Ordinary Differential Equations and Infinite Series

Sam Melkonian

Math 1005

School of Mathematics and Statistics

Carleton University

NELSON EDUCATION

NELSON EDUCATION

COPYRIGHT © 2013 by Nelson
Education Ltd.

Printed and bound in Canada
6 7 8 9   16 15 14 13

For more information contact
Nelson Education Ltd.,
1120 Birchmount Road, Toronto,
Ontario, M1K 5G4. Or you can visit
our Internet site at
http://www.nelson.com

ISBN-13: 978-017-666878-5
ISBN-10: 0-17-666878-0

Consists of Selections from:

*Ordinary Differential Equations
and Infinite Series*
Sam Melkonian

Cover Credit:

EtiAmmos/Shutterstock

Preface

The prerequisites for this book are elementary differential and integral calculus and linear algebra. The exercises at the end of each section follow the progression of the topics in that section, and are approximately in increasing order of difficulty. The exercises at the end of certain chapters cover the material of the entire chapter, may be more difficult, may involve material from earlier chapters, or may be of a more theoretical nature. The solutions of all of the exercises are provided in Appendix C.

Proofs of theorems which are mere computations are furnished in order to provide the reader with a better understanding of the subject. More abstract or otherwise difficult proofs are omitted from the main text. The proofs of selected theorems are given in Appendix B.

Appendix A contains formulas and techniques from trigonometry, calculus and linear algebra which may prove useful to the reader.

Sam Melkonian
August 2012

iv

Contents

Appendices

C Solutions   **347**

Index   **445**

Part I

Ordinary Differential Equations

Chapter 1

Introduction

1.1 Basic Concepts

Definition 1.1. An *ordinary differential equation of order* $n \geq 1$ is a relation which contains the derivative of order n of an unknown function y, called the *dependent variable*, and may also contain lower-order derivatives of y as well as given functions of an *independent variable* x or t.

Example 1.1. $y' + y = x^2 + e^x$ is a first-order ordinary differential equation.

Example 1.2. $y''' = 2y^2 + y' + 1$ is a third-order ordinary differential equation.

The term *ordinary* refers to differential equations in which the unknown function y is a function of a single variable. In contrast, differential equations which contain unknown functions of more than one variable are called *partial differential equations*. This book is concerned only with ordinary differential equations, to which we shall refer simply as *differential equations*, or *equations* for short.

Definition 1.2. A *solution* of a differential equation is any differentiable function f such that, if y is replaced by $f(x)$, y' by $f'(x)$, y'' by $f''(x)$, etc., then the equation is satisfied for *all* x in an interval.

Example 1.3. The function $f(x) = e^{2x}$ is a solution of the equation $y' - 2y = 0$ because $f'(x) = 2e^x$ and, hence, $f'(x) - 2f(x) = 2e^x - 2e^x = 0$ for all x, the relevant interval here being the entire real line $\mathbb{R} = (-\infty, \infty)$.

3

Example 1.4. The first-order equation $y'+x=0$ can be solved simply by integration and requires no special techniques:

$$y' + x = 0 \;\Rightarrow\; y' = -x \;\Rightarrow\; y = \int -x\,dx = -\frac{x^2}{2} + c,$$

where c is an arbitrary constant of integration. Thus, $f(x) = -\dfrac{x^2}{2} + c$ is a solution for every value of c. In particular,

$$f(x) = -\frac{x^2}{2}, \;\; f(x) = -\frac{x^2}{2} + 1 \;\; \text{and} \;\; f(x) = -\frac{x^2}{2} - 2$$

are solutions, corresponding to $c = 0$, $c = 1$ and $c = -2$, respectively. Their graphs are displayed in Figure 1.1.

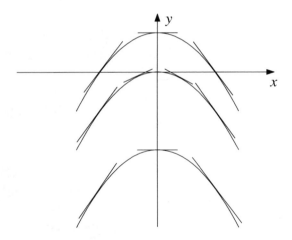

Figure 1.1: Particular solutions of $y' + x = 0$ and directions.

Definition 1.3. The solution of a first-order equation which contains one arbitrary constant is called the *general solution*. It is a *one-parameter family* of solutions, i.e., a set of solutions in which every solution corresponds to a particular value of the *parameter c*. A solution in which c is assigned a particular value is called a *particular solution*.

In Example 1.4, $y = -\dfrac{x^2}{2} + c$ is the general solution, and

$$y = -\frac{x^2}{2}, \;\; y = -\frac{x^2}{2} + 1 \;\; \text{and} \;\; y = -\frac{x^2}{2} - 2$$

are particular solutions. At every point (x, y) on any one of these curves, the slope of the tangent line is $\dfrac{dy}{dx} = -x$, i.e., $y' + x = 0$, which is the differential equation. Thus, the differential equation defines a direction at every point (x, y) in the plane (where it is defined), and the graph of every solution is a curve which follows these directions at every point on the curve. A few directions are indicated in Figure 1.1.

Definition 1.4. The set of directions defined by a first-order differential equation of the form $y' = g(x, y)$ is called a *direction field*, and the graph of a solution is called a *solution curve.*

In Definition 1.4, $g(x, y)$ denotes an expression which may include both x and y. For example, $g(x, y) = x^2 + y^2$ or $g(x, y) = \dfrac{y}{x}$. Such functions of two variables will be discussed at greater length in Section 2.4.

Definition 1.5. An *initial-value problem* for a first-order equation consists of a first-order equation, together with an *initial condition*, which specifies the value of y at a single point x and, thereby, determines a particular solution.

For the equation $y' + x = 0$ in Example 1.4, the initial condition $y(0) = 1$ forces $c = 1$. Hence, the solution of the initial-value problem

$$y' + x = 0, \quad y(0) = 1, \quad \text{is} \quad y = -\frac{x^2}{2} + 1.$$

The initial condition $y(4) = -1$ forces $c = 7$. Hence, the solution of the initial-value problem

$$y' + x = 0, \quad y(4) = -1, \quad \text{is} \quad y = -\frac{x^2}{2} + 7.$$

Example 1.5. Let $y(t) > 0$ denote the amount of a substance present at time t, and suppose that the rate at which y changes with time is proportional to the amount present at time t. This means that

$$\frac{dy}{dt} = ky(t),$$

which is a first-order ordinary differential equation, where k is the proportionality constant. This equation determines, for example, the (approximate) number $y(t)$ of bacteria present in a culture at time t. Since y is an increasing function of t, $y' > 0$ and, hence, $k > 0$. This equation also determines the amount $y(t)$ of a radioactive substance present at time t. Since the substance decays with time, $y' < 0$ and, hence, $k < 0$. If a quantity $y(t)$ is constant in time, then $y' = 0$ and, hence, $k = 0$.

If we attempt to solve the equation as in Example 1.4, we obtain

$$y' = ky \quad \Rightarrow \quad y = \int ky \, dt,$$

and the integral on the right cannot be evaluated because y is not known as a function of t. It is therefore necessary to perform certain algebraic manipulations before an integration can be performed.

Express the equation in the equivalent form $\dfrac{1}{y}y' = k$ and integrate both sides with respect to t to obtain

$$y' = ky \quad \Rightarrow \quad \frac{1}{y}y' = k \quad \Rightarrow \quad \int \frac{1}{y}y' \, dt = \int k \, dt.$$

By the substitution rule,

$$\int \frac{1}{y}y' \, dt = \int \frac{1}{y}\frac{dy}{dt} \, dt = \int \frac{1}{y} \, dy,$$

and the integral on the right can be evaluated without knowledge of y as a function of t. Thus, we obtain

$$\int \frac{1}{y} \, dy = \int k \, dt.$$

Evaluating both integrals, we obtain

$$\ln|y| + c_1 = kt + c_2, \quad \text{or} \quad \ln|y| = kt + c_2 - c_1 = kt + c_3,$$

where c_1 and c_2 are arbitrary constants of integration and the combination $c_2 - c_1$ may be denoted by the single arbitrary constant c_3. Taking the exponential of both sides and employing the fact that $e^{\ln(a)} = a$ for any $a > 0$, we obtain

$$|y| = e^{kt+c_3} = e^{c_3}e^{kt} \quad \Rightarrow \quad y = \pm e^{c_3}e^{kt} = ce^{kt},$$

where $c = \pm e^{c_3}$ is an arbitrary constant since c_3 is arbitrary. At $t = 0$, we obtain $y(0) = c$. Thus, the solution may be expressed as $y(t) = y(0)e^{kt}$. The quantity y grows exponentially if $k > 0$, decays exponentially if $k < 0$, and has the constant value $y(0)$ if $k = 0$.

Example 1.6.   The equation $\dfrac{dy}{dt} = 2y$ has the general solution $y(t) = y(0)e^{2t}$ by Example 1.5 with $k = 2$.

Example 1.7.   The initial-value problem $y' = -3y$, $y(0) = 2$, has the solution $y(t) = 2e^{-3t}$ by Example 1.5 with $k = -3$ and $y(0) = 2$.

Example 1.8. Find the general solution of $y' - xy = 0$ and solve the initial-value problem given the initial condition $y(0) = -2$.

If $y(x) \equiv 0$ (i.e., $y = 0$ for all x), then $y'(x) \equiv 0$, and the equation is satisfied. If $y(x) \not\equiv 0$, then, proceeding as in Example 1.5,

$$y' - xy = 0 \;\Rightarrow\; y' = xy \;\Rightarrow\; \frac{1}{y}y' = x \;\Rightarrow\; \int \frac{1}{y}y'\,dx = \int x\,dx \;\Rightarrow\; \int \frac{1}{y}\,dy = \int x\,dx$$

$$\Rightarrow \ln|y| = \frac{x^2}{2} + c \;\Rightarrow\; |y| = e^c e^{x^2/2} \;\Rightarrow\; y = \pm e^c e^{x^2/2} = K e^{x^2/2}$$

is the general solution, where $K = 0$ corresponds to the solution $y \equiv 0$. $y(0) = -2 \Rightarrow$ $K = -2 \Rightarrow y = -2e^{x^2/2}$ is the solution of the initial-value problem.

The method employed in solving the first-order equations in the present chapter can be applied to all equations of a particular type, and will be discussed in greater generality in Chapter 2, as well as the methods required to solve other types of first-order equation. Second-order equations will be discussed in Chapter 3, where the concepts *general solution*, *particular solution* and *initial-value problem* will be suitably generalized.

Exercises 1.1

1. Find the general solution of the equation $y' + 2x = xe^x$.

2. Find the general solution of the equation $\dfrac{1}{x}y' = 4\cos(2x)$.

3. Find the general solution of the equation $\dfrac{dy}{dx} = 2x\cos(x^2)$.

4. Find the general solution of the equation $\left(\dfrac{dy}{dx}\right)^2 = 4x^2 e^{2x^2}$.

5. Find the general solution of the equation $\dfrac{1}{\cos(x)}\,y' = 2\sin(x)$.

6. Solve the initial-value problem $\dfrac{dy}{dt} = \ln(t)$, $t > 0$, $y(1) = 2$.

7. Solve the initial-value problem $y' = 4\cos^2(x)$, $y\left(\dfrac{\pi}{4}\right) = \dfrac{\pi}{2}$.

8. Find the general solution of the equation $y' = \dfrac{x+3}{x^2 - x - 6}$.

9. Find the general solution of the equation $\dfrac{dy}{dx} = 12e^{2x}\sin(3x)$.

10. Solve the initial-value problem $\dfrac{dy}{dt} = 3y$, $y(0) = 2$.

11. Solve the initial-value problem $\dfrac{dy}{dt} = -2y$, $y(0) = 3$.

12. Solve the initial-value problem $y' + \cos(x)y = 0$, $y(\pi) = -3$.

13. Solve the initial-value problem $3y^2y' = 1$, $y(0) = 2$.

Chapter 2

First-Order Equations

2.1 Separable Equations

Definition 2.1. A first-order differential equation is *separable* if it can be placed in the form

$$g(y)\frac{dy}{dx} = f(x),$$

possibly after some algebraic manipulation.

The essential characteristic of a separable equation is that the quantity $g(y)$ which multiplies $\frac{dy}{dx}$ is independent of x, whereas the right-hand side $f(x)$ of the equation is independent of y. Either or both of these functions may, of course, be constant. The reader may readily verify that the equations in Examples 1.4, 1.5 and 1.8 in Chapter 1 are separable. The method employed in their solution is applicable to any separable equation. Thus, employing the substitution rule, we obtain

$$g(y)\frac{dy}{dx} = f(x) \ \Rightarrow \ \int g(y)\frac{dy}{dx}\, dx = \int f(x)\, dx \ \Rightarrow \ \int g(y)\, dy = \int f(x)\, dx,$$

and evaluation of the last two integrals gives a relation between x and y containing one arbitrary constant. (As seen in the examples in Chapter 1, a difference $c_2 - c_1$ of two arbitrary constants may be replaced by a single one.) It may or may not be possible to solve the relation for y explicitly as a function of x. Nevertheless, it constitutes, at least in principle, the general solution.

Example 2.1. The equation $2\frac{dy}{dx} = \frac{3x^2}{y}$ is separable because it can be placed in the form $2y\frac{dy}{dx} = 3x^2$. Then

$$\int 2y\frac{dy}{dx}\, dx = \int 3x^2\, dx \ \Rightarrow \ \int 2y\, dy = \int 3x^2\, dx \ \Rightarrow \ y^2 = x^3 + c \ \Rightarrow \ y = \pm\sqrt{x^3 + c}$$

is the general solution. If the initial condition $y(0) = 2$ is imposed, then it requires that $2 = \pm\sqrt{c}$, which gives $c = 4$ and we must take the plus sign. The solution of the initial-value problem is then $y = \sqrt{x^3 + 4}$. If, instead, the initial condition is $y(0) = -2$, then, again, $c = 4$, but we must take the minus sign, and $y = -\sqrt{x^3 + 4}$.

Example 2.2. The equation $(x^2 + 4)y' = \dfrac{x}{2y}$ is separable because it can be placed in the form $2yy' = \dfrac{x}{x^2 + 4}$. Then

$$\int 2yy'\,dx = \int \frac{x}{x^2 + 4}\,dx \ \Rightarrow\ \int 2y\,dy = \int \frac{x}{x^2 + 4}\,dx \ \Rightarrow\ y^2 = \frac{1}{2}\ln(x^2 + 4) + c,$$

employing the substitution rule with $u = x^2 + 4$, $\dfrac{du}{dx} = 2x$, to obtain

$$\int \frac{x}{x^2 + 4}\,dx = \frac{1}{2}\int \frac{2x}{x^2 + 4}\,dx = \frac{1}{2}\int \frac{1}{u}\frac{du}{dx}\,dx = \frac{1}{2}\int \frac{1}{u}\,du = \frac{1}{2}\ln(u) + c.$$

Hence, $y = \pm\sqrt{\dfrac{1}{2}\ln(x^2 + 4) + c}$.

Example 2.3. Consider the initial-value problem

$$2xyy' = e^{-y^2}\ln(x), \quad x > 0, \quad y(1) = 2.$$

The equation can be placed in the form $2ye^{y^2}y' = \dfrac{\ln(x)}{x}$, and is separable. Thus,

$$\int 2ye^{y^2}y'\,dx = \int \frac{\ln(x)}{x}\,dx \ \Rightarrow\ \int 2ye^{y^2}\,dy = \int \frac{\ln(x)}{x}\,dx.$$

Employing the substitution rule with $u = y^2$, $\dfrac{du}{dy} = 2y$, in the integral on the left, and $v = \ln(x)$, $\dfrac{dv}{dx} = \dfrac{1}{x}$, in the integral on the right, we obtain

$$\int e^u \frac{du}{dy}\,dy = \int v\frac{dv}{dx}\,dx \Rightarrow \int e^u\,du = \int v\,dv \Rightarrow e^u = \frac{1}{2}v^2 + c \Rightarrow e^{y^2} = \frac{1}{2}[\ln(x)]^2 + c$$

$$\Rightarrow y^2 = \ln\left\{\frac{1}{2}[\ln(x)]^2 + c\right\} \ \Rightarrow\ y = \pm\sqrt{\ln\left\{\frac{1}{2}[\ln(x)]^2 + c\right\}}$$

is the general solution, and

$$y(1) = 2 \Rightarrow \pm\sqrt{\ln(c)} = 2 \Rightarrow \ln(c) = 4 \Rightarrow c = e^4 \Rightarrow y = \sqrt{\ln\left\{\frac{1}{2}[\ln(x)]^2 + e^4\right\}}$$

is the solution of the initial-value problem.

2.1.1 Orthogonal Trajectories

A circle of radius $r > 0$ centred at the origin can be described by the equation $x^2 + y^2 = r^2$. The set (or family or collection) of all such circles constitutes a *one-parameter family of circles*, one circle for each value of the *parameter r*. If we let $f(x, y) = x^2 + y^2$, then the family may be described by the equation $f(x, y) = r^2$ or, alternatively, $g(x, y, r) = x^2 + y^2 - r^2 = 0$.

A straight line through the origin with slope m can be described by the equation $y = mx$. The set of all such lines constitutes a *one-parameter family of lines*, one line for each value of the *parameter m*. With $f(x) = x$, the family may be described by $y = mf(x)$ or, alternatively, $g(x, y, m) = mx - y = 0$.

A few circles centred at the origin and a few lines through the origin are displayed in Figure 2.1.

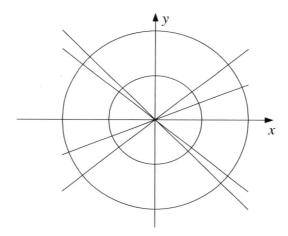

Figure 2.1: Circles centred at the origin and lines through the origin.

More generally, a relation between x and y which includes a parameter (constant) defines a set of curves in the plane, one curve (or more) corresponding to each value of the parameter.

Definition 2.2. A *one-parameter family of curves* is a set of curves defined by an equation of the form $g(x, y, c) = 0$, where c is the *parameter*.

The relation $g(x, y, c) = 0$ my take more particular forms, such as $y = cf(x)$, $y = f(x, c)$, or $f(x, y) = c$. In the first case, $g(x, y, c) = y - cf(x) = 0$, in the second, $g(x, y, c) = y - f(x, c) = 0$, and, in the third, $g(x, y, c) = f(x, y) - c = 0$.

Notice that, in Figure 2.1, every line intersects every circle *orthogonally*, i.e., at right angles. More precisely, at every point of intersection, the line tangent to a circle at that point is *orthogonal* (perpendicular) to the line through the origin.

Definition 2.3. A curve is an *orthogonal trajectory* of a one-parameter family of curves if it intersects every member of the family at right angles.

Thus, every straight line through the origin is an orthogonal trajectory of the family of circles centred at the origin, and every circle centred at the origin is an orthogonal trajectory of the family of lines through the origin.

Given a one-parameter family of curves, it is often necessary to determine its orthogonal trajectories. To this end, we note that if a line L has slope m, then a line perpendicular to L must have slope $-\dfrac{1}{m}$. This fact enables us to determine the orthogonal trajectories of a given family of curves with the aid of differential equations.

Example 2.4. The general solution of the first-order equation $y' = -\dfrac{x}{y}$ is a one-parameter family of curves. Find the general solution and its orthogonal trajectories.

The equation is separable, and

$$yy' = -x \;\Rightarrow\; \frac{y^2}{2} = -\frac{x^2}{2} + c_1 \;\Rightarrow\; y^2 = -x^2 + 2c_1 \;\Rightarrow\; x^2 + y^2 = 2c_1 = c,$$

which defines a one-parameter family of circles centred at the origin for $c > 0$. Its orthogonal trajectories must satisfy the equation $y' = \dfrac{y}{x}$, which is also separable. If $y \not\equiv 0$, then

$$\frac{1}{y}y' = \frac{1}{x} \;\Rightarrow\; \ln|y| = \ln|x| + c \;\Rightarrow\; |y| = e^c|x| \;\Rightarrow\; y = \pm e^c x = Kx,$$

which defines a one-parameter family of lines through the origin, in agreement with the result inferred from Figure 2.1. The constant function $y \equiv 0$ (the x-axis) satisfies the equation and corresponds to $K = 0$. The vertical line $x = 0$ (the y-axis) is an orthogonal trajectory, but is excluded from the solution $y = Kx$. It can be included by regarding x as a function of y, expressing the equation $y' = \dfrac{y}{x}$ as

$$x' = \frac{dx}{dy} = \frac{1}{\frac{dy}{dx}} = \frac{1}{y'} = \frac{x}{y},$$

and noting that $x \equiv 0$ is a solution.

In Example 2.4, the one-parameter family of curves was obtained by solving a first-order equation. If no equation is given, then an equation must be determined for which the given family is the general solution. Thus, given a one-parameter family of curves, $g(x, y, c) = 0$, express the relation as $f(x, y) = c$ and differentiate with respect to x, regarding y as a function of x, to eliminate c. Or, eliminate c from the two equations $g(x, y, c) = 0$ and its derivative with respect to x, regarding y as a function of x.

Example 2.5. Find the orthogonal trajectories of the one-parameter family of parabolas $y = x^2 + c$.

Differentiation with respect to x gives $y' = 2x$. The orthogonal trajectories must therefore satisfy $y' = -\dfrac{1}{2x}$, the general solution of which is $y = -\dfrac{1}{2}\ln|x| + k$, and defines the orthogonal trajectories (Figure 2.2).

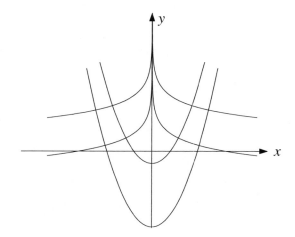

Figure 2.2: The parabolas $y = x^2 + c$ and their orthogonal trajectories.

Example 2.6. Find the orthogonal trajectories of the one-parameter family of parabolas $y = kx^2$.

We may express the equation as $\dfrac{y}{x^2} = k$ and then differentiate to obtain $\dfrac{x^2 y' - 2xy}{x^4} = 0$, i.e., $xy' - 2y = 0$, or $y' = \dfrac{2y}{x}$. Alternatively,

$$y = kx^2 \Rightarrow \frac{y}{x^2} = k \quad \text{and} \quad y' = 2kx \Rightarrow y' = 2x\left(\frac{y}{x^2}\right) = \frac{2y}{x},$$

as before. The orthogonal trajectories must therefore satisfy $y' = -\dfrac{x}{2y}$, which is separable. Thus,

$$y' = -\frac{x}{2y} \;\Rightarrow\; 2yy' = -x \;\Rightarrow\; y^2 = -\frac{x^2}{2} + c \;\Rightarrow\; y = \pm\sqrt{c - \frac{x^2}{2}}, \quad \text{or} \quad \frac{x^2}{2} + y^2 = c,$$

which defines a one-parameter family of ellipses for $c > 0$. A few members of each family are displayed in Figure 2.3

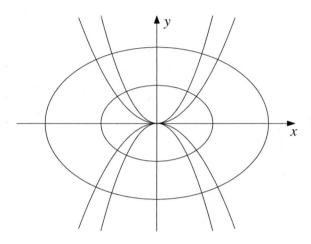

Figure 2.3: The parabolas $y = kx^2$ and their orthogonal trajectories.

Exercises 2.1

1. Solve the initial-value problem $y' = 3x^2y^2$, $y(0) = \dfrac{1}{2}$.

2. Find the general solution of the equation $y' = \dfrac{\sqrt{x+1}}{y^3}$.

3. Solve the initial-value problem $(x^2 + 1)\dfrac{dy}{dx} = \dfrac{2x+1}{3y^2}$, $y(0) = 3$.

4. Find the general solution of the equation $\dfrac{y'}{4x^2 + 3x - 2} = \dfrac{x}{5y^4 - 4y^3 + 1}$.

5. Solve the initial-value problem $xy' - \dfrac{\ln(x)}{y} = 0$, $x > 0$, $y(1) = -3$.

6. Find the general solution of the equation $xy' = (x+1)e^y$.

7. Solve the initial-value problem $y' = \dfrac{xy + x}{xy - y}$, $y(2) = -2$.

8. Solve the initial-value problem $\cos(x) \ln(y) \dfrac{dy}{dx} = y \sin(x)$, $y > 0$, $y(0) = e^2$.

9. Find the general solution of the equation $y' = \dfrac{x^2}{y}$ and its orthogonal trajectories.

10. Find the general solution of the equation $y' = 2x(y^2 + 1)$ and its orthogonal trajectories.

11. Find the orthogonal trajectories of the one-parameter family of curves $y = x^3 + c$.

12. Find the orthogonal trajectories of the one-parameter family of curves $y = kx^4$.

13. Find the orthogonal trajectories of the one-parameter family of curves $y = e^{cx}$.

2.2 Homogeneous Equations

Definition 2.4. A first-order equation is *homogeneous* if it can be placed in the form $y' = f\left(\dfrac{y}{x}\right)$, possibly after some algebraic manipulation.

For example, the equations

$$y' = \frac{y}{x}, \quad y' = \frac{y^2}{x^2} = \left(\frac{y}{x}\right)^2, \quad y' = \frac{x + y}{x} = 1 + \frac{y}{x}$$

and

$$y' = \frac{x^2 + y^2}{xy} = \frac{x}{y} + \frac{y}{x} = \frac{1}{y/x} + \frac{y}{x}$$

are homogeneous, whereas $y' = \dfrac{x^2 + y}{x} = x + \dfrac{y}{x}$ is not, since x and y may appear only as the combination $\dfrac{y}{x}$.

A homogeneous equation is solved by making the substitution (also called a change of variable) $u = \dfrac{y}{x}$, where u is a new function of x. The homogeneous equation for the unknown function y is then transformed into a separable equation for the unknown function u: Employing the product rule, we obtain

$$u = \frac{y}{x} \Rightarrow y = xu \Rightarrow y' = u + xu' \Rightarrow u + xu' = y' = f\left(\frac{y}{x}\right) = f(u)$$

$$\Rightarrow xu' = f(u) - u \Rightarrow \frac{1}{f(u) - u} u' = \frac{1}{x},$$

which has the form $g(u)u' = f(x)$, and is separable. After u is found, y is obtained by $y = xu$.

Example 2.7. The equation

$$y' = \frac{x^2 + y^2}{xy} = \frac{1}{y/x} + \frac{y}{x}$$

is homogeneous, as shown above. The substitution $u = \dfrac{y}{x}$ gives

$$u + xu' = y' = \frac{1}{y/x} + \frac{y}{x} = \frac{1}{u} + u.$$

Then $xu' = \dfrac{1}{u}$, which is separable. Thus,

$$xu' = \frac{1}{u} \;\Rightarrow\; uu' = \frac{1}{x} \;\Rightarrow\; \frac{1}{2}u^2 = \ln|x| + c_1 \;\Rightarrow\; u^2 = 2\ln|x| + 2c_1 = 2\ln|x| + c$$

$$\Rightarrow\; u = \pm\sqrt{2\ln|x| + c} \;\Rightarrow\; y = xu = \pm x\sqrt{2\ln|x| + c}.$$

Example 2.8. The equation

$$xy' = y\ln(y) - y\ln(x), \quad x > 0, \quad y > 0,$$

can be placed in the form

$$y' = \frac{y}{x}\left[\ln(y) - \ln(x)\right] = \frac{y}{x}\ln\left(\frac{y}{x}\right),$$

and is homogeneous. Then $u = \dfrac{y}{x}$ gives $u + xu' = u\ln(u) \Rightarrow xu' = u\ln(u) - u \Rightarrow$

$$\frac{1}{u[\ln(u) - 1]}u' = \frac{1}{x} \;\Rightarrow\; \int \frac{1}{u[\ln(u) - 1]}\,du = \int \frac{1}{x}\,dx = \ln|x| + c_1.$$

In order to evaluate the integral on the left, make the substitution $v = \ln(u) - 1$. Then $\dfrac{dv}{du} = \dfrac{1}{u}$, and we obtain

$$\int \frac{1}{u[\ln(u) - 1]}\,du = \int \frac{1}{v}\frac{dv}{du}\,du = \int \frac{1}{v}\,dv = \ln|v| = \ln|\ln(u) - 1|.$$

Hence, $\ln|\ln(u) - 1| = \ln|x| + c_1 \Rightarrow |\ln(u) - 1| = e^{\ln|x|}e^{c_1} = e^{c_1}|x| \Rightarrow$

$$\ln(u) - 1 = \pm e^{c_1}x = cx \Rightarrow \ln(u) = cx + 1 \Rightarrow u = e^{cx+1} \Rightarrow y = xe^{cx+1}.$$

Example 2.9. Consider the initial-value problem

$$x^2 y' = x^2 + xy + y^2, \quad y(1) = 1.$$

The equation can be placed in the form $y' = 1 + \dfrac{y}{x} + \left(\dfrac{y}{x}\right)^2$, and is homogeneous.

$$u = \frac{y}{x} \;\Rightarrow\; y = xu \;\Rightarrow\; u + xu' = y' = 1 + u + u^2 \;\Rightarrow\; xu' = 1 + u^2 \;\Rightarrow\; \frac{1}{1+u^2} u' = \frac{1}{x}$$

$$\Rightarrow\; \int \frac{1}{1+u^2} \, du = \int \frac{1}{x} \, dx \;\Rightarrow\; \tan^{-1}(u) = \ln|x| + c \;\Rightarrow\; u = \tan(\ln|x| + c).$$

Hence, $y = x \tan(\ln|x| + c)$ is the general solution. $y(1) = 1 \Rightarrow \tan(c) = 1 \Rightarrow c = \dfrac{\pi}{4}$, and the solution of the initial-value problem is $y = x \tan\left(\ln|x| + \dfrac{\pi}{4}\right)$.

Example 2.10. The equation

$$xyy' = y^2 + x^2 e^{-y/x}$$

can be placed in the form $y' = \dfrac{y}{x} + \dfrac{e^{-y/x}}{y/x}$, and is homogeneous.

$$u = \frac{y}{x} \;\Rightarrow\; u + xu' = y' = u + \frac{e^{-u}}{u} \;\Rightarrow\; ue^u u' = \frac{1}{x}$$

$$\Rightarrow\; \int ue^u \, du = \int \frac{1}{x} \, dx = \ln|x| + c.$$

Integration by parts gives $\displaystyle\int ue^u \, du = ue^u - e^u$. Hence, $ue^u - e^u = \ln|x| + c$, i.e.,

$$\frac{y}{x} e^{y/x} - e^{y/x} = \ln|x| + c.$$

It is not possible to solve this relation for y explicitly in terms of x. Nevertheless, this is the general solution, with y defined *implicitly* by the above relation.

Definition 2.5. A solution of a first-order equation defined by a relation between x and y is called an *implicit solution*. If it contains one arbitrary constant, then it is the general solution and has the form $g(x, y, c) = 0$.

In Example 2.10, the solution may be placed in the form

$$g(x, y, c) = \frac{y}{x} e^{y/x} - e^{y/x} - \ln|x| - c = 0.$$

Exercises 2.2

1. Solve the initial-value problem $y' = \dfrac{x+y}{x}$, $y(1) = 2$.

2. Solve the initial-value problem $xyy' = y^2 - x^2$, $y(-1) = 2$.

3. Solve the initial-value problem $y' = \dfrac{\sqrt{x}}{\sqrt{y}} + \dfrac{y}{x}$, $x > 0$, $y > 0$, $y(1) = 9$.

4. Find the general solution of the equation $y' = \dfrac{y}{x} + \dfrac{x}{\sqrt[3]{x^2y} + \sqrt{xy} + x}$.

5. Solve the initial-value problem $y + x\sec\left(\dfrac{y}{x}\right) - xy' = 0$, $y(1) = \dfrac{\pi}{3}$.

6. Find the general solution of the equation $y' = \dfrac{2x + 3y}{3x - 2y}$.

7. Find the general solution of the equation $y' = \dfrac{x^3 + x^2y + xy^2 + y^3}{x^3 + x^2y + xy^2}$.

8. Solve the initial-value problem $yy' = 6x + y$, $y(1) = 4$.

2.3   Linear Equations

Definition 2.6. A first-order equation is *linear* if it has the form

$$a(x)y' + b(x)y = c(x),$$

where $a(x) \not\equiv 0$, $b(x)$ and $c(x)$ may be any functions of x whatsoever (or constants), but are independent of y and y'. An equation which is not linear is called *nonlinear*.

For example, the equations $e^x y' + \ln(x)y = x^3 + 1$, $y' = 6$ and $y' + x^2y = 0$ are linear, but $yy' = 1$, $y' + \sin(y) = 0$ and $y' + y^2 = x$ are nonlinear.

In order to solve a linear equation, divide the equation by $a(x)$ and let $P(x) = \dfrac{b(x)}{a(x)}$

and $Q(x) = \dfrac{c(x)}{a(x)}$ to place the equation in the *standard form*

$$y' + P(x)y = Q(x).$$

Multiply the standard form of the equation by a function $I(x)$, to be determined, to obtain

$$I(x)y' + I(x)P(x)y = I(x)Q(x).$$

The function $I(x)$ is chosen so that the left-hand side $I(x)y' + I(x)P(x)y$ becomes $[I(x)y]'$. Employing the product rule, this requirement becomes

$$I(x)y' + I(x)P(x)y = [I(x)y]' = I(x)y' + I'(x)y,$$

which gives $I(x)P(x)y = I'(x)y$, or $I(x)P(x) = I'(x)$. Then $\dfrac{I'(x)}{I(x)} = P(x)$ and, employing the substitution rule, we obtain

$$\int \frac{1}{I} \frac{dI}{dx}\, dx = \int P(x)\, dx \;\Rightarrow\; \int \frac{1}{I}\, dI = \int P(x)\, dx \;\Rightarrow\; \ln|I(x)| = \int P(x)\, dx,$$

from which we obtain

$$I(x) = e^{\int P(x)\, dx},$$

called an *integrating factor*. Arbitrary constants and $\pm$ signs are not necessary here, since we seek only one function $I(x)$, and not all such functions. The equation then becomes $[I(x)y]' = I(x)Q(x)$, and one integration gives $I(x)y = \int I(x)Q(x)\, dx$, from which we obtain

$$y = \frac{1}{I(x)} \int I(x)Q(x)\, dx.$$

Example 2.11. The equation $y' + 2y = 1$ is linear, with the integrating factor

$$I(x) = e^{\int 2\, dx} = e^{2x}.$$

The equation then becomes

$$e^{2x}y' + 2e^{2x}y = e^{2x}, \quad \text{i.e.,} \quad \left(e^{2x}y\right)' = e^{2x},$$

integration of which gives $e^{2x}y = \displaystyle\int e^{2x}\, dx = \frac{1}{2}e^{2x} + c$ and, hence, $y = \dfrac{1}{2} + ce^{-2x}$.

Example 2.12. Consider the initial-value problem

$$y' - \frac{1}{x}y = \ln(x), \quad x > 0, \quad y(1) = -3.$$

The equation is linear, with the integrating factor $I(x) = e^{\int -\frac{1}{x}\, dx} = e^{-\ln(x)} = \dfrac{1}{x}$. The equation then becomes

$$\frac{1}{x}y' - \frac{1}{x^2}y = \frac{\ln(x)}{x}, \quad \text{i.e.,} \quad \left(\frac{1}{x}y\right)' = \frac{\ln(x)}{x},$$

integration of which, employing the substitution rule with $u = \ln(x)$ and $\dfrac{du}{dx} = \dfrac{1}{x}$, gives

$$\frac{1}{x}y = \int \frac{\ln(x)}{x}\,dx = \int u\frac{du}{dx}\,dx = \int u\,du = \frac{1}{2}u^2 + c = \frac{1}{2}[\ln(x)]^2 + c,$$

and $y = \dfrac{x}{2}[\ln(x)]^2 + cx$. Then $y(1) = -3 \Rightarrow c = -3 \Rightarrow y = \dfrac{x}{2}[\ln(x)]^2 - 3x$.

Example 2.13. The equation $xe^x y' + e^x y = 4xe^{-x}$ is linear. In standard form, it is $y' + \dfrac{1}{x}y = 4e^{-2x}$, with the integrating factor

$$I(x) = e^{\int \frac{1}{x}\,dx} = e^{\ln|x|} = |x| = \pm x,$$

and $I(x) = x$ will do. The equation then becomes

$$xy' + y = 4xe^{-2x}, \quad \text{i.e.,} \quad (xy)' = 4xe^{-2x}.$$

Integration by parts then gives

$$xy = \int 4xe^{-2x}\,dx = -2xe^{-2x} + \int 2e^{-2x}\,dx = -2xe^{-2x} - e^{-2x} + c,$$

and $y = -2e^{-2x} - \dfrac{e^{-2x}}{x} + \dfrac{c}{x}$.

Example 2.14. Consider the initial-value problem

$$\cos(x)y' + \sin(x)y = 2\sin(x)\cos^3(x), \quad y(\pi) = -2.$$

The equation is linear, with the standard form $y' + \tan(x)y = 2\sin(x)\cos^2(x)$. The integrating factor is

$$I(x) = e^{\int \tan(x)\,dx} = e^{\ln|\sec(x)|} = |\sec(x)| = \pm\frac{1}{\cos(x)},$$

and $I(x) = \dfrac{1}{\cos(x)}$ will do. The equation then becomes

$$\frac{1}{\cos(x)}y' + \frac{\sin(x)}{\cos^2(x)}y = 2\sin(x)\cos(x),$$

i.e.,

$$\left[\frac{1}{\cos(x)}y\right]' = 2\sin(x)\cos(x) = \sin(2x),$$

integration of which gives

$$\frac{1}{\cos(x)}y = \int \sin(2x)\,dx = -\frac{1}{2}\cos(2x) + c \Rightarrow y = -\frac{1}{2}\cos(x)\cos(2x) + c\cos(x).$$

Then $y(\pi) = -2 \Rightarrow -2 = \dfrac{1}{2} - c \Rightarrow c = \dfrac{5}{2} \Rightarrow y = -\dfrac{1}{2}\cos(x)\cos(2x) + \dfrac{5}{2}\cos(x)$.

2.3.1 Bernoulli Equations

Definition 2.7. A first-order equation is a *Bernoulli equation* if it has the form

$$a(x)y' + b(x)y = c(x)y^\alpha,$$

where $a(x) \not\equiv 0$, $b(x)$ and $c(x)$ are functions of x (or constants), but are independent of y and y', and α is a real number.

If $\alpha = 0$, then the equation is $a(x)y' + b(x)y = c(x)$, which is linear, and if $\alpha = 1$, then the equation is $a(x)y' + b(x)y = c(x)y$, i.e., $a(x)y' + [b(x) - c(x)]y = 0$, which is also linear. For $\alpha \neq 0, 1$, a Bernoulli equation may be transformed into a linear equation by means of the substitution (change of variable) $u = y^{1-\alpha}$. Then

$$y = u^{\frac{1}{1-\alpha}}, \quad y^\alpha = u^{\frac{\alpha}{1-\alpha}},$$

and, employing the chain rule,

$$y' = \frac{1}{1-\alpha} u^{\frac{1}{1-\alpha}-1} u' = \frac{1}{1-\alpha} u^{\frac{\alpha}{1-\alpha}} u',$$

and the equation becomes

$$\frac{1}{1-\alpha} a(x) u^{\frac{\alpha}{1-\alpha}} u' + b(x) u^{\frac{1}{1-\alpha}} = c(x) u^{\frac{\alpha}{1-\alpha}}.$$

Multiplication by $u^{\frac{-\alpha}{1-\alpha}}$ then gives

$$\frac{1}{1-\alpha} a(x) u' + b(x) u = c(x),$$

which is linear. Once the linear equation is solved for $u(x)$, the solution $y(x)$ of the Bernoulli equation is obtained by $y = u^{\frac{1}{1-\alpha}}$.

Example 2.15. The equation $xy' + 2y = y^2$ is a Bernoulli equation with $\alpha = 2$. With $1 - \alpha = -1$, $u = y^{-1} \Rightarrow y = u^{-1} \Rightarrow y' = -u^{-2}u'$, $y^2 = u^{-2}$, and the equation becomes

$$-xu^{-2}u' + 2u^{-1} = u^{-2}, \quad \text{i.e.,} \quad -xu' + 2u = 1, \quad \text{or} \quad u' - \frac{2}{x}u = -\frac{1}{x},$$

which is linear, with the integrating factor

$$I(x) = e^{\int -\frac{2}{x}\,dx} = e^{-2\ln|x|} = |x|^{-2} = \frac{1}{x^2}.$$

Then

$$\frac{1}{x^2}u' - \frac{2}{x^3}u = -\frac{1}{x^3} \Rightarrow \left(\frac{1}{x^2}u\right)' = -\frac{1}{x^3} \Rightarrow \frac{1}{x^2}u = \int -\frac{1}{x^3}\,dx = \frac{1}{2x^2} + c$$

$$\Rightarrow u = \frac{1}{2} + cx^2 \Rightarrow y = u^{-1} = \frac{1}{\frac{1}{2} + cx^2} = \frac{2}{1 + kx^2}$$

is the general solution.

Example 2.16. The equation $2y' - y = e^x y^3$ is a Bernoulli equation with $\alpha = 3$. With $1 - \alpha = -2$, $u = y^{-2} \Rightarrow y = u^{-1/2} \Rightarrow y' = -\frac{1}{2}u^{-3/2}u'$, $y^3 = u^{-3/2}$, and the equation becomes

$$-u^{-3/2}u' - u^{-1/2} = e^x u^{-3/2}, \quad \text{i.e.,} \quad -u' - u = e^x, \quad \text{or} \quad u' + u = -e^x,$$

which is linear, with the integrating factor $I(x) = e^{\int 1\,dx} = e^x$. Then

$$e^x u' + e^x u = -e^{2x} \Rightarrow (e^x u)' = -e^{2x} \Rightarrow e^x u = -\int e^{2x}\,dx = -\frac{1}{2}e^{2x} + c$$

$$\Rightarrow u = -\frac{1}{2}e^x + ce^{-x} \Rightarrow y = u^{-1/2} = \frac{1}{\pm\sqrt{ce^{-x} - \frac{1}{2}e^x}}$$

is the general solution. Note that $u^{1/2} = \pm\sqrt{u}$. In fact, it is evident from the Bernoulli equation that if y is a solution, then so is $-y$, because

$$2y' - y = e^x y^3 \Rightarrow -2y' + y = -e^x y^3 \Rightarrow 2(-y)' - (-y) = e^x(-y)^3.$$

Example 2.17. Consider the initial-value problem

$$y' + 2x^2 y = \frac{2x^2}{\sqrt{y}}, \quad y > 0, \quad y(0) = 4.$$

The equation is a Bernoulli equation with $\alpha = -\frac{1}{2}$. With $1 - \alpha = \frac{3}{2}$,

$$u = y^{3/2} \Rightarrow y = u^{2/3} \Rightarrow y' = \frac{2}{3}u^{-1/3}u', \quad \frac{1}{\sqrt{y}} = y^{-1/2} = u^{-1/3},$$

and the equation becomes

$$\frac{2}{3}u^{-1/3}u' + 2x^2 u^{2/3} = 2x^2 u^{-1/3}, \quad \text{i.e.,} \quad \frac{2}{3}u' + 2x^2 u = 2x^2, \quad \text{or} \quad u' + 3x^2 u = 3x^2,$$

which is linear, with the integrating factor $I(x) = e^{\int 3x^2\,dx} = e^{x^3}$. Then

$$e^{x^3}u' + 3x^2 e^{x^3} u = 3x^2 e^{x^3} \implies \left(e^{x^3}u\right)' = 3x^2 e^{x^3} \implies e^{x^3}u = \int 3x^2 e^{x^3}\,dx = e^{x^3} + c$$

$$\implies u = 1 + ce^{-x^3} \implies y = u^{2/3} = \left(1 + ce^{-x^3}\right)^{2/3}$$

is the general solution, and $y(0) = 4 \implies (1+c)^{2/3} = 4 \implies c = 4^{3/2} - 1 = 7 \implies$ $y = \left(1 + 7e^{-x^3}\right)^{2/3}$ is the solution of the initial-value problem.

Exercises 2.3

1. Solve the initial-value problem $y' + y = e^{-x}$, $y(0) = -2$.

2. Find the general solution of the equation $y' - 3y = 1$.

3. Solve the initial-value problem $e^x y' + 2e^x y - 1 = 0$, $y(0) = -3$.

4. Find the general solution of the equation $y' + 2xy = 2x$.

5. Solve the initial-value problem $xy' + y = \dfrac{1}{x}$, $x > 0$, $y(1) = 2$.

6. Find the general solution of the equation $x^3 y' - 2y + 1 = 0$.

7. Find the general solution of the equation $x^2 y' + xy = \dfrac{1}{\ln(x)}$, $x > 0$.

8. Solve the initial-value problem $\cos(x)y' + \sin(x)y = \cos^4(x)$, $y(\pi) = \dfrac{\pi}{2}$.

9. Find the general solution of the equation $xy' + 2y = e^{-x}$.

10. Find the general solution of the equation $xy' - y = \dfrac{x^3}{x+1}$.

11. Find the general solution of the equation $y' + y = \dfrac{e^{-x}}{x^2 + 2x + 2}$.

12. Find the general solution of the equation $x\ln(x)y' + y = \dfrac{2x}{x^2 - 1}$, $x > 0$.

13. Solve the initial-value problem $3y' - y = \dfrac{1}{y^2}$, $y(0) = 2$.

14. Find the general solution of the equation $y' + 4y = 2e^{-x}\sqrt{y}$, $y > 0$.

15. Solve the initial-value problem $2x^2 y' - 2xy = -y^3 \sin(x)$, $y\left(\dfrac{\pi}{2}\right) = \pi$.

16. Find the general solution of the equation $xyy' + y^2 - xe^x = 0$.

17. Find the general solution of the equation $x\ln(x)y' + y = 2y\sqrt{y}$, $x > 1$, $y > 0$.

2.4   Functions of Two Variables

The study of a type of first-order equation called *exact*, to be defined in Section 2.5, requires that certain basic properties of functions of two variables be established first.

Definition 2.8. *A function f of two variables* assigns to any pair (x, y) in its domain a real number denoted by $f(x, y)$, where the *domain* of f is either specified or taken to be all points (x, y) in the plane where $f(x, y)$ is defined.

Several such functions have already been encountered in the preceding sections. For example,

$$f(x, y) = x^2 + xy - y^3, \quad g(x, y) = \frac{x}{y} + 1 \ \text{ and } \ h(x, y) = \sqrt{x - y}$$

are functions of two variables. In the above, the domain of f is the entire plane $\mathbb{R}^2$, that of g is the set of all points (x, y) with $y \neq 0$, and that of h is the set of all points (x, y) with $x - y \geq 0$, i.e., $x \geq y$.

It is important to note that, in the definition of a function of two variables, y is *not* a function of x, and that x and y may be assigned values *independently*. In other words, x and y are *independent variables*. For example,

$$f(x, y) = y - x^2 + 1 \ \Rightarrow \ f(1, 2) = 2, \quad f(2, 1) = -2, \ \text{ and } \ f(0, 0) = 1.$$

It is only a *relation*, such as $f(x, y) = 0$ or $f(x, y) = c$, which defines y as a function of x. For example, $f(x, y) = y - x^2 + 1 = 0 \Rightarrow y = x^2 - 1$.

2.4.1   Partial Derivatives

The (first-order) derivative of a function f of a single variable x is the function f' or $\frac{df}{dx}$ defined by

$$f'(x) = \frac{df}{dx}(x) = \lim_{h \to 0} \frac{f(x + h) - f(x)}{h}.$$

If $z = f(x)$, then $\frac{dz}{dx} = f'(x)$ is the rate of change of z with respect to x.

In contrast to functions of one variable, there are different ways in which functions of two variables can be differentiated.

Definition 2.9. Let f be a function of two variables x and y. The *partial derivative of f with respect to x* is the function f_x or $\dfrac{\partial f}{\partial x}$ of two variables defined by

$$f_x(x,y) = \frac{\partial f}{\partial x}(x,y) = \lim_{h \to 0} \frac{f(x+h,y) - f(x,y)}{h}.$$

The *partial derivative of f with respect to y* is the function f_y or $\dfrac{\partial f}{\partial y}$ of two variables defined by

$$f_y(x,y) = \frac{\partial f}{\partial y}(x,y) = \lim_{h \to 0} \frac{f(x,y+h) - f(x,y)}{h}.$$

If $z = f(x,y)$, then $\dfrac{\partial z}{\partial x} = f_x(x,y)$ is the rate of change of z with respect to x with y held constant, and $\dfrac{\partial z}{\partial y} = f_y(x,y)$ is the rate of change of z with respect to y with x held constant.

Example 2.18. Let $f(x,y) = x^4y^2 + 2x - 3y + e^x - \ln(y) - \sin(y) + \cos(x) + 2$. Then

$$f_x(x,y) = 4x^3y^2 + 2 + e^x - \sin(x) \quad \text{and} \quad f_y(x,y) = 2x^4y - 3 - \frac{1}{y} - \cos(y).$$

In the computation of f_x, y is regarded as a constant, and all expressions which are independent of x, such as y, $\ln(y)$ and $\sin(y)$ have derivative with respect to x equal to 0. In the computation of f_y, x is regarded as a constant, and all expressions which are independent of y, such as x, e^x and $\cos(x)$ have derivative with respect to y equal to 0.

A function f of two variables has four *second-order partial derivatives*, namely, the first-order partial derivatives of the two functions f_x and f_y. The four possibilities are as follows:

$$f_{xx} \;=\; \frac{\partial}{\partial x}f_x = \frac{\partial}{\partial x}\frac{\partial f}{\partial x} = \frac{\partial^2 f}{\partial x^2} \;\text{ is the partial derivative of } f_x \text{ with respect to } x,$$

$$f_{xy} \;=\; \frac{\partial}{\partial y}f_x = \frac{\partial}{\partial y}\frac{\partial f}{\partial x} = \frac{\partial^2 f}{\partial y\partial x} \;\text{ is the partial derivative of } f_x \text{ with respect to } y,$$

$$f_{yx} \;=\; \frac{\partial}{\partial x}f_y = \frac{\partial}{\partial x}\frac{\partial f}{\partial y} = \frac{\partial^2 f}{\partial x\partial y} \;\text{ is the partial derivative of } f_y \text{ with respect to } x,$$

$$f_{yy} \;=\; \frac{\partial}{\partial y}f_y = \frac{\partial}{\partial y}\frac{\partial f}{\partial y} = \frac{\partial^2 f}{\partial y^2} \;\text{ is the partial derivative of } f_y \text{ with respect to } y.$$

Example 2.19. Let $f(x, y) = x^3 y^4 + e^{2x} \ln(y) + x^2 - y^3 - 3$. Then

$$
\begin{aligned}
f_x(x, y) &= 3x^2 y^4 + 2e^{2x} \ln(y) + 2x, \\
f_y(x, y) &= 4x^3 y^3 + \frac{e^{2x}}{y} - 3y^2, \\
f_{xx}(x, y) &= 6xy^4 + 4e^{2x} \ln(y) + 2, \\
f_{xy}(x, y) &= 12x^2 y^3 + \frac{2e^{2x}}{y}, \\
f_{yx}(x, y) &= 12x^2 y^3 + \frac{2e^{2x}}{y}, \\
f_{yy}(x, y) &= 12x^3 y^2 - \frac{e^{2x}}{y^2} - 6y.
\end{aligned}
$$

Note that, in this example, $f_{xy} = f_{yx}$. Although this is not true in general, the conditions under which it is true are given by the following:

Theorem 2.1. If f_{xy} and f_{yx} are continuous in an *open* region R of the (x, y)-plane (i.e., R excludes its boundary), then $f_{xy}(x, y) = f_{yx}(x, y)$ for all (x, y) in R.

Continuity of a function of two variables is defined in a manner analogous to the definition for a function of a single variable:

Definition 2.10. A function f of two variables is *continuous at a point* (a, b) if

$$
\lim_{(x,y) \to (a,b)} f(x, y) = f(a, b).
$$

f is *continuous in a region R* if f is continuous at every point (a, b) in R.

2.4.2   The Chain Rule

The chain rule for functions of a single variable states that, if $z = f(x)$ and $x = g(t)$, then the composition $h(t) = f(g(t))$ has derivative

$$
h'(t) = \frac{d}{dt} h(t) = f'(g(t)) g'(t).
$$

In other words, if z is a function of x and x is a function of t, then $\dfrac{dz}{dt} = \dfrac{dz}{dx} \dfrac{dx}{dt}$.

Several versions of the chain rule exist for functions of two (or more) variables. The one of interest in the present study is the following:

Theorem 2.2. (The Chain Rule) If z is a function of two variables and x and y are functions of a single variable t, then the composition $h(t) = f(x(t), y(t))$ has derivative

$$h'(t) = \frac{d}{dt}f(x(t), y(t)) = f_x(x(t), y(t))\frac{dx}{dt} + f_y(x(t), y(t))\frac{dy}{dt}. \tag{2.1}$$

In other words, if $z = f(x, y)$ and x and y are functions of t, then

$$\frac{dz}{dt} = \frac{\partial f}{\partial x}\frac{dx}{dt} + \frac{\partial f}{\partial y}\frac{dy}{dt}.$$

Note that, in the special case where $z = f(x)$ is independent of y, $\dfrac{\partial f}{\partial y} = 0$ and $\dfrac{\partial f}{\partial x} = \dfrac{df}{dx}$, and the above formula reduces to $\dfrac{dz}{dt} = \dfrac{df}{dx}\dfrac{dx}{dt} = \dfrac{dz}{dx}\dfrac{dx}{dt}$, i.e., the chain rule for functions of one variable.

Example 2.20. Let $f(x, y) = x^2 + y^3$, $x(t) = t^3 - 6t + 1$ and $y(t) = e^t + 3t$. Then

$$h(t) = f(x(t), y(t)) = (t^3 - 6t + 1)^2 + (e^t + 3t)^3$$

is a function of t, and

$$\begin{aligned}
h'(t) &= \frac{\partial f}{\partial x}\frac{dx}{dt} + \frac{\partial f}{\partial y}\frac{dy}{dt} = 2x(t)(3t^2 - 6) + 3[y(t)]^2(e^t + 3) \\
&= 2(t^3 - 6t + 1)(3t^2 - 6) + 3(e^t + 3t)^2(e^t + 3).
\end{aligned}$$

In Theorem 2.2, consider the special case where $x(t) = t$. In that case, $\dfrac{dx}{dt} = 1$, and Equation (2.1) reduces to

$$\frac{d}{dt}f(t, y(t)) = f_x(t, y(t)) + f_y(t, y(t))\frac{dy}{dt},$$

or, employing the fact that $x = t$,

$$\frac{d}{dx}f(x, y(x)) = f_x(x, y(x)) + f_y(x, y(x))\frac{dy}{dx}, \tag{2.2}$$

which is the version of the chain rule required in the study of exact equations.

Exercises 2.4

1. Let $f(x, y) = x^3 - y^2 + x^2y^2 + 1$.

   (a) Determine $f(1, 0)$, $f(3, 1)$, $f(1, 3)$ and $f(2, -1)$.

(b) Find $f_x(x, y)$ and $f_y(x, y)$, and the values of these functions at the points $(1, 0)$, $(3, 1)$, $(1, 3)$ and $(2, -1)$.

(c) Find $f_{xx}(x, y)$, $f_{xy}(x, y)$, $f_{yx}(x, y)$ and $f_{yy}(x, y)$, and the values of these functions at the points $(1, 0)$, $(3, 1)$, $(1, 3)$ and $(2, -1)$.

2. Let $f(x, y) = x^2 \ln(y) - y^3 e^x + x^3 - y^2 + 1$. Find f_x, f_y, f_{xx}, f_{xy}, f_{yx} and f_{yy}.

3. Let $f(x, y) = x^4 + 3x^2 y^2 + y^4$, $x(t) = t^2 + 2t$ and $y(t) = t^3 - 2t$. Determine $\dfrac{d}{dt} f(x(t), y(t))$.

4. Let $f(x, y) = x^2 - \cos(y) + x \sin(y)$, $x(t) = 2t^2 + 3t - 1$ and $y(t) = e^t + 2t$. Determine $\dfrac{d}{dt} f(x(t), y(t))$.

5. Let $f(x, y) = \sin(xy) + \sqrt{xy}$, $x(t) = e^t + 1$ and $y(t) = \ln(t)$. Determine $\dfrac{d}{dt} f(x(t), y(t))$.

6. Let $f(x, y) = x^4 + 3x^2 y^2 + y^4$ and $y(x) = x^3 + 6x^2 - x$. Determine $\dfrac{d}{dx} f(x, y(x))$.

7. Let $f(x, y) = e^y - x^2 + y^3 \ln(x)$ and $y(x) = \sin(x)$. Determine $\dfrac{d}{dx} f(x, y(x))$.

8. Let $f(x, y) = \dfrac{1}{x^2 + y^2} + xe^{-y}$ and $y(x) = \sin(2x)$. Determine $\dfrac{d}{dx} f(x, y(x))$.

9. Let $f(x, y) = x^4 - y^4 - 1$. The relation $f(x, y) = 0$ defines y as a function of x. Determine $\dfrac{dy}{dx}$ in terms of x and y.

10. Let $f(x, y) = x^3 + y^2 - e^y$. The relation $f(x, y) = 0$ defines y as a function of x. Determine $\dfrac{dy}{dx}$ in terms of x and y.

2.5   Exact Equations

Consider a first-order equation expressed in the form

$$P(x, y) + Q(x, y) \frac{dy}{dx} = 0, \tag{2.3}$$

where P and Q are functions of two variables.

Suppose that there exists a function f of two variables such that $f_x = P$ and $f_y = Q$. Then Equation (2.3) takes the form

$$f_x + f_y \frac{dy}{dx} = 0$$

which, by Equation (2.2), is $\dfrac{d}{dx}f(x,y(x)) = 0$. Integration with respect to x then yields $f(x,y(x)) = c$, an arbitrary constant. Thus, the general solution of Equation (2.3) is $f(x,y) = c$. The problem, then, is the determination of the function f, called a *potential function*.

Definition 2.11. An equation of the form $P(x,y) + Q(x,y)\dfrac{dy}{dx} = 0$, with P and Q continuous in a region R of the (x,y)-plane, is said to be *exact* in R if there exists a potential function f defined for all (x,y) in R.

Example 2.21. Consider the equation $y + xy' = 0$. Evidently, $f(x,y) = xy$ is a potential function because $f_x = y = P$ and $f_y = x = Q$. Hence, the equation is exact, with the general solution $f(x,y) = c$, i.e., $xy = c$.

Theorem 2.3. Suppose that P and Q have continuous first-order partial derivatives in an open region R of the plane. If the equation $P(x,y) + Q(x,y)y' = 0$ is exact in R, then $P_y(x,y) = Q_x(x,y)$ for all (x,y) in R.

Proof. Since the equation is exact, there exists a potential function f. Then $f_x = P$ and $f_y = Q \Rightarrow f_{xy} = P_y$ and $f_{yx} = Q_x$. Since P_y and Q_x are continuous in R, f_{xy} and f_{yx} are continuous in R, hence equal by Theorem 2.1. Thus, $P_y = Q_x$ in R.

Theorem 2.3 is equivalent to the following:

Theorem 2.4. If $P_y \neq Q_x$ in R, then the equation $P(x,y) + Q(x,y)y' = 0$ is not exact in R.

Proof. Suppose that $P_y \neq Q_x$ in R. If the equation is exact, then $P_y = Q_x$ by Theorem 2.3, which contradicts $P_y \neq Q_x$. Hence, the equation is not exact.

Example 2.22. Consider the equation $x^2 + y^2 + xy\dfrac{dy}{dx} = 0$.

$P(x,y) = x^2 + y^2$, $Q(x,y) = xy$, $P_y = 2y$, $Q_x = y$, $P_y \neq Q_x$, hence, the equation is not exact, by Theorem 2.4.

It is not true, in general, that if $P_y = Q_x$, then the equation $P(x,y) + Q(x,y)y' = 0$ is exact. In order to state a converse of Theorem 2.3, i.e., a theorem which gives the conditions under which exactness follows from $P_y = Q_x$, the following definition is required.

Definition 2.12. A region R in the (x, y)-plane is *connected* if it consists of a single "piece." It is *simply connected* if it is connected and has no "holes" in it.

Definition 2.12 is, of necessity, merely informal, since the mathematically rigorous definitions of *connected* and *simply connected* sets are beyond the scope of this book.

For example, the region R enclosed by a non-self-intersecting closed curve (e.g., a circle) is simply connected. The entire plane is simply connected. However, the plane with the origin excluded is not simply connected due to the "hole" at the origin.

Theorem 2.5. Suppose that P and Q have continuous first-order partial derivatives in an open, simply connected region R of the plane. If $P_y = Q_x$ in R, then the equation $P(x, y) + Q(x, y)y' = 0$ is exact in R.

Note that, if the region R is not simply connected, then the equation may not be exact, even if $P_y = Q_x$.

Example 2.23. Consider the equation $x^2 + y^2 + 2xyy' = 0$.

$P(x, y) = x^2 + y^2$, $Q(x, y) = 2xy$, $P_y = 2y$, $Q_x = 2y$, $P_x = 2x$ and $Q_y = 2x$ are continuous in the plane, which is simply connected, and $P_y = Q_x$. Hence, the equation is exact by Theorem 2.5. A potential function f exists, and satisfies the two conditions $f_x = P$ and $f_y = Q$.

$$f_x = P \quad \Rightarrow \quad f(x, y) = \int P(x, y)\, dx = \int x^2 + y^2\, dx = \frac{x^3}{3} + xy^2 + g(y),$$

where $g(y)$ is an arbitrary function of y. Note that, in the above integration with respect to x, y is regarded as a constant, and $g(y)$ has the role of the arbitrary "constant" of integration, being the most general expression such that $\frac{d}{dx}g(y) = 0$. Then $f_y = Q \Rightarrow$

$$2xy + g'(y) = 2xy \quad \Rightarrow \quad g'(y) = 0 \quad \Rightarrow \quad g(y) = c_1 \quad \Rightarrow \quad f(x, y) = \frac{x^3}{3} + xy^2 + c_1,$$

and the general solution of the equation is

$$f(x, y) = \frac{x^3}{3} + xy^2 + c_1 = c_2, \quad \text{or} \quad \frac{x^3}{3} + xy^2 = c_2 - c_1 = k.$$

Example 2.24. Consider the equation $4x^3 - 2x + 3y + (3x + 2y)y' = 0$.

$P(x, y) = 4x^3 - 2x + 3y$, $Q(x, y) = 3x + 2y$, all first-order partial derivatives of both P and Q are continuous in the plane, which is simply connected, and $P_y = 3 = Q_x$. Hence, the equation is exact by Theorem 2.5. A potential function f exists, and satisfies the two conditions $f_x = P$ and $f_y = Q$.

$$f_x = P \quad \Rightarrow \quad f(x, y) = \int P(x, y)\, dx = \int 4x^3 - 2x + 3y\, dx = x^4 - x^2 + 3xy + g(y),$$

where $g(y)$ is an arbitrary function of y. Then $f_y = Q \Rightarrow$

$$3x + g'(y) = 3x + 2y \quad \Rightarrow \quad g'(y) = 2y \quad \Rightarrow \quad g(y) = y^2 + c_1$$

$$\Rightarrow \quad f(x, y) = x^4 - x^2 + 3xy + y^2 + c_1,$$

and the general solution of the equation is

$$f(x, y) = x^4 - x^2 + 3xy + y^2 + c_1 = c_2, \quad \text{or} \quad x^4 - x^2 + 3xy + y^2 = k.$$

Note that, if we begin with the condition $f_y = Q$ instead of $f_x = P$, then the result will be the same. Thus,

$$f_y = Q \quad \Rightarrow \quad f(x, y) = \int Q(x, y)\, dy = \int 3x + 2y\, dy = 3xy + y^2 + g(x),$$

where $g(x)$ is an arbitrary function of x, being the most general expression such that $\frac{d}{dy}g(x) = 0$. In the above integration with respect to y, x is regarded as a constant. Then $f_x = P \Rightarrow$

$$3y + g'(x) = 4x^3 - 2x + 3y \quad \Rightarrow \quad g'(x) = 4x^3 - 2x \quad \Rightarrow \quad g(x) = x^4 - x^2 + c_1$$

$$\Rightarrow \quad f(x, y) = 3xy + y^2 + x^4 - x^2 + c_1,$$

as before.

Example 2.25. Consider the equation $x^2 + y^2 + xyy' = 0$.

As shown in Example 2.22, this equation is not exact because $P_y \neq Q_x$. Thus, any attempt to determine a function f such that $f_x = P$ and $f_y = Q$ must fail. Proceeding as in the last two examples,

$$f_x = P \quad \Rightarrow \quad f(x, y) = \int P(x, y)\, dx = \int x^2 + y^2\, dx = \frac{x^3}{3} + xy^2 + g(y),$$

and $f_y = Q \Rightarrow$

$$2xy + g'(y) = xy \quad \Rightarrow \quad g'(y) = -xy,$$

which is a contradiction because the left-hand side is independent of x, whereas the right-hand side is not, making their equality impossible. It follows that a function $f(x, y)$ with $f_x = P$ and $f_y = Q$ does not exist.

Example 2.26. Consider the initial-value problem

$$ye^x + \sin(y) + [e^x + x\cos(y) + 1]\frac{dy}{dx} = 0, \quad y(0) = -3.$$

$P(x, y) = ye^x + \sin(y)$, $Q(x, y) = e^x + x\cos(y) + 1$, all first-order partial derivatives of both P and Q are continuous in the plane, and $P_y = e^x + \cos(y) = Q_x$. Hence, the equation is exact by Theorem 2.5.

$$f_x = P \quad \Rightarrow \quad f(x, y) = \int P(x, y)\, dx = \int ye^x + \sin(y)\, dx = ye^x + x\sin(y) + g(y),$$

and $f_y = Q \Rightarrow$

$$e^x + x\cos(y) + g'(y) = e^x + x\cos(y) + 1 \quad \Rightarrow \quad g'(y) = 1 \quad \Rightarrow g(y) = y + c_1$$

$$\Rightarrow \quad f(x, y) = ye^x + x\sin(y) + y + c_1,$$

and the general solution is $ye^x + x\sin(y) + y = k$. Setting $x = 0$ and $y = -3$ then gives $k = -6$, and the solution of the initial-value problem is $ye^x + x\sin(y) + y = -6$.

Example 2.27. Consider the initial-value problem

$$y\ln(x) + 2x - \left[x - x\ln(x) + 3y^2\right] y' = 0, \quad x > 0, \quad y(1) = 2.$$

$P(x, y) = y\ln(x) + 2x$, $Q(x, y) = -x + x\ln(x) - 3y^2$, all first-order partial derivatives of both P and Q are continuous in the right half-plane $x > 0$, which is simply connected, and $P_y = \ln(x) = Q_x$. Hence, the equation is exact by Theorem 2.5.

$$f_y = Q \quad \Rightarrow \quad f(x, y) = \int Q(x, y)\, dy = \int -x + x\ln(x) - 3y^2\, dy$$

$$= -xy + xy\ln(x) - y^3 + g(x),$$

and $f_x = P \Rightarrow$

$$-y + y\ln(x) + y + g'(x) = y\ln(x) + 2x \quad \Rightarrow \quad g'(x) = 2x \quad \Rightarrow \quad g(x) = x^2 + c_1$$

$$\Rightarrow \quad f(x, y) = -xy + xy\ln(x) - y^3 + x^2 + c_1,$$

and the general solution is $xy\ln(x) - xy + x^2 - y^3 = k$. Setting $x = 1$ and $y = 2$ then gives $k = -9$, and the solution of the initial-value problem is

$$xy\ln(x) - xy + x^2 - y^3 = -9.$$

2.5.1 Integrating Factors

If the equation $P(x, y) + Q(x, y)y' = 0$ is not exact because $P_y \neq Q_x$, then it can be made exact by multiplication by an *integrating factor* $I(x, y)$, chosen such that the resulting, equivalent, equation

$$I(x, y)P(x, y) + I(x, y)Q(x, y)y' = 0 \tag{2.4}$$

is exact. The exactness of Equation (2.4) requires that $(IP)_y = (IQ)_x$. Employing the product rule, this condition becomes

$$I_y P + I P_y = I_x Q + I Q_x, \quad \text{or} \quad I_y P - I_x Q = I(Q_x - P_y). \tag{2.5}$$

This partial differential equation for the unknown function $I(x, y)$ is more difficult to solve than the given ordinary differential equation, and simplifying assumptions must be made, which may or may not succeed.

Seek an integrating factor $I(x)$ which is independent of y. Then $I_y = 0$, $I_x = I'(x)$, and the condition (2.5) becomes

$$\frac{I'(x)}{I(x)} = \frac{P_y - Q_x}{Q}. \tag{2.6}$$

If the right-hand side of Equation (2.6) is independent of y, then $I(x)$ is determined by Equation (2.6). Otherwise, Equation (2.6) is a contradiction because the left-hand side is independent of y. In that case, $I(x)$ does not exist.

If $I(x)$ does not exist, then seek an integrating factor $I(y)$ which is independent of x. Then $I_x = 0$, $I_y = I'(y)$, and the condition (2.5) becomes

$$\frac{I'(y)}{I(y)} = \frac{Q_x - P_y}{P}. \tag{2.7}$$

If the right-hand side of Equation (2.7) is independent of x, then $I(y)$ is determined by Equation (2.7). Otherwise, Equation (2.7) is a contradiction because the left-hand side is independent of x. In that case, $I(y)$ does not exist.

Example 2.28. Consider the equation $x^2 + y^2 + xyy' = 0$.

As shown in Example 2.22, this equation is not exact because $P_y \neq Q_x$. Since

$$\frac{P_y - Q_x}{Q} = \frac{2y - y}{xy} = \frac{1}{x}$$

is independent of y, $I(x)$ exists and is determined by

$$\frac{I'(x)}{I(x)} = \frac{1}{x} \quad \Rightarrow \quad \int \frac{1}{I(x)} \frac{dI}{dx} dx = \int \frac{1}{x} dx \quad \Rightarrow \quad \int \frac{1}{I} dI = \int \frac{1}{x} dx$$

$$\Rightarrow \quad \ln|I| = \ln|x| \quad \Rightarrow \quad I(x) = \pm x,$$

where arbitrary constants of integration are unnecessary and have been suppressed, because we seek only one solution $I(x)$, and not all possible solutions. Since both $\pm x$ are integrating factors, we select the simpler one, $I(x) = x$. The equation then becomes

$$x^3 + xy^2 + x^2yy' = 0,$$

and is exact. Then

$$f_x = P \quad \Rightarrow \quad f(x,y) = \int x^3 + xy^2 \, dx = \frac{1}{4}x^4 + \frac{1}{2}x^2y^2 + g(y),$$

and $f_y = Q \Rightarrow$

$$x^2y + g'(y) = x^2y \quad \Rightarrow \quad g'(y) = 0 \quad \Rightarrow \quad g(y) = c_1 \quad \Rightarrow \quad f(x,y) = \frac{1}{4}x^4 + \frac{1}{2}x^2y^2 + c_1,$$

and the general solution is $\frac{1}{4}x^4 + \frac{1}{2}x^2y^2 = k$, or $x^4 + 2x^2y^2 = 4k = k_1$.

Example 2.29. Consider the equation

$$\sqrt{x} + y^3 + 2xy^2y' = 0, \quad x > 0.$$

$P(x,y) = \sqrt{x} + y^3$, $Q(x,y) = 2xy^2$, $P_y(x,y) = 3y^2$, $Q_x(x,y) = 2y^2$, $P_y \neq Q_x$, hence, the equation is not exact. Since

$$\frac{P_y - Q_x}{Q} = \frac{3y^2 - 2y^2}{2xy^2} = \frac{1}{2x}$$

is independent of y, $I(x)$ exists and is determined by

$$\frac{I'(x)}{I(x)} = \frac{1}{2x} \quad \Rightarrow \quad \ln|I(x)| = \frac{1}{2}\ln(x) = \ln\left(x^{1/2}\right) \quad \Rightarrow \quad I(x) = \pm x^{1/2} = \pm\sqrt{x}.$$

With $I(x) = x^{1/2}$, the equation becomes

$$x + x^{1/2}y^3 + 2x^{3/2}y^2y' = 0,$$

and is exact. Then

$$f_x = P \quad \Rightarrow \quad f(x,y) = \int x + x^{1/2}y^3 \, dx = \frac{1}{2}x^2 + \frac{2}{3}x^{3/2}y^3 + g(y),$$

and $f_y = Q \Rightarrow$

$$2x^{3/2}y^2 + g'(y) = 2x^{3/2}y^2 \quad \Rightarrow \quad g(y) = c_1 \quad \Rightarrow \quad f(x,y) = \frac{1}{2}x^2 + \frac{2}{3}x^{3/2}y^3 + c_1,$$

and the general solution is $\frac{1}{2}x^2 + \frac{2}{3}x^{3/2}y^3 = k$, or $3x^2 + 4x^{3/2}y^3 = k_1$.

Example 2.30. Consider the equation

$$x + y + \left(\frac{x^2}{2} + x + xy \right) y' = 0.$$

$P_y = 1$, $Q_x = x + 1 + y$, $P_y \neq Q_x$, hence, the equation is not exact. Since

$$\frac{P_y - Q_x}{Q} = \frac{-x - y}{\frac{x^2}{2} + x + xy}$$

is not independent of y, $I(x)$ does not exist. Since

$$\frac{Q_x - P_y}{P} = \frac{x + y}{x + y} = 1$$

is independent of x, $I(y)$ exists and is determined by $\dfrac{I'(y)}{I(y)} = 1$, which gives $I(y) = e^y$. The equation then becomes

$$(x + y)e^y + \left(\frac{x^2}{2} + x + xy \right) e^y y' = 0,$$

and is exact. Then

$$f_x = P \quad \Rightarrow \quad f(x, y) = \int (x + y)e^y \, dx = \left(\frac{1}{2}x^2 + xy \right) e^y + g(y),$$

and $f_y = Q \Rightarrow$

$$\left(\frac{1}{2}x^2 + xy + x \right) e^y + g'(y) = \left(\frac{1}{2}x^2 + xy + x \right) e^y \quad \Rightarrow \quad g(y) = c_1$$

$$\Rightarrow \quad f(x, y) = \left(\frac{1}{2}x^2 + xy \right) e^y + c_1,$$

and the general solution is $\left(\dfrac{1}{2}x^2 + xy \right) e^y = k$, or $(x^2 + 2xy) e^y = k_1$.

Example 2.31. Consider the initial-value problem

$$4xy + \left(x^2 + \sqrt{y} \right) y' = 0, \quad y > 0, \quad y(1) = 4.$$

$P_y = 4x$, $Q_x = 2x$, $P_y \neq Q_x$, hence, the equation is not exact. An integrating factor $I(y)$ exists and is determined by

$$\frac{I'(y)}{I(y)} = \frac{Q_x - P_y}{P} = \frac{-2x}{4xy} = -\frac{1}{2y} \quad \Rightarrow \quad \ln |I(y)| = -\frac{1}{2} \ln(y) \quad \Rightarrow \quad I(y) = y^{-1/2}.$$

The equation then becomes

$$4xy^{1/2} + \left(x^2 y^{-1/2} + 1\right) y' = 0,$$

and is exact. Then

$$f_x = 4xy^{1/2} \quad \Rightarrow \quad f(x,y) = \int 4xy^{1/2}\, dx = 2x^2 y^{1/2} + g(y),$$

and $f_y = Q \Rightarrow$

$$x^2 y^{-1/2} + g'(y) = x^2 y^{-1/2} + 1 \quad \Rightarrow \quad g'(y) = 1 \quad \Rightarrow \quad g(y) = y + c_1$$

$$\Rightarrow \quad f(x,y) = 2x^2 y^{1/2} + y + c_1,$$

and the general solution is $2x^2 y^{1/2} + y = k$. Setting $x = 1$ and $y = 4$ gives $k = 8$, and the solution of the initial-value problem is $2x^2 y^{1/2} + y = 8$.

Exercises 2.5

1. Find the general solution of $3x^2 + y + 1 - (3y^2 - x + 1)y' = 0$.

2. Find the general solution of $xy + x + 1 + \left(\dfrac{1}{2}x^2 + y + 1\right)\dfrac{dy}{dx} = 0$.

3. Find the general solution of $3x^2 y^2 - 2x + (2x^3 y + 3y^2)y' = 0$.

4. Solve the initial-value problem $y^3 - 3x^2 y^2 + 4x^3 + (3xy^2 - 2x^3 y - 4y^3)y' = 0$, $y(0) = 1$.

5. Solve the initial-value problem $y' = \dfrac{3x^2 y^2 - y - 2xy^3}{3x^2 y^2 - 2x^3 y + x}$, $y(2) = 1$.

6. Solve the initial-value problem $\dfrac{\sqrt{y}}{2\sqrt{x}} + y + \left(\dfrac{\sqrt{x}}{2\sqrt{y}} + x\right)\dfrac{dy}{dx} = 0$, $x > 0$, $y > 0$, $y(1) = 4$.

7. Find the general solution of $(6xy + e^y)y' + xe^x + 3y^2 = 0$.

8. Find the general solution of $2xe^{x^2+y^2} + 4x^3 + \left(2ye^{x^2+y^2} - 2y\right)\dfrac{dy}{dx} = 0$.

9. Find the general solution of $e^{x+y} + x + y + \cos(x) + (e^{x+y} + x - y)y' = 0$.

10. Solve the initial-value problem $\dfrac{x}{x^2 + y^2 + 1} - 2x + \left(\dfrac{y}{x^2 + y^2 + 1} + 2y\right)\dfrac{dy}{dx} = 0$, $y(0) = 0$.

11. Find the general solution of

$$\frac{2x+2}{x^2+y^2+2x-3y+3} + 1 + \frac{2y-3}{x^2+y^2+2x-3y+3}\frac{dy}{dx} = 0.$$

12. Consider the equation $\dfrac{x}{\sqrt{x^2+y^2}} + 1 + \left(\dfrac{y}{\sqrt{x^2+y^2}} + 1\right)\dfrac{dy}{dx} = 0.$

    (a) Show that $P_y = Q_x$ in the region $R = \{(x,y) : (x,y) \neq (0,0)\}$.

    (b) Solve the equation.

    (c) Is the equation exact in R?

13. Consider the equation $\dfrac{y}{x^2+y^2} - \dfrac{x}{x^2+y^2}y' = 0.$

    (a) Show that $P_y = Q_x$ in the region $R = \{(x,y) : (x,y) \neq (0,0)\}$.

    (b) Solve the equation.

    (c) Is the equation exact in R?

14. Solve the initial-value problem $x + 6y^2 + 4xyy' = 0$, $y(2) = 0$, and express y in terms of x.

15. Find the general solution of $x^3 + 2y^2 + xyy' = 0$.

16. Find the general solution of $e^{-x} - \cos(y) + \sin(y)y' = 0$.

17. Find the general solution of $xe^{x^2} + xy^2 + yy' = 0$.

18. Find the general solution of $\sqrt{x} + y^2 + 4xyy' = 0$, $x > 0$.

19. Find the general solution of $x + y^2 + 3xyy' = 0$.

20. Solve the initial-value problem $4xy + (6x^2 + y)y' = 0$, $y(1) = 1$.

21. Find the general solution of $\sin(x) + \left[e^{-y} - \cos(x)\right]y' = 0$.

22. Find the general solution of $y + (1 + 2x + xy)y' = 0$.

23. Find the general solution of $\dfrac{dy}{dx} = \dfrac{-y\ln(y)}{x\ln(y) + 2x}$, $y > 0$.

Chapter 2 Exercises

1. Consider the equation $xy + y^2 - x^2 y' = 0$.

   (a) Solve it as a homogeneous equation.

   (b) Solve it as a Bernoulli equation.

2. Consider the equation $\dfrac{y^2}{x^2} - y' = 0$.

   (a) Solve it as a separable equation.

   (b) Solve it as a homogeneous equation.

   (c) Solve it as a Bernoulli equation.

   (d) Find an integrating factor which makes the equation exact and solve it.

   (e) Find the orthogonal trajectories of the one-parameter family of curves defined by the general solution.

3. Consider the equation $x + y - xy' = 0$.

   (a) Solve it as a homogeneous equation.

   (b) Solve it as a linear equation.

   (c) Find an integrating factor which makes the equation exact and solve it.

   (d) Find the orthogonal trajectories of the one-parameter family of curves defined by the general solution.

4. Consider the equation $3xy' + 2y = 0$.

   (a) Solve it as a separable equation.

   (b) Solve it as a homogeneous equation.

   (c) Solve it as a linear equation.

   (d) Find an integrating factor which makes the equation exact and solve it.

   (e) Find the orthogonal trajectories of the one-parameter family of curves defined by the general solution.

5. Find the orthogonal trajectories of the one-parameter family of curves defined by the equation $2x - 2e^{-x} - y^2 = k$.

6. Find the orthogonal trajectories of the one-parameter family of curves defined by the equation $y = 2x \ln |x| + cx$.

7. The relation $f(x, y) = 0$ defines y as a function of x, and x as a function of y. Determine $\dfrac{dy}{dx}$ and $\dfrac{dx}{dy}$ in terms of f_x and f_y, and express $\dfrac{dy}{dx}$ in terms of $\dfrac{dx}{dy}$.

8. Consider the equation $3x - 2y + (y - 2x)y' = 0$.

   (a) Solve it as an exact equation and express y in terms of x.

   (b) Solve it as a homogeneous equation.

9. Consider the equation $xe^x - x\ln(x) + y + xy' = 0$, $x > 0$.

   (a) Solve it as an exact equation and express y in terms of x.

   (b) Solve it as a linear equation.

10. (a) Show that any separable equation can be expressed as an exact equation.

    (b) Solve the equation $y + x\ln(x)\ln(y)y' = 0$, $x > 0$, $y > 0$, as a separable equation.

    (c) Solve the separable equation in part (b) as an exact equation.

11. Consider an equation of the form $y' = f(ax + by + c)$, $b \neq 0$.

    (a) Show that $u(x) = ax + by + c$ transforms the equation into one which is separable.

    (b) Solve $y' = (x + y + 1)^2$.

    (c) Solve $y' = \dfrac{1}{\sqrt{x + y - 2}}$, $x + y > 2$.

    (d) Solve $y' = (x + y)\ln(x + y) - 1$, $x + y > 0$.

12. Consider an equation of the form $a(y) + [b(y)x - c(y)]y' = 0$.

    (a) Show that an integrating factor $I(y)$ exists.

    (b) Regard y as the independent variable and x as the unknown function of y. Show that the resulting equation for $x(y)$ is linear, employing the fact that $y' = \dfrac{1}{x'}$ by the chain rule (see Exercise 7).

13. Consider the equation $y + [(2y^2 + 1)x - 2y]y' = 0$.

    (a) Find an integrating factor which makes the equation exact and solve it.

    (b) Proceed as in Exercise 12(b) and solve the linear equation.

14. Consider the equation $y^2 + (3xy + 2)y' = 0$.

    (a) Find an integrating factor which makes the equation exact and solve it.

    (b) Proceed as in Exercise 12(b) and solve the linear equation.

15. Solve the equation $1 + (xy - x^{-3}y^3)y' = 0$ by transforming it into an equation for x as a function of y (see Exercise 12(b)).

16. Consider the equation $y' = 2\sqrt{y-1}$.

   (a) Find the general solution.

   (b) By inspection of the equation, find a solution which is not a particular solution, i.e., it does not correspond to any particular value of the arbitrary constant c. Such a solution is called a *singular solution*, and may occur only as the solution of a nonlinear equation.

   (c) The *envelope* of a one-parameter family of curves is a curve C with the property that, at every point of C, it is tangent to the graph of a member of the family. The envelope of the one-parameter family of curves defined by the general solution, if it exists, is a singular solution. However, a singular solution is not necessarily an envelope. Confirm that the graph of the singular solution found in part (b) is the envelope of the one-parameter family of curves defined by the general solution found in part (a).

17. Given the general solution $f(x, y, c) = 0$ of a nonlinear equation, where f is a (single-valued) function with continuous first-order partial derivatives, if a singular solution exists, then it is obtained by the elimination of c from the two equations $f(x, y, c) = 0$ and $\dfrac{\partial f}{\partial c}(x, y, c) = 0$.

   (a) Find the general solution of the equation $(y')^2 = \dfrac{1 - y^2}{y^2}$.

   (b) By inspection of the equation, find two singular solutions.

   (c) Express the general solution as $f(x, y, c) = 0$ and determine the singular solutions by elimination of c from $f(x, y, c) = 0$ and $f_c(x, y, c) = 0$.

   (d) Confirm that each singular solution is an envelope of the general solution.

18. Consider the equation $\dfrac{(y')^2 + 1}{(y - xy')^2} = 1$.

   (a) Show that $y = mx \pm \sqrt{m^2 + 1}$ is the general solution, where m is an arbitrary constant.

   (b) Express the general solution in part (a) as $f(x, y, m) = 0$ and determine x^2 as a function of m^2 from the equations $f(x, y, m) = 0$ and $f_m(x, y, m) = 0$.

   (c) Employ the result of part (b) to determine y^2 as a function of m^2.

   (d) Employ the results of parts (b) and (c) to eliminate m, thereby obtaining a relation $g(x, y) = 0$ between x and y, which defines a singular solution.

   (e) The general solution $y = mx \pm \sqrt{m^2 + 1}$ of part (a) defines a one-parameter family of straight lines of slope m and y-intercept $\pm\sqrt{m^2 + 1}$. Identify the graph of the singular solution obtained in part (d) as a well-known geometrical object, and confirm that it is the envelope of the family of straight lines.

19. *Peano's existence theorem* states that, if f is continuous on a rectangular region R with sides parallel to the axes, and if (x_0, y_0) is an interior point of R, then the initial-value problem $y' = f(x, y)$, $y(x_0) = y_0$, has a solution.

   (a) Find the general solution of the equation $y' = \dfrac{y}{x}$ and express y as a function of x

   (b) Show that the initial-value problem with the initial condition $y(0) = 1$ has no solution, and give the reason.

20. *Picard's existence and uniqueness theorem* states that, if f and f_y are continuous on a rectangular region R with sides parallel to the axes, and if (x_0, y_0) is an interior point of R, then the initial-value problem $y' = f(x, y)$, $y(x_0) = y_0$, has a unique solution.

   (a) Find the general solution of the equation $y' = 3xy^{1/3}$.

   (b) Solve the initial-value problem with the initial condition $y(0) = 0$.

   (c) Find a singular solution (which is not an envelope).

   (d) Show that the solution of the initial-value problem is not unique, and give the reason.

Chapter 3

Second-Order Equations

3.1 Basic Definitions

Definition 3.1. The *general solution* of a second-order equation is the solution which contains two arbitrary constants which cannot be combined. It is a *two-parameter family of solutions*, i.e., a set of solutions such that every solution corresponds to particular values of the arbitrary constants. A solution in which the constants are assigned particular values is called a *particular solution*.

Example 3.1. The second-order equation $y'' = x$ can be solved by two integrations:

$$y'' = x \quad \Rightarrow \quad y' = \frac{1}{2}x^2 + c_1 \quad \Rightarrow \quad y = \frac{1}{6}x^3 + c_1 x + c_2$$

is the general solution since it contains two arbitrary constants c_1 and c_2 which cannot be replaced by a single arbitrary constant. Particular solutions are

$$y = \frac{1}{6}x^3, \quad y = \frac{1}{6}x^3 + 2x + 1, \quad \text{and} \quad y = \frac{1}{6}x^3 - 4x - 3,$$

corresponding to $c_1 = c_2 = 0$, $c_1 = 2$, $c_2 = 1$, and $c_1 = -4$, $c_2 = -3$, respectively.

Definition 3.2. An *initial-value problem* for a second-order equation consists of the equation, together with two *initial conditions*, which specify the values of y and y' at a single point x and, thereby, determine a particular solution.

In Example 3.1, if the initial conditions $y(0) = 2$ and $y'(0) = 3$ are imposed, then

$$y = \frac{1}{6}x^3 + c_1 x + c_2 \text{ and } y(0) = 2 \; \Rightarrow c_2 = 2 \; \Rightarrow y = \frac{1}{6}x^3 + c_1 x + 2 \; \Rightarrow y' = \frac{1}{2}x^2 + c_1,$$

$$\text{and } y'(0) = 3 \; \Rightarrow \; c_1 = 3 \; \Rightarrow \; y = \frac{1}{6}x^3 + 3x + 2$$

43

is the solution of the initial-value problem.

In contrast to first-order equations, only a few types of second-order equation can be solved in terms of elementary functions.

Definition 3.3. A second-order equation is *linear* if it has the form

$$a(x)y'' + b(x)y' + c(x)y = g(x),$$

where $a(x) \not\equiv 0$, $b(x)$, $c(x)$ and $g(x)$ are functions of x (or constants). Otherwise, the equation is *nonlinear*. Dividing the equation by $a(x)$ and letting $p(x) = \dfrac{b(x)}{a(x)}$, $q(x) = \dfrac{c(x)}{a(x)}$ and $f(x) = \dfrac{g(x)}{a(x)}$, the equation may be placed in the *standard form*

$$y'' + p(x)y' + q(x)y = f(x).$$

If $f(x) \equiv 0$, then the equation $y'' + p(x)y' + q(x)y = 0$ (or $a(x)y'' + b(x)y' + c(x)y = 0$) is called *homogeneous*. Otherwise, it is *nonhomogeneous*.

For example, the equation

$$e^x y'' + y' - 2y = 0$$

is linear and homogeneous, with the standard form

$$y'' + e^{-x}y' - 2e^{-x}y = 0.$$

The equation

$$2y'' + 5xy' + y = \sin(x)$$

is linear and nonhomogeneous, with the standard form

$$y'' + \frac{5x}{2}y' + \frac{1}{2}y = \frac{1}{2}\sin(x).$$

The equations

$$yy'' + y = x^2, \quad y'' + yy' = 0 \quad \text{and} \quad y'' + y' + e^y = x$$

are nonlinear.

Definition 3.4. Two functions y_1 and y_2 are *linearly dependent on an interval I* if there exist constants c_1 and c_2, not both zero, such that $c_1 y_1 + c_2 y_2 = 0$ on I (i.e., $c_1 y_1(x) + c_2 y_2(x) = 0$ for all x in I). Two functions y_1 and y_2 are *linearly independent on I* if they are not linearly dependent on I, i.e., if $c_1 y_1 + c_2 y_2 = 0$ on I, then $c_1 = c_2 = 0$.

It follows by Definition 3.4 that two functions are linearly dependent on I if and only if one of the functions is a constant multiple of the other on I: Suppose that $c_1 y_1 + c_2 y_2 = 0$.

$$\text{If} \quad c_1 \neq 0, \quad \text{then} \quad y_1 = \frac{-c_2}{c_1} y_2, \quad \text{and if} \quad c_2 \neq 0, \quad \text{then} \quad y_2 = \frac{-c_1}{c_2} y_1.$$

Conversely, if $y_1 = cy_2$, then $1 \cdot y_1 - cy_2 = 0$ (with $c_1 = 1 \neq 0$ and $c_2 = -c$), and if $y_2 = cy_1$, then $cy_1 - 1 \cdot y_2 = 0$ (with $c_1 = c$ and $c_2 = -1 \neq 0$). Two functions are linearly independent on I if and only if neither one is a constant multiple of the other on I.

Example 3.2. $y_1 = x$ and $y_2 = e^x$ are linearly independent on $\mathbb{R}$ because neither one is a constant multiple of the other. If $c_1 x + c_2 e^x = 0$ for all x, then $x = 0 \Rightarrow c_2 = 0 \Rightarrow c_1 x = 0$ for all x, and $x = 1 \Rightarrow c_1 = 0$.

Example 3.3. $y_1 = e^x$ and $y_2 = e^{2x}$ are linearly independent on $\mathbb{R}$ because neither one is a constant multiple of the other. If $c_1 e^x + c_2 e^{2x} = 0$ for all x, then $x = 0 \Rightarrow c_1 + c_2 = 0 \Rightarrow c_2 = -c_1 \Rightarrow c_1(e^x - e^{2x}) = 0$ for all x, and $x = 1 \Rightarrow c_1(e - e^2) = 0 \Rightarrow c_1 = 0 \Rightarrow c_2 = 0$.

More generally, $y_1 = e^{r_1 x}$ and $y_2 = e^{r_2 x}$ are linearly independent on $\mathbb{R}$ if and only if $r_1 \neq r_2$.

Example 3.4. $y_1 = e^{3x}$ and $y_2 = 2e^{3x}$ are linearly dependent on $\mathbb{R}$ because $y_2 = 2y_1$ for all x. Equivalently, $2y_1 + (-1)y_2 = 0$ for all x, with $c_1 = 2$ and $c_2 = -1$.

Example 3.5. $y_1 = \cos(x)$ and $y_2 = \sin(x)$ are linearly independent on $\mathbb{R}$ because neither one is a constant multiple of the other. If $c_1 \cos(x) + c_2 \sin(x) = 0$ for all x, then $x = 0 \Rightarrow c_1 = 0 \Rightarrow c_2 \sin(x) = 0$ for all x, and $x = \dfrac{\pi}{2} \Rightarrow c_2 = 0$.

The terms "dependent" and "independent" are often employed to mean "linearly dependent" and "linearly independent," respectively. If an interval I is not specified, then it is taken to be any interval on which y_1 and y_2 are defined.

The definitions of linear dependence and independence can be extended to any number of functions:

Definition 3.5. The functions $y_1, y_2, \cdots, y_n$ are *linearly dependent on an interval I* if there exist constants $c_1, c_2, \cdots, c_n$, not all zero, such that $c_1 y_1 + c_2 y_2 + \cdots + c_n y_n = 0$ on I. The functions $y_1, y_2, \cdots, y_n$ are *linearly independent on I* if they are not linearly dependent on I, i.e., if $c_1 y_1 + c_2 y_2 + \cdots + c_n y_n = 0$ on I, then $c_1 = c_2 = \cdots = c_n = 0$.

Exercises 3.1

1. Find the general solution of the equation $y'' + 6x^2 + \sin(x) = 2$.

2. Find the general solution of the equation $xy'' = \ln(x)$, $x > 0$.

3. Solve the initial-value problem $y'' - 4\cos^2(x) = 2$, $y(0) = 0$, $y'(0) = 1$.

4. Solve the initial-value problem $y'' = xe^x$, $y(0) = 1$, $y'(0) = 1$.

5. Determine whether the given equation is linear and homogeneous, linear and nonhomogeneous, or nonlinear.

   (a) $xy'' - y' + 2y = 0$

   (b) $2y'' + \ln(x)y = \sin(x)$

   (c) $y'' + y' + (x^2 + y^2) = 0$

   (d) $y'' + xy' = y^3$

   (e) $x^2y'' + xy' = 2y$

   (f) $y'' + y' + y + x = 0$

   (g) $y'' + yy' + y = 0$

6. Show that the functions $y_1 = e^{r_1 x}$ and $y_2 = e^{r_2 x}$ are linearly dependent on $\mathbb{R}$ if and only if $r_1 = r_2$.

7. Show that the functions $y_1 = x^\alpha$ and $y_2 = x^\beta$ are linearly dependent on I if and only if $\alpha = \beta$, where I is any interval where both functions are defined.

8. Show that the functions $y_1 = x^r$ and $y_2 = e^{sx}$ are linearly dependent on I if and only if $r = 0$ and $s = 0$, where I is any interval where both functions are defined.

9. Show that the functions $y_1, y_2, \cdots, y_n$ are linearly dependent if and only if (at least) one of the functions is a linear combination of the others.

10. Are the functions $y_1 = x$, $y_2 = e^x$ and $y_3 = e^{-x}$ linearly independent?

11. Are the functions $y_1 = x$, $y_2 = e^x$ and $y_3 = 2x$ linearly independent?

12. Under what condition(s) is the single function y linearly independent?

3.2 Linear Homogeneous Equations

Before methods of solution of linear, second-order equations can be discussed, certain fundamental results must be established.

Theorem 3.1. If y_1 and y_2 are any two solutions of a linear, homogeneous equation $y'' + p(x)y' + q(x)y = 0$, then any linear combination $y = c_1 y_1 + c_2 y_2$ is a solution.

Proof.

$$
\begin{aligned}
y'' + p(x)y' + q(x)y &= (c_1 y_1 + c_2 y_2)'' + p(x)(c_1 y_1 + c_2 y_2)' + q(x)(c_1 y_1 + c_2 y_2) \\
&= c_1[y_1'' + p(x)y_1' + q(x)y_1] + c_2[y_2'' + p(x)y_2' + q(x)y_2] \\
&= 0.
\end{aligned}
$$

Theorem 3.2. The equation $y'' + p(x)y' + q(x)y = 0$ has precisely two linearly independent solutions y_1 and y_2, and the general solution is $y = c_1 y_1 + c_2 y_2$, where c_1 and c_2 are arbitrary constants.

Example 3.6. Let $y_1 = \cos(x)$ and $y_2 = \sin(x)$. Then $y_1'' = -y_1 \Rightarrow y_1'' + y_1 = 0$, and $y_2'' = -y_2 \Rightarrow y_2'' + y_2 = 0$. Hence, y_1 and y_2 are solutions of $y'' + y = 0$. Since y_1 and y_2 are linearly independent on $\mathbb{R}$, the general solution of $y'' + y = 0$ is $y = c_1 \cos(x) + c_2 \sin(x)$.

Note that, if we take $y_1 = \cos(x)$ and $y_2 = 2\cos(x)$, then, although both y_1 and y_2 are solutions of $y'' + y = 0$, they are not linearly independent since $y_2 = 2y_1$. Then $y = c_1 y_1 + c_2 y_2 = c_1 \cos(x) + 2c_2 \cos(x) = (c_1 + 2c_2)\cos(x) = k\cos(x)$ is not the general solution. Thus, it is essential that y_1 and y_2 be linearly independent solutions in order for $c_1 y_1 + c_2 y_2$ to be the general solution.

It is often possible to obtain one solution y_1 of an equation easily. The method of *reduction of order*, discussed below, is a method of determining a second, independent solution y_2 (i.e., a solution y_2 such that y_1 and y_2 are independent).

Reduction of Order
Suppose that y_1 is a solution of

$$
y'' + p(x)y' + q(x)y = 0,
$$

i.e., $y_1'' + p(x)y_1' + q(x)y_1 = 0$, and let $y_2 = u(x)y_1$, where u is to be determined. Then, by the product rule,

$$
y_2 = uy_1 \quad \Rightarrow \quad y_2' = u'y_1 + uy_1', \quad y_2'' = u''y_1 + 2u'y_1' + uy_1'',
$$

and y_2 is a solution if and only if $y_2'' + p(x)y_2' + q(x)y_2 = 0$, i.e.,

$$[u''y_1 + 2u'y_1' + uy_1''] + p(x)[u'y_1 + uy_1'] + q(x)[uy_1] = 0.$$

Rearranging terms, we obtain

$$u[y_1'' + p(x)y_1' + q(x)y_1] + u''y_1 + u'[2y_1' + p(x)y_1] = 0. \tag{3.1}$$

Since $y_1'' + p(x)y_1' + q(x)y_1 = 0$, Equation (3.1) reduces to

$$u''y_1 + u'[2y_1' + p(x)y_1] = 0,$$

which is a first-order, separable equation for the unknown function $v = u'$. Thus,

$$v'y_1 + v[2y_1' + p(x)y_1] = 0 \quad \Rightarrow \quad \frac{v'}{v} = -\frac{2y_1'}{y_1} - p(x)$$

$$\Rightarrow \quad \ln|v| = -2\ln|y_1| - \int p(x)\,dx \quad \Rightarrow \quad v = \frac{1}{y_1^2}e^{-\int p(x)\,dx}$$

$$\Rightarrow \quad u = \int v\,dx = \int \frac{1}{y_1^2}e^{-\int p(x)\,dx}\,dx, \tag{3.2}$$

where arbitrary constants of integration and $\pm$ signs have been omitted, since we seek only one function u(x), and not all such functions. Since $\frac{1}{y_1^2}e^{\int p(x)\,dx} \neq 0$, $u(x)$ is not a constant and, hence, y_1 and $y_2 = uy_1$ are linearly independent.

3.2.1   Equations with Constant Coefficients

Definition 3.6. A linear, homogeneous equation with *constant coefficients* has the general form

$$ay'' + by' + cy = 0,$$

where a, b and c are constants.

Seek solutions in the form $y = e^{rx}$, where r is a constant to be determined. Then

$$y = e^{rx} \quad \Rightarrow \quad y' = re^{rx} \quad \text{and} \quad y'' = r^2 e^{rx},$$

and $y = e^{rx}$ is a solution if and only if $ar^2 e^{rx} + bre^{rx} + ce^{rx} = 0$, i.e.,

$$ar^2 + br + c = 0, \tag{3.3}$$

called the *indicial equation*. Employing the quadratic formula, the solutions of the indicial equation (3.3) are given by

$$r = \frac{-b \pm \sqrt{b^2 - 4ac}}{2a}. \tag{3.4}$$

There are three possibilities, namely, $b^2 - 4ac > 0$, $b^2 - 4ac = 0$, and $b^2 - 4ac < 0$, and each must be analysed separately.

Case (i) If $b^2 - 4ac > 0$, then

$$r_1 = \frac{-b + \sqrt{b^2 - 4ac}}{2a} \quad \text{and} \quad r_2 = \frac{-b - \sqrt{b^2 - 4ac}}{2a}$$

are two distinct, real roots, and $y_1 = e^{r_1 x}$ and $y_2 = e^{r_2 x}$ are two independent solutions. The general solution is then $y = c_1 e^{r_1 x} + c_2 e^{r_2 x}$.

Example 3.7. Consider the constant-coefficient equation

$$3y'' + 7y' + 2y = 0.$$

Setting $y = e^{rx}$ gives the indicial equation $3r^2 + 7r + 2 = 0$, with the solutions $r = \dfrac{-7 \pm \sqrt{49 - 24}}{6}$, i.e., $r_1 = -\dfrac{1}{3}$ and $r_2 = -2$. Since the roots of the quadratic are real and distinct, $y_1 = e^{-\frac{1}{3}x}$ and $y_2 = e^{-2x}$ are two independent solutions, and the general solution is $y = c_1 e^{-\frac{1}{3}x} + c_2 e^{-2x}$.

Example 3.8. Consider the initial-value problem

$$y'' - y' - 6y = 0, \quad y(0) = 0, \quad y'(0) = 10.$$

Setting $y = e^{rx}$ gives the indicial equation $r^2 - r - 6 = (r - 3)(r + 2) = 0$, with the solutions $r_1 = 3$ and $r_2 = -2$. Since the roots of the quadratic are real and distinct, $y_1 = e^{3x}$ and $y_2 = e^{-2x}$ are two independent solutions, and the general solution is $y = c_1 e^{3x} + c_2 e^{-2x}$. Then $y(0) = 0 \Rightarrow c_1 + c_2 = 0 \Rightarrow$

$$y = c_1(e^{3x} - e^{-2x}) \quad \Rightarrow \quad y' = c_1(3e^{3x} + 2e^{-2x}),$$

and $y'(0) = 10 \Rightarrow c_1 = 2 \Rightarrow y = 2(e^{3x} - e^{-2x})$ is the solution of the initial-value problem.

Case (ii) If $b^2 - 4ac = 0$, then $r = \dfrac{-b}{2a}$ is the only root, and one solution is $y_1 = e^{rx}$. In order to determine a second, independent solution, employ reduction of order. The standard form of the equation $ay'' + by' + cy = 0$ is $y'' + \dfrac{b}{a}y' + \dfrac{c}{a}y = 0$, with $p(x) = \dfrac{b}{a}$. By Equation (3.2),

$$v = u' = \frac{1}{y_1^2}e^{-\int p(x)\,dx} = \frac{1}{e^{2rx}}e^{-\frac{b}{a}x} = 1 \quad \Rightarrow \quad u(x) = x,$$

and $y_2 = uy_1 = xe^{rx}$. The general solution is $y = c_1 e^{rx} + c_2 xe^{rx} = e^{rx}(c_1 + c_2 x)$.

Example 3.9. Consider the constant-coefficient equation

$$3y'' + 4\sqrt{6}\,y' + 8y = 0.$$

$y = e^{rx} \Rightarrow 3r^2 + 4\sqrt{6}\,r + 8 = 0 \Rightarrow r = \dfrac{-4\sqrt{6} \pm \sqrt{96 - 96}}{6} \Rightarrow r = -\dfrac{2\sqrt{6}}{3}$ is the only root. Thus, two independent solutions are $y_1 = e^{-\frac{2\sqrt{6}}{3}x}$ and $y_2 = xe^{-\frac{2\sqrt{6}}{3}x}$, and the general solution is $y = e^{-\frac{2\sqrt{6}}{3}x}(c_1 + c_2 x)$.

Example 3.10. Consider the initial-value problem

$$4y'' - 12y' + 9y = 0, \quad y(0) = 0, \quad y'(0) = 1.$$

$y = e^{rx} \Rightarrow 4r^2 - 12r + 9 = 0 \Rightarrow r = \dfrac{12 \pm \sqrt{144 - 144}}{8} \Rightarrow r = \dfrac{3}{2}$ is the only root. Note that $4r^2 - 12r + 9 = (2r - 3)^2 = 0$ also gives $r = \dfrac{3}{2}$ as the only root. Thus, two independent solutions are $y_1 = e^{\frac{3}{2}x}$ and $y_2 = xe^{\frac{3}{2}x}$, and the general solution is $y = e^{\frac{3}{2}x}(c_1 + c_2 x)$. Then $y(0) = 0 \Rightarrow c_1 = 0 \Rightarrow$

$$y = c_2 xe^{\frac{3}{2}x} \quad \Rightarrow \quad y' = c_2\left(1 + \frac{3}{2}x\right)e^{\frac{3}{2}x},$$

and $y'(0) = 1 \Rightarrow c_2 = 1 \Rightarrow y = xe^{\frac{3}{2}x}$ is the solution of the initial-value problem.

Case (iii) If $b^2 - 4ac < 0$, then the roots of the quadratic are complex,

$$r = \frac{-b \pm \sqrt{b^2 - 4ac}}{2a} = \frac{-b \pm i\sqrt{4ac - b^2}}{2a} = \alpha \pm i\beta,$$

where $\alpha = \dfrac{-b}{2a}$ and $\beta = \dfrac{\sqrt{4ac - b^2}}{2a}$. Two complex solutions are then given by

$$z_1 = e^{(\alpha + i\beta)x} \quad \text{and} \quad z_2 = \overline{z_1} = e^{(\alpha - i\beta)x},$$

where $\overline{z_1}$ is the *complex conjugate* of z_1.

In order to extract two real, independent solutions from the complex ones, employ the fact that any linear combination of solutions is a solution (by Theorem 3.1), and *Euler's identity*, which states that, for any real θ,

$$e^{i\theta} = \cos(\theta) + i\sin(\theta).$$

Thus, express the complex solutions as

$$\begin{aligned}
z_1 &= e^{(\alpha + i\beta)x} = e^{\alpha x}e^{i\beta x} = e^{\alpha x}[\cos(\beta x) + i\sin(\beta x)] \quad \text{and} \\
z_2 &= e^{(\alpha - i\beta)x} = e^{\alpha x}e^{-i\beta x} = e^{\alpha x}[\cos(\beta x) - i\sin(\beta x)],
\end{aligned}$$

and let

$$
\begin{aligned}
y_1 &= \frac{z_1 + z_2}{2} = \frac{z_1 + \overline{z_1}}{2} = \Re(z_1) = e^{\alpha x} \cos(\beta x) \quad \text{and} \\
y_2 &= \frac{z_1 - z_2}{2i} = \frac{z_1 - \overline{z_1}}{2i} = \Im(z_1) = e^{\alpha x} \sin(\beta x),
\end{aligned}
$$

where $\Re(z_1)$ is the *real part* of z_1 and $\Im(z_1)$ its *imaginary part*. Then y_1 and y_2 are two real, independent solutions, and the general solution is

$$
y = c_1 e^{\alpha x} \cos(\beta x) + c_2 e^{\alpha x} \sin(\beta x) = e^{\alpha x}[c_1 \cos(\beta x) + c_2 \sin(\beta x)].
$$

Example 3.11. Consider the constant-coefficient equation

$$
4y'' + 6y' + 3y = 0.
$$

$$
y = e^{rx} \Rightarrow 4r^2 + 6r + 3 = 0 \Rightarrow r = \frac{-6 \pm \sqrt{36 - 48}}{8} = -\frac{3}{4} \pm \frac{\sqrt{3}}{4} i \Rightarrow
$$

$$
y_1 = e^{-\frac{3}{4}x} \cos\left(\frac{\sqrt{3}}{4}x\right) \quad \text{and} \quad y_2 = e^{-\frac{3}{4}x} \sin\left(\frac{\sqrt{3}}{4}x\right)
$$

are two independent solutions, and the general solution is

$$
y = e^{-\frac{3}{4}x}\left[c_1 \cos\left(\frac{\sqrt{3}}{4}x\right) + c_2 \sin\left(\frac{\sqrt{3}}{4}x\right)\right].
$$

Example 3.12. Consider the initial-value problem

$$
y'' - 6y' + 13y = 0, \quad y(0) = 0, \quad y'(0) = -6.
$$

$$
y = e^{rx} \Rightarrow r^2 - 6r + 13 = 0 \Rightarrow r = \frac{6 \pm \sqrt{36 - 52}}{2} = 3 \pm 2i \Rightarrow
$$

$$
y = e^{3x}[c_1 \cos(2x) + c_2 \sin(2x)]
$$

is the general solution. Then $y(0) = 0 \Rightarrow c_1 = 0 \Rightarrow$

$$
y = c_2 e^{3x} \sin(2x) \quad \Rightarrow \quad y' = c_2[3e^{3x} \sin(2x) + 2e^{3x} \cos(2x)],
$$

and $y'(0) = -6 \Rightarrow c_2 = -3 \Rightarrow y = -3e^{3x} \sin(2x)$ is the solution of the initial-value problem.

3.2.2 Cauchy-Euler Equations

Definition 3.7. An equation of the form

$$ax^2 y'' + bxy' + cy = 0, \qquad (3.5)$$

where a, b and c are constants, is called a *Cauchy-Euler* or *Euler* equation.

The standard form of an Euler equation is $y'' + \dfrac{b}{ax}y' + \dfrac{c}{ax^2}y = 0$. Since $p(x) = \dfrac{b}{ax}$ and $q(x) = \dfrac{c}{ax^2}$ are undefined at $x = 0$, the solution may be undefined at $x = 0$. Such a point is called a *singular point* or *singularity* of the equation.

For $x > 0$, seek solutions of the Euler equation (3.5) in the form $y = x^r$, where r is a constant to be determined. Then

$$y = x^r \quad \Rightarrow \quad y' = rx^{r-1} \quad \Rightarrow \quad y'' = r(r-1)x^{r-2},$$

and $y = x^r$ is a solution if and only if $ar(r-1)x^r + brx^r + cx^r = 0$, i.e.,

$$ar(r-1) + br + c = 0, \quad \text{or} \quad ar^2 + (b-a)r + c = 0, \qquad (3.6)$$

called the *indicial equation*.

The three cases where the quadratic $ar^2 + (b-a)r + c$ in Equation (3.6) has two real, distinct roots, a repeated real root, and two complex conjugate roots must be analysed separately.

Case (i) If the quadratic has two real, distinct roots r_1 and r_2, then two independent solutions of the Euler equation are $y_1 = x^{r_1}$ and $y_2 = x^{r_2}$, and the general solution is $y = c_1 x^{r_1} + c_2 x^{r_2}$.

Case (ii) If the quadratic has a repeated real root $r = \dfrac{a-b}{2a}$, which occurs if and only if $(b-a)^2 - 4ac = 0$, then one solution is $y_1 = x^r$. A second, independent solution $y_2 = u(x)y_1$ is obtained by reduction of order. By Equation (3.2) on page 48,

$$v = u' = \frac{1}{y_1^2}e^{-\int p(x)\,dx} = \frac{1}{x^{2r}}e^{-\int \frac{b}{ax}\,dx} = \frac{1}{x^{2r}}e^{-\frac{b}{a}\ln(x)} = \frac{1}{x^{2r}}e^{(2r-1)\ln(x)} = \frac{x^{2r-1}}{x^{2r}} = \frac{1}{x}$$

$$\Rightarrow \quad u = \ln(x) \quad \Rightarrow \quad y_2 = x^r \ln(x),$$

and the general solution is $y = c_1 x^r + c_2 x^r \ln(x) = x^r[c_1 + c_2 \ln(x)]$.

Case (iii) If the quadratic has two complex conjugate roots $r = \alpha \pm i\beta$, then two complex solutions are $z_1 = x^{\alpha+i\beta}$ and $z_2 = x^{\alpha-i\beta} = \overline{z_1}$. Since $x^\gamma = e^{\ln(x^\gamma)} = e^{\gamma \ln(x)}$ for any real number γ, we define the quantity $x^{i\theta}$ by $x^{i\theta} = e^{i\theta \ln(x)}$. Employing Euler's identity, the two complex solutions may be expressed as

$$
\begin{aligned}
z_1 &= x^{\alpha+i\beta} = x^\alpha x^{i\beta} = x^\alpha e^{i\beta \ln(x)} = x^\alpha \{\cos[\beta \ln(x)] + i \sin[\beta \ln(x)]\}, \text{ and} \\
z_2 &= x^{\alpha-i\beta} = x^\alpha x^{-i\beta} = x^\alpha e^{-i\beta \ln(x)} = x^\alpha \{\cos[\beta \ln(x)] - i \sin[\beta \ln(x)]\}.
\end{aligned}
$$

By Theorem 3.1, since the Euler equation is linear and homogeneous, any linear combination of solutions is a solution. Thus, two real, independent solutions are

$$
\begin{aligned}
y_1 &= \frac{z_1 + z_2}{2} = \frac{z_1 + \overline{z_1}}{2} = \Re(z_1) = x^\alpha \cos[\beta \ln(x)] \quad \text{and} \\
y_2 &= \frac{z_1 - z_2}{2i} = \frac{z_1 - \overline{z_1}}{2i} = \Im(z_1) = x^\alpha \sin[\beta \ln(x)],
\end{aligned}
$$

and the general solution is $y = x^\alpha \{c_1 \cos[\beta \ln(x)] + c_2 \sin[\beta \ln(x)]\}$.

If $x < 0$, let $t = -x > 0$ and $y(x) = z(t)$. Then, by the chain rule,

$$
\frac{dy}{dx} = \frac{dz}{dt}\frac{dt}{dx} = -\frac{dz}{dt}, \quad \frac{d^2y}{dx^2} = \frac{d}{dt}\left(-\frac{dz}{dt}\right) \cdot \frac{dt}{dx} = -\frac{d^2z}{dt^2}(-1) = \frac{d^2z}{dt^2},
$$

and the equation $ax^2 y'' + bxy' + cy = 0$ transforms into $at^2 z'' + btz' + cz = 0$, i.e., an Euler equation for $z(t)$ with $t > 0$. Since $y(x) = z(t) = z(-x)$, the solutions $y(x)$ for $x < 0$ are obtained from the solutions $z(t)$ by replacing t by $-x$. Employing the fact that

$$
|x| = \left\{ \begin{array}{cc} x, & x > 0 \\ -x, & x < 0 \end{array} \right\},
$$

the solutions of an Euler equation for any $x \neq 0$ can be obtained from the solutions for $x > 0$ by replacing x by $|x|$.

Example 3.13. Consider the Euler equation

$$
2x^2 y'' + xy' - 3y = 0.
$$

For $x > 0$, $y = x^r \Rightarrow$

$$
2r(r-1) + r - 3 = 0 \quad \Rightarrow \quad 2r^2 - r - 3 = 0 \quad \Rightarrow \quad r = \frac{1 \pm \sqrt{1+24}}{4}
$$

$\Rightarrow r_1 = \dfrac{3}{2}$ and $r_2 = -1$. Since r_1 and r_2 are real and distinct, the general solution for any $x \neq 0$ is $y = c_1 |x|^{3/2} + c_2 |x|^{-1}$. Since $|x| = \pm x$, the term $c_2 |x|^{-1}$ may be replaced by $c_3 x^{-1}$, where $c_3 = \pm c_2$.

Example 3.14. Consider the initial-value problem

$$x^2 y'' + xy' - y = 0, \quad y(1) = 0, \quad y'(1) = -4.$$

For $x > 0$, $y = x^r \Rightarrow$

$$r(r-1) + r - 1 = r^2 - 1 = (r-1)(r+1) = 0$$

$\Rightarrow r_1 = 1$ and $r_2 = -1$. The general solution for any $x \neq 0$ is

$$y = c_1 |x| + c_2 |x|^{-1} = c_3 x + c_4 x^{-1}.$$

Then $y(1) = 0 \Rightarrow c_3 + c_4 = 0 \Rightarrow y = c_3(x - x^{-1})$, $y'(x) = c_3(1 + x^{-2})$, and $y'(1) = -4$
$\Rightarrow c_3 = -2 \Rightarrow y = -2(x - x^{-1})$ is the solution of the initial-value problem.

Example 3.15. Consider the Euler equation

$$4x^2 y'' + 16xy' + 9y = 0.$$

For $x > 0$, $y = x^r \Rightarrow$

$$4r(r-1) + 16r + 9 = 4r^2 + 12r + 9 = (2r+3)^2 = 0 \quad \Rightarrow \quad r = -\frac{3}{2}$$

is the only root. The general solution, for any $x \neq 0$, is $y = |x|^{-3/2}(c_1 + c_2 \ln |x|)$.
Note that $|x|^{-3/2} \neq \pm x^{-3/2}$, and $x^{-3/2}$ is not real for $x < 0$. Hence, the absolute
values must be retained.

Example 3.16. Consider the initial-value problem

$$x^2 y'' - 5xy' + 9y = 0, \quad y(1) = 0, \quad y'(1) = 2.$$

For $x > 0$, $y = x^r \Rightarrow$

$$r(r-1) - 5r + 9 = r^2 - 6r + 9 = (r-3)^2 = 0 \quad \Rightarrow \quad r = 3$$

is the only root. The general solution for any $x \neq 0$ is

$$y = |x|^3(c_1 + c_2 \ln |x|) = x^3(c_3 + c_4 \ln |x|).$$

Then $y(1) = 0 \Rightarrow c_3 = 0 \Rightarrow y = c_4 x^3 \ln |x|$, $y' = c_4(3x^2 \ln |x| + x^2)$, and $y'(1) = 2 \Rightarrow$
$c_4 = 2 \Rightarrow y = 2x^3 \ln |x|$ is the solution of the initial-value problem.

Example 3.17. Consider the Euler equation

$$3x^2 y'' - 2xy' + 4y = 0.$$

For $x > 0$, $y = x^r \Rightarrow 3r(r-1) - 2r + 4 = 3r^2 - 5r + 4 = 0$

$$\Rightarrow \quad r = \frac{5 \pm \sqrt{25 - 48}}{6} = \frac{5}{6} \pm \frac{\sqrt{23}}{6} i$$

$$\Rightarrow \quad y = |x|^{5/6} \left[c_1 \cos\left(\frac{\sqrt{23}}{6} \ln|x| \right) + c_2 \sin\left(\frac{\sqrt{23}}{6} \ln|x| \right) \right]$$

is the general solution for any $x \neq 0$.

Example 3.18. Consider the initial-value problem

$$x^2 y'' - 5xy' + 13y = 0, \quad y(1) = 0, \quad y'(1) = 6.$$

For $x > 0$, $y = x^r \Rightarrow r(r-1) - 5r + 13 = r^2 - 6r + 13 = 0 \Rightarrow$

$$r = \frac{6 \pm \sqrt{36 - 52}}{2} = 3 \pm 2i \quad \Rightarrow$$

$$y = |x|^3 [c_1 \cos(2\ln|x|) + c_2 \sin(2\ln|x|)] = x^3 [c_3 \cos(2\ln|x|) + c_4 \sin(2\ln|x|)]$$

is the general solution for any $x \neq 0$. Then $y(1) = 0 \Rightarrow c_3 = 0 \Rightarrow$

$$y = c_4 x^3 \sin(2\ln|x|) \quad \Rightarrow \quad y' = c_4 [3x^2 \sin(2\ln|x|) + 2x^2 \cos(2\ln|x|)],$$

and $y'(1) = 6 \Rightarrow c_4 = 3$. Hence, the solution of the initial-value problem is

$$y = 3x^3 \sin(2\ln|x|).$$

Exercises 3.2

1. Find the general solution of the equation $y'' - y' - 2y = 0$.

2. Solve the initial-value problem $y'' + y' - 6y = 0$, $y(0) = 0$, $y'(0) = 10$, and determine $y(1)$ and $y'(1)$.

3. Solve the initial-value problem $y'' + 5y' + 4y = 0$, $y(0) = 0$, $y'(0) = -6$.

4. Find the general solution of the equation $4y'' + y' - 3y = 0$.

5. Find two independent solutions of the equation $y'' - 3y' + y = 0$.

6. Solve the initial-value problem $y'' - y = 0$, $y(0) = 1$, $y'(0) = 2$, and determine $y(1)$ and $y(-1)$.

7. Find two independent solutions of the equation $9y'' - 24y' + 16y = 0$.

8. Solve the initial-value problem $y'' - 10y' + 25y = 0$, $y(0) = 1$, $y'(0) = 1$.

9. Find the general solution of the equation $4y'' - 4y' + 1 = 0$.

10. Employ two different methods to solve the equation $y'' = 0$.

11. Find the general solution of the equation $y'' + y' + y = 0$.

12. Solve the initial-value problem $y'' - 2y' + 2y = 0$, $y(0) = 0$, $y'(0) = 1$.

13. Find the general solution of the equation $2y'' - 4y' + 3y = 0$.

14. Find the general solution of the equation $y'' + 4y = 0$.

15. Consider the equation $y'' + y = 0$.

    (a) Find the general solution.

    (b) Solve the initial-value problem, given the initial conditions $y(0) = 1$, $y'(0) = 0$.

    (c) Solve the initial-value problem, given the initial conditions $y(0) = 0$, $y'(0) = 1$.

16. Find the general solution of the equation $x^2y'' + 2xy' - 6y = 0$.

17. Find the general solution of the equation $6x^2y'' + 7xy' - 2y = 0$.

18. Solve the initial-value problem $x^2y'' - 7xy' + 16y = 0$, $y(1) = 0$, $y'(1) = 2$, and determine $y(-1)$ and $y(e)$.

19. Find the general solution of the equation $9x^2y'' - 3xy' + 4y = 0$.

20. Employ three different methods to solve the equation $x^2y'' + xy' = 0$.

21. Find the general solution of the equation $-2x^2y'' + 2xy' - 5y = 0$.

22. Solve the initial-value problem $x^2y'' - 3xy' + 13y = 0$, $y(1) = 0$, $y'(1) = 6$.

23. Find the general solution of the equation $x^2y'' + xy' + 4y = 0$.

3.3 Linear Nonhomogeneous Equations

Theorem 3.3. The general solution of the nonhomogeneous equation

$$a(x)y'' + b(x)y' + c(x)y = g(x) \tag{3.7}$$

is $y = y_p + y_h$, where y_p is any particular solution, and $y_h = c_1 y_1 + c_2 y_2$ is the general solution of the *associated homogeneous equation*

$$a(x)y'' + b(x)y' + c(x)y = 0, \tag{3.8}$$

with y_1 and y_2 any two linearly independent solutions.

Proof. $y = y_p + y_h$ is a solution of Equation (3.7) because

$$
\begin{aligned}
a(x)y'' + b(x)y' + c(x)y &= a(x)(y_p + y_h)'' + b(x)(y_p + y_h)' + c(x)(y_p + y_h) \\
&= [a(x)y_p'' + b(x)y_p' + c(x)y_p] + [a(x)y_h'' + b(x)y_h' + c(x)y_h] \\
&= g(x) + 0 = g(x).
\end{aligned}
$$

Since y contains two arbitrary constants, it is the general solution of Equation (3.7).

The solutions y_1 and y_2 of Equation (3.8) are called the *homogeneous solutions*, and $g(x)$ in Equation (3.7) is called the *nonhomogeneous term*.

In view of Theorem 3.3, given a nonhomogeneous equation, it is necessary to find a particular solution y_p in order to obtain the general solution, the determination of two independent solutions of the associated homogeneous equation already having been discussed in Section 3.2.

3.3.1 The Method of Undetermined Coefficients

Consider a nonhomogeneous equation

$$ay'' + by' + cy = g(x), \tag{3.9}$$

where a, b and c are constants, i.e., the associated homogeneous equation

$$ay'' + by' + cy = 0 \tag{3.10}$$

has constant coefficients.

If $g(x)$ consists of certain, particular forms, then the form of a particular solution y_p, containing unknown constants, of Equation (3.9) can be deduced. The unknown constants in y_p are then determined by forcing y_p to be a solution of Equation (3.9). This is called the method of *undetermined coefficients*.

 If $g(x) = Ce^{\beta x}$, where C and β are constants, then $y_p = Ae^{\beta x}$, provided that $e^{\beta x}$ is not a solution of Equation (3.10).

Example 3.19. Consider the nonhomogeneous equation

$$y'' - y' - 2y = 3e^x.$$

The associated homogeneous equation is

$$y'' - y' - 2y = 0,$$

and $y = e^{rx} \Rightarrow r^2 - r - 2 = (r-2)(r+1) = 0 \Rightarrow y_1 = e^{2x}$, $y_2 = e^{-x}$, and the general solution of the homogeneous equation is $y_h = c_1 e^{2x} + c_2 e^{-x}$.

Since $g(x) = 3e^x$ and e^x is not a solution of the homogeneous equation, $y_p = Ae^x$. Then $y_p' = Ae^x$, $y_p'' = Ae^x$, and

$$y_p'' - y_p' - 2y_p = 3e^x \quad \text{if and only if} \quad A(e^x - e^x - 2e^x) = 3e^x, \quad \text{i.e.,} \quad A = -\frac{3}{2}.$$

Thus, $y_p = -\frac{3}{2}e^x$ and $y = y_p + y_h = -\frac{3}{2}e^x + c_1 e^{2x} + c_2 e^{-x}$ is the general solution of the nonhomogeneous equation.

Example 3.20. Consider the initial-value problem

$$y'' + y = 4e^x, \quad y(0) = 1, \quad y'(0) = 2.$$

The associated homogeneous equation is

$$y'' + y = 0,$$

and $y = e^{rx} \Rightarrow r^2 + 1 = 0 \Rightarrow r = \pm i \Rightarrow y_1 = \cos(x)$, $y_2 = \sin(x)$, and the general solution of the homogeneous equation is $y_h = c_1 \cos(x) + c_2 \sin(x)$.

Since $g(x) = e^x$, which is not a solution of the homogeneous equation, $y_p = Ae^x$. Then $y_p' = Ae^x$, $y_p'' = Ae^x$, and $y_p'' + y_p = 4e^x$ if and only if $A = 2$. Hence, $y_p = 2e^x$, and the general solution of the nonhomogeneous equation is

$$y = y_p + y_h = 2e^x + c_1 \cos(x) + c_2 \sin(x).$$

Then $y(0) = 1 \Rightarrow c_1 = -1$, and $y'(0) = 2 \Rightarrow c_2 = 0$, and $y = 2e^x - \cos(x)$ is the solution of the initial-value problem.

 If $e^{\beta x}$ is a solution of Equation (3.10), then so is $Ae^{\beta x}$ and, hence, it cannot be a solution of Equation (3.9). In that case, $y_p = Axe^{\beta x}$, provided that $xe^{\beta x}$ is not a solution of Equation (3.10).

Example 3.21. Consider the nonhomogeneous equation

$$y'' - 4y = 8e^{2x}.$$

The associated homogeneous equation is

$$y'' - 4y = 0,$$

and $y = e^{rx} \Rightarrow r^2 - 4 = 0 \Rightarrow r = \pm 2 \Rightarrow y_1 = e^{2x}$, $y_2 = e^{-2x}$, and the general solution of the homogeneous equation is $y_h = c_1 e^{2x} + c_2 e^{-2x}$.

Since $g(x) = 8e^{2x}$ and e^{2x} is a solution of the homogeneous equation but xe^{2x} is not, $y_p = Axe^{2x}$. Then $y_p' = A(e^{2x} + 2xe^{2x}) = Ae^{2x}(1 + 2x)$, $y_p'' = Ae^{2x}(4 + 4x)$, and

$$y_p'' - 4y_p = 8e^{2x} \quad \text{if and only if} \quad Ae^{2x}(4 + 4x) - 4Axe^{2x} = 8e^{2x}, \quad \text{i.e.,} \quad A = 2.$$

Thus, $y_p = 2xe^{2x}$ and $y = y_p + y_h = 2xe^{2x} + c_1 e^{2x} + c_2 e^{-x}$ is the general solution of the nonhomogeneous equation.

If both $e^{\beta x}$ and $xe^{\beta x}$ are solutions of Equation (3.10), then $y_p = x^2 e^{\beta x}$. In this case, $x^2 e^{\beta x}$ cannot be a solution of Equation (3.10) because a linear, second-order equation has precisely two independent solutions (Theorem 3.2).

Example 3.22. Consider the nonhomogeneous equation

$$y'' - 6y' + 9y = 4e^{3x}.$$

The associated homogeneous equation is

$$y'' - 6y' + 9y = 0,$$

and $y = e^{rx} \Rightarrow r^2 - 6r + 9 = (r - 3)^2 = 0 \Rightarrow y_1 = e^{3x}$, $y_2 = xe^{3x}$, and the general solution of the homogeneous equation is $y_h = c_1 e^{3x} + c_2 x e^{3x}$.

Since $g(x) = 4e^{3x}$ and both e^{3x} and xe^{3x} are solutions of the homogeneous equation, $y_p = Ax^2 e^{3x}$. Then $y_p' = Ae^{3x}(2x + 3x^2)$, $y_p'' = Ae^{3x}(2 + 12x + 9x^2)$, and

$$y_p'' - 6y_p' + 9y_p = 4e^{3x}$$

if and only if

$$Ae^{3x}[(2 + 12x + 9x^2) - 6(2x + 3x^2) + 9x^2] = 4e^{3x}, \quad \text{i.e.,} \quad A = 2.$$

Thus, $y_p = 2x^2 e^{3x}$ and $y = y_p + y_h = 2x^2 e^{3x} + c_1 e^{3x} + c_2 x e^{3x}$ is the general solution of the nonhomogeneous equation.

The case where $g(x) = Ce^{\beta x}$ can be summarized by the following:

Theorem 3.4. A particular solution y_p of the nonhomogeneous equation

$$ay'' + by' + cy = Ce^{\beta x},$$

where a, b, c, C and β are constants, is given by

1. $y_p = Ae^{\beta x}$, provided that $e^{\beta x}$ is not a solution of the associated homogeneous equation.

2. $y_p = Axe^{\beta x}$, if $e^{\beta x}$ is a solution of the associated homogeneous equation and $xe^{\beta x}$ is not.

3. $y_p = Ax^2 e^{\beta x}$, if both $e^{\beta x}$ and $xe^{\beta x}$ are solutions of the associated homogeneous equation.

If $g(x) = C\cos(\beta x) + D\sin(\beta x)$, where C, D and β are constants, then

$$y_p = A\cos(\beta x) + B\sin(\beta x),$$

provided that $\cos(\beta x)$ and $\sin(\beta x)$ are not solutions of Equation (3.10).

Example 3.23. Consider the nonhomogeneous equation

$$y'' + 4y' + 4y = 6\sin(3x).$$

The associated homogeneous equation is

$$y'' + 4y' + 4y = 0,$$

and $y = e^{rx} \Rightarrow r^2 + 4r + 4 = (r+2)^2 = 0 \Rightarrow y_1 = e^{-2x}$, $y_2 = xe^{-2x}$, and the general solution of the homogeneous equation is $y_h = c_1 e^{-2x} + c_2 xe^{-2x}$.

Since $g(x) = 6\sin(3x)$ and $\sin(3x)$ and $\cos(3x)$ are not solutions of the associated homogeneous equation, $y_p = A\cos(3x) + B\sin(3x)$. Then

$$y_p' = -3A\sin(3x) + 3B\cos(3x), \quad y_p'' = -9A\cos(3x) - 9B\sin(3x),$$

and $y_p'' + 4y_p' + 4y_p = 6\sin(3x)$ if and only if

$$[-9A\cos(3x) - 9B\sin(3x)] + 4[-3A\sin(3x) + 3B\cos(3x)]$$

$$+4[A\cos(3x) + B\sin(3x)] = 6\sin(3x),$$

i.e.,

$$(12B - 5A)\cos(3x) - (12A + 5B)\sin(3x) = 6\sin(3x),$$

which holds if and only if A and B satisfy the system $\left\{\begin{array}{rcl} -5A + 12B &=& 0 \\ 12A + 5B &=& -6 \end{array}\right\}$, with

the solution $A = -\dfrac{72}{169}$ and $B = -\dfrac{30}{169}$. Thus, $y_p = -\dfrac{72}{169}\cos(3x) - \dfrac{30}{169}\sin(3x)$ and

$$y = y_p + y_h = -\frac{72}{169}\cos(3x) - \frac{30}{169}\sin(3x) + c_1 e^{-2x} + c_2 x e^{-2x}$$

is the general solution of the nonhomogeneous equation. Note that y_p includes both a cosine term and a sine term, even though $g(x)$ includes no cosine term.

If $\cos(\beta x)$ and $\sin(\beta x)$ are solutions of Equation (3.10), then

$$y_p = x[A\cos(\beta x) + B\sin(\beta x)].$$

In this case, $x\cos(\beta x)$ and $x\sin(\beta x)$ cannot be solutions of Equation (3.10) because a linear, second-order equation has precisely two independent solutions (Theorem 3.2).

Example 3.24. Consider the nonhomogeneous equation

$$y'' + y = 2\cos(x).$$

The associated homogeneous equation is

$$y'' + y = 0,$$

and $y = e^{rx} \Rightarrow r^2 + 1 = 0 \Rightarrow r = \pm 1 \Rightarrow y_1 = \cos(x),\ y_2 = \sin(x)$, and the general solution of the homogeneous equation is $y_h = c_1\cos(x) + c_2\sin(x)$.

Since $g(x) = 2\cos(x)$ and $\cos(x)$, $\sin(x)$ satisfy the associated homogeneous equation,

$$y_p = x[A\cos(x) + B\sin(x)].$$

Then

$$\begin{aligned} y_p' &= [A\cos(x) + B\sin(x)] + x[-A\sin(x) + B\cos(x)], \\ y_p'' &= 2[-A\sin(x) + B\cos(x)] + x[-A\cos(x) - B\sin(x)], \end{aligned}$$

and $y_p'' + y_p = 2\cos(x)$ if and only if

$$2[-A\sin(x) + B\cos(x)] = 2\cos(x),$$

i.e., $A = 0$ and $B = 1$. Thus, $y_p = x\sin(x)$ and

$$y = y_p + y_h = x\sin(x) + c_1\cos(x) + c_2\sin(x)$$

is the general solution of the nonhomogeneous equation.

The case where $g(x) = C\cos(\beta x) + D\sin(\beta x)$ can be summarised by the following:

Theorem 3.5. A particular solution y_p of the nonhomogeneous equation

$$ay'' + by' + cy = C\cos(\beta x) + D\sin(\beta x),$$

where C, D and β are constants, is given by

1. $y_p = A\cos(\beta x) + B\sin(\beta x)$, provided that $\cos(\beta x)$ and $\sin(\beta x)$ are not solutions of the associated homogeneous equation.

2. $y_p = x[A\cos(\beta x) + B\sin(\beta x)]$, whenever $\cos(\beta x)$ and $\sin(\beta x)$ are solutions of the associated homogeneous equation.

If $g(x)$ is a polynomial of degree $n \geq 0$, i.e.,

$$g(x) = C_0 + C_1 x + C_2 x^2 + \cdots + C_n x^n,$$

then y_p is a polynomial of degree n,

$$y_p = A_0 + A_1 x + A_2 x^2 + \cdots + A_n x^n,$$

provided that no term in y_p satisfies Equation (3.10).

Example 3.25. Consider the nonhomogeneous equation

$$y'' - 5y' + 6y = 3 + 12x.$$

The associated homogeneous equation is

$$y'' - 5y' + 6y = 0,$$

and $y = e^{rx} \Rightarrow r^2 - 5r + 6 = (r-2)(r-3) = 0 \Rightarrow y_1 = e^{2x}$, $y_2 = e^{3x}$, and the general solution of the homogeneous equation is $y_h = c_1 e^{2x} + c_2 e^{3x}$.

Since $g(x) = 3 + 12x$ and no term in a first-degree polynomial is a solution of the homogeneous equation, $y_p = A + Bx$. Then $y_p' = B$, $y_p'' = 0$, and

$$y_p'' - 5y_p' + 6y_p = 3 + 12x \quad \text{if and only if} \quad -5B + 6(A + Bx) = 3 + 12x,$$

which gives $B = 2$ and $A = \dfrac{13}{6}$. Hence, $y_p = \dfrac{13}{6} + 2x$, and the general solution of the nonhomogeneous equation is $y = y_p + y_h = \dfrac{13}{6} + 2x + c_1 e^{2x} + c_2 e^{3x}$.

If any term in $A_0 + A_1 x + A_2 x^2 + \cdots + A_n x^n$ is a solution of Equation (3.10), then

$$y_p = x(A_0 + A_1 x + A_2 x^2 + \cdots + A_n x^n) = A_0 x + A_1 x^2 + A_2 x^3 + \cdots + A_n x^{n+1},$$

provided that no term in y_p is a solution of Equation (3.10).

Example 3.26. Consider the nonhomogeneous equation

$$y'' - 2y' = 2 - 3x.$$

The associated homogeneous equation is

$$y'' - 2y' = 0,$$

and $y = e^{rx} \Rightarrow r^2 - 2r = r(r-2) = 0 \Rightarrow y_1 = 1$, $y_2 = e^{2x}$, and the general solution of the homogeneous equation is $y_h = c_1 + c_2 e^{2x}$.

Since $g(x) = 2 - 3x$ and a constant is a solution of the homogeneous equation, $y_p \neq A + Bx$, but $y_p = x(A + Bx) = Ax + Bx^2$. Then $y_p' = A + 2Bx$, $y_p'' = 2B$, and

$$y_p'' - 2y_p' = 2 - 3x \quad \text{if and only if} \quad 2B - 2(A + 2Bx) = 2 - 3x,$$

which gives $B = \dfrac{3}{4}$ and $A = -\dfrac{1}{4}$. Hence, $y_p = -\dfrac{1}{4}x + \dfrac{3}{4}x^2$, and the general solution of the nonhomogeneous equation is $y = y_p + y_h = -\dfrac{1}{4}x + \dfrac{3}{4}x^2 + c_1 + c_2 e^{2x}$.

If both $A_0 + A_1 x + A_2 x^2 + \cdots + A_n x^n$ and $A_0 x + A_1 x^2 + A_2 x^3 + \cdots + A_n x^{n+1}$ contain terms which are solutions of Equation (3.10), then

$$y_p = x^2(A_0 + A_1 x + A_2 x^2 + \cdots + A_n x^n) = A_0 x^2 + A_1 x^3 + A_2 x^4 + \cdots + A_n x^{n+2}.$$

The latter cannot contain any terms which satisfy Equation (3.10), because the only polynomial which can satisfy a homogeneous equation with constant coefficients has degree zero or one, and every term in the above polynomial has degree at least two.

Example 3.27. Consider the nonhomogeneous equation

$$y'' = 24 - 36x + 12x^2.$$

The associated homogeneous equation is

$$y'' = 0,$$

and $y = e^{rx} \Rightarrow r^2 = 0 \Rightarrow y_1 = 1$, $y_2 = x$, and the general solution of the homogeneous equation is $y_h = c_1 + c_2 x$.

Since $g(x) = 24 - 36x + 12x^2$ and both a constant and x satisfy the homogeneous equation, $y_p \neq A + Bx + Cx^2$ and $y_p \neq x(A + Bx + Cx^2)$, but

$$y_p = x^2(A + Bx + Cx^2) = Ax^2 + Bx^3 + Cx^4.$$

Then $y_p' = 2Ax + 3Bx^2 + 4Cx^3$, $y_p'' = 2A + 6Bx + 12Cx^2$, and

$$y_p'' = 24 - 36x + 12x^2 \text{ if and only if } 2A + 6Bx + 12Cx^2 = 24 - 36x + 12x^2,$$

which gives $A = 12$, $B = -6$ and $C = 1$, i.e., $y_p = 12x^2 - 6x^3 + x^4$. The general solution of the nonhomogeneous equation is then

$$y = y_p + y_h = 12x^2 - 6x^3 + x^4 + c_1 + c_2 x.$$

Of course, this equation can be solved much more easily simply by two integrations:

$$y'' = 24 - 36x + 12x^2 \quad \Rightarrow \quad y' = 24x - 18x^2 + 4x^3 + k_1$$

$$\Rightarrow \quad y = 12x^2 - 6x^3 + x^4 + k_1 x + k_2,$$

as above.

The case where $g(x) = C_0 + C_1 x + C_2 x^2 + \cdots + C_n x^n$ can be summarised by the following:

Theorem 3.6. A particular solution of the nonhomogeneous equation

$$ay'' + by' + cy = C_0 + C_1 x + C_2 x^2 + \cdots + C_n x^n$$

is given by

1. $y_p = A_0 + A_1 x + A_2 x^2 + \cdots + A_n x^n$, provided that no term in y_p is a solution of the associated homogeneous equation.

2. $y_p = x(A_0 + A_1 x + A_2 x^2 + \cdots + A_n x^n) = A_0 x + A_1 x^2 + A_2 x^3 + \cdots + A_n x^{n+1}$ if $A_0 + A_1 x + A_2 x^2 + \cdots + A_n x^n$ contains a term which satisfies the associated homogeneous equation and $x(A_0 + A_1 x + A_2 x^2 + \cdots + A_n x^n)$ does not.

3. $y_p = x^2(A_0 + A_1 x + A_2 x^2 + \cdots + A_n x^n) = A_0 x^2 + A_1 x^3 + A_2 x^4 + \cdots + A_n x^{n+2}$ if both $A_0 + A_1 x + A_2 x^2 + \cdots + A_n x^n$ and $x(A_0 + A_1 x + A_2 x^2 + \cdots + A_n x^n)$ contain terms which satisfy the associated homogeneous equation.

Theorem 3.7. If y_{p_1} and y_{p_2} are particular solutions of

$$ay'' + by' + cy = g_1(x) \quad \text{and} \quad ay'' + by' + cy = g_2(x),$$

respectively, then $y_p = y_{p_1} + y_{p_2}$ is a particular solution of

$$ay'' + by' + cy = g_1(x) + g_2(x).$$

More generally, if y_{p_i} is a particular solution of

$$ay'' + by' + cy = g_i(x)$$

for $1 \leq i \leq n$, then $y_p = y_{p_1} + y_{p_2} + \cdots + y_{p_n}$ is a particular solution of

$$ay'' + by' + cy = g_1(x) + g_2(x) + \cdots + g_n(x).$$

Proof. For $n = 2$,

$$
\begin{aligned}
ay_p'' + by_p' + cy_p &= a(y_{p_1} + y_{p_2})'' + b(y_{p_1} + y_{p_2})' + c(y_{p_1} + y_{p_2}) \\
&= (ay_{p_1}'' + by_{p_1}' + cy_{p_1}) + (ay_{p_2}'' + by_{p_2}' + cy_{p_2}) \\
&= g_1(x) + g_2(x).
\end{aligned}
$$

The general case is proved similarly.

Example 3.28. Consider the nonhomogeneous equation

$$y'' + 4y = 4x^2 - 5e^x.$$

The associated homogeneous equation is

$$y'' + 4y = 0,$$

and $y = e^{rx} \Rightarrow r^2 + 4 = 0 \Rightarrow r = \pm 2i \Rightarrow y_1 = \cos(2x)$, $y_2 = \sin(2x)$, and the general solution of the homogeneous equation is $y_h = c_1 \cos(2x) + c_2 \sin(2x)$.

For $y'' + 4y = 4x^2$, $y_{p_1} = A + Bx + Cx^2$. Then $y_{p_1}' = B + 2Cx$, $y_{p_1}'' = 2C$, and

$$y_{p_1}'' + 4y_{p_1} = 4x^2 \quad \text{if and only if} \quad 2C + 4(A + Bx + Cx^2) = 4x^2,$$

which gives $C = 1$, $B = 0$, and $A = -\dfrac{1}{2}$. Hence, $y_{p_1} = -\dfrac{1}{2} + x^2$.

For $y'' + 4y = -5e^x$, $y_{p_2} = De^x$. Then $y_{p_2}' = De^x$, $y_{p_2}'' = De^x$, and

$$y_{p_2}'' + 4y_{p_2} = -5e^x \quad \text{if and only if} \quad De^x + 4De^x = -5e^x,$$

which gives $D = -1$. Hence, $y_{p_2} = -e^x$, and $y_p = y_{p_1} + y_{p_2} = -\dfrac{1}{2} + x^2 - e^x$, and

$$y = y_p + y_h = -\frac{1}{2} + x^2 - e^x + c_1 \cos(2x) + c_2 \sin(2x)$$

is the general solution of the nonhomogeneous equation.

If $g(x)$ consists of products such as

$$P(x)e^{\beta x}, \quad P(x)[C\cos(\gamma x) + D\sin(\gamma x)], \quad e^{\beta x}[C\cos(\gamma x) + D\sin(\gamma x)],$$

or

$$P(x)e^{\beta x}[C\cos(\gamma x) + D\sin(\gamma x)],$$

where P is a polynomial and C, D, β and γ are constants, then y_p must have the corresponding forms

$$Q(x)e^{\beta x}, \quad Q(x)\cos(\gamma x) + R(x)\sin(\gamma x), \quad e^{\beta x}[A\cos(\gamma x) + B\sin(\gamma x)],$$

or

$$e^{\beta x}[Q(x)\cos(\gamma x) + R(x)\sin(\gamma x)],$$

multiplied by x or x^2 if necessary, in order that no term in y_p be a solution of the associated homogeneous equation, where Q and R are polynomials of the same degree as that of P.

Example 3.29. Consider the nonhomogeneous equation

$$y'' - 2y' + 2y = e^x\cos(x).$$

The associated homogeneous equation is

$$y'' - 2y' + 2y = 0,$$

and $y = e^{rx} \Rightarrow r^2 - 2r + 2 = 0 \Rightarrow r = 1 \pm i \Rightarrow y_1 = e^x\cos(x)$, $y_2 = e^x\sin(x)$, and the general solution of the homogeneous equation is $y_h = c_1 e^x\cos(x) + c_2 e^x\sin(x)$.

Since $g(x) = e^x\cos(x)$ and $e^x\cos(x)$ is a solution of the associated homogeneous equation, $y_p = xe^x[A\cos(x) + B\sin(x)]$. Then

$$y_p' = e^x[A\cos(x) + B\sin(x)] + xe^x[(A+B)\cos(x) + (B-A)\sin(x)],$$

$$y_p'' = e^x[2(A+B)\cos(x) + 2(B-A)\sin(x)] + xe^x[2B\cos(x) - 2A\sin(x)],$$

and $y_p'' - 2y_p' + 2y_p = e^x\cos(x)$ if and only if

$$e^x[2B\cos(x) - 2A\sin(x)] = e^x\cos(x),$$

which gives $A = 0$ and $B = \dfrac{1}{2}$. Hence, $y_p = \dfrac{1}{2}xe^x\sin(x)$, and

$$y = y_p + y_h = \frac{1}{2}xe^x\sin(x) + c_1 e^x\cos(x) + c_2 e^x\sin(x)$$

is the general solution of the nonhomogeneous equation.

A more efficient method for the determination of particular solutions in examples such as Example 3.29 will be discussed next.

3.3.2   Variation of Parameters

Consider a nonhomogeneous equation

$$y'' + p(x)y' + q(x)y = f(x) \tag{3.11}$$

in standard form. The associated homogeneous equation is

$$y'' + p(x)y' + q(x)y = 0. \tag{3.12}$$

Let y_1 and y_2 be any two linearly independent solutions of Equation (3.12). Seek a particular solution of Equation (3.11) in the form

$$y_p = u_1 y_1 + u_2 y_2, \tag{3.13}$$

where $u_1(x)$ and $u_2(x)$ are functions to be determined by forcing y_p to be a solution of Equation (3.11). Then, by the product rule,

$$y_p' = u_1' y_1 + u_1 y_1' + u_2' y_2 + u_2 y_2' = (u_1' y_1 + u_2' y_2) + (u_1 y_1' + u_2 y_2'). \tag{3.14}$$

The requirement that y_p be a solution of Equation (3.11) imposes one constraint upon the two functions u_1 and u_2. We may therefore impose a second constraint, chosen in order to simplify the procedure. Thus, impose the condition

$$u_1' y_1 + u_2' y_2 = 0. \tag{3.15}$$

Then Equation (3.14) reduces to

$$y_p' = u_1 y_1' + u_2 y_2',$$

from which we obtain

$$y_p'' = u_1' y_1' + u_1 y_1'' + u_2' y_2' + u_2 y_2''.$$

Hence, $y_p'' + p(x)y_p' + q(x)y_p = f(x)$ if and only if

$$[u_1' y_1' + u_1 y_1'' + u_2' y_2' + u_2 y_2''] + p(x)[u_1 y_1' + u_2 y_2'] + q(x)[u_1 y_1 + u_2 y_2] = f(x).$$

Rearranging terms, the latter condition becomes

$$u_1[y_1'' + p(x)y_1' + q(x)y_1] + u_2[y_2'' + p(x)y_2' + q(x)y_2] + u_1' y_1' + u_2' y_2' = f(x). \tag{3.16}$$

Since y_1 and y_2 are solutions of Equation (3.12),

$$y_1'' + p(x)y_1' + q(x)y_1 = 0 \quad \text{and} \quad y_2'' + p(x)y_2' + q(x)y_2 = 0,$$

and condition (3.16) reduces to

$$u_1' y_1' + u_2' y_2' = f(x). \tag{3.17}$$

Combined with condition (3.15), u_1' and u_2' must satisfy the system

$$
\begin{aligned}
y_1 u_1' + y_2 u_2' &= 0 \\
y_1' u_1' + y_2' u_2' &= f(x)
\end{aligned}
\tag{3.18}
$$

of algebraic equations. Employing *Cramer's rule*, we obtain

$$
u_1' = \frac{\begin{vmatrix} 0 & y_2 \\ f(x) & y_2' \end{vmatrix}}{\begin{vmatrix} y_1 & y_2 \\ y_1' & y_2' \end{vmatrix}} = \frac{-y_2 f(x)}{y_1 y_2' - y_1' y_2} \quad \text{and} \quad u_2' = \frac{\begin{vmatrix} y_1 & 0 \\ y_1' & f(x) \end{vmatrix}}{\begin{vmatrix} y_1 & y_2 \\ y_1' & y_2' \end{vmatrix}} = \frac{y_1 f(x)}{y_1 y_2' - y_1' y_2}.
$$

The quantity

$$
\begin{vmatrix} y_1 & y_2 \\ y_1' & y_2' \end{vmatrix} = y_1 y_2' - y_1' y_2
$$

is denoted by $W[y_1, y_2](x)$ or simply by $W(x)$ and called the *Wronskian* of y_1 and y_2. Thus,

$$
u_1 = \int \frac{-y_2 f(x)}{W(x)}\, dx, \quad u_2 = \int \frac{y_1 f(x)}{W(x)}\, dx, \quad \text{and} \quad y_p = u_1 y_1 + u_2 y_2.
$$

This method for the determination of a particular solution of Equation (3.11) is called *variation of parameters* or *variation of constants*.

Note that the above formulas for u_1 and u_2 are defined provided that $W(x) \neq 0$. This is guaranteed by the following:

Theorem 3.8. If p and q are continuous on an interval I, and y_1 and y_2 are solutions of $y'' + p(x)y' + q(x)y = 0$, then either $W \equiv 0$ on I or $W(x) \neq 0$ for any x in I. The solutions y_1 and y_2 are linearly independent on I if and only if $W(x) \neq 0$ on I. (See Chapter 3 Exercise 15 on page 85.)

Example 3.30. Consider the nonhomogeneous equation

$$
y'' - 3y' + 2y = e^{2x}.
$$

The associated homogeneous equation is

$$
y'' - 3y' + 2y = 0,
$$

and $y = e^{rx} \Rightarrow r^2 - 3r + 2 = (r-1)(r-2) = 0 \Rightarrow y_1 = e^x$, $y_2 = e^{2x}$, and the general solution of the homogeneous equation is $y_h = c_1 e^x + c_2 e^{2x}$. The equation is in standard form with $f(x) = e^{2x}$, and the Wronskian of y_1 and y_2 is

$$
W(x) = \begin{vmatrix} y_1 & y_2 \\ y_1' & y_2' \end{vmatrix} = \begin{vmatrix} e^x & e^{2x} \\ e^x & 2e^{2x} \end{vmatrix} = e^{3x}.
$$

Hence,

$$u_1 = \int \frac{-y_2 f(x)}{W(x)}\, dx = \int \frac{-e^{2x} \cdot e^{2x}}{e^{3x}}\, dx = \int -e^x\, dx = -e^x,$$

$$u_2 = \int \frac{y_1 f(x)}{W(x)}\, dx = \int \frac{e^x \cdot e^{2x}}{e^{3x}}\, dx = \int 1\, dx = x,$$

and $y_p = u_1 y_1 + u_2 y_2 = -e^{2x} + x e^{2x}$. Thus,

$$
\begin{aligned}
y = y_p + y_h &= x e^{2x} - e^{2x} + c_1 e^x + c_2 e^{2x} \\
&= x e^{2x} + c_1 e^x + (c_2 - 1) e^{2x} \\
&= x e^{2x} + c_1 e^x + c_3 e^{2x}
\end{aligned}
$$

is the general solution of the nonhomogeneous equation.

Note that the term $-e^{2x} = -y_2$ has been absorbed into the term $c_2 e^{2x}$ in the general solution above. Thus, any term in y_p which satisfies the homogeneous equation may be removed from y_p. In fact, a particular solution of a nonhomogeneous equation is not unique because, if y_p is a particular solution, then so is $y_p + y_i$, where y_i is any solution of the associated homogeneous equation. For this reason, arbitrary constants of integration k_1 and k_2 need not be added to u_1 and u_2, since this would merely add the term $k_1 y_1 + k_2 y_2$ to y_p, and these may be removed.

Example 3.31. Consider the initial-value problem

$$4y'' - y = 4e^{\frac{1}{2}x}, \quad y(0) = 0, \quad y'(0) = 3.$$

The associated homogeneous equation, $4y'' - y = 0$, has the two independent solutions $y_1 = e^{\frac{1}{2}x}$ and $y_2 = e^{-\frac{1}{2}x}$, with the Wronskian $W(x) = -1$. The standard form of the nonhomogeneous equation is $y'' - \frac{1}{4}y = e^{\frac{1}{2}x}$. Hence, $f(x) = e^{\frac{1}{2}x}$,

$$u_1 = \int 1\, dx = x, \quad u_2 = \int -e^x\, dx = -e^x,$$

and $y_p = x e^{\frac{1}{2}x} - e^{\frac{1}{2}x}$, or $y_p = x e^{\frac{1}{2}x}$, since $-e^{\frac{1}{2}x} = -y_1$ satisfies the homogeneous equation and may be removed from y_p. The general solution of the nonhomogeneous equation is $y = y_p + y_h = x e^{\frac{1}{2}x} + c_1 e^{\frac{1}{2}x} + c_2 e^{-\frac{1}{2}x}$. Then $y(0) = 0 \Rightarrow c_2 = -c_1 \Rightarrow$

$$y = x e^{\frac{1}{2}x} + c_1 \left(e^{\frac{1}{2}x} - e^{-\frac{1}{2}x} \right), \quad y' = e^{\frac{1}{2}x} + \frac{1}{2} x e^{\frac{1}{2}x} + \frac{1}{2} c_1 \left(e^{\frac{1}{2}x} + e^{-\frac{1}{2}x} \right),$$

and $y'(0) = 3 \Rightarrow c_1 = 2$. Hence, the solution of the initial-value problem is

$$y = x e^{\frac{1}{2}x} + 2 \left(e^{\frac{1}{2}x} - e^{-\frac{1}{2}x} \right).$$

Example 3.32. Consider the nonhomogeneous equation

$$y'' - 2y' + 2y = e^x \cos(x),$$

which has been solved in Example 3.29 by the method of undetermined coefficients. Here, we shall solve it by variation of parameters. Two independent solutions of the associated homogeneous equation were found to be $y_1 = e^x \cos(x)$ and $y_2 = e^x \sin(x)$. With $f(x) = e^x \cos(x)$ and

$$W(x) = \begin{vmatrix} y_1 & y_2 \\ y_1' & y_2' \end{vmatrix} = \begin{vmatrix} e^x \cos(x) & e^x \sin(x) \\ e^x \cos(x) - e^x \sin(x) & e^x \sin(x) + e^x \cos(x) \end{vmatrix} = e^{2x},$$

$$u_1 = -\int \sin(x) \cos(x)\, dx = -\frac{1}{2}\int \sin(2x)\, dx = \frac{1}{4}\cos(2x),$$

$$u_2 = \int \cos^2(x)\, dx = \frac{1}{2}\int 1 + \cos(2x)\, dx = \frac{1}{2}x + \frac{1}{4}\sin(2x),$$

and

$$\begin{aligned}
y_p &= \frac{1}{4}\cos(2x)[e^x \cos(x)] + \left[\frac{1}{2}x + \frac{1}{4}\sin(2x)\right][e^x \sin(x)] \\
&= \frac{1}{2}xe^x \sin(x) + \frac{1}{4}e^x[\cos(2x)\cos(x) + \sin(2x)\sin(x)] \\
&= \frac{1}{2}xe^x \sin(x) + \frac{1}{4}e^x \cos(x).
\end{aligned}$$

Since $\frac{1}{4}e^x \cos(x) = \frac{1}{4}y_1$ satisfies the homogeneous equation, it suffices to take as a particular solution $y_p = \frac{1}{2}xe^x \sin(x)$, in agreement with the result of Example 3.29.

Example 3.33. Consider the nonhomogeneous equation

$$y'' + 6y' + 9y = \frac{2\ln(x)}{xe^{3x}}, \quad x > 0.$$

The associated homogeneous equation has the two independent solutions $y_1 = e^{-3x}$ and $y_2 = xe^{-3x}$, with $f(x) = \frac{2\ln(x)}{xe^{3x}}$ and

$$W(x) = \begin{vmatrix} e^{-3x} & xe^{-3x} \\ -3e^{-3x} & e^{-3x} - 3xe^{-3x} \end{vmatrix} = e^{-6x}.$$

Then, by integration by parts and by substitution,

$$u_1 = -\int \frac{xe^{-3x}}{e^{-6x}}\frac{2\ln(x)}{xe^{3x}}\, dx = -2\int \ln(x)\, dx = -2x\ln(x) + 2x,$$

$$u_2 = \int \frac{e^{-3x}}{e^{-6x}}\frac{2\ln(x)}{xe^{3x}}\, dx = 2\int \frac{\ln(x)}{x}\, dx = [\ln(x)]^2,$$

and

$$y_p = [2x - 2x \ln(x)]e^{-3x} + [\ln(x)]^2 x e^{-3x}, \quad \text{or} \quad y_p = x e^{-3x}[\ln(x)]^2 - 2x e^{-3x} \ln(x),$$

since $2xe^{-3x} = 2y_2$. Thus,

$$y = y_p + y_h = xe^{-3x}[\ln(x)]^2 - 2xe^{-3x}\ln(x) + c_1 e^{-3x} + c_2 x e^{-3x}$$

is the general solution of the nonhomogeneous equation.

Example 3.34. Consider the nonhomogeneous equation

$$x^2 y'' - 6xy' + 12y = x^5 e^x.$$

The associated homogeneous equation is the Euler equation

$$x^2 y'' - 6xy' + 12y = 0$$

and, for $x > 0$, $y = x^r \Rightarrow r^2 - 7r + 12 = (r-3)(r-4) = 0 \Rightarrow y_1 = x^3$ and $y_2 = x^4$. Since $|x|^3 = \pm x^3$ and $|x|^4 = x^4$, these solutions are defined for all real x, with the Wronskian

$$W(x) = \begin{vmatrix} x^3 & x^4 \\ 3x^2 & 4x^3 \end{vmatrix} = x^6.$$

The nonhomogeneous equation in standard form is $y'' - \dfrac{6}{x}y' + \dfrac{12}{x^2}y = x^3 e^x$. Thus, $f(x) = x^3 e^x$. By integration by parts,

$$\begin{aligned} u_1 &= -\int \frac{x^4 \cdot x^3 e^x}{x^6}\, dx = -\int x e^x\, dx = -xe^x + e^x, \\ u_2 &= \int \frac{x^3 \cdot x^3 e^x}{x^6}\, dx = \int e^x\, dx = e^x, \end{aligned}$$

and $y_p = (e^x - xe^x)x^3 + e^x x^4 = x^3 e^x$. Hence, $y = y_p + y_h = x^3 e^x + c_1 x^3 + c_2 x^4$ is the general solution of the nonhomogeneous equation.

Example 3.35. Consider the nonhomogeneous equation

$$x^2 y'' - 3xy' + 3y = 4x^5 e^{x^2}.$$

The associated homogeneous equation is the Euler equation

$$x^2 y'' - 3xy' + 3y = 0$$

and, for $x > 0$, $y = x^r \Rightarrow r^2 - 4r + 3 = (r-1)(r-3) = 0 \Rightarrow y_1 = x$ and $y_2 = x^3$. Since $|x| = \pm x$ and $|x|^3 = \pm x^3$, these solutions are defined for all real x, with the Wronskian

$$W(x) = \begin{vmatrix} x & x^3 \\ 1 & 3x^2 \end{vmatrix} = 2x^3.$$

The standard form of the nonhomogeneous equation is $y'' - \dfrac{3}{x}y' + \dfrac{3}{x^2}y = 4x^3 e^{x^2}$, with $f(x) = 4x^3 e^{x^2}$. Thus, by integration by parts,

$$
\begin{aligned}
u_1 &= -\int \frac{x^3 \cdot 4x^3 e^{x^2}}{2x^3}\, dx = -\int x^2 \cdot 2x e^{x^2}\, dx \\
&= -x^2 e^{x^2} + \int 2x e^{x^2}\, dx = -x^2 e^{x^2} + e^{x^2}, \\
u_2 &= \int \frac{x \cdot 4x^3 e^{x^2}}{2x^3}\, dx = \int 2x e^{x^2}\, dx = e^{x^2},
\end{aligned}
$$

and $y_p = x e^{x^2}(1 - x^2) + x^3 e^{x^2} = x e^{x^2}$. The general solution of the nonhomogeneous equation is then $y = y_p + y_h = x e^{x^2} + c_1 x + c_2 x^3$.

Example 3.36. Consider the nonhomogeneous equation

$$x^2 y'' - 3xy' + 5y = x^2, \quad x > 0.$$

The associated homogeneous equation is the Euler equation

$$x^2 y'' - 3xy' + 5y = 0,$$

and $y = x^r \Rightarrow r^2 - 4r + 5 = 0 \Rightarrow r = \dfrac{4 \pm \sqrt{-4}}{2} = 2 \pm i \Rightarrow y_1 = x^2 \cos[\ln(x)]$ and $y_2 = x^2 \sin[\ln(x)]$, with the Wronskian

$$
W(x) = \begin{vmatrix} x^2 \cos[\ln(x)] & x^2 \sin[\ln(x)] \\ 2x\cos[\ln(x)] - x\sin[\ln(x)] & 2x\sin[\ln(x)] + x\cos[\ln(x)] \end{vmatrix} = x^3.
$$

The nonhomogeneous equation in standard form is $y'' - \dfrac{3}{x}y' + \dfrac{5}{x^2} = 1$, and $f(x) = 1$. By integration by substitution with $u = \ln(x)$ and $\dfrac{du}{dx} = \dfrac{1}{x}$,

$$
\begin{aligned}
u_1 &= -\int \frac{x^2 \sin[\ln(x)]}{x^3}\, dx = -\int \frac{\sin[\ln(x)]}{x}\, dx = \cos[\ln(x)], \\
u_2 &= \int \frac{x^2 \cos[\ln(x)]}{x^3}\, dx = \int \frac{\cos[\ln(x)]}{x}\, dx = \sin[\ln(x)],
\end{aligned}
$$

and $y_p = x^2 \cos^2[\ln(x)] + x^2 \sin^2[\ln(x)] = x^2$. Hence,

$$y = y_p + y_h = x^2\{1 + c_1 \cos[\ln(x)] + c_2 \sin[\ln(x)]\}.$$

is the general solution of the nonhomogeneous equation.

Example 3.37. Consider the initial-value problem

$$x^2 y'' - xy' + y = 27x^4 \ln(x), \quad x > 0, \quad y(1) = 3, \quad y'(1) = -3.$$

The associated homogeneous equation is the Euler equation

$$x^2 y'' - xy' + y = 0,$$

and $y = x^r \Rightarrow r^2 - 2r + 1 = (r-1)^2 = 0 \Rightarrow y_1 = x$ and $y_2 = x \ln(x)$, with the Wronskian

$$W(x) = \begin{vmatrix} x & x \ln(x) \\ 1 & \ln(x) + 1 \end{vmatrix} = x.$$

The nonhomogeneous equation in standard form is $y'' - \dfrac{1}{x} y' + \dfrac{1}{x^2} y = 27x^2 \ln(x)$, and $f(x) = 27x^2 \ln(x)$. By integration by parts,

$$
\begin{aligned}
u_1 &= -\int \frac{x \ln(x) \cdot 27x^2 \ln(x)}{x} \, dx = -\int 27x^2 [\ln(x)]^2 \, dx \\
&= -9x^3 [\ln(x)]^2 + \int 18x^2 \ln(x) \, dx \\
&= -9x^3 [\ln(x)]^2 + 6x^3 \ln(x) - \int 6x^2 \, dx \\
&= -9x^3 [\ln(x)]^2 + 6x^3 \ln(x) - 2x^3, \\
u_2 &= \int \frac{x \cdot 27x^2 \ln(x)}{x} \, dx = \int 27x^2 \ln(x) \, dx \\
&= 9x^3 \ln(x) - \int 9x^2 \, dx \\
&= 9x^3 \ln(x) - 3x^3,
\end{aligned}
$$

and

$$
\begin{aligned}
y_p &= \{-9x^3 [\ln(x)]^2 + 6x^3 \ln(x) - 2x^3\} x + [9x^3 \ln(x) - 3x^3] x \ln(x) \\
&= 3x^4 \ln(x) - 2x^4.
\end{aligned}
$$

Hence, the general solution of the nonhomogeneous equation is

$$y = y_p + y_h = 3x^4 \ln(x) - 2x^4 + c_1 x + c_2 x \ln(x).$$

Then $y(1) = 3 \Rightarrow c_1 = 5$, $y' = 12x^3 \ln(x) - 5x^3 + 5 + c_2 [\ln(x) + 1]$, and $y'(1) = -3 \Rightarrow c_2 = -3$. Hence,

$$y = 3x^4 \ln(x) - 2x^4 + 5x - 3x \ln(x)$$

is the solution of the initial-value problem.

Example 3.38. Consider the nonhomogeneous equation

$$4x^2 y'' + 4xy' - y = x.$$

The associated homogeneous equation is the Euler equation

$$4x^2 y'' + 4xy' - y = 0$$

and, for $x > 0$, $y = x^r \Rightarrow 4r(r-1) + 4r - 1 = 4r^2 - 1 = 0 \Rightarrow r = \pm\frac{1}{2} \Rightarrow y_1 = x^{1/2}$ and $y_2 = x^{-1/2}$, with the Wronskian

$$W(x) = \begin{vmatrix} x^{1/2} & x^{-1/2} \\ \frac{1}{2}x^{-1/2} & -\frac{1}{2}x^{-3/2} \end{vmatrix} = -x^{-1}.$$

The nonhomogeneous equation in standard form is $y'' + \dfrac{1}{x}y' - \dfrac{1}{4x^2} = \dfrac{1}{4x}$ and, hence, $f(x) = \dfrac{1}{4x}$. Then

$$u_1 = -\int \frac{x^{-1/2} \cdot \frac{1}{4x}}{-x^{-1}}\, dx = \frac{1}{4}\int x^{-1/2}\, dx = \frac{1}{2}x^{1/2},$$

$$u_2 = \int \frac{x^{1/2} \cdot \frac{1}{4x}}{-x^{-1}}\, dx = -\frac{1}{4}\int x^{1/2}\, dx = -\frac{1}{6}x^{3/2},$$

and

$$y_p = \frac{1}{2}x^{1/2} \cdot x^{1/2} - \frac{1}{6}x^{3/2} \cdot x^{-1/2} = \frac{1}{3}x.$$

Since y_p is a particular solution of the nonhomogeneous equation for any real x, the general solution for any $x \neq 0$ is

$$y = y_p + y_h = \frac{1}{3}x + c_1|x|^{1/2} + c_2|x|^{-1/2}.$$

The absolute values are required only in y_h.

Exercises 3.3

In Exercises 1-17, solve the equation or the initial-value problem by the method of undetermined coefficients.

1. $y'' + 4y' = -5e^x$

2. $y'' - y = 6e^{2x}$, $y(0) = 2$, $y'(0) = 4$

3. $y'' - 5y' + 6y = 4e^{-2x}$

4. $y'' + 3y' - 4y = -10e^x$

5. $y'' + 6y' + 9y = 6e^{-3x}$

6. $6y'' + y' - 2y = 65\sin(x)$

7. $y'' + 2y' + y = 50\cos(3x),\ y(0) = 0,\ y'(0) = 2$

8. $y'' + y = 4\sin(x)$

9. $y'' + 4y = 8\cos(2x) + 12\sin(2x)$

10. $y'' + 4y' + 4y = 4\sin(x) - 3\cos(x)$

11. $y'' - y = 4$

12. $y'' - y' - 12y = 3 + 12x$

13. $y'' + 2y' + 3y = -9x$

14. $y'' - 9y = 2 - 3x + x^2$

15. $y'' + y' = 1 + x,\ y(0) = 1,\ y'(0) = 1$

16. $y'' - y' = 4x^3$

17. $y'' - y = -2x + 4e^x + 2\sin(x),\ y(0) = 0,\ y'(0) = 9$

In Exercises 18-37, solve the equation or the initial-value problem by variation of parameters.

18. $y'' + y' - 2y = 9e^x$

19. $y'' - 4y' + 4y = 6xe^{2x}$

20. $y'' + y' = 1,\ y(0) = 2,\ y'(0) = 4$

21. $y'' + 9y = 6\sin(3x)$

22. $y'' + y = \sec(x)$

23. $y'' + 6y' + 13y = 16e^{-3x}\cos(2x)$

24. $y'' - 4y' + 13y = \dfrac{9e^{2x}}{\cos(3x)}$

25. $y'' - 2y' + y = e^x \ln(x),\ x > 0$

26. $y'' + 3y' + 2y = \sin(e^x)$

27. $x^2 y'' - 6y = 10x^5$

28. $x^2 y'' - 4xy' + 6y = x^4 e^x$

29. $x^2 y'' + 5xy' + 3y = 4xe^{x^2}$, $y(1) = e$, $y'(1) = e$

30. $x^2 y'' - 2xy' + 2y = x^3 \cos(x)$

31. $x^2 y'' + xy' - y = x^2 \sin(x)$

32. $x^2 y'' + 3xy' + y = \dfrac{\ln(x)}{x}$, $x > 0$

33. $x^2 y'' - 3xy' + 4y = x^2 \ln(x)$, $x > 0$

34. $x^2 y'' - 3xy' + 13y = 9x^2$

35. $x^2 y'' + 7xy' + 13y = \dfrac{4}{x^3 \cos^2[2\ln(x)]}$, $x > 0$

36. $x^2 y'' - 5xy' + 13y = 8x^3 \sin[2\ln(x)]$, $x > 0$

37. $4x^2 y'' + 4xy' - y = x^2$

3.4   Equations Reducible to First-Order Equations

Consider a second-order equation in which the dependent variable y does not appear explicitly. For example,

$$y'y'' + x^2 = 0.$$

Let $y'(x) = z(x)$. Then $y'' = z'$, and the equation becomes $zz' + x^2 = 0$, which is of the first order. If the first-order equation can be solved for z, then y is obtained by

$$y = \int y' \, dx = \int z \, dx.$$

The general solution z of the first-order equation includes one arbitrary constant, and its integral y contains a second arbitrary constant, and is therefore the general solution of the second-order equation.

Example 3.39. Consider the equation

$$\frac{y''}{y' + 1} = \frac{1}{x} + x.$$

Since y does not appear explicitly, let $z(x) = y'(x)$ to obtain the first-order equation

$$\frac{z'}{z + 1} = \frac{1}{x} + x,$$

which is separable. Then

$$\int \frac{1}{z+1}\,dz = \int \frac{1}{x} + x\,dx \quad \Rightarrow \quad \ln|z+1| = \ln|x| + \frac{1}{2}x^2 + c_1$$

$$\Rightarrow \quad z + 1 = k_1 x e^{x^2/2} \quad \Rightarrow \quad y = \int z\,dx = \int k_1 x e^{x^2/2} - 1\,dx = k_1 e^{x^2/2} - x + c_2$$

is the general solution.

Example 3.40. Consider the equation

$$x\sqrt{x}\,y'' = \sqrt{x}\,y' + 2x\sqrt{y'}, \quad x > 0.$$

Since y does not appear explicitly, let $z(x) = y'(x)$ to obtain the first-order equation

$$x\sqrt{x}\,z' = \sqrt{x}\,z + 2x\sqrt{z},$$

which is homogeneous (also a Bernoulli equation). Then $u = \dfrac{z}{x} \Rightarrow$

$$u + xu' = z' = \frac{z}{x} + 2\sqrt{\frac{z}{x}} = u + 2\sqrt{u} \quad \Rightarrow \quad \frac{1}{2\sqrt{u}}u' = \frac{1}{x} \quad \Rightarrow \quad \sqrt{u} = \ln(x) + c_1$$

$$\Rightarrow \quad u = [\ln(x) + c_1]^2 \quad \Rightarrow \quad z = x[\ln(x) + c_1]^2 \quad \Rightarrow \quad y = \int z\,dx$$

and, by integration by parts,

$$
\begin{aligned}
y &= \int x[\ln(x) + c_1]^2\,dx = \frac{x^2}{2}[\ln(x) + c_1]^2 - \int x[\ln(x) + c_1]\,dx \\
&= \frac{x^2}{2}[\ln(x) + c_1]^2 - \frac{x^2}{2}[\ln(x) + c_1] + \int \frac{x}{2}\,dx \\
&= \frac{x^2}{2}[\ln(x) + c_1]^2 - \frac{x^2}{2}[\ln(x) + c_1] + \frac{x^2}{4} + c_2
\end{aligned}
$$

is the general solution.

Example 3.41. Consider the equation

$$y'' = \frac{-1}{(x + y' + 1)^2} - 1.$$

Since y does not appear explicitly, let $z(x) = y'(x)$ to obtain the first-order equation

$$z' = \frac{-1}{(x + z + 1)^2} - 1,$$

which has the form $z' = f(x + z + 1)$. By Exercise 11 in the Chapter 2 Exercises on page 39, let $u = x + z + 1$ to obtain

$$u' = 1 + z' = -\frac{1}{u^2} \quad \Rightarrow \quad u^2 u' = -1 \quad \Rightarrow \quad \frac{u^3}{3} = -x + c_1 \quad \Rightarrow \quad u^3 = -3x + k_1$$

$$\Rightarrow \quad u = (k_1 - 3x)^{1/3} \quad \Rightarrow \quad z = (k_1 - 3x)^{1/3} - x - 1$$

$$\Rightarrow \quad y = \int z \, dx = \int (k_1 - 3x)^{1/3} - x - 1 \, dx = -\frac{1}{4}(k_1 - 3x)^{4/3} - \frac{1}{2}x^2 - x + c_2$$

is the general solution.

Example 3.42. Consider the equation

$$y'y'' = x.$$

Since y does not appear explicitly, let $z(x) = y'(x)$ to obtain the first-order equation

$$zz' = x,$$

which is separable. Then

$$\frac{1}{2}z^2 = \frac{1}{2}x^2 + c_1 \quad \Rightarrow \quad z^2 = x^2 + k \quad \Rightarrow \quad z = \pm\sqrt{x^2 + k} \quad \Rightarrow \quad y = \pm\int \sqrt{x^2 + k} \, dx.$$

The value of the last integral depends upon the sign of k. If $k = 0$, then

$$y = \pm\int x \, dx = \pm\frac{x^2}{2} + c_2.$$

If $k > 0$, let $k = \mu^2$ and make the trigonometric substitution

$$x = \mu \tan(t), \quad -\frac{\pi}{2} < t < \frac{\pi}{2}, \quad \frac{dx}{dt} = \mu \sec^2(t), \quad \sqrt{x^2 + \mu^2} = \mu \sec(t),$$

to obtain

$$y = \pm\int \sqrt{x^2 + \mu^2} \, dx = \pm\mu^2 \int \sec^3(t) \, dt.$$

By integration by parts,

$$
\begin{aligned}
\int \sec^3(t)\,dt &= \int \sec(t)\cdot\sec^2(t)\,dt \\
&= \sec(t)\tan(t) - \int \tan(t)\cdot\sec(t)\tan(t)\,dt \\
&= \sec(t)\tan(t) - \int \sec(t)\tan^2(t)\,dt \\
&= \sec(t)\tan(t) - \int \sec(t)[\sec^2(t)-1]\,dt \\
&= \sec(t)\tan(t) - \int \sec^3(t)\,dt + \int \sec(t)\,dt \\
\Rightarrow\quad 2\int \sec^3(t)\,dt &= \sec(t)\tan(t) + \ln|\sec(t)+\tan(t)| + c_3 \\
\Rightarrow\quad \int \sec^3(t)\,dt &= \frac{1}{2}\Big[\sec(t)\tan(t)+\ln|\sec(t)+\tan(t)|\Big] + c_4.
\end{aligned}
$$

Hence, employing $\tan(t)=\dfrac{x}{\mu}$ and $\sec(t)=\dfrac{1}{\mu}\sqrt{x^2+\mu^2}$,

$$
y = \pm\frac{\mu^2}{2}\left[\frac{x\sqrt{x^2+\mu^2}}{\mu^2}+\ln\left|\frac{\sqrt{x^2+\mu^2}}{\mu}+\frac{x}{\mu}\right|\right] + c_5.
$$

If $k<0$, let $k=-\mu^2$ and make the trigonometric substitution

$$
x=\mu\sec(t),\ 0\le t<\frac{\pi}{2}\ \text{or}\ \pi\le t<\frac{3\pi}{2},\ \frac{dx}{dt}=\mu\sec(t)\tan(t),\ \sqrt{x^2-\mu^2}=\mu\tan(t),
$$

to obtain

$$
\begin{aligned}
y &= \pm\int\sqrt{x^2-\mu^2}\,dx = \pm\mu^2\int\sec(t)\tan^2(t)\,dt = \pm\mu^2\int\sec^3(t)-\sec(t)\,dt \\
&= \pm\mu^2\left\{\frac{1}{2}\big[\sec(t)\tan(t)+\ln|\sec(t)+\tan(t)|\big]-\ln|\sec(t)+\tan(t)|\right\} + c_6 \\
&= \pm\frac{\mu^2}{2}\big[\sec(t)\tan(t)-\ln|\sec(t)+\tan(t)|\big] + c_6.
\end{aligned}
$$

Hence, employing $\sec(t)=\dfrac{x}{\mu}$ and $\tan(t)=\dfrac{1}{\mu}\sqrt{x^2-\mu^2}$,

$$
y = \pm\frac{\mu^2}{2}\left[\frac{x\sqrt{x^2-\mu^2}}{\mu^2}-\ln\left|\frac{x}{\mu}+\frac{\sqrt{x^2-\mu^2}}{\mu}\right|\right] + c_6.
$$

Consider a second-order equation in which the independent variable x does not appear explicitly. For example,

$$y'y'' + y^3 = 0.$$

Let $y'(x) = v(y)$. Then, by the chain rule,

$$y''(x) = \frac{dv}{dy}\frac{dy}{dx} = v'v,$$

and the equation becomes $v^2v' + y^3 = 0$, which is of the first order. The general solution $v(y)$ of the latter equation contains one arbitrary constant. Once $v(y)$ is found, $y' = v(y)$ is a separable equation, and

$$y' = v(y) \quad \Rightarrow \quad \frac{y'}{v(y)} = 1 \quad \Rightarrow \quad \int \frac{1}{v(y)}\,dy = \int 1\,dx = x + c,$$

yielding a second arbitrary constant and, therefore, the general solution of the second-order equation.

Example 3.43. Consider the equation

$$y'' = (y')^2 \left(2y - \frac{1}{y} \right).$$

Since x does not appear explicitly, let $v(y) = y'(x)$ to obtain the first-order equation

$$vv' = v^2 \left(2y - \frac{1}{y} \right),$$

which is separable. One solution is $v = 0$ and gives $y' = 0$, i.e., $y = c_1$. If $v \neq 0$, then

$$\frac{v'}{v} = 2y - \frac{1}{y} \quad \Rightarrow \quad \ln|v| = y^2 - \ln|y| + c_2 \quad \Rightarrow \quad v = k_1 y^{-1} e^{y^2} \quad \Rightarrow \quad y e^{-y^2} y' = k_1$$

$$\Rightarrow \quad \int y e^{-y^2}\,dy = \int k_1\,dx \quad \Rightarrow \quad -\frac{1}{2} e^{-y^2} = k_1 x + k_2$$

$$\Rightarrow \quad -y^2 = \ln(k_3 x + k_4) \quad \Rightarrow \quad y = \pm\sqrt{-\ln(k_3 x + k_4)}$$

is the general solution.

Example 3.44. Consider the equation

$$y'' + (1 + 2y)(y')^3 = 0.$$

Since x does not appear explicitly, let $v(y) = y'(x)$ to obtain the first-order equation

$$vv' + (1 + 2y)v^3 = 0,$$

which is separable. One solution is $v = 0$ and gives $y' = 0$, i.e., $y = c_1$. If $v \neq 0$, then

$$-\frac{v'}{v^2} = 1 + 2y \quad \Rightarrow \quad \frac{1}{v} = y + y^2 + c_2 \quad \Rightarrow \quad (y + y^2 + c_2)y' = 1$$

$$\Rightarrow \quad \int y + y^2 + c_2 \, dy = \int 1 \, dx \quad \Rightarrow \quad \frac{1}{2}y^2 + \frac{1}{3}y^3 + c_2 y = x + c_3$$

is the general solution.

Example 3.45. Consider the equation

$$yy'' + 3y^2(y')^3 + (y')^2 = 0.$$

Since x does not appear explicitly, let $v(y) = y'(x)$ to obtain the first-order equation

$$yvv' + 3y^2v^3 + v^2 = 0.$$

One solution is $v = 0$ and gives $y' = 0$, i.e., $y = c_1$. If $v \neq 0$, then

$$yv' + v = -3y^2v^2$$

is a Bernoulli equation with $\alpha = 2$. Hence, $u = v^{-1} \Rightarrow v = u^{-1} \Rightarrow v' = -u^{-2}u'$, and the equation for v transforms into

$$-yu^{-2}u' + u^{-1} = -3y^2u^{-2}, \quad \text{or} \quad -yu' + u = -3y^2,$$

which is linear. Its standard form is

$$u' - \frac{1}{y}u = 3y,$$

with the integrating factor $I(y) = e^{\int -\frac{1}{y} dy} = e^{-\ln|y|} = |y|^{-1} = \pm y^{-1}$ and, with $I(y) = y^{-1}$, the equation becomes

$$\frac{1}{y}u' - \frac{1}{y^2}u = 3, \quad \text{i.e.,} \quad \left(\frac{1}{y}u\right)' = 3.$$

Hence,

$$\frac{1}{y}u = 3y + c_2 \quad \Rightarrow \quad u = 3y^2 + c_2 y \quad \Rightarrow \quad v = (3y^2 + c_2 y)^{-1} \quad \Rightarrow \quad (3y^2 + c_2 y)y' = 1$$

$$\Rightarrow \quad \int 3y^2 + c_2 y \, dy = \int 1 \, dx \quad \Rightarrow \quad y^3 + \frac{1}{2}c_2 y^2 = x + c_3$$

is the general solution.

Example 3.46. Consider the equation

$$y'' + (y')^2 = y'. \tag{3.19}$$

Since x does not appear explicitly, let $v(y) = y'(x)$ to obtain the first-order equation

$$vv' + v^2 = v,$$

which is separable. One solution is $v = 0$ and gives $y' = 0$, i.e., $y = c_1$. If $v \neq 0$, then

$$v' + v = 1 \quad \Rightarrow \quad \frac{v'}{1 - v} = 1 \quad \Rightarrow \quad -\ln|1 - v| = y + c_2$$

$$\Rightarrow \quad 1 - v = ke^{-y} \quad \Rightarrow \quad v = 1 - ke^{-y} \quad \Rightarrow \quad \frac{y'}{1 - ke^{-y}} = 1$$

$$\Rightarrow \quad \int \frac{1}{1 - ke^{-y}} \, dy = \int 1 \, dx \quad \Rightarrow \quad \int \frac{e^y}{e^y - k} \, dy = x + c_3$$

$$\Rightarrow \quad \ln|e^y - k| = x + c_3 \quad \Rightarrow \quad e^y - k = k_1 e^x \quad \Rightarrow \quad y = \ln(k_1 e^x + k)$$

is the general solution.

Note that y also does not appear in Equation (3.19). It may therefore also be solved by letting $z(x) = y'(x)$. The equation then becomes

$$z' + z^2 = z,$$

which is separable. Then

$$\frac{z'}{z - z^2} = 1 \quad \Rightarrow \quad \left(\frac{1}{1 - z} + \frac{1}{z} \right) z' = 1 \quad \Rightarrow \quad -\ln|1 - z| + \ln|z| = x + c_1$$

$$\Rightarrow \quad \ln \left| \frac{z}{1 - z} \right| = x + c_1 \quad \Rightarrow \quad \frac{z}{1 - z} = ke^x \quad \Rightarrow \quad z = \frac{ke^x}{ke^x + 1}$$

$$\Rightarrow \quad y = \int \frac{ke^x}{ke^x + 1} \, dx = \ln|ke^x + 1| + k_1$$

is the general solution, and is equivalent to the solution obtained earlier because

$$\ln|ke^x + 1| + k_1 = \ln|ke^x + 1| + \ln(e^{k_1}) = \ln(e^{k_1}|ke^x + 1|) = \ln(k_2 e^x + k_3).$$

Exercises 3.4

Find the general solution of the given equation.

1. $\dfrac{y''}{y'-2} = \dfrac{2}{x} + 3x^2$

2. $x^2 y'' = (y')^2$

3. $y'' - x(y')^3 = 0$

4. $y'y'' + x = 0$

5. $xy'' = y' \ln(y') - y' \ln(x), \ x > 0$

6. $y'' + 2y' = 2e^{-x}\sqrt{y'}$

7. $x^4 + (y')^2 - xy'y'' = 0$

8. $y'' = (2x - y' + 3)^2 + 2$

9. $y'' + (2 - 6y + 12y^2)(y')^3 = 0$

10. $y'' = (y')^2 \tan(y)$

11. $yy'' = y'(y' - 1)\ln(y' - 1)$

12. $\sin(y)y'' + \cos(y)(y')^2 = (y')^3$

13. $y'' = 2yy'$

14. $y'' - (y')^2 = 1$

15. $\sqrt{1 + y'}\, y'' = 1$

16. $e^{y'} y'' = 1$

17. $\cos(y')y'' = 1$

18. $y'' = y'\sqrt{1 - (y')^2}$

Chapter 3 Exercises

1. Consider the equation $x^2 y'' + xy' + \left(x^2 - \dfrac{1}{4}\right) y = 0$, $x > 0$. Given that one solution is $y_1 = \dfrac{\cos(x)}{\sqrt{x}}$, find a second, independent solution y_2 by reduction of order.

2. Consider the equation $y'' + xy' + y = 0$. Given that one solution is $y_1 = e^{-x^2/2}$, find a second, independent solution y_2 by reduction of order. Note that y_2 includes an integral which cannot be evaluated in terms of elementary functions.

3. Consider the equation $2x^2 y'' + (2x^2 + x)y' - y = 0$, $x > 0$. Given that one solution is $y_1 = x^{-1/2} e^{-x}$, find a second, independent solution y_2 by reduction of order. Note that y_2 includes an integral which cannot be evaluated in terms of elementary functions.

4. Consider the equation $y'' + y = \cos(x)$.

   (a) Solve the equation by the method of undetermined coefficients.

   (b) Solve the equation by variation of parameters.

5. Consider the equation $y'' - y' - 2y = 8x^2$.

   (a) Solve the equation by the method of undetermined coefficients.

   (b) Solve the equation by variation of parameters.

6. Consider the equation $y'' - y = \cos(x) - 5\sin(2x)$.

   (a) Solve the equation by the method of undetermined coefficients.

   (b) Solve the equation by variation of parameters.

7. Consider the equation $y'' - 2y' - 8y = 24(x^2 + 1)e^{4x}$.

   (a) Solve the equation by the method of undetermined coefficients.

   (b) Solve the equation by variation of parameters.

8. Consider the equation $a(x - x_0)^2 y'' + b(x - x_0)y' + cy = 0$, where a, b, c and x_0 are constants.

   (a) Show that the change of variables $t = x - x_0$ and $y(x) = z(t)$ transforms the equation into an Euler equation for $z(t)$.

   (b) Solve the equation $2(x - 3)^2 y'' + 3(x - 3)y' + y = 0$ for $x \neq 3$.

9. Consider the Euler equation $ax^2 y'' + bxy' + cy = 0$, $x > 0$.

(a) Show that the change of variables $t = \ln(x)$ and $y(x) = z(t)$ transforms the Euler equation for $y(x)$ into an equation for $z(t)$ with constant coefficients.

(b) Show that the indicial equation for $z = e^{rt}$ is identical to the one for $y = x^r$.

(c) Express the three cases of solution $z = c_1 e^{r_1 t} + c_2 e^{r_2 t}$, $z = e^{rt}(c_1 + c_2 t)$ and $z = e^{\alpha t}[c_1 \cos(\beta t) + c_2 \sin(\beta t)]$ in terms of x to obtain the three cases of solution for $y(x)$.

10. Consider the equation $x^2 y'' - xy' + y = \dfrac{x}{\ln(x)}$, $x > 0$.

   (a) Solve the equation by variation of parameters.

   (b) Let $t = \ln(x)$ and $y(x) = z(t)$ to transform the equation for $y(x)$ into an equation for $z(t)$ (see Exercise 9).

   (c) Solve the equation obtained in part (b) for $z(t)$.

   (d) Obtain $y(x)$ from $z(t)$ and compare with the result of part (a).

11. Consider the equation $4x^2 y'' + 4xy' - y = x^2 |x|^{1/2}$.

   (a) Solve the equation for $x > 0$.

   (b) Solve the equation for $x < 0$. (You will need to employ the fact that $|x| = -x$ for $x < 0$, and that $\dfrac{d}{dx}(-x)^\alpha = -\alpha(-x)^{\alpha-1}$, by the chain rule.)

   (c) Combine the solutions in parts (a) and (b) into a solution which is valid for any $x \neq 0$.

12. Consider the equation $y'' + y' = 2x$.

   (a) Solve the equation by the method of undetermined coefficients.

   (b) Solve the equation by variation of parameters.

   (c) Solve the equation by letting $z(x) = y'(x)$.

13. Consider the equation $x^2 y'' + xy' = 1$, $x > 0$.

   (a) Solve the equation by variation of parameters.

   (b) Solve the equation by letting $z(x) = y'(x)$.

14. Consider the equation $3y'y'' = 1$.

   (a) Solve the equation by letting $z(x) = y'(x)$.

   (b) Solve the equation by letting $v(y) = y'(x)$.

15. Suppose that the functions p and q are continuous on an interval I and let y_1 and y_2 be solutions of the equation $y'' + p(x)y' + q(x)y = 0$.

(a) Show that the Wronskian $W(x) = W[y_1, y_2](x) = y_1 y_2' - y_1' y_2$ satisfies the first-order equation $W'(x) + p(x)W(x) = 0$. (*Hint:* Multiply the equation $y_2'' + p(x)y_2' + q(x)y_2 = 0$ by y_1, $y_1'' + p(x)y_1' + q(x)y_1 = 0$ by y_2, and subtract the latter from the former.)

(b) Solve the first-order equation in part (a) for $W(x)$.

(c) Deduce from the result of part (b) that either $W(x) = 0$ on I, or $W(x) \neq 0$ for any x in I.

(d) Prove that y_1 and y_2 are linearly dependent on I if and only if $W(x) = 0$ on I.

(e) Deduce from the result of part (d) that y_1 and y_2 are linearly independent on I if and only if $W(x) \neq 0$ on I.

16. Consider the equation $x^2 y'' - xy' = 0$ on the interval $I = (-1, 1)$.

(a) Find two linearly independent solutions y_1 and y_2.

(b) Compute the Wronskian $W(x)$.

(c) Show that there is a point x_0 in I with $W(x_0) = 0$.

(d) Why does the result of part (c) not contradict the result of part (e) in Exercise 15?

Chapter 4

Higher-Order Linear Equations

The definitions and certain of the methods of solution discussed in Chapter 3 can be extended to equations of any order $n \geq 2$.

Definition 4.1. The *general solution* of an equation of order $n \geq 2$ is the solution which contains n arbitrary constants which cannot be combined. It is an *n-parameter family of solutions*, i.e., a set of solutions such that every solution corresponds to particular values of the arbitrary constants. A solution in which the constants are assigned particular values is called a *particular solution*.

Definition 4.2. An *initial-value problem* for an equation of order $n \geq 2$ consists of the equation, together with n *initial conditions*, which specify the values of

$$y, \; y', \; y'', \; \cdots, \; y^{(n-1)}$$

at a single point x and, thereby, determine a particular solution.

Definition 4.3. An equation of order $n \geq 2$ is *linear* if it has the form

$$a_n(x)y^{(n)} + a_{n-1}(x)y^{(n-1)} + \cdots + a_2(x)y'' + a_1(x)y' + a_0(x)y = g(x). \qquad (4.1)$$

Otherwise, it is *nonlinear*. The *standard form* of Equation (4.1) is

$$y^{(n)} + p_{n-1}(x)y^{(n-1)} + \cdots + p_2(x)y'' + p_1(x)y' + p_0(x)y = f(x). \qquad (4.2)$$

The equation is called *homogeneous* if $g(x) \equiv 0$ (or $f(x) \equiv 0$). Otherwise, it is *nonhomogeneous*.

4.1 Homogeneous Equations

Theorem 4.1. If y_1, y_2, $\cdots$, y_n are solutions of the linear, homogeneous equation

$$a_n(x)y^{(n)} + a_{n-1}(x)y^{(n-1)} + \cdots + a_2(x)y'' + a_1(x)y' + a_0(x)y = 0, \qquad (4.3)$$

then any linear combination

$$y = c_1 y_1 + c_2 y_2 + \cdots + c_n y_n$$

is also a solution.

Theorem 4.2. The homogeneous equation (4.3) has precisely n linearly independent solutions y_1, y_2, $\cdots$, y_n, and the general solution is

$$y = c_1 y_1 + c_2 y_2 + \cdots + c_n y_n,$$

where c_1, c_2, $\cdots$, c_n are arbitrary constants.

4.1.1 Equations with Constant Coefficients

Consider the equation

$$a_n y^{(n)} + a_{n-1}y^{(n-1)} + \cdots + a_2 y'' + a_1 y' + a_0 y = 0, \qquad (4.4)$$

where a_1, a_2, $\cdots$, a_n are constants.

As in the case $n = 2$ discussed in Chapter 3, seek solutions in the form $y = e^{rx}$. Then

$$y' = re^{rx}, \quad y'' = r^2 e^{rx}, \quad \cdots, \quad y^{(n-1)} = r^{n-1}e^{rx}, \quad y^{(n)} = r^n e^{rx},$$

and substitution into Equation (4.4) yields

$$(a_n r^n + a_{n-1}r^{n-1} + \cdots + a_2 r^2 + a_1 r + a_0)e^{rx} = 0$$

or, upon division by $e^{rx} \neq 0$, the *indicial equation*

$$P(r) = a_n r^n + a_{n-1}r^{n-1} + \cdots + a_2 r^2 + a_1 r + a_0 = 0. \qquad (4.5)$$

In the case $n = 2$ discussed in Chapter 3, there are three possibilities for the roots of the polynomial P in Equation (4.5), namely, two distinct real roots, one real repeated root, or two complex-conjugate roots.

In the cases $n \geq 3$, there are more possibilities, such as repeated complex roots, or real roots which are repeated more than once, but the forms of the solutions are analogous to the ones for $n = 2$, and are given by Theorems 4.3–4.5.

Theorem 4.3. If P has n distinct real roots r_i, $1 \le i \le n$, i.e.,

$$P(r) = (r - r_1)(r - r_2) \cdots (r - r_n),$$

where $r_i \ne r_j$ if $i \ne j$, then n independent solutions of Equation (4.4) are given by

$$y_1 = e^{r_1 x}, \quad y_2 = e^{r_2 x}, \quad \cdots, \quad y_n = e^{r_n x},$$

and the general solution is $y = c_1 y_1 + c_2 y_2 + \cdots + c_n y_n$.

Example 4.1. Consider the equation

$$4y''' - 4y'' - y' + y = 0.$$

$y = e^{rx} \Rightarrow$

$$P(r) = 4r^3 - 4r^2 - r + 1 = 0.$$

Since $r = 1$ is a root, $r - 1$ must be a factor. Long division of $r - 1$ into $4r^3 - 4r^2 - r + 1$ gives the other factor $4r^2 - 1$. Alternatively,

$$
\begin{aligned}
4r^3 - 4r^2 - r + 1 &= (r - 1)(4r^2 + ar - 1) \\
&= 4r^3 + (a - 4)r^2 - (a + 1)r + 1 \Rightarrow a = 0 \Rightarrow \\
4r^3 - 4r^2 - r + 1 &= (r - 1)(4r^2 - 1),
\end{aligned}
$$

as above. Thus,

$$P(r) = 4r^3 - 4r^2 - r + 1 = (r - 1)(2r - 1)(2r + 1) = 0$$

$\Rightarrow r_1 = 1$, $r_2 = \dfrac{1}{2}$ and $r_3 = -\dfrac{1}{2} \Rightarrow y_1 = e^x$, $y_2 = e^{\frac{1}{2}x}$ and $y_3 = e^{-\frac{1}{2}x}$, and

$$y = c_1 e^x + c_2 e^{\frac{1}{2}x} + c_3 e^{-\frac{1}{2}x}$$

is the general solution.

Example 4.2. Consider the initial-value problem

$$y''' - 4y'' + y' + 6y = 0, \quad y(0) = 0, \quad y'(0) = 0, \quad y''(0) = 12.$$

$y = e^{rx} \Rightarrow$

$$P(r) = r^3 - 4r^2 + r + 6 = 0.$$

Since $r = -1$ is a root, $r + 1$ must be a factor. Long division of $r + 1$ into $r^3 - 4r^2 + r + 6$ gives the other factor $r^2 - 5r + 6$. Alternatively,

$$
\begin{aligned}
r^3 - 4r^2 + r + 6 &= (r + 1)(r^2 + ar + 6) \\
&= r^3 + (a + 1)r^2 + (a + 6)r + 6 \Rightarrow a = -5 \Rightarrow \\
r^3 - 4r^2 + r + 6 &= (r + 1)(r^2 - 5r + 6) = (r + 1)(r - 2)(r - 3) = 0
\end{aligned}
$$

$\Rightarrow r_1 = -1$, $r_2 = 2$ and $r_3 = 3$, $y_1 = e^{-x}$, $y_2 = e^{2x}$ and $y_3 = e^{3x}$, and

$$y = c_1 e^{-x} + c_2 e^{2x} + c_3 e^{3x}$$

is the general solution. Then $y' = -c_1 e^{-x} + 2c_2 e^{2x} + 3c_3 e^{3x}$, $y'' = c_1 e^{-x} + 4c_2 e^{2x} + 9c_3 e^{3x}$, and the initial conditions $y(0) = 0$, $y'(0) = 0$ and $y''(0) = 12$ require that

$$\left\{ \begin{array}{ccccccc} c_1 & + & c_2 & + & c_3 & = & 0 \\ -c_1 & + & 2c_2 & + & 3c_3 & = & 0 \\ c_1 & + & 4c_2 & + & 9c_3 & = & 12 \end{array} \right\}.$$

The sum of the first two equations gives $3c_2 + 4c_3 = 0$, and the sum of the last two gives $6c_2 + 12c_3 = 12$. The solution of the system

$$\left\{ \begin{array}{ccccc} 3c_2 & + & 4c_3 & = & 0 \\ 6c_2 & + & 12c_3 & = & 12 \end{array} \right\}$$

is $c_2 = -4$ and $c_3 = 3$. Then $c_1 = 1$, and

$$y = e^{-x} - 4e^{2x} + 3e^{3x}$$

is the solution of the initial-value problem.

Example 4.3. Consider the equation

$$y^{(4)} - 5y''' + 5y'' + 5y' - 6y = 0.$$

$y = e^{rx} \Rightarrow$

$$P(r) = r^4 - 5r^3 + 5r^2 + 5r - 6 = 0.$$

Since $r = 1$ and $r = -1$ are roots, $r - 1$ and $r + 1$ must be factors. Long division of $(r - 1)(r + 1) = r^2 - 1$ into $r^4 - 5r^3 + 5r^2 + 5r - 6$ gives the other factor $r^2 - 5r + 6$. Alternatively,

$$\begin{array}{rcl} r^4 - 5r^3 + 5r^2 + 5r - 6 & = & (r^2 - 1)(r^2 + ar + 6) \\ & = & r^4 + ar^3 + 5r^2 - ar - 6 \Rightarrow a = -5 \Rightarrow \\ r^4 - 5r^3 + 5r^2 + 5r - 6 & = & (r^2 - 1)(r^2 - 5r + 6) \\ & = & (r - 1)(r + 1)(r - 2)(r - 3) = 0 \end{array}$$

$\Rightarrow r_1 = 1$, $r_2 = -1$, $r_3 = 2$ and $r_4 = 3$, and $y_1 = e^x$, $y_2 = e^{-x}$, $y_3 = e^{2x}$ and $y_4 = e^{3x}$, and

$$y = c_1 e^x + c_2 e^{-x} + c_3 e^{2x} + c_4 e^{3x}$$

is the general solution.

Definition 4.4. Let P be a polynomial and suppose that

$$P(r) = Q(r)(r - r_0)^m,$$

where Q is a polynomial with $Q(r_0) \neq 0$ and $m \geq 1$ is an integer. Then r_0 is a root of $P(r)$ and m is called the *multiplicity* of the root r_0.

For example, if $P(r) = r^3 - 3r + 2 = (r + 2)(r - 1)^2$, then $r_0 = -2$ is a root of multiplicity 1 and $r_1 = 1$ is a root of multiplicity 2.

If $P(r) = r^4 - r^3 - 3r^2 + 5r - 2 = (r^2 + r - 2)(r - 1)^2$, then the multiplicity of the root $r_0 = 1$ is *not* 2 because $Q(r) = r^2 + r - 2$ and $Q(r_0) = Q(1) = 0$. Since $P(r) = (r + 2)(r - 1)^3$ and $Q(r) = r + 2$ with $Q(1) = 3 \neq 0$, the multiplicity of $r_0 = 1$ is $m = 3$.

Thus, the multiplicity of a root r_0 of a polynomial P is the largest power of $r - r_0$ which occurs in the factorization of P.

Theorem 4.4. Let r_0 be a root of the indicial equation (4.5) obtained by letting $y = e^{rx}$ in Equation (4.4). If r_0 has multiplicity $m \geq 1$, i.e., $P(r) = Q(r)(r - r_0)^m$ with $Q(r_0) \neq 0$, then m linearly independent solutions of Equation (4.4) are given by

$$y_1 = e^{r_0 x}, \quad y_2 = x e^{r_0 x}, \quad y_3 = x^2 e^{r_0 x}, \quad \cdots, \quad y_m = x^{m-1} e^{r_0 x}.$$

Proof. Define the *linear operator* L by

$$L[y] = a_n y^{(n)} + a_{n-1} y^{(n-1)} + \cdots + a_2 y'' + a_1 y' + a_0 y,$$

i.e., L assigns to a function y the expression on the left-hand side of Equation (4.4). Thus, y is a solution of Equation (4.4) if and only if $L[y] = 0$. Then

$$
\begin{aligned}
L[e^{rx}] &= (a_n r^n + a_{n-1} r^{n-1} + \cdots + a_2 r^2 + a_1 r + a_0) e^{rx} \\
&= P(r) e^{rx} = Q(r)(r - r_0)^m e^{rx} = 0 \text{ when } r = r_0, \text{ if } m \geq 1, \\
L[x e^{rx}] &= L\left[\frac{d}{dr} e^{rx}\right] = \frac{d}{dr} L[e^{rx}] = \frac{d}{dr}[Q(r)(r - r_0)^m e^{rx}] \\
&= (r - r_0)^m \frac{d}{dr}[Q(r) e^{rx}] + m(r - r_0)^{m-1}[Q(r) e^{rx}] = 0 \\
&\quad \text{when } r = r_0, \text{ if } m \geq 2, \\
L[x^2 e^{rx}] &= L\left[\frac{d^2}{dr^2} e^{rx}\right] = \frac{d^2}{dr^2} L[e^{rx}] = \frac{d^2}{dr^2}[Q(r)(r - r_0)^m e^{rx}] \\
&= (r - r_0)^m \frac{d^2}{dr^2}[Q(r) e^{rx}] + 2m(r - r_0)^{m-1} \frac{d}{dr}[Q(r) e^{rx}] \\
&\quad + m(m-1)(r - r_0)^{m-2}[Q(r) e^{rx}] = 0 \text{ when } r = r_0, \text{ if } m \geq 3,
\end{aligned}
$$

and, in general, $L[x^k e^{rx}] = 0$ when $r = r_0$, if $m > k$. Thus, for $k = 0, 1, \cdots, m-1$, $x^k e^{r_0 x}$ is a solution. Note that the order of differentiation with respect to r and x has been reversed. This is permissible by Theorem 2.1 in Section 2.4.1 since the partial derivatives of all orders of e^{rx} are continuous everywhere.

Theorem 4.3 is the special case of Theorem 4.4 in which all of the roots of P are real and distinct (i.e., of multiplicity $m = 1$).

Example 4.4. Consider the equation

$$y''' - 4y'' + 5y' - 2y = 0.$$

$y = e^{rx} \Rightarrow$

$$P(r) = r^3 - 4r^2 + 5r - 2 = 0.$$

Since $r = 1$ is a root, $r - 1$ is a factor. Long division of $r - 1$ into $r^3 - 4r^2 + 5r - 2$ gives the other factor $r^2 - 3r + 2$. Hence,

$$r^3 - 4r^2 + 5r - 2 = (r - 1)(r^2 - 3r + 2) = (r - 1)^2(r - 2) = 0$$

$\Rightarrow r_1 = 1$ is a root of multiplicity 2 and $r_2 = 2$ is a root of multiplicity 1. Three linearly independent solutions are therefore given by $y_1 = e^x$, $y_2 = xe^x$ and $y_3 = e^{2x}$, and

$$y = c_1 e^x + c_2 x e^x + c_3 e^{2x}$$

is the general solution.

Example 4.5. Consider the initial-value problem

$$y''' - 3y'' + 3y' - y = 0, \quad y(0) = 1, \quad y'(0) = 2, \quad y''(0) = 9.$$

$y = e^{rx} \Rightarrow$

$$P(r) = r^3 - 3r^2 + 3r - 1 = 0.$$

Since $r = 1$ is a root, $r - 1$ is a factor. Long division of $r - 1$ into $r^3 - 3r^2 + 3r - 1$ gives the other factor $r^2 - 2r + 1$. Hence,

$$r^3 - 3r^2 + 3r - 1 = (r - 1)(r^2 - 2r + 1) = (r - 1)^3 = 0$$

$\Rightarrow r_1 = 1$ is a root of multiplicity 3, and three linearly independent solutions are given by $y_1 = e^x$, $y_2 = xe^x$ and $y_3 = x^2 e^x$, and

$$y = c_1 e^x + c_2 x e^x + c_3 x^2 e^x = (c_1 + c_2 x + c_3 x^2)e^x$$

is the general solution. Then

$$\begin{aligned} y' &= c_1 e^x + c_2(e^x + xe^x) + c_3(2xe^x + x^2 e^x) \\ &= (c_1 + c_2)e^x + (c_2 + 2c_3)xe^x + c_3 x^2 e^x, \\ y'' &= (c_1 + c_2)e^x + (c_2 + 2c_3)(e^x + xe^x) + c_3(2xe^x + x^2 e^x) \\ &= (c_1 + 2c_2 + 2c_3)e^x + (c_2 + 4c_3)xe^x + c_3 x^2 e^x, \end{aligned}$$

$y(0) = c_1 = 1$, $y'(0) = c_1 + c_2 = 2 \Rightarrow c_2 = 1$, $y''(0) = c_1 + 2c_2 + 2c_3 = 9 \Rightarrow c_3 = 3 \Rightarrow$ $y = e^x + xe^x + 3x^2 e^x$ is the solution of the initial-value problem.

Example 4.6. Consider the equation

$$y^{(4)} - 4y''' + 3y'' + 4y' - 4y = 0.$$

$y = e^{rx} \Rightarrow$

$$P(r) = r^4 - 4r^3 + 3r^2 + 4r - 4 = 0.$$

Since $r = 1$ and $r = -1$ are roots, $r - 1$ and $r + 1$ are factors. Long division of $(r - 1)(r + 1) = r^2 - 1$ into $r^4 - 4r^3 + 3r^2 + 4r - 4$ gives the other factor $r^2 - 4r + 4$. Hence,

$$r^4 - 4r^3 + 3r^2 + 4r - 4 = (r^2 - 1)(r^2 - 4r + 4) = (r - 1)(r + 1)(r - 2)^2 = 0$$

$\Rightarrow r_1 = 1$ and $r_2 = -1$ are roots of multiplicity 1, and $r_3 = 2$ is a root of multiplicity 2. Four independent solutions are therefore given by $y_1 = e^x$, $y_2 = e^{-x}$, $y_3 = e^{2x}$ and $y_4 = xe^{2x}$, and

$$y = c_1 e^x + c_2 e^{-x} + c_3 e^{2x} + c_4 xe^{2x}$$

is the general solution.

Example 4.7. Consider the equation

$$y^{(4)} - 2y''' - 3y'' + 4y' + 4y = 0.$$

$y = e^{rx} \Rightarrow$

$$P(r) = r^4 - 2r^3 - 3r^2 + 4r + 4 = 0.$$

Since $r = -1$ and $r = 2$ are roots, $r + 1$ and $r - 2$ are factors. Long division of $(r + 1)(r - 2) = r^2 - r - 2$ into $r^4 - 2r^3 - 3r^2 + 4r + 4$ gives the other factor $r^2 - r - 2$. Hence,

$$r^4 - 2r^3 - 3r^2 + 4r + 4 = (r^2 - r - 2)^2 = (r + 1)^2(r - 2)^2 = 0$$

$\Rightarrow r_1 = -1$ and $r_2 = 2$ are roots of multiplicity 2. Four independent solutions are therefore given by $y_1 = e^{-x}$, $y_2 = xe^{-x}$, $y_3 = e^{2x}$ and $y_4 = xe^{2x}$, and

$$y = c_1 e^{-x} + c_2 xe^{-x} + c_3 e^{2x} + c_4 xe^{2x}$$

is the general solution.

Example 4.8. Consider the equation

$$y^{(4)} - 5y''' + 6y'' + 4y' - 8y = 0.$$

$y = e^{rx} \Rightarrow$

$$P(r) = r^4 - 5r^3 + 6r^2 + 4r - 8 = 0.$$

Since $r = -1$ and $r = 2$ are roots, $r + 1$ and $r - 2$ are factors. Long division of $(r+1)(r-2) = r^2 - r - 2$ into $r^4 - 5r^3 + 6r^2 + 4r - 8$ gives the other factor $r^2 - 4r + 4$. Hence,

$$r^4 - 5r^3 + 6r^2 + 4r - 8 = (r+1)(r-2)(r^2 - 4r + 4) = (r+1)(r-2)^3 = 0$$

$\Rightarrow r_1 = -1$ is a root of multiplicity 1 and $r_2 = 2$ is a root of multiplicity 3. Four independent solutions are therefore given by $y_1 = e^{-x}$, $y_2 = e^{2x}$, $y_3 = xe^{2x}$ and $y_4 = x^2 e^{2x}$, and

$$y = c_1 e^{-x} + c_2 e^{2x} + c_3 x e^{2x} + c_4 x^2 e^{2x}$$

is the general solution.

Example 4.9. Consider the equation

$$y^{(4)} - 8y''' + 24y'' - 32y' + 16y = 0.$$

$y = e^{rx} \Rightarrow$

$$P(r) = r^4 - 8r^3 + 24r^2 - 32r + 16 = 0.$$

Since $r = 2$ is a root, $r - 2$ is a factor. Long division of $r-2$ into $r^4 - 8r^3 + 24r^2 - 32r + 16$ gives the other factor $r^3 - 6r^2 + 12r - 8$. Since $r = 2$ is a root of the cubic, $r - 2$ is a factor. Long division of $r - 2$ into $r^3 - 6r^2 + 12r - 8$ gives $r^2 - 4r + 4$. Hence,

$$r^4 - 8r^3 + 24r^2 - 32r + 16 = (r - 2)^2 (r^2 - 4r + 4) = (r - 2)^4 = 0$$

$\Rightarrow r_1 = 2$ is a root of multiplicity 4. Four independent solutions are therefore given by $y_1 = e^{2x}$, $y_2 = xe^{2x}$, $y_3 = x^2 e^{2x}$ and $y_4 = x^3 e^{2x}$, and

$$y = c_1 e^{2x} + c_2 x e^{2x} + c_3 x^2 e^{2x} + c_4 x^3 e^{2x} = (c_1 + c_2 x + c_3 x^2 + c_4 x^3)e^{2x}$$

is the general solution. Note that, since no root of $P(r)$ other than $r_1 = 2$ could be found, it may be beneficial to determine whether or not $r_1 = 2$ is also a root of $P'(r)$.

$$P'(r) = 4r^3 - 24r^2 + 48r - 32,$$

and $r_1 = 2$ is a root. Since $r_1 = 2$ is a root of both $P(r)$ and $P'(r)$, $(r - 2)^2$ must be a factor of $P(r)$, and long division needs to be performed only once in order to determine the other factor $r^2 - 4r + 4$.

In general, if $P(r)$ is a polynomial of degree $n \geq 1$ and $1 \leq k \leq n$, then $(r - r_0)^k$ is a factor of $P(r)$ if and only if r_0 is a root of $P(r)$, $P'(r)$, $\cdots$, and $P^{(k-1)}(r)$.

Theorem 4.5. Let $r_0 = \alpha + i\beta$ and $\overline{r_0} = \alpha - i\beta$ be two complex-conjugate roots of the indicial equation (4.5) obtained by letting $y = e^{rx}$ in Equation (4.4). Then two real, linearly independent solutions of Equation (4.4) are given by

$$y_1 = e^{\alpha x} \cos(\beta x) \quad \text{and} \quad y_2 = e^{\alpha x} \sin(\beta x).$$

More generally, if r_0 and $\overline{r_0}$ have multiplicity $m \geq 1$, i.e.,

$$P(r) = Q(r)(r - r_0)^m (r - \overline{r_0})^m,$$

then $2m$ real, linearly independent solutions of Equation (4.4) are given by

$$e^{\alpha x} \cos(\beta x), \quad x e^{\alpha x} \cos(\beta x), \quad x^2 e^{\alpha x} \cos(\beta x), \quad \cdots, \quad x^{m-1} e^{\alpha x} \cos(\beta x),$$

$$e^{\alpha x} \sin(\beta x), \quad x e^{\alpha x} \sin(\beta x), \quad x^2 e^{\alpha x} \sin(\beta x), \quad \cdots, \quad x^{m-1} e^{\alpha x} \sin(\beta x).$$

The remaining $n - 2m$ independent solutions of Equation (4.4) are determined by the roots of the polynomial Q of degree $n - 2m$.

Proof. By the proof of Theorem 4.4, the complex-conjugate functions $x^k e^{r_0 x}$ and $\overline{x^k e^{\overline{r_0} x}}$, $0 \leq k \leq m - 1$, are solutions. As in the case $n = 2$ derived in Section 3.2.1, from every one of the m pairs of complex-conjugate solutions $z_k = x^k e^{r_0 x}$ and $\overline{z_k} = x^k e^{\overline{r_0} x}$, $0 \leq k \leq m - 1$, two real solutions

$$\frac{z_k + \overline{z_k}}{2} = x^k e^{\alpha x} \cos(\beta x) \quad \text{and} \quad \frac{z_k - \overline{z_k}}{2i} = x^k e^{\alpha x} \sin(\beta x)$$

are obtained, for a total of $2m$ real, independent solutions. By the first part of this theorem and/or Theorem 4.4, an additional $n - 2m$ real, independent solutions are determined by the roots of Q.

Example 4.10. Consider the equation

$$y''' - 8y'' + 25y' - 26y = 0.$$

$y = e^{rx} \Rightarrow$

$$P(r) = r^3 - 8r^2 + 25r - 26 = 0.$$

Since $r = 2$ is a root, $r - 2$ is a factor. Long division of $r - 2$ into $r^3 - 8r^2 + 25r - 26$ gives the other factor $r^2 - 6r + 13$, and

$$r^2 - 6r + 13 = 0 \quad \Rightarrow \quad r = \frac{6 \pm \sqrt{36 - 52}}{2} = 3 \pm 2i.$$

Hence, P has the real root $r_1 = 2$ of multiplicity 1 and the complex-conjugate roots $3 \pm 2i$ of multiplicity 1. Three real, independent solutions are therefore given by $y_1 = e^{2x}$, $y_2 = e^{3x}\cos(2x)$ and $y_3 = e^{3x}\sin(2x)$, and

$$y = c_1 e^{2x} + c_2 e^{3x}\cos(2x) + c_3 e^{3x}\sin(2x)$$

is the general solution.

Example 4.11. Consider the equation

$$y^{(4)} - 7y''' + 27y'' - 47y' + 26y = 0.$$

$y = e^{rx} \Rightarrow$

$$P(r) = r^4 - 7r^3 + 27r^2 - 47r + 26 = 0.$$

Since $r = 1$ and $r = 2$ are roots, $(r-1)$ and $(r-2)$ are factors. Long division of $(r-1)(r-2) = r^2 - 3r + 2$ into $r^4 - 7r^3 + 27r^2 - 47r + 26$ gives the other factor $r^2 - 4r + 13$, and

$$r^2 - 4r + 13 = 0 \quad \Rightarrow \quad r = \frac{4 \pm \sqrt{16 - 52}}{2} = 2 \pm 3i.$$

Hence, four real, independent solutions are given by $y_1 = e^x$, $y_2 = e^{2x}$, $y_3 = e^{2x}\cos(3x)$ and $y_4 = e^{2x}\sin(3x)$, and

$$y = c_1 e^x + c_2 e^{2x} + c_3 e^{2x}\cos(3x) + c_4 e^{2x}\sin(3x)$$

is the general solution.

Example 4.12. Consider the equation

$$y^{(4)} - 8y''' + 26y'' - 32y' + 13y = 0.$$

$y = e^{rx} \Rightarrow$

$$P(r) = r^4 - 8r^3 + 26r^2 - 32r + 13 = 0.$$

Since $r = 1$ is a root of both $P(r)$ and $P'(r) = 4r^3 - 24r^2 + 52r - 32$, $(r-1)^2$ is a factor of $P(r)$. Long division of $(r-1)^2 = r^2 - 2r + 1$ into $r^4 - 8r^3 + 26r^2 - 32r + 13$ gives the other factor $r^2 - 6r + 13$, and

$$r^2 - 6r + 13 = 0 \quad \Rightarrow \quad r = \frac{6 \pm \sqrt{36 - 52}}{2} = 3 \pm 2i.$$

Hence, $r_1 = 1$ is a root of multiplicity 2 and $3 \pm 2i$ are two complex-conjugate roots of multiplicity 1. Four real, independent solutions are therefore given by $y_1 = e^x$, $y_2 = xe^x$, $y_3 = e^{3x}\cos(2x)$ and $y_4 = e^{3x}\sin(2x)$, and

$$y = c_1 e^x + c_2 xe^x + c_3 e^{3x}\cos(2x) + c_4 e^{3x}\sin(2x)$$

is the general solution.

Example 4.13. Consider the equation

$$y^{(4)} + y'' + y = 0.$$

$y = e^{rx} \Rightarrow$

$$P(r) = r^4 + r^2 + 1 = 0.$$

Since no real roots are immediately evident, write

$$\begin{aligned}
r^4 + r^2 + 1 &= (r^2 + ar + 1)(r^2 + br + 1) \\
&= r^4 + (a+b)r^3 + (ab+2)r^2 + (a+b)r + 1
\end{aligned}$$

and solve for a and b to obtain $a = \pm 1$ and $b = \mp 1$. Choosing $a = 1$ and $b = -1$ gives

$$r^4 + r^2 + 1 = (r^2 + r + 1)(r^2 - r + 1).$$

Choosing $a = -1$ and $b = 1$ gives the same result.

$$r^2 + r + 1 = 0 \quad \Rightarrow \quad r = \frac{-1 \pm \sqrt{1-4}}{2} = -\frac{1}{2} \pm i\frac{\sqrt{3}}{2}, \text{ and}$$

$$r^2 - r + 1 = 0 \quad \Rightarrow \quad r = \frac{1 \pm \sqrt{1-4}}{2} = \frac{1}{2} \pm i\frac{\sqrt{3}}{2}.$$

Hence, $P(r)$ has two pairs of complex-conjugate roots of multiplicity 1. Four real, independent solutions are therefore given by

$$y_1 = e^{-\frac{1}{2}x} \cos\left(\frac{\sqrt{3}}{2}x\right), \quad y_2 = e^{-\frac{1}{2}x} \sin\left(\frac{\sqrt{3}}{2}x\right),$$

$$y_3 = e^{\frac{1}{2}x} \cos\left(\frac{\sqrt{3}}{2}x\right), \quad y_4 = e^{\frac{1}{2}x} \sin\left(\frac{\sqrt{3}}{2}x\right),$$

and the general solution is $y = c_1y_1 + c_2y_2 + c_3y_3 + c_4y_4$.

Example 4.14. Consider the equation

$$y^{(4)} - 4y''' + 14y'' - 20y' + 25y = 0.$$

$y = e^{rx} \Rightarrow$

$$P(r) = r^4 - 4r^3 + 14r^2 - 20r + 25 = 0.$$

Since no real roots are immediately evident,

$$\begin{aligned}
r^4 - 4r^3 + 14r^2 - 20r + 25 &= (r^2 + ar + 5)(r^2 + br + 5) \\
&= r^4 + (a+b)r^3 + (ab+10)r^2 + 5(a+b)r + 25
\end{aligned}$$

$\Rightarrow a + b = -4$ and $ab + 10 = 14 \Rightarrow b = -4 - a \Rightarrow -a^2 - 4a = 4 \Rightarrow a^2 + 4a + 4 = 0$
$\Rightarrow (a + 2)^2 = 0 \Rightarrow a = -2 \Rightarrow b = -2 \Rightarrow$

$$r^4 - 4r^3 + 14r^2 - 20r + 25 = (r^2 - 2r + 5)^2,$$

and

$$r^2 - 2r + 5 = 0 \quad \Rightarrow \quad r = \frac{2 \pm \sqrt{4 - 20}}{2} = 1 \pm 2i.$$

Hence, $1 \pm 2i$ are complex-conjugate roots of multiplicity 2. Four real, independent solutions are therefore given by

$$y_1 = e^x \cos(2x), \quad y_2 = xe^x \cos(2x), \quad y_3 = e^x \sin(2x), \quad y_4 = xe^x \sin(2x),$$

and the general solution is $y = c_1 y_1 + c_2 y_2 + c_3 y_3 + c_4 y_4$. Note that, if $P(r)$ is expressed as

$$\begin{aligned}
r^4 - 4r^3 + 14r^2 - 20r + 25 &= (r^2 + ar + 1)(r^2 + br + 25) \\
&= r^4 + (a + b)r^3 + (ab + 26)r^2 + (25a + b)r + 25,
\end{aligned}$$

then the equations $a + b = -4$, $25a + b = -20$ and $ab + 26 = 14$ are inconsistent and lead to a contradiction.

4.1.2 Cauchy-Euler Equations

Definition 4.5. An equation of the form

$$a_n x^n y^{(n)} + a_{n-1} x^{n-1} y^{(n-1)} + \cdots + a_2 x^2 y'' + a_1 x y' + a_0 y = 0, \quad n \geq 2, \tag{4.6}$$

where a_i, $0 \leq i \leq n$, are constants, is called a *Cauchy-Euler* or *Euler* equation.

Definition 4.5 is a generalization of Definition 3.7 given in Section 3.2.2 for $n = 2$ to equations of order $n \geq 2$. The solutions are analogous to the ones obtained therein for $n = 2$, and are given by the following:

Theorem 4.6. Let $P(r) = 0$ denote the indicial equation which results from the substitution of $y = x^r$ into Equation (4.6) for $x > 0$. If $r = r_0$ is a real root of multiplicity $m \geq 1$, then m independent solutions of Equation 4.6 for $x > 0$ are given by

$$x^{r_0}, \quad x^{r_0} \ln(x), \quad x^{r_0} [\ln(x)]^2, \quad \cdots, \quad x^{r_0} [\ln(x)]^{m-1}.$$

If $\alpha \pm i\beta$ are complex-conjugate roots of multiplicity $m \geq 1$, then $2m$ independent solutions of Equation 4.6 for $x > 0$ are given by

$$x^\alpha \cos[\beta \ln(x)], \quad x^\alpha \ln(x) \cos[\beta \ln(x)], \quad \cdots, \quad x^\alpha [\ln(x)]^{m-1} \cos[\beta \ln(x)],$$

$$x^\alpha \sin[\beta \ln(x)], \quad x^\alpha \ln(x) \sin[\beta \ln(x)], \quad \cdots, \quad x^\alpha [\ln(x)]^{m-1} \sin[\beta \ln(x)].$$

The solutions for $x \neq 0$ are obtained from the ones for $x > 0$ by replacing x by $|x|$.

Proof. For $x > 0$, make the change of variables $t = \ln(x)$ and $y(x) = z(t)$. Then, by the chain rule,

$$
\begin{aligned}
\frac{dy}{dx} &= \frac{dz}{dt}\frac{dt}{dx} = \frac{1}{x}\frac{dz}{dt} & \Rightarrow \quad xy'(x) = z'(t), \\
\frac{d^2y}{dx^2} &= \frac{1}{x^2}\frac{d^2z}{dt^2} - \frac{1}{x^2}\frac{dz}{dt} = \frac{1}{x^2}\left[\frac{d^2z}{dt^2} - \frac{dz}{dt}\right] & \Rightarrow \quad x^2y''(x) = z''(t) - z'(t), \\
\frac{d^3y}{dx^3} &= \frac{1}{x^3}\left[\frac{d^3z}{dt^3} - \frac{d^2z}{dt^2}\right] - \frac{2}{x^3}\left[\frac{d^2z}{dt^2} - \frac{dz}{dt}\right] = \frac{1}{x^3}\left[\frac{d^3z}{dt^3} - 3\frac{d^2z}{dt^2} + 2\frac{dz}{dt}\right] \\
&\Rightarrow \quad x^3y'''(x) = z'''(t) - 3z''(t) + 2z'(t),
\end{aligned}
$$

etc., i.e., every term $x^k y^{(k)}(x)$ in the Euler equation transforms into an expression with constant coefficients. Thus, the Euler equation for $y(x)$ transforms into an equation for $z(t)$ with constant coefficients. Moreover, the indicial equation $P(r) = 0$ for $y(x)$ is identical to the one for $z(t)$ because $z(t) = e^{rt}$ if and only if $y(x) = e^{r\ln(x)} = x^r$. The forms of the solutions for $y(x)$ then follow from the corresponding forms of the solutions for $z(t)$ as given by Theorems 4.4 and 4.5 in Section 4.1.1. Replacing x by $|x|$ then gives the solutions for both $x > 0$ and $x < 0$.

Example 4.15. Consider the Euler equation

$$x^3y''' + 3x^2y'' - 2xy' + 2y = 0.$$

For $x > 0$, $y = x^r \Rightarrow$

$$
\begin{aligned}
P(r) &= r(r-1)(r-2) + 3r(r-1) - 2r + 2 \\
&= r(r-1)(r-2) + 3r(r-1) - 2(r-1) \\
&= (r-1)[r(r-2) + 3r - 2] \\
&= (r-1)(r^2 + r - 2) \\
&= (r-1)^2(r+2) = 0
\end{aligned}
$$

$\Rightarrow r_1 = 1$ is a root of multiplicity 2 and $r_2 = -2$ is a root of multiplicity 1. Hence, $y_1 = x$, $y_2 = x\ln(x)$ and $y_3 = x^{-2}$ for $x > 0$, and

$$y = c_1|x| + c_2|x|\ln|x| + c_3|x|^{-2} = c_4 x + c_5 x\ln|x| + c_6 x^{-2}$$

is the general solution for $x \neq 0$.

Example 4.16. Consider the Euler equation

$$x^3y''' - 4x^2y'' + 13xy' - 13y = 0.$$

For $x > 0$, $y = x^r \Rightarrow$

$$
\begin{aligned}
P(r) &= r(r-1)(r-2) - 4r(r-1) + 13r - 13 \\
&= r(r-1)(r-2) - 4r(r-1) + 13(r-1) \\
&= (r-1)[r(r-2) - 4r + 13] \\
&= (r-1)(r^2 - 6r + 13) = 0
\end{aligned}
$$

$\Rightarrow r_1 = 1$ and

$$
r^2 - 6r + 13 = 0 \quad \Rightarrow \quad r = \frac{6 \pm \sqrt{36 - 52}}{2} = 3 \pm 2i.
$$

Hence, $y_1 = x$, $y_2 = x^3 \cos[2\ln(x)]$ and $y_3 = x^3 \sin[2\ln(x)]$ for $x > 0$, and

$$
y = c_1 x + c_2 x^3 \cos(2\ln|x|) + c_3 x^3 \sin(2\ln|x|)
$$

is the general solution for $x \neq 0$.

Example 4.17. Consider the initial-value problem

$$
x^3 y''' - x^2 y'' - 2xy' + 6y = 0, \quad y(1) = 0, \quad y'(1) = 1, \quad y''(1) = 16.
$$

For $x > 0$, $y = x^r \Rightarrow$

$$
\begin{aligned}
P(r) &= r(r-1)(r-2) - r(r-1) - 2r + 6 \\
&= r(r-1)(r-2) - (r^2 + r - 6) \\
&= r(r-1)(r-2) - (r+3)(r-2) \\
&= (r-2)[r(r-1) - (r+3)] \\
&= (r-2)(r^2 - 2r - 3) \\
&= (r-2)(r-3)(r+1) = 0
\end{aligned}
$$

$\Rightarrow y = c_1 x^2 + c_2 x^3 + c_3 x^{-1}$ is the general solution for $x \neq 0$. Then

$$
\begin{aligned}
y' &= 2c_1 x + 3c_2 x^2 - c_3 x^{-2}, \\
y'' &= 2c_1 + 6c_2 x + 2c_3 x^{-3},
\end{aligned}
$$

and $y(1) = 0$, $y'(1) = 1$ and $y''(1) = 16 \Rightarrow$

$$
\begin{aligned}
y(1) &= c_1 + c_2 + c_3 = 0, \\
y'(1) &= 2c_1 + 3c_2 - c_3 = 1, \\
y''(1) &= 2c_1 + 6c_2 + 2c_3 = 16.
\end{aligned}
$$

Subtracting twice the first equation from third gives $c_2 = 4$. Adding the first two gives $3c_1 + 4c_2 = 1 \Rightarrow c_1 = -5$, and the first equation then gives $c_3 = 1$. Hence, $y = -5x^2 + 4x^3 + x^{-1}$ is the solution of the initial-value problem.

Example 4.18.   Consider the Euler equation

$$x^4 y^{(4)} - x^3 y''' + 4x^2 y'' - 8xy' + 8y = 0.$$

For $x > 0$, $y = x^r \Rightarrow$

$$
\begin{aligned}
P(r) &= r(r-1)(r-2)(r-3) - r(r-1)(r-2) + 4r(r-1) - 8r + 8 \\
&= r(r-1)(r-2)(r-3) - r(r-1)(r-2) + 4r(r-1) - 8(r-1) \\
&= (r-1)[r(r-2)(r-3) - r(r-2) + 4r - 8] \\
&= (r-1)[r(r-2)(r-3) - r(r-2) + 4(r-2)] \\
&= (r-1)(r-2)[r(r-3) - r + 4] \\
&= (r-1)(r-2)(r^2 - 4r + 4) \\
&= (r-1)(r-2)^3 = 0
\end{aligned}
$$

$\Rightarrow y = c_1 x + c_2 x^2 + c_3 x^2 \ln|x| + c_4 x^2 (\ln|x|)^2$ is the general solution for $x \neq 0$.

Example 4.19.   Consider the Euler equation

$$x^4 y^{(4)} + 7x^3 y''' + 13x^2 y'' - 26xy' + 26y = 0.$$

For $x > 0$, $y = x^r \Rightarrow$

$$
\begin{aligned}
P(r) &= r(r-1)(r-2)(r-3) + 7r(r-1)(r-2) + 13r(r-1) - 26r + 26 \\
&= r(r-1)(r-2)(r-3) + 7r(r-1)(r-2) + 13r(r-1) - 26(r-1) \\
&= (r-1)[r(r-2)(r-3) + 7r(r-2) + 13r - 26] \\
&= (r-1)[r(r-2)(r-3) + 7r(r-2) + 13(r-2)] \\
&= (r-1)(r-2)[r(r-3) + 7r + 13] \\
&= (r-1)(r-2)(r^2 + 4r + 13) = 0
\end{aligned}
$$

$\Rightarrow r_1 = 1$, $r_2 = 2$, and

$$r^2 + 4r + 13 = 0 \;\Rightarrow\; r = \frac{-4 \pm \sqrt{16 - 52}}{2} = -2 \pm 3i.$$

Hence, $y = c_1 x + c_2 x^2 + c_3 x^{-2} \cos(3 \ln|x|) + c_4 x^{-2} \sin(3 \ln|x|)$ is the general solution for $x \neq 0$.

Exercises 4.1

1. Find the general solution of the equation $y''' - 6y'' + 11y' - 6y = 0$.

2. Solve the initial-value problem $y''' - 2y'' - y' + 2y = 0$, $y(0) = 6$, $y'(0) = 0$, $y''(0) = 0$.

3. Find the general solution of the equation $9y''' + 9y'' - y' - y = 0$.

4. Find the general solution of the equation $y''' - 5y'' + 8y' - 4y = 0$.

5. Find the general solution of the equation $y''' - 6y'' + 12y' - 8y = 0$.

6. Solve the initial-value problem $y''' + y'' - y' - y = 0$, $y(0) = 0$, $y'(0) = 3$, $y''(0) = 2$.

7. Find the general solution of the equation $y''' - 5y'' + 17y' - 13y = 0$.

8. Find the general solution of the equation $y^{(4)} - 5y'' + 4y = 0$.

9. Solve the initial-value problem $y^{(4)} - 2y''' - y'' + 2y' = 0$, $y(0) = 0$, $y'(0) = 2$, $y''(0) = 0$, $y'''(0) = 8$.

10. Find the general solution of the equation $y^{(4)} - 7y''' + 17y'' - 17y' + 6y = 0$.

11. Find the general solution of the equation $y^{(4)} - y''' - 3y'' + 5y' - 2y = 0$.

12. Find the general solution of the equation $y^{(4)} - 4y''' + 6y'' - 4y' + y = 0$.

13. Find the general solution of the equation $y^{(4)} - 6y''' + 13y'' - 12y' + 4y = 0$.

14. Find the general solution of the equation $y^{(4)} + 2y''' + 4y'' - 2y' - 5y = 0$.

15. Find the general solution of the equation $y^{(4)} + 10y''' + 41y'' + 76y' + 52y = 0$.

16. Find the general solution of the equation $y^{(4)} + 5y'' + 4y = 0$.

17. Find the general solution of the equation $y^{(4)} + 4y = 0$.

18. Find the general solution of the equation $y^{(4)} - 8y''' + 26y'' - 40y' + 25y = 0$.

19. Find the general solution of the equation $x^3 y''' + x^2 y'' - 2xy' + 2y = 0$.

20. Find the general solution of the equation $x^3 y''' - 2x^2 y'' + 3xy' - 3y = 0$.

21. Find the general solution of the equation $x^3 y''' + xy' - y = 0$.

22. Solve the initial-value problem $x^3 y''' + 8x^2 y'' + 13xy' - 13y = 0$, $x > 0$, $y(1) = 0$, $y'(1) = 6$, $y''(1) = -2$.

23. Find the general solution of the equation $x^4 y^{(4)} + x^3 y''' + x^2 y'' - 2xy' + 2y = 0$.

24. Find the general solution of the equation $x^4 y^{(4)} - x^3 y''' + 5x^2 y'' - 10xy' + 10y = 0$.

25. Find the general solution of the equation $x^4 y^{(4)} + 6x^3 y''' + 6x^2 y'' - 2xy' + 2y = 0$.

26. Find the general solution of the equation $x^4 y^{(4)} + 2x^3 y''' + 3x^2 y'' - 3xy' + 4y = 0$.

4.2 Nonhomogeneous Equations

Theorem 4.7. The general solution of the linear, nonhomogeneous equation of order $n \geq 2$,

$$a_n(x)y^{(n)} + a_{n-1}(x)y^{(n-1)} + \cdots + a_2(x)y'' + a_1(x)y' + a_0(x)y = g(x), \qquad (4.7)$$

is $y = y_p + y_h$, where y_p is any particular solution, and $y_h = c_1 y_1 + c_2 y_2 + \cdots + c_n y_n$ is the general solution of the *associated homogeneous equation*

$$a_n(x)y^{(n)} + a_{n-1}(x)y^{(n-1)} + \cdots + a_2(x)y'' + a_1(x)y' + a_0(x)y = 0, \qquad (4.8)$$

where y_k, $1 \leq k \leq n$, are n linearly independent solutions.

Theorem 4.7 is a generalization of Theorem 3.3 given in Section 3.3 for $n = 2$, and the proof is similar. The general solution of Equation (4.8) is obtained by the methods discussed in Sections 4.1.1 and 4.1.2 for equations with constant coefficients and Cauchy-Euler equations. A particular solution of Equation (4.7) is obtained by variation of parameters or, where applicable, the method of undetermined coefficients, suitably generalized to equations of order $n \geq 2$.

4.2.1 Variation of Parameters

Definition 4.6. The *Wronskian* of n solutions y_1, y_2, $\cdots$, y_n of Equation (4.8) is

$$W(x) = W[y_1, y_2, \cdots, y_n](x) = \begin{vmatrix} y_1 & y_2 & \cdots & y_n \\ y_1' & y_2' & \cdots & y_n' \\ \vdots & \vdots & \cdots & \vdots \\ y_1^{(n-1)} & y_2^{(n-1)} & \cdots & y_n^{(n-1)} \end{vmatrix}.$$

Theorem 4.8. Consider the *standard form* of Equation (4.7),

$$y^{(n)} + p_{n-1}(x)y^{(n-1)} + \cdots + p_2(x)y'' + p_1(x)y' + p_0(x)y = f(x), \qquad (4.9)$$

and the *associated homogeneous equation*

$$y^{(n)} + p_{n-1}(x)y^{(n-1)} + \cdots + p_2(x)y'' + p_1(x)y' + p_0(x)y = 0. \qquad (4.10)$$

If p_k, $0 \leq k \leq n-1$, are continuous on an interval I, and y_k, $1 \leq k \leq n$, are solutions of Equation (4.10), then either $W \equiv 0$ on I or $W(x) \neq 0$ for any x in I. The solutions y_1, y_2, $\cdots$, y_n are linearly independent on I if and only if $W \neq 0$ on I.

The method of *variation of parameters* for equations of order $n \geq 2$ is given by the theorem which follows, and is an extension of the one for $n = 2$.

Theorem 4.9. Let y_1, y_2, $\cdots$, y_n be n linearly independent solutions of Equation (4.10) and let $W(x)$ be the Wronskian. Let $\Delta_j(x)$, $1 \leq j \leq n$, denote the Wronskian with its jth column replaced by the column vector $[0, 0, \cdots, 0, f(t)]^t$, i.e.,

$$\Delta_j(x) = \begin{vmatrix} y_1 & y_2 & \cdots & 0 & \cdots & y_n \\ y_1' & y_2' & \cdots & 0 & \cdots & y_n' \\ \vdots & \vdots & \cdots & \vdots & \cdots & \vdots \\ y_1^{(n-1)} & y_2^{(n-1)} & \cdots & f(t) & \cdots & y_n^{(n-1)} \end{vmatrix}.$$

Then a particular solution y_p of Equation (4.9) is given by

$$y_p = u_1 y_1 + u_2 y_2 + \cdots + u_n y_n,$$

where

$$u_j(x) = \int \frac{\Delta_j(x)}{W(x)}\, dx, \quad 1 \leq j \leq n.$$

Example 4.20. Consider the nonhomogeneous equation

$$y''' - 3y' - 2y = 27e^{-x}.$$

For the associated homogeneous equation

$$y''' - 3y' - 2y = 0,$$

$y = e^{rx} \Rightarrow P(r) = r^3 - 3r - 2 = (r+1)(r^2 - r - 2) = (r+1)^2(r-2) = 0 \Rightarrow y_1 = e^{-x}$, $y_2 = xe^{-x}$ and $y_3 = e^{2x}$ are three independent solutions. With $f(x) = 27e^{-x}$,

$$\begin{aligned} W(x) &= \begin{vmatrix} e^{-x} & xe^{-x} & e^{2x} \\ -e^{-x} & e^{-x} - xe^{-x} & 2e^{2x} \\ e^{-x} & -2e^{-x} + xe^{-x} & 4e^{2x} \end{vmatrix} \\ &= e^{-x}(8e^x - 6xe^x) - xe^{-x}(-6e^x) + e^{2x}\left(e^{-2x}\right) = 9, \\ \Delta_1(x) &= \begin{vmatrix} 0 & xe^{-x} & e^{2x} \\ 0 & e^{-x} - xe^{-x} & 2e^{2x} \\ 27e^{-x} & -2e^{-x} + xe^{-x} & 4e^{2x} \end{vmatrix} = 27e^{-x}(3xe^x - e^x) = 27(3x - 1), \\ \Delta_2(x) &= \begin{vmatrix} e^{-x} & 0 & e^{2x} \\ -e^{-x} & 0 & 2e^{2x} \\ e^{-x} & 27e^{-x} & 4e^{2x} \end{vmatrix} = -27e^{-x}(3e^x) = -81, \\ \Delta_3(x) &= \begin{vmatrix} e^{-x} & xe^{-x} & 0 \\ -e^{-x} & e^{-x} - xe^{-x} & 0 \\ e^{-x} & -2e^{-x} + xe^{-x} & 27e^{-x} \end{vmatrix} = 27e^{-x}\left(e^{-2x}\right) = 27e^{-3x}. \end{aligned}$$

Then

$$u_1 = \int 3(3x - 1)\, dx = \frac{9}{2}x^2 - 3x,$$

$$u_2 = \int -9\, dx = -9x,$$

$$u_3 = \int 3e^{-3x}\, dx = -e^{-3x},$$

and

$$y_p = \left(\frac{9}{2}x^2 - 3x\right)e^{-x} - 9x(xe^{-x}) - e^{-3x}\left(e^{2x}\right)$$

$$= -\frac{9}{2}x^2 e^{-x} - 3xe^{-x} - e^{-x},$$

or $y_p = -\dfrac{9}{2}x^2 e^{-x}$, since $-3xe^{-x} - e^{-x}$ is a solution of the homogeneous equation. Hence,

$$y = -\frac{9}{2}x^2 e^{-x} + c_1 e^{-x} + c_2 xe^{-x} + c_3 e^{2x}$$

is the general solution of the nonhomogeneous equation.

Example 4.21. Consider the initial-value problem

$$y''' - y' = 8xe^x, \quad y(0) = 0, \quad y'(0) = 0, \quad y''(0) = 0.$$

For the associated homogeneous equation

$$y''' - y' = 0,$$

$y = e^{rx} \Rightarrow P(r) = r^3 - r = r(r^2 - 1) = r(r-1)(r+1) = 0 \Rightarrow y_1 = 1$, $y_2 = e^x$ and $y_3 = e^{-x}$ are three independent solutions. With $f(x) = 8xe^x$,

$$W(x) = \begin{vmatrix} 1 & e^x & e^{-x} \\ 0 & e^x & -e^{-x} \\ 0 & e^x & e^{-x} \end{vmatrix} = 2,$$

$$\Delta_1(x) = \begin{vmatrix} 0 & e^x & e^{-x} \\ 0 & e^x & -e^{-x} \\ 8xe^x & e^x & e^{-x} \end{vmatrix} = -16xe^x,$$

$$\Delta_2(x) = \begin{vmatrix} 1 & 0 & e^{-x} \\ 0 & 0 & -e^{-x} \\ 0 & 8xe^x & e^{-x} \end{vmatrix} = 8x,$$

$$\Delta_3(x) = \begin{vmatrix} 1 & e^x & 0 \\ 0 & e^x & 0 \\ 0 & e^x & 8xe^x \end{vmatrix} = 8xe^{2x}.$$

Then

$$u_1 = \int -8xe^x \, dx = -8xe^x + 8e^x,$$

$$u_2 = \int 4x \, dx = 2x^2,$$

$$u_3 = \int 4xe^{2x} \, dx = 2xe^{2x} - e^{2x},$$

and

$$y_p = -8xe^x + 8e^x + 2x^2 e^x + 2xe^x - e^x = 2x^2 e^x - 6xe^x + 7e^x,$$

or $y_p = 2x^2 e^x - 6xe^x$, since $7e^x$ is a solution of the homogeneous equation. Hence,

$$y = 2x^2 e^x - 6xe^x + c_1 + c_2 e^x + c_3 e^{-x}$$

is the general solution of the nonhomogeneous equation. Then

$$y' = 2x^2 e^x - 2xe^x - 6e^x + c_2 e^x - c_3 e^{-x},$$
$$y'' = 2x^2 e^x + 2xe^x - 8e^x + c_2 e^x + c_3 e^{-x},$$

and $y(0) = 0$, $y'(0) = 0$ and $y''(0) = 0 \Rightarrow$

$$\left\{ \begin{array}{rrrrrrl} c_1 & + & c_2 & + & c_3 & = & 0 \\ -6 & + & c_2 & - & c_3 & = & 0 \\ -8 & + & c_2 & + & c_3 & = & 0 \end{array} \right\} \Rightarrow \left\{ \begin{array}{rrrrrrl} c_1 & + & c_2 & + & c_3 & = & 0 \\ & & c_2 & - & c_3 & = & 6 \\ & & c_2 & + & c_3 & = & 8 \end{array} \right\}$$

$\Rightarrow c_1 = -8$, $c_2 = 7$, $c_3 = 1$, and $y = 2x^2 e^x - 6xe^x - 8 + 7e^x + e^{-x}$ is the solution of the initial-value problem.

Example 4.22. Consider the nonhomogeneous equation

$$y''' - 3y'' + 7y' - 5y = 32e^x \sin(2x).$$

For the associated homogeneous equation

$$y''' - 3y'' + 7y' - 5y = 0,$$

$y = e^{rx} \Rightarrow P(r) = r^3 - 3r^2 + 7r - 5 = (r-1)(r^2 - 2r + 5) = 0 \Rightarrow r_1 = 1$ and $r = \dfrac{2 \pm \sqrt{-16}}{2} = 1 \pm 2i \Rightarrow y_1 = e^x$, $y_2 = e^x \cos(2x)$ and $y_3 = e^x \sin(2x)$ are three independent solutions. With $f(x) = 32e^x \sin(2x)$,

$$
W(x) = \begin{vmatrix} e^x & e^x \cos(2x) & e^x \sin(2x) \\ e^x & e^x \cos(2x) - 2e^x \sin(2x) & e^x \sin(2x) + 2e^x \cos(2x) \\ e^x & -3e^x \cos(2x) - 4e^x \sin(2x) & 4e^x \cos(2x) - 3e^x \sin(2x) \end{vmatrix}
$$

$$
= e^x \left(10e^{2x}\right) - e^x \left(4e^{2x}\right) + e^x \left(2e^{2x}\right) = 8e^{3x},
$$

$$
\Delta_1(x) = \begin{vmatrix} 0 & e^x \cos(2x) & e^x \sin(2x) \\ 0 & e^x \cos(2x) - 2e^x \sin(2x) & e^x \sin(2x) + 2e^x \cos(2x) \\ 32e^x \sin(2x) & -3e^x \cos(2x) - 4e^x \sin(2x) & 4e^x \cos(2x) - 3e^x \sin(2x) \end{vmatrix}
$$

$$
= 32e^x \sin(2x) \left(2e^{2x}\right) = 64e^{3x} \sin(2x),
$$

$$
\Delta_2(x) = \begin{vmatrix} e^x & 0 & e^x \sin(2x) \\ e^x & 0 & e^x \sin(2x) + 2e^x \cos(2x) \\ e^x & 32e^x \sin(2x) & 4e^x \cos(2x) - 3e^x \sin(2x) \end{vmatrix}
$$

$$
= -32e^x \sin(2x) \left[2e^{2x} \cos(2x)\right] = -64e^{3x} \sin(2x) \cos(2x),
$$

$$
\Delta_3(x) = \begin{vmatrix} e^x & e^x \cos(2x) & 0 \\ e^x & e^x \cos(2x) - 2e^x \sin(2x) & 0 \\ e^x & -3e^x \cos(2x) - 4e^x \sin(2x) & 32e^x \sin(2x) \end{vmatrix}
$$

$$
= 32e^x \sin(2x) \left[-2e^{2x} \sin(2x)\right] = -64e^{3x} \sin^2(2x).
$$

Then

$$
u_1 = \int 8 \sin(2x)\, dx = -4 \cos(2x),
$$

$$
u_2 = \int -8 \sin(2x) \cos(2x)\, dx = -4 \int \sin(4x)\, dx = \cos(4x),
$$

$$
u_3 = \int -8 \sin^2(2x)\, dx = 4 \int \cos(4x) - 1\, dx = \sin(4x) - 4x,
$$

and

$$
\begin{aligned}
y_p &= -4e^x \cos(2x) + e^x \cos(2x) \cos(4x) + [\sin(4x) - 4x]e^x \sin(2x) \\
&= -4e^x \cos(2x) - 4xe^x \sin(2x) + e^x[\cos(2x) \cos(4x) + \sin(2x) \sin(4x)] \\
&= -4e^x \cos(2x) - 4xe^x \sin(2x) + e^x \cos(2x) \\
&= -3e^x \cos(2x) - 4xe^x \sin(2x),
\end{aligned}
$$

or $y_p = -4xe^x \sin(2x)$, since $-3e^x \cos(2x)$ is a solution of the homogeneous equation. Hence,

$$
y = -4xe^x \sin(2x) + c_1 e^x + c_2 e^x \cos(2x) + c_3 e^x \sin(2x)
$$

is the general solution of the nonhomogeneous equation.

Example 4.23. Consider the nonhomogeneous equation
$$y^{(4)} - 6y''' + 11y'' - 6y' = 36e^{3x}.$$
For the associated homogeneous equation
$$y^{(4)} - 6y''' + 11y'' - 6y' = 0,$$
$y = e^{rx} \Rightarrow P(r) = r^4 - 6r^3 + 11r^2 - 6r = 0 \Rightarrow$

$$
\begin{aligned}
r(r^3 - 6r^2 + 11r - 6) &= r(r-1)(r^2 - 5r + 6) \\
&= r(r-1)(r-2)(r-3) \\
&= 0
\end{aligned}
$$

$\Rightarrow y_1 = 1$, $y_2 = e^x$, $y_3 = e^{2x}$ and $y_4 = e^{3x}$ are four independent solutions, with the Wronskian

$$
W(x) = \begin{vmatrix}
1 & e^x & e^{2x} & e^{3x} \\
0 & e^x & 2e^{2x} & 3e^{3x} \\
0 & e^x & 4e^{2x} & 9e^{3x} \\
0 & e^x & 8e^{2x} & 27e^{3x}
\end{vmatrix}.
$$

Computing the determinant along the fourth row, we obtain

$$
W(x) = e^x \begin{vmatrix} 1 & e^{2x} & e^{3x} \\ 0 & 2e^{2x} & 3e^{3x} \\ 0 & 4e^{2x} & 9e^{3x} \end{vmatrix} - 8e^{2x} \begin{vmatrix} 1 & e^x & e^{3x} \\ 0 & e^x & 3e^{3x} \\ 0 & e^x & 9e^{3x} \end{vmatrix} + 27e^{3x} \begin{vmatrix} 1 & e^x & e^{2x} \\ 0 & e^x & 2e^{2x} \\ 0 & e^x & 4e^{2x} \end{vmatrix}
$$

$$
= e^x \left(6e^{5x}\right) - 8e^{2x} \left(6e^{4x}\right) + 27e^{3x} \left(2e^{3x}\right) = 12e^{6x}.
$$

With $f(x) = 36e^{3x}$,

$$
\begin{aligned}
\Delta_1(x) &= \begin{vmatrix}
0 & e^x & e^{2x} & e^{3x} \\
0 & e^x & 2e^{2x} & 3e^{3x} \\
0 & e^x & 4e^{2x} & 9e^{3x} \\
f(x) & e^x & 8e^{2x} & 27e^{3x}
\end{vmatrix} = -f(x) \begin{vmatrix} e^x & e^{2x} & e^{3x} \\ e^x & 2e^{2x} & 3e^{3x} \\ e^x & 4e^{2x} & 9e^{3x} \end{vmatrix} \\
&= -f(x) \left[e^x \left(6e^{5x}\right) - e^x \left(5e^{5x}\right) + e^x \left(e^{5x}\right) \right] = -2e^{6x} f(x) = -72e^{9x},
\end{aligned}
$$

$$
\begin{aligned}
\Delta_2(x) &= \begin{vmatrix}
1 & 0 & e^{2x} & e^{3x} \\
0 & 0 & 2e^{2x} & 3e^{3x} \\
0 & 0 & 4e^{2x} & 9e^{3x} \\
0 & f(x) & 8e^{2x} & 27e^{3x}
\end{vmatrix} = f(x) \begin{vmatrix} 1 & e^{2x} & e^{3x} \\ 0 & 2e^{2x} & 3e^{3x} \\ 0 & 4e^{2x} & 9e^{3x} \end{vmatrix} = 6e^{5x} f(x) = 216e^{8x},
\end{aligned}
$$

$$
\begin{aligned}
\Delta_3(x) &= \begin{vmatrix}
1 & e^x & 0 & e^{3x} \\
0 & e^x & 0 & 3e^{3x} \\
0 & e^x & 0 & 9e^{3x} \\
0 & e^x & f(x) & 27e^{3x}
\end{vmatrix} = -f(x) \begin{vmatrix} 1 & e^x & e^{3x} \\ 0 & e^x & 3e^{3x} \\ 0 & e^x & 9e^{3x} \end{vmatrix} = -6e^{4x} f(x) = -216e^{7x},
\end{aligned}
$$

$$
\begin{aligned}
\Delta_4(x) &= \begin{vmatrix}
1 & e^x & e^{2x} & 0 \\
0 & e^x & 2e^{2x} & 0 \\
0 & e^x & 4e^{2x} & 0 \\
0 & e^x & 8e^{2x} & f(x)
\end{vmatrix} = f(x) \begin{vmatrix} 1 & e^x & e^{2x} \\ 0 & e^x & 2e^{2x} \\ 0 & e^x & 4e^{2x} \end{vmatrix} = 2e^{3x} f(x) = 72e^{6x}.
\end{aligned}
$$

Then

$$u_1 = -6\int e^{3x}\,dx = -2e^{3x},$$

$$u_2 = 18\int e^{2x}\,dx = 9e^{2x},$$

$$u_3 = -18\int e^{x}\,dx = -18e^{x},$$

$$u_4 = 6\int 1\,dx = 6x.$$

Hence, $y_p = -2e^{3x} + 9e^{2x}e^{x} - 18e^{x}e^{2x} + 6xe^{3x} = -11e^{3x} + 6xe^{3x}$, or $y_p = 6xe^{3x}$, since $-11e^{3x}$ is a solution of the homogeneous equation. Thus,

$$y = 6xe^{3x} + c_1 + c_2 e^{x} + c_3 e^{2x} + c_4 e^{3x}$$

is the general solution of the nonhomogeneous equation.

Example 4.24. Consider the nonhomogeneous equation

$$x^3 y''' - 3x^2 y'' + 6xy' - 6y = 8x^3 \ln(x), \quad x > 0.$$

The associated homogeneous equation is the Euler equation

$$x^3 y''' - 3x^2 y'' + 6xy' - 6y = 0,$$

for which $y = x^r \Rightarrow P(r) = r(r-1)(r-2) - 3r(r-1) + 6r - 6 = 0 \Rightarrow$

$$(r-1)[r(r-2) - 3r + 6] = (r-1)(r^2 - 5r + 6) = (r-1)(r-2)(r-3) = 0$$

$\Rightarrow y_1 = x$, $y_2 = x^2$ and $y_3 = x^3$ are three independent solutions. With $f(x) = 8\ln(x)$,

$$W(x) = \begin{vmatrix} x & x^2 & x^3 \\ 1 & 2x & 3x^2 \\ 0 & 2 & 6x \end{vmatrix} = x\left(6x^2\right) - 4x^3 = 2x^3,$$

$$\Delta_1(x) = \begin{vmatrix} 0 & x^2 & x^3 \\ 0 & 2x & 3x^2 \\ f(x) & 2 & 6x \end{vmatrix} = f(x)\left[x^4\right] = 8x^4 \ln(x),$$

$$\Delta_2(x) = \begin{vmatrix} x & 0 & x^3 \\ 1 & 0 & 3x^2 \\ 0 & f(x) & 6x \end{vmatrix} = -f(x)\left[2x^3\right] = -16x^3 \ln(x),$$

$$\Delta_3(x) = \begin{vmatrix} x & x^2 & 0 \\ 1 & 2x & 0 \\ 0 & 2 & f(x) \end{vmatrix} = f(x)\left[x^2\right] = 8x^2 \ln(x).$$

Then

$$u_1 = 4 \int x \ln(x)\, dx = 2x^2 \ln(x) - x^2,$$

$$u_2 = -8 \int \ln(x)\, dx = -8x \ln(x) + 8x,$$

$$u_3 = 4 \int \frac{\ln(x)}{x}\, dx = 2[\ln(x)]^2.$$

Hence,

$$y_p = \left[2x^2 \ln(x) - x^2\right] x + \left[-8x \ln(x) + 8x\right] x^2 + 2[\ln(x)]^2 x^3$$
$$= -6x^3 \ln(x) + 7x^3 + 2x^3 [\ln(x)]^2,$$

or $y_p = 2x^3[\ln(x)]^2 - 6x^3 \ln(x)$, since $7x^3$ is a solution of the homogeneous equation. Thus,

$$y = 2x^3[\ln(x)]^2 - 6x^3 \ln(x) + c_1 x + c_2 x^2 + c_3 x^3$$

is the general solution of the nonhomogeneous equation for $x > 0$.

Example 4.25. Consider the nonhomogeneous equation

$$x^3 y''' + 2xy' - 2y = x, \quad x > 0.$$

The associated homogeneous equation is the Euler equation

$$x^3 y''' + 2xy' - 2y = 0,$$

for which $y = x^r \Rightarrow P(r) = r(r-1)(r-2) + 2r - 2 = 0 \Rightarrow$

$$(r-1)[r(r-2) + 2] = (r-1)(r^2 - 2r + 2) = 0$$

$$\Rightarrow r_1 = 1 \text{ and } r^2 - 2r + 2 = 0 \Rightarrow r = \frac{2 \pm \sqrt{-4}}{2} = 1 \pm i \Rightarrow y_1 = x,\ y_2 = x \cos[\ln(x)]$$

and $y_3 = x\sin[\ln(x)]$ are three independent solutions. With $f(x) = \dfrac{1}{x^2}$,

$$W(x) = \begin{vmatrix} x & x\cos[\ln(x)] & x\sin[\ln(x)] \\ 1 & \cos[\ln(x)] - \sin[\ln(x)] & \sin[\ln(x)] + \cos[\ln(x)] \\ 0 & -\frac{1}{x}\sin[\ln(x)] - \frac{1}{x}\cos[\ln(x)] & \frac{1}{x}\cos[\ln(x)] - \frac{1}{x}\sin[\ln(x)] \end{vmatrix}$$

$$= x\left[\frac{2}{x}\right] - 1[1] = 1,$$

$$\Delta_1(x) = \begin{vmatrix} 0 & x\cos[\ln(x)] & x\sin[\ln(x)] \\ 0 & \cos[\ln(x)] - \sin[\ln(x)] & \sin[\ln(x)] + \cos[\ln(x)] \\ f(x) & -\frac{1}{x}\sin[\ln(x)] - \frac{1}{x}\cos[\ln(x)] & \frac{1}{x}\cos[\ln(x)] - \frac{1}{x}\sin[\ln(x)] \end{vmatrix}$$

$$= f(x)[x] = \frac{1}{x},$$

$$\Delta_2(x) = \begin{vmatrix} x & 0 & x\sin[\ln(x)] \\ 1 & 0 & \sin[\ln(x)] + \cos[\ln(x)] \\ 0 & f(x) & \frac{1}{x}\cos[\ln(x)] - \frac{1}{x}\sin[\ln(x)] \end{vmatrix}$$

$$= -f(x)\{x\cos[\ln(x)]\} = -\frac{\cos[\ln(x)]}{x},$$

$$\Delta_3(x) = \begin{vmatrix} x & x\cos[\ln(x)] & 0 \\ 1 & \cos[\ln(x)] - \sin[\ln(x)] & 0 \\ 0 & -\frac{1}{x}\sin[\ln(x)] - \frac{1}{x}\cos[\ln(x)] & f(x) \end{vmatrix}$$

$$= f(x)\{-x\sin[\ln(x)]\} = -\frac{\sin[\ln(x)]}{x}.$$

Then

$$u_1 = \int \frac{1}{x}\,dx = \ln(x),$$

$$u_2 = -\int \frac{\cos[\ln(x)]}{x}\,dx = -\sin[\ln(x)],$$

$$u_3 = -\int \frac{\sin[\ln(x)]}{x}\,dx = \cos[\ln(x)].$$

Hence, $y_p = x\ln(x) - x\cos[\ln(x)]\sin[\ln(x)] + x\sin[\ln(x)]\cos[\ln(x)] = x\ln(x)$, and

$$y = x\ln(x) + c_1 x + c_2 x\cos[\ln(x)] + c_3 x\sin[\ln(x)]$$

is the general solution of the nonhomogeneous equation for $x > 0$.

4.2.2 Undetermined Coefficients–Annihilators

In Section 3.3.1, the method of undetermined coefficients was employed to determine particular solutions y_p of second-order nonhomogeneous equations. The same method can be applied to the higher-order equations considered in the present chapter, with a slight difference. Instead of listing the form of y_p for every type of nonhomogeneous term $g(x)$, the form of y_p will be *determined* by $g(x)$. The unknown constants in y_p are then determined by substitution into the nonhomogeneous equation, as before.

Definition 4.7. Let D denote the *linear operator* defined by

$$Df = D[f] = \frac{d}{dx}f = f',$$

where f is a differentiable function. Let D^2 denote the linear operator defined by

$$D^2 f = D^2[f] = D[D[f]] = D[f'] = f'',$$

and, more generally, for any integer $n \geq 1$,

$$D^n f = D^n[f] = f^{(n)},$$

the derivative of f of order n. If $n = 0$, $D^0 f$ is defined by $D^0 f = f$. The abuse of notation $D[f(x)]$ is customary, and denotes the value of the function $Df = f'$ at x, i.e.,

$$D[f(x)] = (Df)(x) = f'(x),$$

and, more generally,

$$D^n[f(x)] = (D^n f)(x) = f^{(n)}(x), \quad n \geq 0.$$

Let $P(r)$ be a polynomial of degree $n \geq 0$, i.e.,

$$P(r) = a_n r^n + a_{n-1} r^{n-1} + \cdots + a_2 r^2 + a_1 r + a_0,$$

where a_k, $0 \leq k \leq n$, are constants. The linear operator $P(D)$ is defined by

$$\begin{aligned}
P(D)f &= \left(a_n D^n + a_{n-1} D^{n-1} + \cdots + a_2 D^2 + a_1 D + a_0 D^0\right) f \\
&= a_n D^n f + a_{n-1} D^{n-1} f + \cdots + a_2 D^2 f + a_1 Df + a_0 D^0 f \\
&= a_n f^{(n)} + a_{n-1} f^{(n-1)} + \cdots + a_2 f'' + a_1 f' + a_0 f.
\end{aligned}$$

If $P(D)f(x) = 0$ for all x, then $P(D)$ is called an *annihilator* of the function f, and the function f is said to be *annihilated* by $P(D)$.

Example 4.26. Let $P(r) = r - 1$. Then $P(D) = D - 1$, and $(D - 1)f = f' - f$ for any differentiable function f. If $f(x) = e^x$, then

$$P(D)[e^x] = (D - 1)e^x = De^x - e^x = e^x - e^x = 0.$$

Thus, $D - 1$ is an annihilator of the function e^x.

Example 4.27. Let $P(r) = r^2 + 4$. Then $P(D) = D^2 + 4$, and $(D^2 + 4)f = f'' + 4f$ for any differentiable function f. If $f(x) = \sin(2x)$, then

$$P(D)[\sin(2x)] = (D^2 + 4)\sin(2x) = D^2\sin(2x) + 4\sin(2x) = -4\sin(2x) + 4\sin(2x) = 0.$$

Thus, $D^2 + 1$ is an annihilator of the function $\sin(2x)$.

Example 4.28. Let $f(x) = \cos(3x)$. Then

$$Df(x) = -3\sin(3x) \quad \text{and} \quad D^2 f(x) = -9\cos(3x) = -9f(x).$$

Hence, $(D^2 + 9)\cos(3x) = 0$, i.e., $P(D) = D^2 + 9$ is an annihilator of the function $f(x) = \cos(3x)$.

Example 4.29. Let $f(x) = e^{3x}\sin(2x)$. How can an annihilator of f be determined? Recall that $e^{3x}\cos(2x)$ and $e^{3x}\sin(2x)$ are solutions of a second-order homogeneous equation for which the indicial equation has the roots $r = 3 \pm 2i$. Then

$$r - 3 = \pm 2i \quad \Rightarrow \quad (r - 3)^2 = -4 \quad \Rightarrow \quad P(r) = r^2 - 6r + 13 = 0$$

is the indicial equation. Hence, $e^{3x}\cos(2x)$ and $e^{3x}\sin(2x)$ are the solutions of the equation $y'' - 6y' + 13y = 0$, i.e., they are annihilated by $P(D) = D^2 - 6D + 13$.

Example 4.30. Let $f(x) = x^2 e^{2x}$. Recall that e^{2x}, xe^{2x} and $x^2 e^{2x}$ are solutions of a third-order homogeneous equation for which the indicial equation has the root $r = 2$ of multiplicity 3, i.e., the indicial equation is $P(r) = (r-2)^3$. Hence, $P(D) = (D-2)^3$ is an annihilator of $x^2 e^{2x}$, as well as e^{2x} and xe^{2x}.

Consider a nonhomogeneous equation of order $n \geq 2$ with constant coefficients,

$$a_n y^{(n)} + a_{n-1} y^{(n-1)} + \cdots + a_2 y'' + a_1 y' + a_0 y = g(x), \tag{4.11}$$

where the nonhomogeneous term is denoted by $g(x)$ since the equation need not be in standard form. With

$$P(r) = a_n r^n + a_{n-1} r^{n-1} + \cdots + a_2 r^2 + a_1 r + a_0,$$

Equation (4.11) can be expressed as

$$P(D)y = g(x).$$

If $Q(D)$ is an annihilator of $g(x)$, then

$$P(D)y = g(x) \quad \Rightarrow \quad Q(D)P(D)y = Q(D)g(x) = 0,$$

i.e., if y is a solution of the nonhomogeneous equation $P(D)y = g(x)$, then it is a solution of the homogeneous equation $Q(D)P(D)y = 0$. From the solutions of the latter equation, the form of y_p can be deduced by means of the following:

Theorem 4.10. Consider the nonhomogeneous equation (4.11), and let Q be a polynomial of the least degree $m \geq 1$ such that $Q(D)$ is an annihilator of g. Let

$$y_1, \ y_2, \ \cdots, \ y_n, \ z_1, \ z_2, \ \cdots, \ z_m$$

be $n+m$ independent solutions of the equation $Q(D)P(D)y = 0$ of order $n+m$, where $y_1, \ y_2, \ \cdots, \ y_n$ are independent solutions of $P(D)y = 0$. Then there exist constants $c_1, \ c_2, \ \cdots, \ c_m$ such that

$$y_p = c_1 z_1 + c_2 z_2 + \cdots + c_m z_m. \tag{4.12}$$

Equation (4.12) gives the form of y_p, and the constants c_i, $1 \leq i \leq m$, are determined by substitution of y_p into Equation (4.11).

Proof. Since $Q(D)P(D)z_i = 0$, $1 \leq i \leq m$, $P(D)z_i$ are solutions of $Q(D)y = 0$. They are linearly independent because if $d_1 P(D)z_1 + d_2 P(D)z_2 + \cdots + d_m P(D)z_m = 0$, then $P(D)(d_1 z_1 + d_2 z_2 + \cdots + d_m z_m) = 0$, i.e., $z = d_1 z_1 + d_2 z_2 + \cdots + d_m z_m$ is a solution of $P(D)y = 0$. Hence, there exist constants $b_1, \ b_2, \ \cdots, \ b_n$ such that

$$z = b_1 y_1 + b_2 y_2 + \cdots + b_n y_n.$$

Then

$$d_1 z_1 + d_2 z_2 + \cdots + d_m z_m = b_1 y_1 + b_2 y_2 + \cdots + b_n y_n$$

$$\Rightarrow \ d_1 z_1 + d_2 z_2 + \cdots + d_m z_m - b_1 y_1 - b_2 y_2 - \cdots - b_n y_n = 0$$

$$\Rightarrow \ d_i = 0, \ b_j = 0, \ 1 \leq i \leq m, \ 1 \leq j \leq n,$$

since

$$y_1, \ y_2, \ \cdots, \ y_n, \ z_1, \ z_2, \ \cdots, \ z_m$$

are linearly independent. Thus, $P(D)z_i$, $1 \leq i \leq m$, are m linearly independent solutions of $Q(D)y = 0$. Since $g(x)$ is a solution of $Q(D)g = 0$, there exist constants $c_1, \ c_2, \ \cdots, \ c_m$ such that

$$\begin{aligned} g(x) &= c_1 P(D)z_1 + c_2 P(D)z_2 + \cdots + c_m P(D)z_m \\ &= P(D)(c_1 z_1 + c_2 z_2 + \cdots + c_m z_m), \end{aligned}$$

which shows that $y_p = c_1 z_1 + c_2 z_2 + \cdots + c_m z_m$ satisfies $P(D)y_p = g(x)$.

Example 4.31. Consider the nonhomogeneous equation

$$y''' - 3y' - 2y = 27e^{-x},$$

which has been solved by variation of parameters in Section 4.2.1, Example 4.20. The *indicial polynomial* is $P(r) = (r + 1)^2 (r - 2)$. Hence, the nonhomogeneous equation is

$$P(D)y = (D + 1)^2 (D - 2)y = 27e^{-x}.$$

The annihilator of $g(x) = 27e^{-x}$ of minimal degree is $Q(D) = D + 1$. Thus,

$$Q(D)P(D)y = (D+1)^3(D-2)y = (D+1)[27e^{-x}] = 0$$

$$\Rightarrow \ y = c_1 e^{-x} + c_2 x e^{-x} + c_3 x^2 e^{-x} + c_4 e^{2x}.$$

Since e^{-x}, xe^{-x} and e^{2x} are solutions of the homogeneous equation $P(D)y = 0$, $y_p = c_3 x^2 e^{-x}$, or $y_p = cx^2 e^{-x}$, where c is to be determined. Then

$$\begin{aligned}
y_p' &= c[2xe^{-x} - x^2 e^{-x}], \\
y_p'' &= c[2e^{-x} - 4xe^{-x} + x^2 e^{-x}], \\
y_p''' &= c[-6e^{-x} + 6xe^{-x} - x^2 e^{-x}],
\end{aligned}$$

and $y_p''' - 3y_p' - 2y_p = 27e^{-x} \Rightarrow$

$$c[-6e^{-x} + 6xe^{-x} - x^2 e^{-x}] - 3c[2xe^{-x} - x^2 e^{-x}] - 2c[x^2 e^{-x}] = 27e^{-x}$$

$$\Rightarrow -6c = 27 \Rightarrow c = -\frac{9}{2} \Rightarrow y_p = -\frac{9}{2}x^2 e^{-x} \Rightarrow$$

$$y = -\frac{9}{2}x^2 e^{-x} + c_1 e^{-x} + c_2 x e^{-x} + c_4 e^{2x}$$

is the general solution of the nonhomogeneous equation.

Example 4.32. Consider the nonhomogeneous equation

$$y''' - y' = 8xe^x,$$

which has been solved by variation of parameters in Section 4.2.1, Example 4.21. The indicial polynomial is $P(r) = r(r-1)(r+1)$. Hence, the nonhomogeneous equation is

$$P(D)y = D(D-1)(D+1)y = 8xe^x.$$

The annihilator of $g(x) = 8xe^x$ of minimal degree is $Q(D) = (D-1)^2$. Thus,

$$\begin{aligned}
Q(D)P(D)y &= (D-1)^2 D(D-1)(D+1)y \\
&= D(D-1)^3(D+1)y = (D-1)^2[8xe^x] = 0
\end{aligned}$$

$$\Rightarrow \ y = c_1 + c_2 e^x + c_3 x e^x + c_4 x^2 e^x + c_5 e^{-x}.$$

Since 1, e^x and e^{-x} are solutions of the homogeneous equation $P(D)y = 0$,

$$y_p = c_3 x e^x + c_4 x^2 e^x = (ax^2 + bx)e^x,$$

where a and b are to be determined. Then

$$
\begin{aligned}
y_p' &= (2ax + b)e^x + (ax^2 + bx)e^x \\
&= [ax^2 + (2a + b)x + b]e^x, \\
y_p'' &= [2ax + 2a + b]e^x + [ax^2 + (2a + b)x + b]e^x \\
&= [ax^2 + (4a + b)x + (2a + 2b)]e^x, \\
y_p''' &= [2ax + 4a + b]e^x + [ax^2 + (4a + b)x + (2a + 2b)]e^x \\
&= [ax^2 + (6a + b)x + (6a + 3b)]e^x,
\end{aligned}
$$

and $y_p''' - y_p' = 8xe^x \Rightarrow$

$$[ax^2 + (6a + b)x + (6a + 3b)]e^x - [ax^2 + (2a + b)x + b]e^x = 8xe^x$$

$$\Rightarrow \quad 4ax + (6a + 2b) = 8x$$

$\Rightarrow a = 2$ and $b = -6 \Rightarrow y_p = (2x^2 - 6x)e^x \Rightarrow$

$$y = (2x^2 - 6x)e^x + c_1 + c_2e^x + c_5e^{-x}$$

is the general solution of the nonhomogeneous equation.

Example 4.33. Consider the nonhomogeneous equation

$$y''' - 3y'' + 7y' - 5y = 32e^x \sin(2x),$$

which has been solved by variation of parameters in Section 4.2.1, Example 4.22. The indicial polynomial is $P(r) = (r - 1)(r^2 - 2r + 5)$. Hence, the nonhomogeneous equation is

$$P(D)y = (D - 1)(D^2 - 2D + 5)y = 32e^x \sin(2x).$$

Since $e^x \cos(2x)$ and $e^x \sin(2x)$ are solutions of a homogeneous equation for which the indicial equation has the roots $r = 1 \pm 2i$, $r - 1 = \pm 2i \Rightarrow (r - 1)^2 = -4 \Rightarrow r^2 - 2r + 5 = 0$ is the indicial equation. Hence, the annihilator of $g(x) = 32e^x \sin(2x)$ of minimal degree is $Q(D) = D^2 - 2D + 5$. Then

$$
\begin{aligned}
Q(D)P(D)y &= (D^2 - 2D + 5)(D - 1)(D^2 - 2D + 5)y \\
&= (D - 1)(D^2 - 2D + 5)^2 y = (D^2 - 2D + 5)[32e^x \sin(2x)] = 0
\end{aligned}
$$

$$\Rightarrow \quad y = c_1 e^x + c_2 e^x \cos(2x) + c_3 e^x \sin(2x) + c_4 x e^x \cos(2x) + c_5 x e^x \sin(2x).$$

Since $c_1 e^x + c_2 e^x \cos(2x) + c_3 e^x \sin(2x)$ satisfies the homogeneous equation $P(D)y = 0$,

$$y_p = c_4 x e^x \cos(2x) + c_5 x e^x \sin(2x) = x e^x [a \cos(2x) + b \sin(2x)],$$

where a and b are to be determined. Then

$$\begin{aligned}
y'_p &= e^x[a\cos(2x) + b\sin(2x)] + xe^x[a\cos(2x) + b\sin(2x)] \\
&\quad + xe^x[-2a\sin(2x) + 2b\cos(2x)] \\
&= e^x[a\cos(2x) + b\sin(2x)] + xe^x[(a+2b)\cos(2x) + (b-2a)\sin(2x)], \\
y''_p &= e^x[a\cos(2x) + b\sin(2x)] + e^x[-2a\sin(2x) + 2b\cos(2x)] \\
&\quad + e^x[(a+2b)\cos(2x) + (b-2a)\sin(2x)] \\
&\quad + xe^x[(a+2b)\cos(2x) + (b-2a)\sin(2x)] \\
&\quad + xe^x[(-2a-4b)\sin(2x) + (2b-4a)\cos(2x)] \\
&= e^x[(2a+4b)\cos(2x) + (2b-4a)\sin(2x)] \\
&\quad + xe^x[(4b-3a)\cos(2x) + (-4a-3b)\sin(2x)], \\
y'''_p &= e^x[(2a+4b)\cos(2x) + (2b-4a)\sin(2x)] \\
&\quad + e^x[(-4a-8b)\sin(2x) + (4b-8a)\cos(2x)] \\
&\quad + e^x[(4b-3a)\cos(2x) + (-4a-3b)\sin(2x)] \\
&\quad + xe^x[(4b-3a)\cos(2x) + (-4a-3b)\sin(2x)] \\
&\quad + xe^x[(-8b+6a)\sin(2x) + (-8a-6b)\cos(2x)] \\
&= e^x[(12b-9a)\cos(2x) + (-12a-9b)\sin(2x)] \\
&\quad + xe^x[(-11a-2b)\cos(2x) + (2a-11b)\sin(2x)],
\end{aligned}$$

and $y'''_p - 3y''_p + 7y'_p - 5y_p = 32e^x\sin(2x) \Rightarrow$

$$\begin{aligned}
y'''_p - 3y''_p + 7y'_p - 5y_p &= e^x\cos(2x)[(12b-9a) - 3(2a+4b) + 7a] \\
&\quad + e^x\sin(2x)[(-12a-9b) - 3(2b-4a) + 7b] \\
&\quad + xe^x\cos(2x)[(-11a-2b) - 3(4b-3a) + 7(a+2b) - 5a] \\
&\quad + xe^x\sin(2x)[(2a-11b) - 3(-4a-3b) + 7(b-2a) - 5b] \\
&= 32e^x\sin(2x)
\end{aligned}$$

$$\Rightarrow \quad -8ae^x\cos(2x) - 8be^x\sin(2x) = 32e^x\sin(2x)$$

$\Rightarrow a = 0$ and $b = -4 \Rightarrow y_p = -4xe^x\sin(2x) \Rightarrow$

$$y = -4xe^x\sin(2x) + c_1e^x + c_2e^x\cos(2x) + c_3e^x\sin(2x)$$

is the general solution of the nonhomogeneous equation.

Example 4.34. Consider the nonhomogeneous equation

$$y^{(4)} - 6y''' + 11y'' - 6y' = 36e^{3x},$$

which has been solved by variation of parameters in Section 4.2.1, Example 4.23. The indicial polynomial is $P(r) = r(r-1)(r-2)(r-3)$. Hence, the nonhomogeneous equation is

$$P(D)y = D(D-1)(D-2)(D-3)y = 36e^{3x}.$$

The annihilator of $g(x) = 36e^{3x}$ of minimal degree is $Q(D) = D - 3$. Thus,

$$\begin{aligned} Q(D)P(D)y &= (D-3)D(D-1)(D-2)(D-3)y \\ &= D(D-1)(D-2)(D-3)^2 y = (D-3)[36e^{3x}] = 0 \end{aligned}$$

$$\Rightarrow \ y = c_1 + c_2 e^x + c_3 e^{2x} + c_4 e^{3x} + c_5 x e^{3x}.$$

Since $c_1 + c_2 e^x + c_3 e^{2x} + c_4 e^{3x}$ is a solution of the homogeneous equation $P(D)y = 0$, $y_p = c_5 x e^{3x}$, or $y_p = ax e^{3x}$, where a is to be determined. Then

$$\begin{aligned} y_p' &= a[e^{3x} + 3xe^{3x}], \\ y_p'' &= a[6e^{3x} + 9xe^{3x}], \\ y_p''' &= a[27e^{3x} + 27xe^{3x}], \\ y_p^{(4)} &= a[108e^{3x} + 81xe^{3x}], \end{aligned}$$

and $y_p^{(4)} - 6y_p''' + 11y_p'' - 6y_p' = 36e^{3x} \Rightarrow$

$$\begin{aligned} y_p^{(4)} - 6y_p''' + 11y_p'' - 6y_p' &= a[108e^{3x} + 81xe^{3x}] - 6a[27e^{3x} + 27xe^{3x}] \\ &\quad + 11a[6e^{3x} + 9xe^{3x}] - 6a[e^{3x} + 3xe^{3x}] \\ &= 36e^{3x} \end{aligned}$$

$$\Rightarrow 6a = 36 \Rightarrow a = 6 \Rightarrow y_p = 6xe^{3x} \Rightarrow$$

$$y = 6xe^{3x} + c_1 + c_2 e^x + c_3 e^{2x} + c_4 e^{3x}$$

is the general solution of the nonhomogeneous equation.

Exercises 4.2

In Exercises 1-15, employ variation of parameters to find the general solution or to solve the initial-value problem.

1. $y''' - 3y'' - y' + 3y = 8e^{2x}$

2. $y''' - 3y'' + 2y' = 8xe^{2x}$

3. $y''' - 2y'' + y' = -2e^x \cos(x)$

4. $y''' - y'' + 2y = 10e^x$

5. $y''' - y'' + y' - y = 4\sin(x) + 4\cos(x)$

6. $y''' - y'' = 20x^3$, $y(0) = 20$, $y'(0) = 0$, $y''(0) = -20$

7. $y''' - 2y'' = 5\sin(x)$

8. $y^{(4)} - y'' = 2$

9. $y^{(4)} + y'' = 6x$

10. $x^3 y''' - x^2 y'' + 2xy' - 2y = x, \ x > 0$

11. $x^3 y''' + 5x^2 y'' + 2xy' - 2y = \dfrac{1}{x}, \ x > 0$

12. $x^3 y''' + 2x^2 y'' = 1, \ x > 0, \ y(1) = 5, \ y'(1) = 1, \ y''(1) = 0$

13. $x^3 y''' + x^2 y'' - xy' = 4x^2, \ x > 0$

14. $x^3 y''' + 2x^2 y'' - 2xy' = x^3 \cos(x), \ x > 0$

15. $x^3 y''' + 3x^2 y'' + 2xy' = 1, \ x > 0$

16. $x^3 y''' + 3x^2 y'' = x^2 \sin(x), \ x > 0$

In Exercises 17-25, employ annihilators to determine a particular solution.

17. $y''' - 3y'' - y' + 3y = 8e^{2x}$ (see Exercise 1)

18. $y''' - y'' + 2y = 10e^x$ (see Exercise 4)

19. $y''' - y'' = 20x^3$ (see Exercise 6)

20. $y''' - 2y'' = 5\sin(x)$ (see Exercise 7)

21. $y''' - 3y'' + 2y' = 8xe^{2x}$ (see Exercise 2)

22. $y''' - y'' + y' - y = 4\sin(x) + 4\cos(x)$ (see Exercise 5)

23. $y''' - 2y'' + y' = -2e^x \cos(x)$ (see Exercise 3)

24. $y^{(4)} - y'' = 2$ (see Exercise 8)

25. $y^{(4)} + y'' = 6x$ (see Exercise 9)

Chapter 4 Exercises

1. Consider the equation $y''' - y'' - 2y' = 12$.

    (a) Employ variation of parameters to solve the equation.

    (b) Employ annihilators to solve the equation.

    (c) Integrate the equation once and solve the resulting second-order equation.

2. Solve the equation $x^3 y''' + x^2 y'' = x, \ x > 0$.

3. Solve the equation $x^3 y''' + x^2 y'' = \dfrac{4}{x}$, $x > 0$ (see Exercise 2).

4. Integrate the equation $y''' - y'' = 20x^3$ twice and solve the resulting first-order equation (see Exercise 6 in Section 4.2 on page 118).

5. Solve the equation $x^4 y^{(4)} - 4x^3 y''' + 12x^2 y'' - 24xy' + 24y = x^4$, $x > 0$.

6. Solve the equation $x^3 y''' - x^2 y'' + 10xy' = 156x^2 \sin[3\ln(x)]$, $x > 0$.

7. Let $P(r)$ be a polynomial with real coefficients. Show that if z is a complex root, then its complex conjugate $\bar{z}$ is also a root.

8. Let $p(x)$ and $q(x)$ be continuous on the interval $I = (-1, 1)$. Is it possible for the equation $y'' + p(x)y' + q(x)y = 0$ to have the solutions $y_1 = 1$, $y_2 = x$ and $y_3 = x^3$ on I?

9. Solve the equation $y''' + 3y'' + 3y' + y = 2xe^{-x}\cos(x)$ by variation of parameters.

10. Employ annihilators to solve the equation in Exercise 9.

Chapter 5

Linear Systems

Definition 5.1. A set of n first-order differential equations which involve n unknown functions of an independent variable t, where $n \geq 2$, is called a *system of first-order equations*. A system is *linear* if it has the form

$$
\begin{aligned}
x_1' &= a_{11}(t)x_1 + a_{12}(t)x_2 + \cdots + a_{1n}(t)x_n(t) + f_1(t) \\
x_2' &= a_{21}(t)x_1 + a_{22}(t)x_2 + \cdots + a_{2n}(t)x_n(t) + f_2(t) \\
&\vdots \\
x_n' &= a_{n1}(t)x_1 + a_{n2}(t)x_2 + \cdots + a_{nn}(t)x_n(t) + f_n(t),
\end{aligned}
\tag{5.1}
$$

where x_1, x_2, $\cdots$, x_n are unknown functions of t, and $a_{ij}(t)$, $1 \leq i, j \leq n$, and $f_j(t)$, $1 \leq j \leq n$, are given functions of t. A linear system is *homogeneous* if $f_j(t) \equiv 0$, $1 \leq j \leq n$. Otherwise, it is *nonhomogeneous*. It has *constant coefficients* if $a_{ij}(t) = a_{ij}$ is constant, $1 \leq i, j \leq n$.

For example, if $n = 2$, writing $x_1 = x$ and $x_2 = y$ for convenience, the system

$$
\begin{aligned}
x' &= 3x + 2y \\
y' &= 2x - y
\end{aligned}
$$

is linear and homogeneous with constant coefficients, whereas

$$
\begin{aligned}
x' &= x - 3y + t^2 \\
y' &= 6x + 4y + e^t
\end{aligned}
$$

is linear and nonhomogeneous with constant coefficients.

Definition 5.2. A *solution* of a system is a set of n differentiable functions $x_1(t)$, $x_2(t)$, $\cdots$, $x_n(t)$ which satisfy *every* equation in the system for all t in an interval I.

For example, $x(t) = 2e^t$, $y(t) = e^t$ is a solution of the system

$$
\begin{aligned}
x' &= 3x - 4y \\
y' &= x - y
\end{aligned}
\tag{5.2}
$$

because

$$
\begin{aligned}
x'(t) &= 2e^t = 3(2e^t) - 4(e^t) = 3x(t) - 4y(t) \\
y'(t) &= e^t = 2e^t - e^t = x(t) - y(t)
\end{aligned}
$$

for all t in the interval $I = \mathbb{R}$.

In the following sections, methods will be developed for the determination of all solutions of linear systems with constant coefficients. This is achieved most efficiently, especially for large n, by expressing a linear system in *matrix form*. For example, with

$$
\mathbf{x} = \begin{pmatrix} x \\ y \end{pmatrix}, \quad \mathbf{x}' = \begin{pmatrix} x \\ y \end{pmatrix}' = \begin{pmatrix} x' \\ y' \end{pmatrix} \quad \text{and} \quad A = \begin{pmatrix} 3 & -4 \\ 1 & -1 \end{pmatrix},
$$

the system (5.2) can be expressed as

$$
\begin{pmatrix} x' \\ y' \end{pmatrix} = \begin{pmatrix} 3 & -4 \\ 1 & -1 \end{pmatrix} \begin{pmatrix} x \\ y \end{pmatrix}, \quad \text{i.e., } \mathbf{x}' = A\mathbf{x},
$$

and the solution $x(t) = 2e^t$, $y(t) = e^t$ can be expressed as the vector (or *vector-valued*) function

$$
\mathbf{x}(t) = \begin{pmatrix} x(t) \\ y(t) \end{pmatrix} = \begin{pmatrix} 2e^t \\ e^t \end{pmatrix} = e^t \begin{pmatrix} 2 \\ 1 \end{pmatrix}.
$$

Similarly, the system of three nonhomogenous equations

$$
\begin{aligned}
x' &= 2x + 3y - z + t^2 \\
y' &= x - 4z - e^t \\
z' &= -y + 6z + 5
\end{aligned}
$$

can be expressed as $\mathbf{x}' = A\mathbf{x} + \mathbf{f}(t)$ by letting

$$
\mathbf{x} = \begin{pmatrix} x \\ y \\ z \end{pmatrix}, \quad A = \begin{pmatrix} 2 & 3 & -1 \\ 1 & 0 & -4 \\ 0 & -1 & 6 \end{pmatrix} \quad \text{and} \quad \mathbf{f}(t) = \begin{pmatrix} t^2 \\ -e^t \\ 5 \end{pmatrix}.
$$

More generally, the system (5.1) can be expressed as $\mathbf{x}' = A(t)\mathbf{x} + \mathbf{f}(t)$ by letting

$$
\mathbf{x} = \begin{pmatrix} x_1 \\ x_2 \\ \vdots \\ x_n \end{pmatrix}, \quad \mathbf{f}(t) = \begin{pmatrix} f_1(t) \\ f_2(t) \\ \vdots \\ f_n(t) \end{pmatrix} \quad \text{and}
$$

$$A(t) = (a_{ij}(t)) = \begin{pmatrix} a_{11}(t) & a_{12}(t) & \cdots & a_{1n}(t) \\ a_{21}(t) & a_{22}(t) & \cdots & a_{2n}(t) \\ \vdots & \vdots & \cdots & \vdots \\ a_{n1}(t) & a_{n2}(t) & \cdots & a_{nn}(t) \end{pmatrix}.$$

For a homogeneous system, $\mathbf{f}(t) \equiv 0$, and, for a system with constant coefficients, $A(t) = A$ has constant entries a_{ij}, $1 \le i, j \le n$.

5.1 Homogeneous Systems

5.1.1 General Theory

Theorem 5.1. Let $A(t)$ be an $n \times n$ matrix with entries $a_{ij}(t)$ and consider the homogeneous system $\mathbf{x}' = A(t)\mathbf{x}$. If $\mathbf{x}_1(t), \mathbf{x}_2(t), \cdots, \mathbf{x}_k(t)$, $k \ge 1$, are solutions, then any linear combination

$$\mathbf{x}(t) = c_1\mathbf{x}_1(t) + c_2\mathbf{x}_2(t) + \cdots + c_k\mathbf{x}_k(t)$$

is also a solution.

Proof.

$$\begin{aligned} \mathbf{x}'(t) &= (c_1\mathbf{x}_1(t) + c_2\mathbf{x}_2(t) + \cdots + c_k\mathbf{x}_k(t))' \\ &= c_1\mathbf{x}_1'(t) + c_2\mathbf{x}_2'(t) + \cdots + c_k\mathbf{x}_k'(t) \\ &= c_1 A(t)\mathbf{x}_1(t) + c_2 A(t)\mathbf{x}_2(t) + \cdots + c_k A(t)\mathbf{x}_k(t) \\ &= A(t)(c_1\mathbf{x}_1(t) + c_2\mathbf{x}_2(t) + \cdots + c_k\mathbf{x}_k(t)) \\ &= A(t)\mathbf{x}(t). \end{aligned}$$

Definition 5.3. The vector-valued functions $\mathbf{x}_1(t), \mathbf{x}_2(t), \cdots, \mathbf{x}_k(t)$, $k \ge 1$, are *linearly dependent* on an interval I if there exist constants $c_1, c_2, \cdots, c_k$, not all zero, such that

$$c_1\mathbf{x}_1(t) + c_2\mathbf{x}_2(t) + \cdots + c_k\mathbf{x}_k(t) = 0$$

for all t in I. Otherwise, they are *linearly independent* on I.

Definition 5.4. Let $\mathbf{x}_1(t), \mathbf{x}_2(t), \cdots, \mathbf{x}_n(t)$ be n-vector-valued functions, i.e.,

$$\mathbf{x}_i(t) = \begin{pmatrix} x_{1i}(t) \\ x_{2i}(t) \\ \vdots \\ x_{ni}(t) \end{pmatrix}, \quad 1 \le i \le n.$$

The *Wronskian* $W(t) \equiv W[\mathbf{x}_1(t), \mathbf{x}_2(t), \cdots, \mathbf{x}_n(t)]$ is defined by

$$W(t) = \det(\mathbf{x}_1(t)\ \mathbf{x}_2(t)\ \cdots\ \mathbf{x}_n(t)) = \begin{vmatrix} x_{11}(t) & x_{12}(t) & \cdots & x_{1n}(t) \\ x_{21}(t) & x_{22}(t) & \cdots & x_{2n}(t) \\ \vdots & \vdots & \cdots & \vdots \\ x_{n1}(t) & x_{n2}(t) & \cdots & x_{nn}(t) \end{vmatrix}.$$

Theorem 5.2. Suppose that $A(t) = (a_{ij}(t))$ is continuous on an interval I, i.e., $a_{ij}(t)$ is continuous for $1 \leq i, j \leq n$, and let $\mathbf{x}_1(t), \mathbf{x}_2(t), \cdots, \mathbf{x}_n(t)$ be solutions of $\mathbf{x}' = A(t)\mathbf{x}$. Then either $W(t) = 0$ on I, or $W(t) \neq 0$ for any t in I. The solutions $\mathbf{x}_1(t), \mathbf{x}_2(t), \cdots, \mathbf{x}_n(t)$ are linearly independent on I if and only if $W(t) \neq 0$ on I.

Definition 5.5. Let $\mathbf{x}_1(t), \mathbf{x}_2(t), \cdots, \mathbf{x}_n(t)$ be n linearly independent solutions of $\mathbf{x}' = A(t)\mathbf{x}$. The set $\{\mathbf{x}_1(t), \mathbf{x}_2(t), \cdots, \mathbf{x}_n(t)\}$ is called a *fundamental set* of solutions. The matrix

$$X(t) = (\mathbf{x}_1(t)\ \mathbf{x}_2(t)\ \cdots\ \mathbf{x}_n(t)) = \begin{pmatrix} x_{11}(t) & x_{12}(t) & \cdots & x_{1n}(t) \\ x_{21}(t) & x_{22}(t) & \cdots & x_{2n}(t) \\ \vdots & \vdots & \cdots & \vdots \\ x_{n1}(t) & x_{n2}(t) & \cdots & x_{nn}(t) \end{pmatrix}$$

is called a *fundamental matrix* for the system. The *general solution* of the system is

$$\mathbf{x}(t) = c_1\mathbf{x}_1(t) + c_2\mathbf{x}_2(t) + \cdots + c_n\mathbf{x}_n(t),$$

where c_1, c_2, $\cdots$, c_n are arbitrary constants, and may be expressed more concisely as

$$\mathbf{x}(t) = (\mathbf{x}_1(t)\ \mathbf{x}_2(t)\ \cdots\ \mathbf{x}_n(t)) \begin{pmatrix} c_1 \\ c_2 \\ \vdots \\ c_n \end{pmatrix} = X(t)\mathbf{c}, \quad \text{where} \quad \mathbf{c} = \begin{pmatrix} c_1 \\ c_2 \\ \vdots \\ c_n \end{pmatrix}.$$

A solution in which c_1, c_2, $\cdots$, c_n are assigned particular values is called a *particular solution*.

Theorem 5.3. A fundamental matrix $X(t)$ for a system $\mathbf{x}' = A(t)\mathbf{x}$, where $A(t)$ is continuous on an interval I, is nonsingular on I, i.e., $\det(X(t)) \neq 0$ on I, and satisfies the matrix equation $X'(t) = A(t)X(t)$, where $X'(t) = (x_{ij}'(t))$.

Proof. Since $\mathbf{x}_1(t)$, $\mathbf{x}_2(t)$, $\cdots$, $\mathbf{x}_n(t)$ are linearly independent, $\det(X(t)) = W(t) \neq 0$ on I, and, since $\mathbf{x}_i' = A(t)\mathbf{x}_i$, $1 \leq i \leq n$,

$$\begin{aligned} X'(t) &= (\mathbf{x}_1'(t)\ \mathbf{x}_2'(t)\ \cdots\ \mathbf{x}_n'(t)) \\ &= (A\mathbf{x}_1(t)\ A\mathbf{x}_2(t)\ \cdots\ A\mathbf{x}_n(t)) \\ &= A(\mathbf{x}_1(t)\ \mathbf{x}_2(t)\ \cdots\ \mathbf{x}_n(t)) \\ &= AX(t). \end{aligned}$$

Theorem 5.4. Let $A(t)$ be continuous on an interval I. If $X(t)$ is a fundamental matrix for the system $\mathbf{x}' = A(t)\mathbf{x}$, then $X(t)C$ is also a fundamental matrix for any nonsingular $n \times n$ matrix C. If $X(t)$ and $Y(t)$ are any two fundamental matrices, then there exists a nonsingular constant $n \times n$ matrix C such that

$$Y(t) = X(t)C.$$

Equivalently, $X(t) = Y(t)C^{-1}$.

Proof. $Z(t) = X(t)C$ satisfies the matrix equation $Z'(t) = AZ(t)$ because

$$Z'(t) = [X(t)C]' = X'(t)C = [AX(t)]C = A[X(t)C] = AZ(t).$$

Since $\det(X(t)) \neq 0$ and $\det(C) \neq 0$, $\det(Z(t)) = \det(X(t))\det(C) \neq 0$. Hence, the columns of $Z(t)$ are linearly independent, and each column $\mathbf{z}_j$ is a solution of the system because

$$\begin{aligned}
(\mathbf{z}_1'(t) \ \mathbf{z}_2'(t) \ \cdots \ \mathbf{z}_n'(t)) &= (\mathbf{z}_1(t) \ \mathbf{z}_2(t) \ \cdots \ \mathbf{z}_n(t))' \\
&= A(\mathbf{z}_1(t) \ \mathbf{z}_2(t) \ \cdots \ \mathbf{z}_n(t)) \\
&= (A\mathbf{z}_1(t) \ A\mathbf{z}_2(t) \ \cdots \ A\mathbf{z}_n(t)) \\
\Rightarrow \quad \mathbf{z}_j'(t) &= A\mathbf{z}_j(t), \ 1 \leq j \leq n.
\end{aligned}$$

Thus, $Z(t)$ is a fundamental matrix. If $X(t)$ and $Y(t)$ are any two fundamental matrices, let $C(t) = X(t)^{-1}Y(t)$. Then $X(t)C(t) = Y(t)$

$$\begin{aligned}
\Rightarrow \quad & X'(t)C(t) + X(t)C'(t) = Y'(t) \\
\Rightarrow \quad & A(t)X(t)C(t) + X(t)C'(t) = A(t)Y(t) \\
\Rightarrow \quad & A(t)Y(t) + X(t)C'(t) = A(t)Y(t) \\
\Rightarrow \quad & X(t)C'(t) = 0 \\
\Rightarrow \quad & C'(t) = X(t)^{-1}X(t)C'(t) = 0.
\end{aligned}$$

Hence, $C(t) = C$ is a constant matrix, and $Y(t) = X(t)C$.

Definition 5.6. An *initial-value problem* for a homogeneous system consists of a system $\mathbf{x}' = A(t)\mathbf{x}$, together with an *initial condition* $\mathbf{x}(t_0) = \mathbf{x}_0$, which requires that the solution $\mathbf{x}(t)$ be equal to $\mathbf{x}_0$ at $t = t_0$, and determines the arbitrary constant vector $\mathbf{c}$.

Theorem 5.5. Let $A(t)$ be continuous on an interval I containing the point t_0 in its interior. The solution of the initial-value problem

$$\mathbf{x}' = A(t)\mathbf{x}, \ \ \mathbf{x}(t_0) = \mathbf{x}_0,$$

is given by $\mathbf{x}(t) = X(t)X(t_0)^{-1}\mathbf{x}_0$, where $X(t)$ is a fundamental matrix.

Proof. $\mathbf{x}(t) = X(t)\mathbf{c}$ and $\mathbf{x}(t_0) = \mathbf{x}_0 \Rightarrow \mathbf{x}(t_0) = X(t_0)\mathbf{c} = \mathbf{x}_0 \Rightarrow \mathbf{c} = X(t_0)^{-1}\mathbf{x}_0 \Rightarrow$

$$\mathbf{x}(t) = X(t)\mathbf{c} = X(t)X(t_0)^{-1}\mathbf{x}_0.$$

5.1.2   Systems with Constant Coefficients

Let $A = (a_{ij})$ be an $n \times n$ matrix, where a_{ij}, $1 \leq i, j \leq n$, are constants, and consider the system

$$\mathbf{x}' = A\mathbf{x}. \tag{5.3}$$

Analogous to single equations with constant coefficients, seek solutions in the form

$$\mathbf{x}(t) = e^{\lambda t}\mathbf{v}, \tag{5.4}$$

where λ is a scalar and $\mathbf{v} \neq \mathbf{0}$ is a vector, to be determined. The case $\mathbf{v} = \mathbf{0}$ is omitted because it yields only the trivial solution $\mathbf{x}(t) \equiv \mathbf{0}$. Then

$$\mathbf{x}'(t) = \lambda e^{\lambda t}\mathbf{v},$$

and $\mathbf{x}'(t) = A\mathbf{x}(t)$ if and only if $\lambda e^{\lambda t}\mathbf{v} = A e^{\lambda t}\mathbf{v}$, or $A\mathbf{v} = \lambda\mathbf{v}$, i.e., λ is an *eigenvalue* of A and $\mathbf{v}$ is a corresponding *eigenvector*.

The equation $A\mathbf{v} = \lambda\mathbf{v}$ is equivalent to

$$(\lambda I - A)\mathbf{v} = \mathbf{0}, \tag{5.5}$$

where I is the $n \times n$ identity matrix. Equation (5.5) is a homogeneous algebraic system, and admits nontrivial (i.e., nonzero) solutions $\mathbf{v}$ if and only if the coefficient matrix $\lambda I - A$ is singular, i.e.,

$$\det(\lambda I - A) = 0. \tag{5.6}$$

The eigenvalues of A are determined by solving Equation (5.6) for λ, and for each eigenvalue λ_i, the eigenvectors which correspond to λ_i are obtained by setting $\lambda = \lambda_i$ in Equation (5.5) and solving for $\mathbf{v}$.

If the $n \times n$ matrix A admits n real, linearly independent eigenvectors $\mathbf{v}_1, \mathbf{v}_2, \cdots$, $\mathbf{v}_n$, corresponding to the eigenvalues $\lambda_1, \lambda_2, \cdots, \lambda_n$ (not necessarily distinct), then n linearly independent solutions of the system $\mathbf{x}' = A\mathbf{x}$ are given by

$$\mathbf{x}_1(t) = e^{\lambda_1 t}\mathbf{v}_1, \quad \mathbf{x}_2(t) = e^{\lambda_2 t}\mathbf{v}_2, \quad \cdots, \quad \mathbf{x}_n(t) = e^{\lambda_n t}\mathbf{v}_n.$$

This is automatically true in case A possesses n real, distinct eigenvalues, because eigenvectors which correspond to distinct eigenvalues are linearly independent. The cases where A has complex eigenvalues or fewer than n independent eigenvectors will be dicussed later.

Example 5.1.   Consider the system

$$\left\{ \begin{array}{rcrcr} x' & = & 2x & + & 2y \\ y' & = & -2x & + & 7y \end{array} \right\}. \tag{5.7}$$

This system may be expressed in matrix form as $\mathbf{x}' = A\mathbf{x}$, where

$$\mathbf{x} = \begin{pmatrix} x \\ y \end{pmatrix} \quad \text{and} \quad A = \begin{pmatrix} 2 & 2 \\ -2 & 7 \end{pmatrix}.$$

Then

$$\det(\lambda I - A) = \begin{vmatrix} \lambda - 2 & -2 \\ 2 & \lambda - 7 \end{vmatrix} = (\lambda - 2)(\lambda - 7) + 4 = \lambda^2 - 9\lambda + 18$$

$$= (\lambda - 3)(\lambda - 6) = 0$$

$\Rightarrow \lambda_1 = 3$ and $\lambda_2 = 6$ are the eigenvalues of A.

For $\lambda_1 = 3$, $(\lambda_1 I - A)\mathbf{v} = \mathbf{0}$ with $\mathbf{v} = \begin{pmatrix} a \\ b \end{pmatrix} \Rightarrow$

$$\begin{pmatrix} 1 & -2 \\ 2 & -4 \end{pmatrix} \begin{pmatrix} a \\ b \end{pmatrix} = \begin{pmatrix} 0 \\ 0 \end{pmatrix}$$

$\Rightarrow a - 2b = 0$, and $b = 1 \Rightarrow \mathbf{v} = \mathbf{v}_1 = \begin{pmatrix} 2 \\ 1 \end{pmatrix}$ is an eigenvector which corresponds to the eigenvalue $\lambda_1 = 3$.

For $\lambda_2 = 6$, $(\lambda_2 I - A)\mathbf{v} = \mathbf{0}$ with $\mathbf{v} = \begin{pmatrix} a \\ b \end{pmatrix} \Rightarrow$

$$\begin{pmatrix} 4 & -2 \\ 2 & -1 \end{pmatrix} \begin{pmatrix} a \\ b \end{pmatrix} = \begin{pmatrix} 0 \\ 0 \end{pmatrix}$$

$\Rightarrow 2a - b = 0$, and $a = 1 \Rightarrow \mathbf{v} = \mathbf{v}_2 = \begin{pmatrix} 1 \\ 2 \end{pmatrix}$ is an eigenvector which corresponds to the eigenvalue $\lambda_2 = 6$.

Thus, two independent solutions of the system (5.7) are given in vector form by

$$\mathbf{x}_1(t) = e^{3t} \begin{pmatrix} 2 \\ 1 \end{pmatrix} = \begin{pmatrix} 2e^{3t} \\ e^{3t} \end{pmatrix} \quad \text{and} \quad \mathbf{x}_2(t) = e^{6t} \begin{pmatrix} 1 \\ 2 \end{pmatrix} = \begin{pmatrix} e^{6t} \\ 2e^{6t} \end{pmatrix},$$

and $X(t) = (\mathbf{x}_1(t)\ \mathbf{x}_2(t)) = \begin{pmatrix} 2e^{3t} & e^{6t} \\ e^{3t} & 2e^{6t} \end{pmatrix}$ is a fundamental matrix. The general solution in vector form is

$$\mathbf{x}(t) = c_1 \mathbf{x}_1(t) + c_2 \mathbf{x}_2(t) = X(t)\mathbf{c} = \begin{pmatrix} 2e^{3t} & e^{6t} \\ e^{3t} & 2e^{6t} \end{pmatrix} \begin{pmatrix} c_1 \\ c_2 \end{pmatrix} = \begin{pmatrix} 2c_1 e^{3t} + c_2 e^{6t} \\ c_1 e^{3t} + 2c_2 e^{6t} \end{pmatrix},$$

from which the general solution $x(t) = 2c_1 e^{3t} + c_2 e^{6t}$ and $y(t) = c_1 e^{3t} + 2c_2 e^{6t}$ of the system (5.7) is obtained in scalar form. Note that if $\mathbf{v}$ is an eigenvector of A, then so is $c\mathbf{v}$ for any constant $c \neq 0$. Thus, the choice of an eigenvector is not unique, and we may take $\mathbf{v}_1 = \begin{pmatrix} 4 \\ 2 \end{pmatrix}$ and $\mathbf{v}_2 = \begin{pmatrix} 2 \\ 4 \end{pmatrix}$. Then $Y(t) = \begin{pmatrix} 4e^{3t} & 2e^{6t} \\ 2e^{3t} & 4e^{6t} \end{pmatrix}$ is also a fundamental matrix. By Theorem 5.4, $X(t)^{-1}Y(t) = \begin{pmatrix} 2 & 0 \\ 0 & 2 \end{pmatrix}$ is a constant matrix.

Example 5.2. Consider the system

$$\left\{ \begin{array}{rcrcr} x' & = & -x & + & 3y \\ y' & = & -4x & + & 6y \end{array} \right\}. \tag{5.8}$$

This system may be expressed in matrix form as $\mathbf{x}' = A\mathbf{x}$, where

$$\mathbf{x} = \begin{pmatrix} x \\ y \end{pmatrix} \quad \text{and} \quad A = \begin{pmatrix} -1 & 3 \\ -4 & 6 \end{pmatrix}.$$

Then

$$\begin{aligned} \det(\lambda I - A) & = \begin{vmatrix} \lambda+1 & -3 \\ 4 & \lambda-6 \end{vmatrix} = (\lambda+1)(\lambda-6) + 12 = \lambda^2 - 5\lambda + 6 \\ & = (\lambda-2)(\lambda-3) = 0 \end{aligned}$$

$\Rightarrow \lambda_1 = 2$ and $\lambda_2 = 3$ are the eigenvalues of A.

For $\lambda_1 = 2$, $(\lambda_1 I - A)\mathbf{v} = \mathbf{0}$ with $\mathbf{v} = \begin{pmatrix} a \\ b \end{pmatrix} \Rightarrow$

$$\begin{pmatrix} 3 & -3 \\ 4 & -4 \end{pmatrix} \begin{pmatrix} a \\ b \end{pmatrix} = \begin{pmatrix} 0 \\ 0 \end{pmatrix}$$

$\Rightarrow 3a - 3b = 0$, and $a = 1 \Rightarrow \mathbf{v} = \mathbf{v}_1 = \begin{pmatrix} 1 \\ 1 \end{pmatrix}$ is an eigenvector which corresponds to the eigenvalue $\lambda_1 = 2$.

For $\lambda_2 = 3$, $(\lambda_2 I - A)\mathbf{v} = \mathbf{0}$ with $\mathbf{v} = \begin{pmatrix} a \\ b \end{pmatrix} \Rightarrow$

$$\begin{pmatrix} 4 & -3 \\ 4 & -3 \end{pmatrix} \begin{pmatrix} a \\ b \end{pmatrix} = \begin{pmatrix} 0 \\ 0 \end{pmatrix}$$

$\Rightarrow 4a - 3b = 0$, and $a = 3 \Rightarrow \mathbf{v} = \mathbf{v}_2 = \begin{pmatrix} 3 \\ 4 \end{pmatrix}$ is an eigenvector which corresponds to the eigenvalue $\lambda_2 = 3$.

Thus, two independent solutions of the system (5.8) are given in vector form by

$$\mathbf{x}_1(t) = e^{2t} \begin{pmatrix} 1 \\ 1 \end{pmatrix} = \begin{pmatrix} e^{2t} \\ e^{2t} \end{pmatrix} \quad \text{and} \quad \mathbf{x}_2(t) = e^{3t} \begin{pmatrix} 3 \\ 4 \end{pmatrix} = \begin{pmatrix} 3e^{3t} \\ 4e^{3t} \end{pmatrix},$$

and $X(t) = (\mathbf{x}_1(t)\ \mathbf{x}_2(t)) = \begin{pmatrix} e^{2t} & 3e^{3t} \\ e^{2t} & 4e^{3t} \end{pmatrix}$ is a fundamental matrix. The general solution in vector form is

$$\mathbf{x}(t) = c_1\mathbf{x}_1(t) + c_2\mathbf{x}_2(t) = X(t)\mathbf{c} = \begin{pmatrix} e^{2t} & 3e^{3t} \\ e^{2t} & 4e^{3t} \end{pmatrix} \begin{pmatrix} c_1 \\ c_2 \end{pmatrix} = \begin{pmatrix} c_1e^{2t} + 3c_2e^{3t} \\ c_1e^{2t} + 4c_2e^{3t} \end{pmatrix},$$

from which the general solution $x(t) = c_1e^{2t} + 3c_2e^{3t}$ and $y(t) = c_1e^{2t} + 4c_2e^{3t}$ of the system (5.8) is obtained in scalar form.

Example 5.3. Consider the system

$$\left\{ \begin{array}{rcl} x' & = & -x \\ y' & = & -y \end{array} \right\}. \tag{5.9}$$

This system may be expressed in matrix form as $\mathbf{x}' = A\mathbf{x}$, where

$$\mathbf{x} = \begin{pmatrix} x \\ y \end{pmatrix} \quad \text{and} \quad A = \begin{pmatrix} -1 & 0 \\ 0 & -1 \end{pmatrix}.$$

Then

$$\det(\lambda I - A) = \begin{vmatrix} \lambda + 1 & 0 \\ 0 & \lambda + 1 \end{vmatrix} = (\lambda + 1)^2 = 0$$

$\Rightarrow \lambda_1 = -1$ is the only eigenvalues of A, with multiplicity 2.

For $\lambda_1 = -1$, $(\lambda_1 I - A)\mathbf{v} = \mathbf{0}$ with $\mathbf{v} = \begin{pmatrix} a \\ b \end{pmatrix} \Rightarrow$

$$\begin{pmatrix} 0 & 0 \\ 0 & 0 \end{pmatrix} \begin{pmatrix} a \\ b \end{pmatrix} = \begin{pmatrix} 0 \\ 0 \end{pmatrix},$$

which states that both a and b are free. Hence, $a = 1$ and $b = 0$ gives the eigenvector $\mathbf{v}_1 = \begin{pmatrix} 1 \\ 0 \end{pmatrix}$, and $a = 0$ and $b = 1$ gives the eigenvector $\mathbf{v}_2 = \begin{pmatrix} 0 \\ 1 \end{pmatrix}$. Since $\mathbf{v}_1$ and $\mathbf{v}_2$ are linearly independent, two independent solutions of the system (5.9) are given in vector form by

$$\mathbf{x}_1(t) = e^{-t} \begin{pmatrix} 1 \\ 0 \end{pmatrix} = \begin{pmatrix} e^{-t} \\ 0 \end{pmatrix} \quad \text{and} \quad \mathbf{x}_2(t) = e^{-t} \begin{pmatrix} 0 \\ 1 \end{pmatrix} = \begin{pmatrix} 0 \\ e^{-t} \end{pmatrix},$$

and $X(t) = (\mathbf{x}_1(t) \; \mathbf{x}_2(t)) = \begin{pmatrix} e^{-t} & 0 \\ 0 & e^{-t} \end{pmatrix}$ is a fundamental matrix. The general solution in vector form is

$$\mathbf{x}(t) = c_1 \mathbf{x}_1(t) + c_2 \mathbf{x}_2(t) = X(t)\mathbf{c} = \begin{pmatrix} e^{-t} & 0 \\ 0 & e^{-t} \end{pmatrix} \begin{pmatrix} c_1 \\ c_2 \end{pmatrix} = \begin{pmatrix} c_1 e^{-t} \\ c_2 e^{-t} \end{pmatrix},$$

from which the general solution $x(t) = c_1 e^{-t}$ and $y(t) = c_2 e^{-t}$ of the system (5.9) is obtained in scalar form.

Note that, even though the 2×2 matrix A has only one eigenvalue λ_1, the general solution is obtained as in the preceding examples because there are two independent eigenvectors which correspond to λ_1.

A system such as (5.9) is said to be *decoupled* because each equation involves only one of the unknown functions, and can be solved independently of the other(s). Thus, $x' = -x \Rightarrow x(t) = c_1 e^{-t}$, and $y' = -y \Rightarrow y(t) = c_2 e^{-t}$, as above.

Example 5.4. Consider the initial-value problem

$$\left\{ \begin{array}{rcrcr} x' & = & 3x & + & y \\ y' & = & -4x & - & 2y \end{array} \right\}, \quad x(0) = 1, \quad y(0) = 5. \tag{5.10}$$

This problem may be expressed in matrix form as $\mathbf{x}' = A\mathbf{x}$, $\mathbf{x}(0) = \mathbf{x}_0$, where

$$\mathbf{x} = \begin{pmatrix} x \\ y \end{pmatrix}, \quad A = \begin{pmatrix} 3 & 1 \\ -4 & -2 \end{pmatrix} \quad \text{and} \quad \mathbf{x}_0 = \begin{pmatrix} 1 \\ 5 \end{pmatrix}.$$

Then

$$\begin{aligned} \det(\lambda I - A) &= \begin{vmatrix} \lambda - 3 & -1 \\ 4 & \lambda + 2 \end{vmatrix} = (\lambda - 3)(\lambda + 2) + 4 = \lambda^2 - \lambda - 2 \\ &= (\lambda + 1)(\lambda - 2) = 0 \end{aligned}$$

$\Rightarrow \lambda_1 = -1$ and $\lambda_2 = 2$ are the eigenvalues of A.

For $\lambda_1 = -1$, $(\lambda_1 I - A)\mathbf{v} = \mathbf{0}$ with $\mathbf{v} = \begin{pmatrix} a \\ b \end{pmatrix} \Rightarrow$

$$\begin{pmatrix} -4 & -1 \\ 4 & 1 \end{pmatrix} \begin{pmatrix} a \\ b \end{pmatrix} = \begin{pmatrix} 0 \\ 0 \end{pmatrix}$$

$\Rightarrow 4a + b = 0$, and $a = 1 \Rightarrow \mathbf{v} = \mathbf{v}_1 = \begin{pmatrix} 1 \\ -4 \end{pmatrix}$ is an eigenvector which corresponds to the eigenvalue $\lambda_1 = -1$.

For $\lambda_2 = 2$, $(\lambda_2 I - A)\mathbf{v} = \mathbf{0}$ with $\mathbf{v} = \begin{pmatrix} a \\ b \end{pmatrix} \Rightarrow$

$$\begin{pmatrix} -1 & -1 \\ 4 & 4 \end{pmatrix} \begin{pmatrix} a \\ b \end{pmatrix} = \begin{pmatrix} 0 \\ 0 \end{pmatrix}$$

$\Rightarrow -a - b = 0$, and $a = 1 \Rightarrow \mathbf{v} = \mathbf{v}_2 = \begin{pmatrix} 1 \\ -1 \end{pmatrix}$ is an eigenvector which corresponds to the eigenvalue $\lambda_2 = 2$.

Thus, two independent solutions of the system (5.10) are given in vector form by

$$\mathbf{x}_1(t) = e^{-t} \begin{pmatrix} 1 \\ -4 \end{pmatrix} = \begin{pmatrix} e^{-t} \\ -4e^{-t} \end{pmatrix} \quad \text{and} \quad \mathbf{x}_2(t) = e^{2t} \begin{pmatrix} 1 \\ -1 \end{pmatrix} = \begin{pmatrix} e^{2t} \\ -e^{2t} \end{pmatrix},$$

and $X(t) = (\mathbf{x}_1(t)\ \mathbf{x}_2(t)) = \begin{pmatrix} e^{-t} & e^{2t} \\ -4e^{-t} & -e^{2t} \end{pmatrix}$ is a fundamental matrix. The solution of the initial-value problem (5.10) is then given by $\mathbf{x}(t) = X(t)X(0)^{-1}\mathbf{x}_0$.

Note that the inverse of a 2×2 matrix $\begin{pmatrix} a & b \\ c & d \end{pmatrix}$ is obtained simply as

$$\begin{pmatrix} a & b \\ c & d \end{pmatrix}^{-1} = \frac{1}{\det(A)} \begin{pmatrix} d & -b \\ -c & a \end{pmatrix} = \frac{1}{ad - bc} \begin{pmatrix} d & -b \\ -c & a \end{pmatrix}.$$

Thus, $X(0)^{-1} = \begin{pmatrix} 1 & 1 \\ -4 & -1 \end{pmatrix}^{-1} = \frac{1}{3} \begin{pmatrix} -1 & -1 \\ 4 & 1 \end{pmatrix}$, and

$$\begin{aligned} \mathbf{x}(t) &= \frac{1}{3} \begin{pmatrix} e^{-t} & e^{2t} \\ -4e^{-t} & -e^{2t} \end{pmatrix} \begin{pmatrix} -1 & -1 \\ 4 & 1 \end{pmatrix} \begin{pmatrix} 1 \\ 5 \end{pmatrix} = \begin{pmatrix} e^{-t} & e^{2t} \\ -4e^{-t} & -e^{2t} \end{pmatrix} \begin{pmatrix} -2 \\ 3 \end{pmatrix} \\ &= \begin{pmatrix} -2e^{-t} + 3e^{2t} \\ 8e^{-t} - 3e^{2t} \end{pmatrix}, \end{aligned}$$

i.e., $x(t) = -2e^{-t} + 3e^{2t}$ and $y(t) = 8e^{-t} - 3e^{2t}$.

Example 5.5. Consider the system

$$\left\{ \begin{array}{rcrcrcr} x' & = & & - & 2y & + & 2z \\ y' & = & -3x & + & y & + & 3z \\ z' & = & -x & + & y & + & 3z \end{array} \right\}. \tag{5.11}$$

This system may be expressed in matrix form as $\mathbf{x}' = A\mathbf{x}$, where

$$\mathbf{x} = \begin{pmatrix} x \\ y \\ z \end{pmatrix} \quad \text{and} \quad A = \begin{pmatrix} 0 & -2 & 2 \\ -3 & 1 & 3 \\ -1 & 1 & 3 \end{pmatrix}.$$

Then

$$\det(\lambda I - A) = \begin{vmatrix} \lambda & 2 & -2 \\ 3 & \lambda - 1 & -3 \\ 1 & -1 & \lambda - 3 \end{vmatrix}$$

$$= \lambda[(\lambda - 1)(\lambda - 3) - 3] - 2[3(\lambda - 3) + 3] - 2[-3 - (\lambda - 1)]$$

$$= \lambda[\lambda^2 - 4\lambda] - 4\lambda + 16$$

$$= \lambda^2(\lambda - 4) - 4(\lambda - 4)$$

$$= (\lambda - 4)(\lambda^2 - 4)$$

$$= (\lambda - 4)(\lambda - 2)(\lambda + 2) = 0$$

$\Rightarrow \lambda_1 = 2$, $\lambda_2 = -2$ and $\lambda_3 = 4$ are the eigenvalues of A.

For $\lambda_1 = 2$, $(\lambda_1 I - A)\mathbf{v} = \mathbf{0}$ with $\mathbf{v} = \begin{pmatrix} a \\ b \\ c \end{pmatrix} \Rightarrow$

$$\begin{pmatrix} 2 & 2 & -2 \\ 3 & 1 & -3 \\ 1 & -1 & -1 \end{pmatrix} \begin{pmatrix} a \\ b \\ c \end{pmatrix} = \begin{pmatrix} 0 \\ 0 \\ 0 \end{pmatrix}.$$

Row reduction of the coefficient matrix ($R_2 \to R_2 - 3R_3$ and $R_3 \to R_1 - 2R_3$, where R_i denotes row i) then gives

$$\begin{pmatrix} 2 & 2 & -2 \\ 0 & 4 & 0 \\ 0 & 4 & 0 \end{pmatrix} \begin{pmatrix} a \\ b \\ c \end{pmatrix} = \begin{pmatrix} 0 \\ 0 \\ 0 \end{pmatrix}$$

$\Rightarrow b = 0$ and $a + b - c = 0 \Rightarrow a = c$, and $a = 1 \Rightarrow \mathbf{v}_1 = \begin{pmatrix} 1 \\ 0 \\ 1 \end{pmatrix}$ is an eigenvector

which corresponds to the eigenvalue $\lambda_1 = 2$.

For $\lambda_2 = -2$, $(\lambda_2 I - A)\mathbf{v} = \mathbf{0}$ with $\mathbf{v} = \begin{pmatrix} a \\ b \\ c \end{pmatrix} \Rightarrow$

$$\begin{pmatrix} -2 & 2 & -2 \\ 3 & -3 & -3 \\ 1 & -1 & -5 \end{pmatrix} \begin{pmatrix} a \\ b \\ c \end{pmatrix} = \begin{pmatrix} 0 \\ 0 \\ 0 \end{pmatrix}.$$

Row reduction of the coefficient matrix gives

$$\begin{pmatrix} -2 & 2 & -2 \\ 3 & -3 & -3 \\ 1 & -1 & -5 \end{pmatrix} \to \begin{pmatrix} -1 & 1 & -1 \\ 1 & -1 & -1 \\ 1 & -1 & -5 \end{pmatrix} \to \begin{pmatrix} -1 & 1 & -1 \\ 0 & 0 & -2 \\ 0 & 0 & -6 \end{pmatrix}$$

$$\Rightarrow \begin{pmatrix} -1 & 1 & -1 \\ 0 & 0 & -2 \\ 0 & 0 & -6 \end{pmatrix} \begin{pmatrix} a \\ b \\ c \end{pmatrix} = \begin{pmatrix} 0 \\ 0 \\ 0 \end{pmatrix}$$

$\Rightarrow c = 0$ and $-a + b - c = 0 \Rightarrow a = b$, and $a = 1 \Rightarrow \mathbf{v}_2 = \begin{pmatrix} 1 \\ 1 \\ 0 \end{pmatrix}$ is an eigenvector

which corresponds to the eigenvalue $\lambda_2 = -2$.

For $\lambda_3 = 4$, $(\lambda_3 I - A)\mathbf{v} = \mathbf{0}$ with $\mathbf{v} = \begin{pmatrix} a \\ b \\ c \end{pmatrix} \Rightarrow$

$$\begin{pmatrix} 4 & 2 & -2 \\ 3 & 3 & -3 \\ 1 & -1 & 1 \end{pmatrix} \begin{pmatrix} a \\ b \\ c \end{pmatrix} = \begin{pmatrix} 0 \\ 0 \\ 0 \end{pmatrix}.$$

Row reduction of the coefficient matrix gives

$$\begin{pmatrix} 4 & 2 & -2 \\ 3 & 3 & -3 \\ 1 & -1 & 1 \end{pmatrix} \rightarrow \begin{pmatrix} 2 & 1 & -1 \\ 1 & 1 & -1 \\ 1 & -1 & 1 \end{pmatrix} \rightarrow \begin{pmatrix} 2 & 1 & -1 \\ 0 & -1 & 1 \\ 0 & 3 & -3 \end{pmatrix}$$

$$\Rightarrow \begin{pmatrix} 2 & 1 & -1 \\ 0 & -1 & 1 \\ 0 & 3 & -3 \end{pmatrix} \begin{pmatrix} a \\ b \\ c \end{pmatrix} = \begin{pmatrix} 0 \\ 0 \\ 0 \end{pmatrix}$$

$\Rightarrow -b + c = 0$ and $2a + b - c = 0 \Rightarrow a = 0$, and $b = 1 \Rightarrow \mathbf{v}_3 = \begin{pmatrix} 0 \\ 1 \\ 1 \end{pmatrix}$ is an eigenvector

which corresponds to the eigenvalue $\lambda_3 = 4$.

Thus, three independent solutions of the system (5.11) are given in vector form by

$$\mathbf{x}_1(t) = e^{2t} \begin{pmatrix} 1 \\ 0 \\ 1 \end{pmatrix}, \quad \mathbf{x}_2(t) = e^{-2t} \begin{pmatrix} 1 \\ 1 \\ 0 \end{pmatrix} \quad \text{and} \quad \mathbf{x}_3(t) = e^{4t} \begin{pmatrix} 0 \\ 1 \\ 1 \end{pmatrix},$$

and $X(t) = (\mathbf{x}_1(t) \ \mathbf{x}_2(t) \ \mathbf{x}_3(t)) = \begin{pmatrix} e^{2t} & e^{-2t} & 0 \\ 0 & e^{-2t} & e^{4t} \\ e^{2t} & 0 & e^{4t} \end{pmatrix}$ is a fundamental matrix. The

general solution of the system (5.11) is

$$\begin{aligned} \mathbf{x}(t) &= c_1 \mathbf{x}_1(t) + c_2 \mathbf{x}_2(t) + c_3 \mathbf{x}_3(t) \\ &= X(t)\mathbf{c} \\ &= \begin{pmatrix} e^{2t} & e^{-2t} & 0 \\ 0 & e^{-2t} & e^{4t} \\ e^{2t} & 0 & e^{4t} \end{pmatrix} \begin{pmatrix} c_1 \\ c_2 \\ c_3 \end{pmatrix} = \begin{pmatrix} c_1 e^{2t} + c_2 e^{-2t} \\ c_2 e^{-2t} + c_3 e^{4t} \\ c_1 e^{2t} + c_3 e^{4t} \end{pmatrix}, \end{aligned}$$

i.e., $x(t) = c_1 e^{2t} + c_2 e^{-2t}$, $y(t) = c_2 e^{-2t} + c_3 e^{4t}$ and $z(t) = c_1 e^{2t} + c_3 e^{4t}$.

Example 5.6. Consider the system

$$\left\{ \begin{array}{rcrcr} x' & = & x & & \\ y' & = & & y & \\ z' & = & -x & + & 2z \end{array} \right\}. \tag{5.12}$$

This system may be expressed in matrix form as $\mathbf{x}' = A\mathbf{x}$, where

$$\mathbf{x} = \begin{pmatrix} x \\ y \\ z \end{pmatrix} \quad \text{and} \quad A = \begin{pmatrix} 1 & 0 & 0 \\ 0 & 1 & 0 \\ -1 & 0 & 2 \end{pmatrix}.$$

Then

$$\det(\lambda I - A) = \begin{vmatrix} \lambda - 1 & 0 & 0 \\ 0 & \lambda - 1 & 0 \\ 1 & 0 & \lambda - 2 \end{vmatrix} = (\lambda - 1)^2 (\lambda - 2) = 0$$

$\Rightarrow \lambda_1 = 1$, of multiplicity 2, and $\lambda_2 = 2$ are the eigenvalues of A.

For $\lambda_1 = 1$, $(\lambda_1 I - A)\mathbf{v} = \mathbf{0}$ with $\mathbf{v} = \begin{pmatrix} a \\ b \\ c \end{pmatrix} \Rightarrow$

$$\begin{pmatrix} 0 & 0 & 0 \\ 0 & 0 & 0 \\ 1 & 0 & -1 \end{pmatrix} \begin{pmatrix} a \\ b \\ c \end{pmatrix} = \begin{pmatrix} 0 \\ 0 \\ 0 \end{pmatrix}$$

$\Rightarrow a - c = 0 \Rightarrow a = c$ and b is free. Thus, $a = 1$ and $b = 0 \Rightarrow \mathbf{v}_1 = \begin{pmatrix} 1 \\ 0 \\ 1 \end{pmatrix}$, and

$a = 0$ and $b = 1 \Rightarrow \mathbf{v}_2 = \begin{pmatrix} 0 \\ 1 \\ 0 \end{pmatrix}$ are independent eigenvectors which correspond to

the eigenvalue $\lambda_1 = 1$.

For $\lambda_2 = 2$, $(\lambda_2 I - A)\mathbf{v} = \mathbf{0}$ with $\mathbf{v} = \begin{pmatrix} a \\ b \\ c \end{pmatrix} \Rightarrow$

$$\begin{pmatrix} 1 & 0 & 0 \\ 0 & 1 & 0 \\ 1 & 0 & 0 \end{pmatrix} \begin{pmatrix} a \\ b \\ c \end{pmatrix} = \begin{pmatrix} 0 \\ 0 \\ 0 \end{pmatrix}$$

$\Rightarrow a = 0$ and $b = 0$, and $c = 1 \Rightarrow \mathbf{v}_3 = \begin{pmatrix} 0 \\ 0 \\ 1 \end{pmatrix}$ is an eigenvector which corresponds to the eigenvalue $\lambda_2 = 2$.

Thus, three independent solutions of the system (5.12) are given in vector form by

$$\mathbf{x}_1(t) = e^t \begin{pmatrix} 1 \\ 0 \\ 1 \end{pmatrix}, \quad \mathbf{x}_2(t) = e^t \begin{pmatrix} 0 \\ 1 \\ 0 \end{pmatrix} \quad \text{and} \quad \mathbf{x}_3(t) = e^{2t} \begin{pmatrix} 0 \\ 0 \\ 1 \end{pmatrix},$$

and $X(t) = (\mathbf{x}_1(t) \ \mathbf{x}_2(t) \ \mathbf{x}_3(t)) = \begin{pmatrix} e^t & 0 & 0 \\ 0 & e^t & 0 \\ e^t & 0 & e^{2t} \end{pmatrix}$ is a fundamental matrix. The general solution of the system (5.12) is

$$
\begin{aligned}
\mathbf{x}(t) &= c_1 \mathbf{x}_1(t) + c_2 \mathbf{x}_2(t) + c_3 \mathbf{x}_3(t) \\
&= X(t)\mathbf{c} \\
&= \begin{pmatrix} e^t & 0 & 0 \\ 0 & e^t & 0 \\ e^t & 0 & e^{2t} \end{pmatrix} \begin{pmatrix} c_1 \\ c_2 \\ c_3 \end{pmatrix} = \begin{pmatrix} c_1 e^t \\ c_2 e^t \\ c_1 e^t + c_3 e^{2t} \end{pmatrix},
\end{aligned}
$$

i.e., $x(t) = c_1 e^t$, $y(t) = c_2 e^t$ and $z(t) = c_1 e^t + c_3 e^{2t}$.

Complex Eigenvalues

Let A be an $n \times n$ matrix with real entries, and suppose that $\lambda = \alpha + i\beta$, $\beta \neq 0$, is a complex eigenvalue. Then $\overline{\lambda} = \alpha - i\beta$ is also an eigenvalue since $\det(\lambda I - A)$ is a polynomial with real coefficients. If $\mathbf{v}$ is an eigenvector corresponding to λ, then $\overline{\mathbf{v}}$ is an eigenvector which corresponds to $\overline{\lambda}$ because

$$A\mathbf{v} = \lambda\mathbf{v} \quad \Rightarrow \quad \overline{A\mathbf{v}} = \overline{\lambda\mathbf{v}} \quad \Rightarrow \quad \overline{A}\,\overline{\mathbf{v}} = \overline{\lambda}\,\overline{\mathbf{v}} \quad \Rightarrow \quad A\overline{\mathbf{v}} = \overline{\lambda}\overline{\mathbf{v}}.$$

Then $\mathbf{z}(t) = e^{\lambda t}\mathbf{v}$ and $\overline{\mathbf{z}}(t) = e^{\overline{\lambda} t}\overline{\mathbf{v}}$ are two complex solutions of the system $\mathbf{x}' = A\mathbf{x}$. Let $\mathbf{v} = \mathbf{a} + i\mathbf{b}$, where $\mathbf{a}$ and $\mathbf{b}$ are real vectors. Then $\overline{\mathbf{v}} = \mathbf{a} - i\mathbf{b}$ and, employing Euler's identity, we obtain

$$
\begin{aligned}
\mathbf{z}(t) &= e^{(\alpha + i\beta)t}[\mathbf{a} + i\mathbf{b}] = e^{\alpha t}e^{i\beta t}[\mathbf{a} + i\mathbf{b}] \\
&= e^{\alpha t}[\cos(\beta t) + i\sin(\beta t)][\mathbf{a} + i\mathbf{b}] \\
&= e^{\alpha t}\{[\cos(\beta t)\mathbf{a} - \sin(\beta t)\mathbf{b}] + i[\sin(\beta t)\mathbf{a} + \cos(\beta t)\mathbf{b}]\}, \\
\overline{\mathbf{z}}(t) &= e^{\alpha t}\{[\cos(\beta t)\mathbf{a} - \sin(\beta t)\mathbf{b}] - i[\sin(\beta t)\mathbf{a} + \cos(\beta t)\mathbf{b}]\}.
\end{aligned}
$$

Since the system is linear and homogeneous, any linear combination of solutions is a solution. Thus,

$$\mathbf{x}_1(t) \;=\; \frac{\mathbf{z}(t) + \overline{\mathbf{z}}(t)}{2} = \Re(\mathbf{z}(t)) = e^{\alpha t}[\cos(\beta t)\mathbf{a} - \sin(\beta t)\mathbf{b}],$$

$$\mathbf{x}_2(t) \;=\; \frac{\mathbf{z}(t) - \overline{\mathbf{z}}(t)}{2i} = \Im(\mathbf{z}(t)) = e^{\alpha t}[\sin(\beta t)\mathbf{a} + \cos(\beta t)\mathbf{b}]$$

are two real solutions which are linearly independent.

Example 5.7.   Consider the system

$$\left\{ \begin{array}{rcrcr} x' & = & 2x & + & 3y \\ y' & = & -3x & + & 2y \end{array} \right\}. \tag{5.13}$$

This system may be expressed in matrix form as $\mathbf{x}' = A\mathbf{x}$, where

$$\mathbf{x} = \left(\begin{array}{c} x \\ y \end{array} \right) \quad \text{and} \quad A = \left(\begin{array}{cc} 2 & 3 \\ -3 & 2 \end{array} \right).$$

Then

$$\det(\lambda I - A) = \left| \begin{array}{cc} \lambda - 2 & -3 \\ 3 & \lambda - 2 \end{array} \right| = (\lambda - 2)^2 + 9 = \lambda^2 - 4\lambda + 13 = 0$$

$$\Rightarrow \lambda, \overline{\lambda} = \frac{4 \pm \sqrt{-36}}{2} = 2 \pm 3i \text{ are the complex eigenvalues of } A.$$

For $\lambda = 2 + 3i$, $(\lambda I - A)\mathbf{v} = \mathbf{0}$ with $\mathbf{v} = \left(\begin{array}{c} a \\ b \end{array} \right) \Rightarrow$

$$\left(\begin{array}{cc} 3i & -3 \\ 3 & 3i \end{array} \right) \left(\begin{array}{c} a \\ b \end{array} \right) = \left(\begin{array}{c} 0 \\ 0 \end{array} \right)$$

$\Rightarrow 3ia - 3b = 0$, and $a = 1 \Rightarrow$

$$\mathbf{v} = \left(\begin{array}{c} 1 \\ i \end{array} \right) = \left(\begin{array}{c} 1 \\ 0 \end{array} \right) + i \left(\begin{array}{c} 0 \\ 1 \end{array} \right)$$

is an eigenvector which corresponds to the eigenvalue $\lambda = 2 + 3i$. Then

$$\begin{aligned} \mathbf{z}(t) \;=\;& e^{2t}[\cos(3t) + i\sin(3t)] \left[\left(\begin{array}{c} 1 \\ 0 \end{array} \right) + i \left(\begin{array}{c} 0 \\ 1 \end{array} \right) \right] \\ =\;& e^{2t} \left\{ \left[\cos(3t) \left(\begin{array}{c} 1 \\ 0 \end{array} \right) - \sin(3t) \left(\begin{array}{c} 0 \\ 1 \end{array} \right) \right] + i \left[\sin(3t) \left(\begin{array}{c} 1 \\ 0 \end{array} \right) + \cos(3t) \left(\begin{array}{c} 0 \\ 1 \end{array} \right) \right] \right\} \end{aligned}$$

is a complex solution, and

$$
\begin{aligned}
\mathbf{x}_1(t) &= \Re(\mathbf{z}(t)) = e^{2t}\left[\cos(3t)\begin{pmatrix}1\\0\end{pmatrix} - \sin(3t)\begin{pmatrix}0\\1\end{pmatrix}\right]\\
&= e^{2t}\begin{pmatrix}\cos(3t)\\-\sin(3t)\end{pmatrix} = \begin{pmatrix}e^{2t}\cos(3t)\\-e^{2t}\sin(3t)\end{pmatrix},\\
\mathbf{x}_2(t) &= \Im(\mathbf{z}(t)) = e^{2t}\left[\sin(3t)\begin{pmatrix}1\\0\end{pmatrix} + \cos(3t)\begin{pmatrix}0\\1\end{pmatrix}\right]\\
&= e^{2t}\begin{pmatrix}\sin(3t)\\\cos(3t)\end{pmatrix} = \begin{pmatrix}e^{2t}\sin(3t)\\e^{2t}\cos(3t)\end{pmatrix}
\end{aligned}
$$

are two real, independent solutions of the system (5.13).

$$
X(t) = (\mathbf{x}_1(t)\ \mathbf{x}_2(t)) = e^{2t}\begin{pmatrix}\cos(3t) & \sin(3t)\\-\sin(3t) & \cos(3t)\end{pmatrix} = \begin{pmatrix}e^{2t}\cos(3t) & e^{2t}\sin(3t)\\-e^{2t}\sin(3t) & e^{2t}\cos(3t)\end{pmatrix}
$$

is a fundamental matrix, and the general solution is

$$
\begin{aligned}
\mathbf{x}(t) &= c_1\mathbf{x}_1(t) + c_2\mathbf{x}_2(t) = X(t)\mathbf{c} = e^{2t}\begin{pmatrix}\cos(3t) & \sin(3t)\\-\sin(3t) & \cos(3t)\end{pmatrix}\begin{pmatrix}c_1\\c_2\end{pmatrix}\\
&= e^{2t}\begin{pmatrix}c_1\cos(3t) + c_2\sin(3t)\\-c_1\sin(3t) + c_2\cos(3t)\end{pmatrix} = \begin{pmatrix}c_1 e^{2t}\cos(3t) + c_2 e^{2t}\sin(3t)\\-c_1 e^{2t}\sin(3t) + c_2 e^{2t}\cos(3t)\end{pmatrix},
\end{aligned}
$$

i.e., $x(t) = e^{2t}[c_1\cos(3t) + c_2\sin(3t)]$ and $y(t) = e^{2t}[-c_1\sin(3t) + c_2\cos(3t)]$.

Example 5.8. Consider the system

$$
\left\{\begin{array}{rcl}x' &=& 4x + 13y\\y' &=& -x\end{array}\right\}.
\tag{5.14}
$$

This system may be expressed in matrix form as $\mathbf{x}' = A\mathbf{x}$, where

$$
\mathbf{x} = \begin{pmatrix}x\\y\end{pmatrix} \quad\text{and}\quad A = \begin{pmatrix}4 & 13\\-1 & 0\end{pmatrix}.
$$

Then

$$
\det(\lambda I - A) = \begin{vmatrix}\lambda - 4 & -13\\1 & \lambda\end{vmatrix} = \lambda(\lambda - 4) + 13 = \lambda^2 - 4\lambda + 13 = 0
$$

$$
\Rightarrow \lambda, \overline{\lambda} = \frac{4 \pm \sqrt{-36}}{2} = 2 \pm 3i \text{ are the complex eigenvalues of } A.
$$

For $\lambda = 2 + 3i$, $(\lambda I - A)\mathbf{v} = \mathbf{0}$ with $\mathbf{v} = \begin{pmatrix}a\\b\end{pmatrix} \Rightarrow$

$$
\begin{pmatrix}-2 + 3i & -13\\1 & 2 + 3i\end{pmatrix}\begin{pmatrix}a\\b\end{pmatrix} = \begin{pmatrix}0\\0\end{pmatrix}
$$

$\Rightarrow a + (2 + 3i)b = 0$, and $b = -1 \Rightarrow$

$$\mathbf{v} = \begin{pmatrix} 2 + 3i \\ -1 \end{pmatrix} = \begin{pmatrix} 2 \\ -1 \end{pmatrix} + i \begin{pmatrix} 3 \\ 0 \end{pmatrix}$$

is an eigenvector which corresponds to the eigenvalue $\lambda = 2 + 3i$. Then

$$
\begin{aligned}
\mathbf{z}(t) &= e^{2t}[\cos(3t) + i\sin(3t)]\left[\begin{pmatrix} 2 \\ -1 \end{pmatrix} + i\begin{pmatrix} 3 \\ 0 \end{pmatrix}\right] \\
&= e^{2t}\left\{\left[\cos(3t)\begin{pmatrix} 2 \\ -1 \end{pmatrix} - \sin(3t)\begin{pmatrix} 3 \\ 0 \end{pmatrix}\right] \right. \\
&\quad \left. + i\left[\sin(3t)\begin{pmatrix} 2 \\ -1 \end{pmatrix} + \cos(3t)\begin{pmatrix} 3 \\ 0 \end{pmatrix}\right]\right\}
\end{aligned}
$$

is a complex solution, and

$$
\begin{aligned}
\mathbf{x}_1(t) &= \Re(\mathbf{z}(t)) = e^{2t}\left[\cos(3t)\begin{pmatrix} 2 \\ -1 \end{pmatrix} - \sin(3t)\begin{pmatrix} 3 \\ 0 \end{pmatrix}\right] \\
&= e^{2t}\begin{pmatrix} 2\cos(3t) - 3\sin(3t) \\ -\cos(3t) \end{pmatrix} = \begin{pmatrix} e^{2t}[2\cos(3t) - 3\sin(3t)] \\ -e^{2t}\cos(3t) \end{pmatrix}, \\
\mathbf{x}_2(t) &= \Im(\mathbf{z}(t)) = e^{2t}\left[\sin(3t)\begin{pmatrix} 2 \\ -1 \end{pmatrix} + \cos(3t)\begin{pmatrix} 3 \\ 0 \end{pmatrix}\right] \\
&= e^{2t}\begin{pmatrix} 2\sin(3t) + 3\cos(3t) \\ -\sin(3t) \end{pmatrix} = \begin{pmatrix} e^{2t}[2\sin(3t) + 3\cos(3t)] \\ -e^{2t}\sin(3t) \end{pmatrix}
\end{aligned}
$$

are two real, independent solutions of the system (5.14).

$$
\begin{aligned}
X(t) &= (\mathbf{x}_1(t)\ \mathbf{x}_2(t)) \\
&= e^{2t}\begin{pmatrix} 2\cos(3t) - 3\sin(3t) & 2\sin(3t) + 3\cos(3t) \\ -\cos(3t) & -\sin(3t) \end{pmatrix} \\
&= \begin{pmatrix} e^{2t}[2\cos(3t) - 3\sin(3t)] & e^{2t}[2\sin(3t) + 3\cos(3t)] \\ -e^{2t}\cos(3t) & -e^{2t}\sin(3t) \end{pmatrix}
\end{aligned}
$$

is a fundamental matrix, and the general solution is

$$
\begin{aligned}
\mathbf{x}(t) &= c_1\mathbf{x}_1(t) + c_2\mathbf{x}_2(t) = X(t)\mathbf{c} \\
&= e^{2t}\begin{pmatrix} 2\cos(3t) - 3\sin(3t) & 2\sin(3t) + 3\cos(3t) \\ -\cos 3t & -\sin(3t) \end{pmatrix}\begin{pmatrix} c_1 \\ c_2 \end{pmatrix} \\
&= e^{2t}\begin{pmatrix} c_1[2\cos(3t) - 3\sin(3t)] + c_2[2\sin(3t) + 3\cos(3t)] \\ -c_1\cos(3t) - c_2\sin(3t) \end{pmatrix},
\end{aligned}
$$

i.e.,

$$
\begin{aligned}
x(t) &= e^{2t}[(2c_1 + 3c_2)\cos(3t) + (2c_2 - 3c_1)\sin(3t)], \\
y(t) &= e^{2t}[-c_1\cos(3t) - c_2\sin(3t)].
\end{aligned}
$$

Example 5.9. Consider the initial-value problem

$$\left\{ \begin{array}{rcrcr} x' & = & x & + & y \\ y' & = & -5x & + & 5y \end{array} \right\}, \quad x(0) = 1, \quad y(0) = 3. \tag{5.15}$$

This problem may be expressed in matrix form as $\mathbf{x}' = A\mathbf{x}$, where

$$\mathbf{x} = \left(\begin{array}{c} x \\ y \end{array} \right), \quad A = \left(\begin{array}{cc} 1 & 1 \\ -5 & 5 \end{array} \right) \quad \text{and} \quad \mathbf{x}(0) = \left(\begin{array}{c} 1 \\ 3 \end{array} \right).$$

Then

$$\det(\lambda I - A) = \left| \begin{array}{cc} \lambda - 1 & -1 \\ 5 & \lambda - 5 \end{array} \right| = (\lambda - 1)(\lambda - 5) + 5 = \lambda^2 - 6\lambda + 10 = 0$$

$$\Rightarrow \lambda, \bar{\lambda} = \frac{6 \pm \sqrt{-4}}{2} = 3 \pm i \text{ are the complex eigenvalues of } A.$$

For $\lambda = 3 + i$, $(\lambda I - A)\mathbf{v} = \mathbf{0}$ with $\mathbf{v} = \left(\begin{array}{c} a \\ b \end{array} \right) \Rightarrow$

$$\left(\begin{array}{cc} 2 + i & -1 \\ 5 & -2 + i \end{array} \right) \left(\begin{array}{c} a \\ b \end{array} \right) = \left(\begin{array}{c} 0 \\ 0 \end{array} \right)$$

$\Rightarrow (2 + i)a - b = 0$, and $a = 1 \Rightarrow$

$$\mathbf{v} = \left(\begin{array}{c} 1 \\ 2 + i \end{array} \right) = \left(\begin{array}{c} 1 \\ 2 \end{array} \right) + i \left(\begin{array}{c} 0 \\ 1 \end{array} \right)$$

is an eigenvector which corresponds to the eigenvalue $\lambda = 3 + i$. Then

$$\begin{array}{rcl} \mathbf{z}(t) & = & e^{3t}[\cos(t) + i\sin(t)] \left[\left(\begin{array}{c} 1 \\ 2 \end{array} \right) + i \left(\begin{array}{c} 0 \\ 1 \end{array} \right) \right] \\[2mm] & = & e^{3t} \left\{ \left[\cos(t) \left(\begin{array}{c} 1 \\ 2 \end{array} \right) - \sin(t) \left(\begin{array}{c} 0 \\ 1 \end{array} \right) \right] + i \left[\sin(t) \left(\begin{array}{c} 1 \\ 2 \end{array} \right) + \cos(t) \left(\begin{array}{c} 0 \\ 1 \end{array} \right) \right] \right\} \end{array}$$

is a complex solution, and

$$\begin{array}{rcl} \mathbf{x}_1(t) & = & \Re(\mathbf{z}(t)) = e^{3t} \left[\cos(t) \left(\begin{array}{c} 1 \\ 2 \end{array} \right) - \sin(t) \left(\begin{array}{c} 0 \\ 1 \end{array} \right) \right] \\[2mm] & = & e^{3t} \left(\begin{array}{c} \cos(t) \\ 2\cos(t) - \sin(t) \end{array} \right), \\[3mm] \mathbf{x}_2(t) & = & \Im(\mathbf{z}(t)) = e^{3t} \left[\sin(t) \left(\begin{array}{c} 1 \\ 2 \end{array} \right) + \cos(t) \left(\begin{array}{c} 0 \\ 1 \end{array} \right) \right] \\[2mm] & = & e^{3t} \left(\begin{array}{c} \sin(t) \\ 2\sin(t) + \cos(t) \end{array} \right) \end{array}$$

are two real, independent solutions of the system (5.15). Thus,

$$X(t) \;=\; (\mathbf{x}_1(t)\,\mathbf{x}_2(t)) = e^{3t}\begin{pmatrix} \cos(t) & \sin(t) \\ 2\cos(t) - \sin(t) & 2\sin(t) + \cos(t) \end{pmatrix}$$

is a fundamental matrix,

$$X(0) = \begin{pmatrix} 1 & 0 \\ 2 & 1 \end{pmatrix}, \quad X(0)^{-1} = \begin{pmatrix} 1 & 0 \\ -2 & 1 \end{pmatrix},$$

and $\mathbf{x}(0) = \begin{pmatrix} 1 \\ 3 \end{pmatrix} \Rightarrow$

$$\begin{aligned}
\mathbf{x}(t) \;&=\; X(t)X(0)^{-1}\mathbf{x}(0) \\
&=\; e^{3t}\begin{pmatrix} \cos(t) & \sin(t) \\ 2\cos(t) - \sin(t) & 2\sin(t) + \cos(t) \end{pmatrix}\begin{pmatrix} 1 & 0 \\ -2 & 1 \end{pmatrix}\begin{pmatrix} 1 \\ 3 \end{pmatrix} \\
&=\; e^{3t}\begin{pmatrix} \cos(t) & \sin(t) \\ 2\cos(t) - \sin(t) & 2\sin(t) + \cos(t) \end{pmatrix}\begin{pmatrix} 1 \\ 1 \end{pmatrix} \\
&=\; e^{3t}\begin{pmatrix} \cos(t) + \sin(t) \\ 3\cos(t) + \sin(t) \end{pmatrix},
\end{aligned}$$

i.e., $x(t) = e^{3t}[\cos(t) + \sin(t)]$ and $y(t) = e^{3t}[3\cos(t) + \sin(t)]$.

Example 5.10. Consider the system

$$\left\{\begin{array}{rcrcrcr}
x' &=& -x &+& 4y &+& 3z \\
y' &=& 2x &+& y &+& z \\
z' &=& -4x &+& 4y &+& z
\end{array}\right\}. \tag{5.16}$$

This system may be expressed in matrix form as $\mathbf{x}' = A\mathbf{x}$, where

$$\mathbf{x} = \begin{pmatrix} x \\ y \\ z \end{pmatrix} \quad \text{and} \quad A = \begin{pmatrix} -1 & 4 & 3 \\ 2 & 1 & 1 \\ -4 & 4 & 1 \end{pmatrix}.$$

Then

$$\begin{aligned}
\det(\lambda I - A) \;&=\; \begin{vmatrix} \lambda + 1 & -4 & -3 \\ -2 & \lambda - 1 & -1 \\ 4 & -4 & \lambda - 1 \end{vmatrix} \\
&=\; (\lambda + 1)[(\lambda - 1)^2 - 4] + 4[-2(\lambda - 1) + 4] - 3[8 - 4(\lambda - 1)] \\
&=\; (\lambda + 1)[\lambda^2 - 2\lambda - 3] + 4\lambda - 12 \\
&=\; (\lambda + 1)(\lambda - 3)(\lambda + 1) + 4(\lambda - 3) \\
&=\; (\lambda - 3)[(\lambda + 1)^2 + 4] \\
&=\; (\lambda - 3)[\lambda^2 + 2\lambda + 5] = 0
\end{aligned}$$

$\Rightarrow \lambda_1 = 3$ and $\lambda_2, \overline{\lambda}_2 = \dfrac{-2 \pm \sqrt{-16}}{2} = -1 \pm 2i$ are the eigenvalues of A.

For $\lambda_1 = 3$, $(\lambda_1 I - A)\mathbf{v} = \mathbf{0}$ with $\mathbf{v} = \begin{pmatrix} a \\ b \\ c \end{pmatrix} \Rightarrow$

$$\begin{pmatrix} 4 & -4 & -3 \\ -2 & 2 & -1 \\ 4 & -4 & 2 \end{pmatrix} \begin{pmatrix} a \\ b \\ c \end{pmatrix} = \begin{pmatrix} 0 \\ 0 \\ 0 \end{pmatrix}.$$

Row reduction of the coefficient matrix gives

$$\begin{pmatrix} 4 & -4 & -3 \\ -2 & 2 & -1 \\ 4 & -4 & 2 \end{pmatrix} \rightarrow \begin{pmatrix} 4 & -4 & -3 \\ 0 & 0 & -5 \\ 0 & 0 & -5 \end{pmatrix} \Rightarrow \begin{pmatrix} 4 & -4 & -3 \\ 0 & 0 & -5 \\ 0 & 0 & -5 \end{pmatrix} \begin{pmatrix} a \\ b \\ c \end{pmatrix} = \begin{pmatrix} 0 \\ 0 \\ 0 \end{pmatrix}$$

$\Rightarrow c = 0$ and $a - b = 0$, and $a = 1 \Rightarrow \mathbf{v}_1 = \begin{pmatrix} 1 \\ 1 \\ 0 \end{pmatrix}$ is an eigenvector which corresponds

to the eigenvalue $\lambda_1 = 3$. Hence,

$$\mathbf{x}_1(t) = e^{\lambda_1 t}\mathbf{v}_1 = e^{3t} \begin{pmatrix} 1 \\ 1 \\ 0 \end{pmatrix} = \begin{pmatrix} e^{3t} \\ e^{3t} \\ 0 \end{pmatrix}$$

is one solution of the system (5.16).

For $\lambda_2 = -1 + 2i$, $(\lambda_2 I - A)\mathbf{v} = \mathbf{0}$ with $\mathbf{v} = \begin{pmatrix} a \\ b \\ c \end{pmatrix} \Rightarrow$

$$\begin{pmatrix} 2i & -4 & -3 \\ -2 & 2i - 2 & -1 \\ 4 & -4 & 2i - 2 \end{pmatrix} \begin{pmatrix} a \\ b \\ c \end{pmatrix} = \begin{pmatrix} 0 \\ 0 \\ 0 \end{pmatrix}.$$

Row reduction of the coefficient matrix gives

$$\begin{pmatrix} 2i & -4 & -3 \\ -2 & 2i - 2 & -1 \\ 4 & -4 & 2i - 2 \end{pmatrix} \rightarrow \begin{pmatrix} 2i & -4 & -3 \\ 0 & -2i - 6 & -i - 3 \\ 0 & -8i - 4 & -4i - 2 \end{pmatrix} \rightarrow$$

$$\begin{pmatrix} 2i & -4 & -3 \\ 0 & -2i - 6 & -i - 3 \\ 0 & 0 & 0 \end{pmatrix} \rightarrow \begin{pmatrix} 2i & -4 & -3 \\ 0 & 2 & 1 \\ 0 & 0 & 0 \end{pmatrix}$$

$$\Rightarrow \begin{pmatrix} 2i & -4 & -3 \\ 0 & 2 & 1 \\ 0 & 0 & 0 \end{pmatrix} \begin{pmatrix} a \\ b \\ c \end{pmatrix} = \begin{pmatrix} 0 \\ 0 \\ 0 \end{pmatrix}$$

$\Rightarrow 2b + c = 0 \Rightarrow c = -2b$ and $2ia - 4b - 3c = 0 \Rightarrow 2ia + 2b = 0$, and $b = 1 \Rightarrow c = -2$ and $a = i \Rightarrow$

$$\mathbf{v}_2 = \begin{pmatrix} i \\ 1 \\ -2 \end{pmatrix} = \begin{pmatrix} 0 \\ 1 \\ -2 \end{pmatrix} + i \begin{pmatrix} 1 \\ 0 \\ 0 \end{pmatrix}$$

is an eigenvector which corresponds to the eigenvalue $\lambda_2 = -1 + 2i$. Then

$$\begin{aligned} \mathbf{z}(t) &= e^{-t}[\cos(2t) + i\sin(2t)] \left[\begin{pmatrix} 0 \\ 1 \\ -2 \end{pmatrix} + i \begin{pmatrix} 1 \\ 0 \\ 0 \end{pmatrix} \right] \\ &= e^{-t} \left\{ \left[\cos(2t) \begin{pmatrix} 0 \\ 1 \\ -2 \end{pmatrix} - \sin(2t) \begin{pmatrix} 1 \\ 0 \\ 0 \end{pmatrix} \right] \right. \\ &\qquad \left. + i \left[\sin(2t) \begin{pmatrix} 0 \\ 1 \\ -2 \end{pmatrix} + \cos(2t) \begin{pmatrix} 1 \\ 0 \\ 0 \end{pmatrix} \right] \right\} \\ &= e^{-t} \begin{pmatrix} -\sin(2t) \\ \cos(2t) \\ -2\cos(2t) \end{pmatrix} + ie^{-t} \begin{pmatrix} \cos(2t) \\ \sin(2t) \\ -2\sin(2t) \end{pmatrix} \end{aligned}$$

is a complex solution, and

$$\begin{aligned} \mathbf{x}_2(t) &= \Re(\mathbf{z}(t)) = e^{-t} \begin{pmatrix} -\sin(2t) \\ \cos(2t) \\ -2\cos(2t) \end{pmatrix} = \begin{pmatrix} -e^{-t}\sin(2t) \\ e^{-t}\cos(2t) \\ -2e^{-t}\cos(2t) \end{pmatrix}, \\ \mathbf{x}_3(t) &= \Im(\mathbf{z}(t)) = e^{-t} \begin{pmatrix} \cos(2t) \\ \sin(2t) \\ -2\sin(2t) \end{pmatrix} = \begin{pmatrix} e^{-t}\cos(2t) \\ e^{-t}\sin(2t) \\ -2e^{-t}\sin(2t) \end{pmatrix} \end{aligned}$$

are two real, independent solutions of the system (5.16). Thus, three independent solutions are $\mathbf{x}_1(t)$, $\mathbf{x}_2(t)$ and $\mathbf{x}_3(t)$,

$$X(t) = (\mathbf{x}_1(t)\ \mathbf{x}_2(t)\ \mathbf{x}_3(t)) = \begin{pmatrix} e^{3t} & -e^{-t}\sin(2t) & e^{-t}\cos(2t) \\ e^{3t} & e^{-t}\cos(2t) & e^{-t}\sin(2t) \\ 0 & -2e^{-t}\cos(2t) & -2e^{-t}\sin(2t) \end{pmatrix}$$

is a fundamental matrix, and

$$\begin{aligned} \mathbf{x}(t) &= c_1\mathbf{x}_1(t) + c_2\mathbf{x}_2(t) + c_3\mathbf{x}_3(t) \\ &= X(t)\mathbf{c} \\ &= \begin{pmatrix} e^{3t} & -e^{-t}\sin(2t) & e^{-t}\cos(2t) \\ e^{3t} & e^{-t}\cos(2t) & e^{-t}\sin(2t) \\ 0 & -2e^{-t}\cos(2t) & -2e^{-t}\sin(2t) \end{pmatrix} \begin{pmatrix} c_1 \\ c_2 \\ c_3 \end{pmatrix}, \end{aligned}$$

i.e.,

$$\begin{aligned} x(t) &= c_1 e^{3t} - c_2 e^{-t} \sin(2t) + c_3 e^{-t} \cos(2t), \\ y(t) &= c_1 e^{3t} + c_2 e^{-t} \cos(2t) + c_3 e^{-t} \sin(2t), \\ z(t) &= -2c_2 e^{-t} \cos(2t) - 2c_3 e^{-t} \sin(2t) \end{aligned}$$

is the general solution of the system (5.16).

Example 5.11. Consider the system

$$\left\{ \begin{array}{rcl} x' &=& -4z \\ y' &=& -2w \\ z' &=& x \\ w' &=& 8y \end{array} \right\}. \tag{5.17}$$

This system may be expressed in matrix form as $\mathbf{x}' = A\mathbf{x}$, where

$$\mathbf{x} = \begin{pmatrix} x \\ y \\ z \\ w \end{pmatrix} \quad \text{and} \quad A = \begin{pmatrix} 0 & 0 & -4 & 0 \\ 0 & 0 & 0 & -2 \\ 1 & 0 & 0 & 0 \\ 0 & 8 & 0 & 0 \end{pmatrix}.$$

Then

$$\begin{aligned} \det(\lambda I - A) &= \begin{vmatrix} \lambda & 0 & 4 & 0 \\ 0 & \lambda & 0 & 2 \\ -1 & 0 & \lambda & 0 \\ 0 & -8 & 0 & \lambda \end{vmatrix} = \lambda \begin{vmatrix} \lambda & 0 & 2 \\ 0 & \lambda & 0 \\ -8 & 0 & \lambda \end{vmatrix} + 4 \begin{vmatrix} 0 & \lambda & 2 \\ -1 & 0 & 0 \\ 0 & -8 & \lambda \end{vmatrix} \\ &= \lambda[\lambda(\lambda^2 + 16)] + 4[\lambda^2 + 16] \\ &= (\lambda^2 + 16)(\lambda^2 + 4) = 0 \end{aligned}$$

$\Rightarrow \lambda_1, \overline{\lambda}_1 = \pm 2i$ and $\lambda_2, \overline{\lambda}_2 = \pm 4i$ are the eigenvalues of A.

For $\lambda_1 = 2i$, $(\lambda_1 I - A)\mathbf{v} = 0$ with $\mathbf{v} = \begin{pmatrix} a \\ b \\ c \\ d \end{pmatrix} \Rightarrow$

$$\begin{pmatrix} 2i & 0 & 4 & 0 \\ 0 & 2i & 0 & 2 \\ -1 & 0 & 2i & 0 \\ 0 & -8 & 0 & 2i \end{pmatrix} \begin{pmatrix} a \\ b \\ c \\ d \end{pmatrix} = \begin{pmatrix} 0 \\ 0 \\ 0 \\ 0 \end{pmatrix}.$$

Row reduction of the coefficient matrix gives

$$\begin{pmatrix} 2i & 0 & 4 & 0 \\ 0 & 2i & 0 & 2 \\ -1 & 0 & 2i & 0 \\ 0 & -8 & 0 & 2i \end{pmatrix} \rightarrow \begin{pmatrix} 2i & 0 & 4 & 0 \\ 0 & 2i & 0 & 2 \\ 0 & 0 & 0 & 0 \\ 0 & 0 & 0 & 6 \end{pmatrix} \Rightarrow \begin{pmatrix} 2i & 0 & 4 & 0 \\ 0 & 2i & 0 & 2 \\ 0 & 0 & 0 & 0 \\ 0 & 0 & 0 & 6 \end{pmatrix} \begin{pmatrix} a \\ b \\ c \\ d \end{pmatrix} = \begin{pmatrix} 0 \\ 0 \\ 0 \\ 0 \end{pmatrix}$$

$\Rightarrow d = 0 \Rightarrow b = 0$ and $2ia + 4c = 0$, and $c = 1 \Rightarrow a = 2i \Rightarrow$

$$\mathbf{v}_1 = \begin{pmatrix} 2i \\ 0 \\ 1 \\ 0 \end{pmatrix} = \begin{pmatrix} 0 \\ 0 \\ 1 \\ 0 \end{pmatrix} + i \begin{pmatrix} 2 \\ 0 \\ 0 \\ 0 \end{pmatrix}$$

is an eigenvector of A which corresponds to the eigenvalue $\lambda_1 = 2i$. Then

$$\mathbf{z}_1(t) = [\cos(2t) + i\sin(2t)] \left[\begin{pmatrix} 0 \\ 0 \\ 1 \\ 0 \end{pmatrix} + i \begin{pmatrix} 2 \\ 0 \\ 0 \\ 0 \end{pmatrix} \right]$$

$$= \left[\cos(2t) \begin{pmatrix} 0 \\ 0 \\ 1 \\ 0 \end{pmatrix} - \sin(2t) \begin{pmatrix} 2 \\ 0 \\ 0 \\ 0 \end{pmatrix} \right] + i \left[\sin(2t) \begin{pmatrix} 0 \\ 0 \\ 1 \\ 0 \end{pmatrix} + \cos(2t) \begin{pmatrix} 2 \\ 0 \\ 0 \\ 0 \end{pmatrix} \right]$$

is a complex solution, and

$$\mathbf{x}_1(t) = \Re(\mathbf{z}_1(t)) = \left[\cos(2t) \begin{pmatrix} 0 \\ 0 \\ 1 \\ 0 \end{pmatrix} - \sin(2t) \begin{pmatrix} 2 \\ 0 \\ 0 \\ 0 \end{pmatrix} \right] = \begin{pmatrix} -2\sin(2t) \\ 0 \\ \cos(2t) \\ 0 \end{pmatrix},$$

$$\mathbf{x}_2(t) = \Im(\mathbf{z}_1(t)) = \left[\sin(2t) \begin{pmatrix} 0 \\ 0 \\ 1 \\ 0 \end{pmatrix} + \cos(2t) \begin{pmatrix} 2 \\ 0 \\ 0 \\ 0 \end{pmatrix} \right] = \begin{pmatrix} 2\cos(2t) \\ 0 \\ \sin(2t) \\ 0 \end{pmatrix}$$

are two real, independent solutions of the system (5.17).

For $\lambda_2 = 4i$, $(\lambda_2 I - A)\mathbf{v} = 0$ with $\mathbf{v} = \begin{pmatrix} a \\ b \\ c \\ d \end{pmatrix} \Rightarrow$

$$\begin{pmatrix} 4i & 0 & 4 & 0 \\ 0 & 4i & 0 & 2 \\ -1 & 0 & 4i & 0 \\ 0 & -8 & 0 & 4i \end{pmatrix} \begin{pmatrix} a \\ b \\ c \\ d \end{pmatrix} = \begin{pmatrix} 0 \\ 0 \\ 0 \\ 0 \end{pmatrix}.$$

Row reduction of the coefficient matrix gives

$$\begin{pmatrix} 4i & 0 & 4 & 0 \\ 0 & 4i & 0 & 2 \\ -1 & 0 & 4i & 0 \\ 0 & -8 & 0 & 4i \end{pmatrix} \rightarrow \begin{pmatrix} 4i & 0 & 4 & 0 \\ 0 & 4i & 0 & 2 \\ 0 & 0 & -12 & 0 \\ 0 & 0 & 0 & 0 \end{pmatrix}$$

$$\Rightarrow \begin{pmatrix} 4i & 0 & 4 & 0 \\ 0 & 4i & 0 & 2 \\ 0 & 0 & -12 & 0 \\ 0 & 0 & 0 & 0 \end{pmatrix} \begin{pmatrix} a \\ b \\ c \\ d \end{pmatrix} = \begin{pmatrix} 0 \\ 0 \\ 0 \\ 0 \end{pmatrix}$$

$\Rightarrow c = 0 \Rightarrow a = 0$ and $4ib + 2d = 0$, and $d = 2 \Rightarrow b = i \Rightarrow$

$$\mathbf{v}_2 = \begin{pmatrix} 0 \\ i \\ 0 \\ 2 \end{pmatrix} = \begin{pmatrix} 0 \\ 0 \\ 0 \\ 2 \end{pmatrix} + i \begin{pmatrix} 0 \\ 1 \\ 0 \\ 0 \end{pmatrix}$$

is an eigenvector of A which corresponds to the eigenvalue $\lambda_2 = 4i$. Then

$$\mathbf{z}_2(t) = [\cos(4t) + i\sin(4t)] \left[\begin{pmatrix} 0 \\ 0 \\ 0 \\ 2 \end{pmatrix} + i \begin{pmatrix} 0 \\ 1 \\ 0 \\ 0 \end{pmatrix} \right]$$

$$= \left[\cos(4t) \begin{pmatrix} 0 \\ 0 \\ 0 \\ 2 \end{pmatrix} - \sin(4t) \begin{pmatrix} 0 \\ 1 \\ 0 \\ 0 \end{pmatrix} \right] + i \left[\sin(4t) \begin{pmatrix} 0 \\ 0 \\ 0 \\ 2 \end{pmatrix} + \cos(4t) \begin{pmatrix} 0 \\ 1 \\ 0 \\ 0 \end{pmatrix} \right]$$

is a complex solution, and

$$\mathbf{x}_3(t) = \Re(\mathbf{z}_2(t)) = \left[\cos(4t) \begin{pmatrix} 0 \\ 0 \\ 0 \\ 2 \end{pmatrix} - \sin(4t) \begin{pmatrix} 0 \\ 1 \\ 0 \\ 0 \end{pmatrix} \right] = \begin{pmatrix} 0 \\ -\sin(4t) \\ 0 \\ 2\cos(4t) \end{pmatrix},$$

$$\mathbf{x}_4(t) = \Im(\mathbf{z}_2(t)) = \left[\sin(4t) \begin{pmatrix} 0 \\ 0 \\ 0 \\ 2 \end{pmatrix} + \cos(4t) \begin{pmatrix} 0 \\ 1 \\ 0 \\ 0 \end{pmatrix} \right] = \begin{pmatrix} 0 \\ \cos(4t) \\ 0 \\ 2\sin(4t) \end{pmatrix}$$

are two real, independent solutions of the system (5.17). Thus, $\mathbf{x}_1(t)$, $\mathbf{x}_2(t)$, $\mathbf{x}_3(t)$ and $\mathbf{x}_4(t)$ are four real, independent solutions,

$$X(t) = \begin{pmatrix} -2\sin(2t) & 2\cos(2t) & 0 & 0 \\ 0 & 0 & -\sin(4t) & \cos(4t) \\ \cos(2t) & \sin(2t) & 0 & 0 \\ 0 & 0 & 2\cos(4t) & 2\sin(4t) \end{pmatrix}$$

is a fundamental matrix, and

$$
\begin{aligned}
\mathbf{x}(t) &= c_1\mathbf{x}_1(t) + c_2\mathbf{x}_2(t) + c_3\mathbf{x}_3(t) + c_4\mathbf{x}_4(t) \\
&= X(t)\mathbf{c} \\
&= \begin{pmatrix} -2\sin(2t) & 2\cos(2t) & 0 & 0 \\ 0 & 0 & -\sin(4t) & \cos(4t) \\ \cos(2t) & \sin(2t) & 0 & 0 \\ 0 & 0 & 2\cos(4t) & 2\sin(4t) \end{pmatrix} \begin{pmatrix} c_1 \\ c_2 \\ c_3 \\ c_4 \end{pmatrix},
\end{aligned}
$$

i.e.,

$$
\begin{aligned}
x(t) &= -2c_1\sin(2t) + 2c_2\cos(2t), \\
y(t) &= -c_3\sin(4t) + c_4\cos(4t), \\
z(t) &= c_1\cos(2t) + c_2\sin(2t), \\
w(t) &= 2c_3\cos(4t) + 2c_4\sin(4t)
\end{aligned}
$$

is the general solution of the system (5.17).

Generalized Eigenvectors

Consider the system $\mathbf{x}' = A\mathbf{x}$, where A is a 2×2 matrix. If A possesses two distinct eigenvalues λ_1 and λ_2, with corresponding eigenvectors $\mathbf{v}_1$ and $\mathbf{v}_2$, then two linearly independent solutions of the system are

$$
\mathbf{x}_1(t) = e^{\lambda_1 t}\mathbf{v}_1 \quad \text{and} \quad \mathbf{x}_2(t) = e^{\lambda_2 t}\mathbf{v}_2.
$$

If A possesses only one eigenvalue λ_1 of multiplicity two, i.e., $\det(\lambda I - A) = (\lambda - \lambda_1)^2$, and if A has two independent eigenvectors $\mathbf{v}_1$ and $\mathbf{v}_2$ corresponding to λ_1, then two independent solutions of the system are

$$
\mathbf{x}_1(t) = e^{\lambda_1 t}\mathbf{v}_1 \quad \text{and} \quad \mathbf{x}_2(t) = e^{\lambda_1 t}\mathbf{v}_2.
$$

More generally, if an $n \times n$ matrix A possesses n independent eigenvectors (real or complex), then n independent solutions of the system $\mathbf{x}' = A\mathbf{x}$ can be determined by the methods already discussed.

If an $n \times n$ matrix A admits only k linearly independent eigenvectors, where $k < n$, which occurs whenever an eigenvalue of A of multiplicity $m > 1$ has fewer than m independent eigenvectors, then the methods employed thus far yield only k linearly independent solutions of the system $\mathbf{x}' = A\mathbf{x}$, and additional independent solutions are required in order to obtain all n independent solutions.

Given an $n \times n$ matrix A, $\det(\lambda I - A)$ is a polynomial of degree n, called the *characteristic polynomial* of A. If $\lambda_1, \lambda_2, \cdots, \lambda_r$ are the distinct eigenvalues of A, with multiplicities $m_1, m_2, \cdots, m_r$, respectively, then

$$
\det(\lambda I - A) = (\lambda - \lambda_1)^{m_1}(\lambda - \lambda_2)^{m_2} \cdots (\lambda - \lambda_r)^{m_r},
$$

with

$$m_1 + m_2 + \cdots + m_r = n.$$

Thus, n independent solutions of the system $\mathbf{x}' = A\mathbf{x}$ can be determined provided that, for every eigenvalue λ_i of multiplicity m_i, a total of m_i independent solutions of the system can be found. Several cases are possible, and will be considered for $n = 2$, $n = 3$ and $n = 4$, from which the suitable procedures for any $n \geq 2$ can be deduced.

Let A be a 2×2 matrix with only one eigenvalue λ_1 of multiplicity 2, and with only one independent eigenvector $\mathbf{v}_1$. Then one solution of the system $\mathbf{x}' = A\mathbf{x}$ is $\mathbf{x}_1(t) = e^{\lambda_1 t}\mathbf{v}_1$. A second, independent solution $\mathbf{x}_2(t)$ is sought in the form

$$\mathbf{x}_2(t) = e^{\lambda_1 t}(t\mathbf{u}_0 + \mathbf{u}_1), \tag{5.18}$$

where $\mathbf{u}_0$ and $\mathbf{u}_1$ are vectors to be determined. Then

$$\mathbf{x}_2'(t) = \lambda_1 e^{\lambda_1 t}(t\mathbf{u}_0 + \mathbf{u}_1) + e^{\lambda_1 t}\mathbf{u}_0,$$

and, hence, $\mathbf{x}_2'(t) = A\mathbf{x}_2(t)$ if and only if

$$\lambda_1 e^{\lambda_1 t}(t\mathbf{u}_0 + \mathbf{u}_1) + e^{\lambda_1 t}\mathbf{u}_0 = Ae^{\lambda_1 t}(t\mathbf{u}_0 + \mathbf{u}_1).$$

Division by $e^{\lambda_1 t} \neq 0$ yields the condition

$$\lambda_1(t\mathbf{u}_0 + \mathbf{u}_1) + \mathbf{u}_0 = A(t\mathbf{u}_0 + \mathbf{u}_1),$$

which holds for all real t if and only if

$$\lambda_1 \mathbf{u}_0 = A\mathbf{u}_0 \quad \text{and} \quad \lambda_1 \mathbf{u}_1 + \mathbf{u}_0 = A\mathbf{u}_1. \tag{5.19}$$

The first condition in (5.19) is equivalent to

$$(\lambda_1 I - A)\mathbf{u}_0 = 0,$$

i.e., $\mathbf{u}_0$ is an eigenvector of A corresponding to the eigenvalue λ_1. We may, therefore, take $\mathbf{u}_0 = \mathbf{v}_1$, or $\mathbf{u}_0 = c\mathbf{v}_1$ for any constant $c \neq 0$. The second condition in (5.19) is equivalent to

$$(A - \lambda_1 I)\mathbf{u}_1 = \mathbf{u}_0. \tag{5.20}$$

A solution $\mathbf{u}_1$ of Equation (5.20) is called a *generalized eigenvector* of the matrix A corresponding to the eigenvalue λ_1.

Note that Equation (5.20) is a nonhomogeneous algebraic system with a singular coefficient matrix $A - \lambda_1 I$, and such a system may have no solution, in general. In the present case, however, it can be shown that, since $\mathbf{u}_0$ is an eigenvector which corresponds to λ_1 of multiplicity $m_1 > 1$, a solution $\mathbf{u}_1$ exists.

Thus, two independent solutions of the system $\mathbf{x}' = A\mathbf{x}$ are given by

$$\mathbf{x}_1(t) = e^{\lambda_1 t}\mathbf{v}_1 \quad \text{and} \quad \mathbf{x}_2(t) = e^{\lambda_1 t}(t\mathbf{u}_0 + \mathbf{u}_1),$$

where $\mathbf{u}_0$ is an eigenvector and $\mathbf{u}_1$ is a generalized eigenvector corresponding to the eigenvalue λ_1 of multiplicity 2.

Example 5.12. Consider the system

$$\left\{ \begin{array}{rcrcr} x' & = & 5x & - & y \\ y' & = & 4x & + & y \end{array} \right\}. \tag{5.21}$$

This system may be expressed in matrix form as $\mathbf{x}' = A\mathbf{x}$, where

$$\mathbf{x} = \left(\begin{array}{c} x \\ y \end{array} \right) \quad \text{and} \quad A = \left(\begin{array}{cc} 5 & -1 \\ 4 & 1 \end{array} \right).$$

Then

$$\begin{array}{rcl} \det(\lambda I - A) & = & \left| \begin{array}{cc} \lambda - 5 & 1 \\ -4 & \lambda - 1 \end{array} \right| = (\lambda - 5)(\lambda - 1) + 4 = \lambda^2 - 6\lambda + 9 \\ & = & (\lambda - 3)^2 = 0 \end{array}$$

$\Rightarrow \lambda_1 = 3$ is the only eigenvalue of A, of multiplicity 2.

For $\lambda_1 = 3$, $(\lambda_1 I - A)\mathbf{v} = \mathbf{0}$ with $\mathbf{v} = \left(\begin{array}{c} a \\ b \end{array} \right) \Rightarrow$

$$\left(\begin{array}{cc} -2 & 1 \\ -4 & 2 \end{array} \right) \left(\begin{array}{c} a \\ b \end{array} \right) = \left(\begin{array}{c} 0 \\ 0 \end{array} \right)$$

$\Rightarrow -2a + b = 0$, and $a = 1 \Rightarrow \mathbf{v} = \mathbf{v}_1 = \left(\begin{array}{c} 1 \\ 2 \end{array} \right)$ is an eigenvector which corresponds to the eigenvalue $\lambda_1 = 3$. Thus, one solution of the system (5.21) is

$$\mathbf{x}_1(t) = e^{3t}\left(\begin{array}{c} 1 \\ 2 \end{array} \right) = \left(\begin{array}{c} e^{3t} \\ 2e^{3t} \end{array} \right).$$

Since A has only one independent eigenvector which corresponds to the eigenvalue λ_1 of multiplicity 2, a second, independent solution of the system must be sought in the form

$$\mathbf{x}_2(t) = e^{3t}(t\mathbf{u}_0 + \mathbf{u}_1),$$

where $\mathbf{u}_0 = \mathbf{v}_1$ is an eigenvector corresponding to λ_1 and $\mathbf{u}_1$ is a solution of the algebraic system $(A - \lambda_1 I)\mathbf{u}_1 = \mathbf{u}_0$, i.e., a generalized eigenvector. Employing the fact that $(A - \lambda_1 I) = -(\lambda_1 I - A)$, $(A - \lambda_1 I)\mathbf{u}_1 = \mathbf{u}_0$ with $\mathbf{u}_1 = \left(\begin{array}{c} a \\ b \end{array} \right) \Rightarrow$

$$\left(\begin{array}{cc} 2 & -1 \\ 4 & -2 \end{array} \right) \left(\begin{array}{c} a \\ b \end{array} \right) = \left(\begin{array}{c} 1 \\ 2 \end{array} \right)$$

$\Rightarrow 2a - b = 1$, and $a = 0 \Rightarrow b = -1 \Rightarrow \mathbf{u}_1 = \begin{pmatrix} 0 \\ -1 \end{pmatrix}$. Hence,

$$\mathbf{x}_2(t) = e^{3t} \left[t \begin{pmatrix} 1 \\ 2 \end{pmatrix} + \begin{pmatrix} 0 \\ -1 \end{pmatrix} \right] = e^{3t} \begin{pmatrix} t \\ 2t - 1 \end{pmatrix}.$$

Thus, two independent solutions of the system (5.21) are given by

$$\mathbf{x}_1(t) = e^{3t} \begin{pmatrix} 1 \\ 2 \end{pmatrix} \quad \text{and} \quad \mathbf{x}_2(t) = e^{3t} \begin{pmatrix} t \\ 2t - 1 \end{pmatrix},$$

and

$$X(t) = (\mathbf{x}_1(t) \ \mathbf{x}_2(t)) = e^{3t} \begin{pmatrix} 1 & t \\ 2 & 2t - 1 \end{pmatrix}$$

is a fundamental matrix. The general solution is

$$\begin{aligned} \mathbf{x}(t) &= c_1 \mathbf{x}_1(t) + c_2 \mathbf{x}_2(t) = X(t)\mathbf{c} \\ &= e^{3t} \begin{pmatrix} 1 & t \\ 2 & 2t - 1 \end{pmatrix} \begin{pmatrix} c_1 \\ c_2 \end{pmatrix} = \begin{pmatrix} c_1 e^{3t} + c_2 t e^{3t} \\ 2c_1 e^{3t} + c_2 (2t - 1)e^{3t} \end{pmatrix}, \end{aligned}$$

i.e., $x(t) = c_1 e^{3t} + c_2 t e^{3t}$ and $y(t) = 2c_1 e^{3t} + c_2(2t - 1)e^{3t}$.

Example 5.13. Consider the system

$$\left\{ \begin{array}{rcrcr} x' &=& -5x &+& 4y \\ y' &=& -x &-& y \end{array} \right\}. \tag{5.22}$$

This system may be expressed in matrix form as $\mathbf{x}' = A\mathbf{x}$, where

$$\mathbf{x} = \begin{pmatrix} x \\ y \end{pmatrix} \quad \text{and} \quad A = \begin{pmatrix} -5 & 4 \\ -1 & -1 \end{pmatrix}.$$

Then

$$\begin{aligned} \det(\lambda I - A) &= \begin{vmatrix} \lambda + 5 & -4 \\ 1 & \lambda + 1 \end{vmatrix} = (\lambda + 5)(\lambda + 1) + 4 = \lambda^2 + 6\lambda + 9 \\ &= (\lambda + 3)^2 = 0 \end{aligned}$$

$\Rightarrow \lambda_1 = -3$ is the only eigenvalue of A, of multiplicity 2.

For $\lambda_1 = -3$, $(\lambda_1 I - A)\mathbf{v} = \mathbf{0}$ with $\mathbf{v} = \begin{pmatrix} a \\ b \end{pmatrix} \Rightarrow$

$$\begin{pmatrix} 2 & -4 \\ 1 & -2 \end{pmatrix} \begin{pmatrix} a \\ b \end{pmatrix} = \begin{pmatrix} 0 \\ 0 \end{pmatrix}$$

$\Rightarrow a - 2b = 0$, and $b = 1 \Rightarrow \mathbf{v} = \mathbf{v}_1 = \begin{pmatrix} 2 \\ 1 \end{pmatrix}$ is an eigenvector which corresponds to the eigenvalue $\lambda_1 = -3$. Thus, one solution of the system (5.22) is

$$\mathbf{x}_1(t) = e^{-3t} \begin{pmatrix} 2 \\ 1 \end{pmatrix} = \begin{pmatrix} 2e^{-3t} \\ e^{-3t} \end{pmatrix}.$$

Since A has only one independent eigenvector which corresponds to the eigenvalue λ_1 of multiplicity 2, a second, independent solution of the system must be sought in the form

$$\mathbf{x}_2(t) = e^{-3t}(t\mathbf{u}_0 + \mathbf{u}_1),$$

where $\mathbf{u}_0 = \mathbf{v}_1$ is an eigenvector corresponding to λ_1 and $\mathbf{u}_1$ is a solution of the algebraic system $(A - \lambda_1 I)\mathbf{u}_1 = \mathbf{u}_0$, i.e., a generalized eigenvector. With $\mathbf{u}_1 = \begin{pmatrix} a \\ b \end{pmatrix}$, $(A - \lambda_1 I)\mathbf{u}_1 = \mathbf{u}_0 \Rightarrow$

$$\begin{pmatrix} -2 & 4 \\ -1 & 2 \end{pmatrix} \begin{pmatrix} a \\ b \end{pmatrix} = \begin{pmatrix} 2 \\ 1 \end{pmatrix}$$

$\Rightarrow -a + 2b = 1$, and $b = 0 \Rightarrow a = -1 \Rightarrow \mathbf{u}_1 = \begin{pmatrix} -1 \\ 0 \end{pmatrix}$. Hence,

$$\mathbf{x}_2(t) = e^{-3t} \left[t \begin{pmatrix} 2 \\ 1 \end{pmatrix} + \begin{pmatrix} -1 \\ 0 \end{pmatrix} \right] = e^{-3t} \begin{pmatrix} 2t - 1 \\ t \end{pmatrix}.$$

Thus, two independent solutions of the system (5.22) are given by

$$\mathbf{x}_1(t) = e^{-3t} \begin{pmatrix} 2 \\ 1 \end{pmatrix} \quad \text{and} \quad \mathbf{x}_2(t) = e^{-3t} \begin{pmatrix} 2t - 1 \\ t \end{pmatrix},$$

and

$$X(t) = (\mathbf{x}_1(t) \ \mathbf{x}_2(t)) = e^{-3t} \begin{pmatrix} 2 & 2t - 1 \\ 1 & t \end{pmatrix}$$

is a fundamental matrix. The general solution is

$$\begin{aligned} \mathbf{x}(t) &= c_1\mathbf{x}_1(t) + c_2\mathbf{x}_2(t) = X(t)\mathbf{c} \\ &= e^{-3t} \begin{pmatrix} 2 & 2t - 1 \\ 1 & t \end{pmatrix} \begin{pmatrix} c_1 \\ c_2 \end{pmatrix} = \begin{pmatrix} 2c_1e^{-3t} + c_2(2t - 1)e^{-3t} \\ c_1e^{-3t} + c_2te^{-3t} \end{pmatrix}, \end{aligned}$$

i.e., $x(t) = 2c_1e^{-3t} + c_2(2t - 1)e^{-3t}$ and $y(t) = c_1e^{-3t} + c_2te^{-3t}$.

If A is a 3×3 matrix with fewer than three independent eigenvectors, then there are three possibilities, depending upon the number of distinct eigenvalues and the number of independent eigenvectors which correspond to each eigenvalue.

Let A be a 3×3 matrix with only two distinct eigenvalues, λ_1 of multiplicity $m_1 = 1$ and λ_2 of multiplicity $m_2 = 2$, and with only two independent eigenvectors $\mathbf{v}_1$ and $\mathbf{v}_2$, corresponding to λ_1 and λ_2, respectively. Then three independent solutions of the system $\mathbf{x}' = A\mathbf{x}$ are given by

$$\mathbf{x}_1(t) = e^{\lambda_1 t}\mathbf{v}_1, \quad \mathbf{x}_2(t) = e^{\lambda_2 t}\mathbf{v}_2 \quad \text{and} \quad \mathbf{x}_3(t) = e^{\lambda_2 t}(t\mathbf{u}_0 + \mathbf{u}_1),$$

where $\mathbf{u}_0$ is an eigenvector which corresponds to λ_2 and $\mathbf{u}_1$ is a generalized eigenvector which corresponds to λ_2, i.e., $\mathbf{u}_1$ is a solution of the algebraic system $(A - \lambda_2 I)\mathbf{u}_1 = \mathbf{u}_0$.

Example 5.14. Consider the system

$$\left\{ \begin{array}{rcrcrcr} x' & = & 2x & + & 3y & - & 9z \\ y' & = & & & 3y & - & 4z \\ z' & = & & & y & - & z \end{array} \right\}. \tag{5.23}$$

This system may be expressed in matrix form as $\mathbf{x}' = A\mathbf{x}$, where

$$\mathbf{x} = \begin{pmatrix} x \\ y \\ z \end{pmatrix} \quad \text{and} \quad A = \begin{pmatrix} 2 & 3 & -9 \\ 0 & 3 & -4 \\ 0 & 1 & -1 \end{pmatrix}.$$

Then

$$\begin{aligned} \det(\lambda I - A) &= \begin{vmatrix} \lambda - 2 & -3 & 9 \\ 0 & \lambda - 3 & 4 \\ 0 & -1 & \lambda + 1 \end{vmatrix} = (\lambda - 2)[(\lambda - 3)(\lambda + 1) + 4] \\ &= (\lambda - 2)(\lambda^2 - 2\lambda + 1) = (\lambda - 2)(\lambda - 1)^2 = 0 \end{aligned}$$

$\Rightarrow \lambda_1 = 2$ of multiplicity 1 and $\lambda_2 = 1$ of multiplicity 2.

For $\lambda_1 = 2$, $(\lambda_1 I - A)\mathbf{v} = \mathbf{0}$ with $\mathbf{v} = \begin{pmatrix} a \\ b \\ c \end{pmatrix} \Rightarrow$

$$\begin{pmatrix} 0 & -3 & 9 \\ 0 & -1 & 4 \\ 0 & -1 & 3 \end{pmatrix} \begin{pmatrix} a \\ b \\ c \end{pmatrix} = \begin{pmatrix} 0 \\ 0 \\ 0 \end{pmatrix}$$

$\Rightarrow -b + 4c = 0$ and $-b + 3c = 0 \Rightarrow b = c = 0$, and $a = 1 \Rightarrow \mathbf{v} = \mathbf{v}_1 = \begin{pmatrix} 1 \\ 0 \\ 0 \end{pmatrix}$ is

an eigenvector which corresponds to the eigenvalue $\lambda_1 = 2$. Thus, one solution of the system (5.23) is

$$\mathbf{x}_1(t) = e^{2t} \begin{pmatrix} 1 \\ 0 \\ 0 \end{pmatrix} = \begin{pmatrix} e^{2t} \\ 0 \\ 0 \end{pmatrix}.$$

For $\lambda_2 = 1$, $(\lambda_2 I - A)\mathbf{v} = \mathbf{0}$ with $\mathbf{v} = \begin{pmatrix} a \\ b \\ c \end{pmatrix} \Rightarrow$

$$\begin{pmatrix} -1 & -3 & 9 \\ 0 & -2 & 4 \\ 0 & -1 & 2 \end{pmatrix} \begin{pmatrix} a \\ b \\ c \end{pmatrix} = \begin{pmatrix} 0 \\ 0 \\ 0 \end{pmatrix}$$

$\Rightarrow -b + 2c = 0$ and $-a - 3b + 9c = 0 \Rightarrow b = 2c$ and $-a + 3c = 0$, and $c = 1 \Rightarrow$
$\mathbf{v} = \mathbf{v}_2 = \begin{pmatrix} 3 \\ 2 \\ 1 \end{pmatrix}$ is an eigenvector which corresponds to the eigenvalue $\lambda_2 = 1$. Thus,
a second, independent solution of the system (5.23) is

$$\mathbf{x}_2(t) = e^t \begin{pmatrix} 3 \\ 2 \\ 1 \end{pmatrix} = \begin{pmatrix} 3e^t \\ 2e^t \\ e^t \end{pmatrix}.$$

Since A has only one independent eigenvector which corresponds to the eigenvalue λ_2 of multiplicity 2, a third, independent solution of the system must be sought in the form

$$\mathbf{x}_3(t) = e^t(t\mathbf{u}_0 + \mathbf{u}_1),$$

where $\mathbf{u}_0 = \mathbf{v}_2$ is an eigenvector corresponding to λ_2 and $\mathbf{u}_1$ is a solution of the algebraic system $(A - \lambda_2 I)\mathbf{u}_1 = \mathbf{u}_0$, i.e., a generalized eigenvector. With $\mathbf{u}_1 = \begin{pmatrix} a \\ b \\ c \end{pmatrix}$,

$(A - \lambda_2 I)\mathbf{u}_1 = \mathbf{u}_0 \Rightarrow$

$$\begin{pmatrix} 1 & 3 & -9 \\ 0 & 2 & -4 \\ 0 & 1 & -2 \end{pmatrix} \begin{pmatrix} a \\ b \\ c \end{pmatrix} = \begin{pmatrix} 3 \\ 2 \\ 1 \end{pmatrix}$$

$\Rightarrow a + 3b - 9c = 3$ and $b - 2c = 1$, and $c = 0 \Rightarrow a = 0$ and $b = 1 \Rightarrow \mathbf{u}_1 = \begin{pmatrix} 0 \\ 1 \\ 0 \end{pmatrix}$.

Hence,

$$\mathbf{x}_3(t) = e^t \left[t \begin{pmatrix} 3 \\ 2 \\ 1 \end{pmatrix} + \begin{pmatrix} 0 \\ 1 \\ 0 \end{pmatrix} \right] = e^t \begin{pmatrix} 3t \\ 2t + 1 \\ t \end{pmatrix}.$$

Thus, three independent solutions of the system (5.23) are given by

$$\mathbf{x}_1(t) = e^{2t} \begin{pmatrix} 1 \\ 0 \\ 0 \end{pmatrix}, \quad \mathbf{x}_2(t) = e^t \begin{pmatrix} 3 \\ 2 \\ 1 \end{pmatrix} \quad \text{and} \quad \mathbf{x}_3(t) = e^t \begin{pmatrix} 3t \\ 2t + 1 \\ t \end{pmatrix},$$

and

$$X(t) = (\mathbf{x}_1(t)\ \mathbf{x}_2(t)\ \mathbf{x}_3(t)) = \begin{pmatrix} e^{2t} & 3e^t & 3te^t \\ 0 & 2e^t & (2t+1)e^t \\ 0 & e^t & te^t \end{pmatrix}$$

is a fundamental matrix. The general solution is

$$\begin{aligned} \mathbf{x}(t) &= c_1\mathbf{x}_1(t) + c_2\mathbf{x}_2(t) + c_3\mathbf{x}_3(t) = X(t)\mathbf{c} \\ &= \begin{pmatrix} e^{2t} & 3e^t & 3te^t \\ 0 & 2e^t & (2t+1)e^t \\ 0 & e^t & te^t \end{pmatrix} \begin{pmatrix} c_1 \\ c_2 \\ c_3 \end{pmatrix} = \begin{pmatrix} c_1e^{2t} + 3c_2e^t + 3c_3te^t \\ 2c_2e^t + c_3(2t+1)e^t \\ c_2e^t + c_3te^t \end{pmatrix}, \end{aligned}$$

i.e., $x(t) = c_1e^{2t} + 3c_2e^t + 3c_3te^t$, $y(t) = 2c_2e^t + c_3(2t+1)e^t$ and $z(t) = c_2e^t + c_3te^t$.

Let A be a 3×3 matrix with only one eigenvalue λ_1 of multiplicity $m_1 = 3$, and with only two independent eigenvectors $\mathbf{v}_1$ and $\mathbf{v}_2$ corresponding to λ_1. Then two independent solutions of the system $\mathbf{x}' = A\mathbf{x}$ are given by

$$\mathbf{x}_1(t) = e^{\lambda_1 t}\mathbf{v}_1 \quad \text{and} \quad \mathbf{x}_2(t) = e^{\lambda_1 t}\mathbf{v}_2.$$

A third, independent solution is sought in the form

$$\mathbf{x}_3(t) = e^{\lambda_1 t}(t\mathbf{u}_0 + \mathbf{u}_1),$$

where, as before, $\mathbf{u}_0$ is an eigenvector which corresponds to λ_1 and $\mathbf{u}_1$ is a generalized eigenvector which corresponds to λ_1, i.e., $\mathbf{u}_1$ is a solution of the algebraic system $(A - \lambda_1 I)\mathbf{u}_1 = \mathbf{u}_0$. In the present case, since there are two independent eigenvectors $\mathbf{v}_1$ and $\mathbf{v}_2$ corresponding to λ_1, we must set $\mathbf{u}_0 = \alpha\mathbf{v}_1 + \beta\mathbf{v}_2$, and choose α and β in order that the nonhomogeneous algebraic system

$$(A - \lambda_1 I)\mathbf{u}_1 = \mathbf{u}_0 = \alpha\mathbf{v}_1 + \beta\mathbf{v}_2$$

be consistent and have a solution $\mathbf{u}_1$.

Example 5.15. Consider the system

$$\left\{ \begin{array}{rcrcrcr} x' &=& x &+& y &-& 2z \\ y' &=& -3x &+& 5y &-& 6z \\ z' &=& -x &+& y & & \end{array} \right\}. \tag{5.24}$$

This system may be expressed in matrix form as $\mathbf{x}' = A\mathbf{x}$, where

$$\mathbf{x} = \begin{pmatrix} x \\ y \\ z \end{pmatrix} \quad \text{and} \quad A = \begin{pmatrix} 1 & 1 & -2 \\ -3 & 5 & -6 \\ -1 & 1 & 0 \end{pmatrix}.$$

Then

$$\det(\lambda I - A) = \begin{vmatrix} \lambda - 1 & -1 & 2 \\ 3 & \lambda - 5 & 6 \\ 1 & -1 & \lambda \end{vmatrix}$$

$$= (\lambda - 1)[\lambda(\lambda - 5) + 6] + [3\lambda - 6] + 2[-3 - (\lambda - 5)]$$
$$= (\lambda - 1)(\lambda^2 - 5\lambda + 6) + (\lambda - 2)$$
$$= (\lambda - 1)(\lambda - 2)(\lambda - 3) + (\lambda - 2)$$
$$= (\lambda - 2)[(\lambda - 1)(\lambda - 3) + 1]$$
$$= (\lambda - 2)[\lambda^2 - 4\lambda + 4] = (\lambda - 2)^3 = 0$$

$\Rightarrow \lambda_1 = 2$ is the only eigenvalue of A, of multiplicity 3.

For $\lambda_1 = 2$, $(\lambda_1 I - A)\mathbf{v} = \mathbf{0}$ with $\mathbf{v} = \begin{pmatrix} a \\ b \\ c \end{pmatrix} \Rightarrow$

$$\begin{pmatrix} 1 & -1 & 2 \\ 3 & -3 & 6 \\ 1 & -1 & 2 \end{pmatrix} \begin{pmatrix} a \\ b \\ c \end{pmatrix} = \begin{pmatrix} 0 \\ 0 \\ 0 \end{pmatrix}$$

$\Rightarrow a - b + 2c = 0.$ $c = 0 \Rightarrow a = b \Rightarrow \mathbf{v} = \mathbf{v}_1 = \begin{pmatrix} 1 \\ 1 \\ 0 \end{pmatrix}$, and $a = 0 \Rightarrow b = 2c$

$\Rightarrow \mathbf{v} = \mathbf{v}_2 = \begin{pmatrix} 0 \\ 2 \\ 1 \end{pmatrix}$ are two independent eigenvectors which correspond to the eigenvalue $\lambda_1 = 2$. Thus, two independent solutions of the system (5.24) are

$$\mathbf{x}_1(t) = e^{2t} \begin{pmatrix} 1 \\ 1 \\ 0 \end{pmatrix} \quad \text{and} \quad \mathbf{x}_2(t) = e^{2t} \begin{pmatrix} 0 \\ 2 \\ 1 \end{pmatrix}.$$

Since A has only two independent eigenvectors which correspond to the eigenvalue λ_1 of multiplicity 3, a third, independent solution of the system must be sought in the form

$$\mathbf{x}_3(t) = e^{2t}(t\mathbf{u}_0 + \mathbf{u}_1),$$

where $\mathbf{u}_0 = \alpha\mathbf{v}_1 + \beta\mathbf{v}_2$ is an eigenvector corresponding to λ_1 and $\mathbf{u}_1$ is a solution of the algebraic system $(A - \lambda_1 I)\mathbf{u}_1 = \mathbf{u}_0$, i.e., a generalized eigenvector. With $\mathbf{u}_1 = \begin{pmatrix} a \\ b \\ c \end{pmatrix}$

and $\mathbf{u}_0 = \alpha \begin{pmatrix} 1 \\ 1 \\ 0 \end{pmatrix} + \beta \begin{pmatrix} 0 \\ 2 \\ 1 \end{pmatrix} = \begin{pmatrix} \alpha \\ \alpha + 2\beta \\ \beta \end{pmatrix}$, $(A - \lambda_1 I)\mathbf{u}_1 = \mathbf{u}_0 \Rightarrow$

$$\begin{pmatrix} -1 & 1 & -2 \\ -3 & 3 & -6 \\ -1 & 1 & -2 \end{pmatrix} \begin{pmatrix} a \\ b \\ c \end{pmatrix} = \begin{pmatrix} \alpha \\ \alpha + 2\beta \\ \beta \end{pmatrix},$$

which is consistent if and only if $\alpha = \beta$. Then $-a + b - 2c = \alpha$, and $\alpha = 1$ and

$a = c = 0 \Rightarrow b = 1 \Rightarrow \mathbf{u}_1 = \begin{pmatrix} 0 \\ 1 \\ 0 \end{pmatrix}$ and $\mathbf{u}_0 = \begin{pmatrix} 1 \\ 3 \\ 1 \end{pmatrix}$. Hence,

$$\mathbf{x}_3(t) = e^{2t} \left[t \begin{pmatrix} 1 \\ 3 \\ 1 \end{pmatrix} + \begin{pmatrix} 0 \\ 1 \\ 0 \end{pmatrix} \right] = e^{2t} \begin{pmatrix} t \\ 3t + 1 \\ t \end{pmatrix}.$$

Thus, three independent solutions of the system (5.24) are given by

$$\mathbf{x}_1(t) = e^{2t} \begin{pmatrix} 1 \\ 1 \\ 0 \end{pmatrix}, \quad \mathbf{x}_2(t) = e^{2t} \begin{pmatrix} 0 \\ 2 \\ 1 \end{pmatrix} \quad \text{and} \quad \mathbf{x}_3(t) = e^{2t} \begin{pmatrix} t \\ 3t + 1 \\ t \end{pmatrix},$$

and

$$X(t) = (\mathbf{x}_1(t)\ \mathbf{x}_2(t)\ \mathbf{x}_3(t)) = e^{2t} \begin{pmatrix} 1 & 0 & t \\ 1 & 2 & 3t + 1 \\ 0 & 1 & t \end{pmatrix}$$

is a fundamental matrix. The general solution is

$$\begin{aligned} \mathbf{x}(t) &= c_1\mathbf{x}_1(t) + c_2\mathbf{x}_2(t) + c_3\mathbf{x}_3(t) = X(t)\mathbf{c} \\ &= e^{2t} \begin{pmatrix} 1 & 0 & t \\ 1 & 2 & 3t + 1 \\ 0 & 1 & t \end{pmatrix} \begin{pmatrix} c_1 \\ c_2 \\ c_3 \end{pmatrix} = e^{2t} \begin{pmatrix} c_1 + c_3 t \\ c_1 + 2c_2 + c_3(3t + 1) \\ c_2 + c_3 t \end{pmatrix}, \end{aligned}$$

i.e., $x(t) = (c_1 + c_3 t)e^{2t}$, $y(t) = [c_1 + 2c_2 + c_3(3t + 1)]e^{2t}$ and $z(t) = (c_2 + c_3 t)e^{2t}$.

Example 5.16. Consider the system

$$\left\{ \begin{array}{rcrcrcr} x' &=& x & & & & \\ y' &=& & & y & & \\ z' &=& -x &+& y &+& z \end{array} \right\}. \tag{5.25}$$

This system may be expressed in matrix form as $\mathbf{x}' = A\mathbf{x}$, where

$$\mathbf{x} = \begin{pmatrix} x \\ y \\ z \end{pmatrix} \quad \text{and} \quad A = \begin{pmatrix} 1 & 0 & 0 \\ 0 & 1 & 0 \\ -1 & 1 & 1 \end{pmatrix}.$$

Then

$$\det(\lambda I - A) = \begin{vmatrix} \lambda - 1 & 0 & 0 \\ 0 & \lambda - 1 & 0 \\ 1 & -1 & \lambda - 1 \end{vmatrix} = (\lambda - 1)^3 = 0$$

$\Rightarrow \lambda_1 = 1$ is the only eigenvalue of A, of multiplicity 3.

For $\lambda_1 = 1$, $(\lambda_1 I - A)\mathbf{v} = \mathbf{0}$ with $\mathbf{v} = \begin{pmatrix} a \\ b \\ c \end{pmatrix} \Rightarrow$

$$\begin{pmatrix} 0 & 0 & 0 \\ 0 & 0 & 0 \\ 1 & -1 & 0 \end{pmatrix} \begin{pmatrix} a \\ b \\ c \end{pmatrix} = \begin{pmatrix} 0 \\ 0 \\ 0 \end{pmatrix}$$

$\Rightarrow a - b = 0.$ $a = 1$ and $c = 0 \Rightarrow \mathbf{v} = \mathbf{v}_1 = \begin{pmatrix} 1 \\ 1 \\ 0 \end{pmatrix}$, and $a = 0$ and $c = 1$

$\Rightarrow \mathbf{v} = \mathbf{v}_2 = \begin{pmatrix} 0 \\ 0 \\ 1 \end{pmatrix}$ are two independent eigenvectors which correspond to the eigenvalue $\lambda_1 = 1$. Thus, two independent solutions of the system (5.25) are

$$\mathbf{x}_1(t) = e^t \begin{pmatrix} 1 \\ 1 \\ 0 \end{pmatrix} \quad \text{and} \quad \mathbf{x}_2(t) = e^t \begin{pmatrix} 0 \\ 0 \\ 1 \end{pmatrix}.$$

Since A has only two independent eigenvectors which correspond to the eigenvalue λ_1 of multiplicity 3, a third, independent solution of the system must be sought in the form

$$\mathbf{x}_3(t) = e^t(t\mathbf{u}_0 + \mathbf{u}_1),$$

where $\mathbf{u}_0 = \alpha \mathbf{v}_1 + \beta \mathbf{v}_2$ is an eigenvector corresponding to λ_1 and $\mathbf{u}_1$ is a solution of the algebraic system $(A - \lambda_1 I)\mathbf{u}_1 = \mathbf{u}_0$, i.e., a generalized eigenvector. With $\mathbf{u}_1 = \begin{pmatrix} a \\ b \\ c \end{pmatrix}$

and $\mathbf{u}_0 = \alpha \begin{pmatrix} 1 \\ 1 \\ 0 \end{pmatrix} + \beta \begin{pmatrix} 0 \\ 0 \\ 1 \end{pmatrix} = \begin{pmatrix} \alpha \\ \alpha \\ \beta \end{pmatrix}$, $(A - \lambda_1 I)\mathbf{u}_1 = \mathbf{u}_0 \Rightarrow$

$$\begin{pmatrix} 0 & 0 & 0 \\ 0 & 0 & 0 \\ -1 & 1 & 0 \end{pmatrix} \begin{pmatrix} a \\ b \\ c \end{pmatrix} = \begin{pmatrix} \alpha \\ \alpha \\ \beta \end{pmatrix},$$

which is consistent if and only if $\alpha = 0$. Then $-a + b = \beta$, and $\beta = 1$ and $a = c = 0$

$$\Rightarrow b = 1 \Rightarrow \mathbf{u}_1 = \begin{pmatrix} 0 \\ 1 \\ 0 \end{pmatrix} \text{ and } \mathbf{u}_0 = \begin{pmatrix} 0 \\ 0 \\ 1 \end{pmatrix}. \text{ Hence,}$$

$$\mathbf{x}_3(t) = e^t \left[t \begin{pmatrix} 0 \\ 0 \\ 1 \end{pmatrix} + \begin{pmatrix} 0 \\ 1 \\ 0 \end{pmatrix} \right] = e^t \begin{pmatrix} 0 \\ 1 \\ t \end{pmatrix}.$$

Thus, three independent solutions of the system (5.25) are given by

$$\mathbf{x}_1(t) = e^t \begin{pmatrix} 1 \\ 1 \\ 0 \end{pmatrix}, \quad \mathbf{x}_2(t) = e^t \begin{pmatrix} 0 \\ 0 \\ 1 \end{pmatrix} \quad \text{and} \quad \mathbf{x}_3(t) = e^t \begin{pmatrix} 0 \\ 1 \\ t \end{pmatrix},$$

and

$$X(t) = (\mathbf{x}_1(t) \ \mathbf{x}_2(t) \ \mathbf{x}_3(t)) = e^t \begin{pmatrix} 1 & 0 & 0 \\ 1 & 0 & 1 \\ 0 & 1 & t \end{pmatrix}$$

is a fundamental matrix. The general solution is

$$\begin{aligned} \mathbf{x}(t) &= c_1 \mathbf{x}_1(t) + c_2 \mathbf{x}_2(t) + c_3 \mathbf{x}_3(t) = X(t)\mathbf{c} \\ &= e^t \begin{pmatrix} 1 & 0 & 0 \\ 1 & 0 & 1 \\ 0 & 1 & t \end{pmatrix} \begin{pmatrix} c_1 \\ c_2 \\ c_3 \end{pmatrix} = e^t \begin{pmatrix} c_1 \\ c_1 + c_3 \\ c_2 + c_3 t \end{pmatrix}, \end{aligned}$$

i.e., $x(t) = c_1 e^t$, $y(t) = (c_1 + c_3)e^t$ and $z(t) = (c_2 + c_3 t)e^t$.

Let A be a 3×3 matrix with only one eigenvalue λ_1 of multiplicity $m_1 = 3$, and with only one independent eigenvector $\mathbf{v}_1$ corresponding to λ_1. Then one solution of the system $\mathbf{x}' = A\mathbf{x}$ is given by

$$\mathbf{x}_1(t) = e^{\lambda_1 t}\mathbf{v}_1.$$

A second, independent solution is sought in the form

$$\mathbf{x}_2(t) = e^{\lambda_1 t}(t\mathbf{u}_0 + \mathbf{u}_1),$$

where, as before, $\mathbf{u}_0$ is an eigenvector which corresponds to λ_1 and $\mathbf{u}_1$ is a generalized eigenvector which corresponds to λ_1, i.e., $\mathbf{u}_1$ is a solution of the algebraic system $(A - \lambda_1 I)\mathbf{u}_1 = \mathbf{u}_0$. A third, independent solution is sought in the form

$$\mathbf{x}_3(t) = e^{\lambda_1 t}\left(\frac{1}{2}t^2\mathbf{u}_0 + t\mathbf{u}_1 + \mathbf{u}_2\right),$$

where $\mathbf{u}_0$, $\mathbf{u}_1$ and $\mathbf{u}_2$ are vectors to be determined. Then

$$\mathbf{x}_3'(t) = \lambda_1 e^{\lambda_1 t}\left(\frac{1}{2}t^2\mathbf{u}_0 + t\mathbf{u}_1 + \mathbf{u}_2\right) + e^{\lambda_1 t}(t\mathbf{u}_0 + \mathbf{u}_1),$$

and, hence, $\mathbf{x}_3'(t) = A\mathbf{x}_3(t)$ if and only if

$$\lambda_1 e^{\lambda_1 t}\left(\frac{1}{2}t^2\mathbf{u}_0 + t\mathbf{u}_1 + \mathbf{u}_2\right) + e^{\lambda_1 t}(t\mathbf{u}_0 + \mathbf{u}_1) = Ae^{\lambda_1 t}\left(\frac{1}{2}t^2\mathbf{u}_0 + t\mathbf{u}_1 + \mathbf{u}_2\right).$$

Division by $e^{\lambda_1 t} \neq 0$ yields the condition

$$\lambda_1\left(\frac{1}{2}t^2\mathbf{u}_0 + t\mathbf{u}_1 + \mathbf{u}_2\right) + (t\mathbf{u}_0 + \mathbf{u}_1) = A\left(\frac{1}{2}t^2\mathbf{u}_0 + t\mathbf{u}_1 + \mathbf{u}_2\right),$$

which holds for all real t if and only if

$$\lambda_1\mathbf{u}_0 = A\mathbf{u}_0, \quad \lambda_1\mathbf{u}_1 + \mathbf{u}_0 = A\mathbf{u}_1 \quad \text{and} \quad \lambda_1\mathbf{u}_2 + \mathbf{u}_1 = A\mathbf{u}_2. \tag{5.26}$$

The first two conditions in (5.26) are equivalent to

$$(\lambda_1 I - A)\mathbf{u}_0 = 0 \quad \text{and} \quad (A - \lambda_1 I)\mathbf{u}_1 = \mathbf{u}_0,$$

respectively, as before. The third condition in (5.26) is equivalent to

$$(A - \lambda_1 I)\mathbf{u}_2 = \mathbf{u}_1,$$

a solution $\mathbf{u}_2$ of which is also called a *generalized eigenvector* corresponding to the eigenvalue λ_1 of multiplicity 3.

Example 5.17. Consider the system

$$\left\{\begin{array}{rcrcrcr} x' &=& x &+& 2y &-& z \\ y' &=& -x &+& 4y &-& z \\ z' &=& && y &+& z \end{array}\right\}. \tag{5.27}$$

This system may be expressed in matrix form as $\mathbf{x}' = A\mathbf{x}$, where

$$\mathbf{x} = \begin{pmatrix} x \\ y \\ z \end{pmatrix} \quad \text{and} \quad A = \begin{pmatrix} 1 & 2 & -1 \\ -1 & 4 & -1 \\ 0 & 1 & 1 \end{pmatrix}.$$

Then

$$\begin{aligned} \det(\lambda I - A) &= \begin{vmatrix} \lambda - 1 & -2 & 1 \\ 1 & \lambda - 4 & 1 \\ 0 & -1 & \lambda - 1 \end{vmatrix} \\ &= (\lambda - 1)[(\lambda - 4)(\lambda - 1) + 1] - [-2(\lambda - 1) + 1] \\ &= (\lambda - 1)(\lambda^2 - 5\lambda + 5) + (2\lambda - 3) \\ &= \lambda^3 - 6\lambda^2 + 12\lambda - 8 \\ &= (\lambda - 2)^3 = 0 \end{aligned}$$

$\Rightarrow \lambda_1 = 2$ is the only eigenvalue of A, of multiplicity 3.

For $\lambda_1 = 2$, $(\lambda_1 I - A)\mathbf{v} = \mathbf{0}$ with $\mathbf{v} = \begin{pmatrix} a \\ b \\ c \end{pmatrix} \Rightarrow$

$$\begin{pmatrix} 1 & -2 & 1 \\ 1 & -2 & 1 \\ 0 & -1 & 1 \end{pmatrix} \begin{pmatrix} a \\ b \\ c \end{pmatrix} = \begin{pmatrix} 0 \\ 0 \\ 0 \end{pmatrix}$$

$\Rightarrow -b+c = 0$ and $a - 2b + c = 0 \Rightarrow b = c$ and $a = c$, and $c = 1 \Rightarrow \mathbf{v} = \mathbf{v}_1 = \begin{pmatrix} 1 \\ 1 \\ 1 \end{pmatrix}$ is

the only independent eigenvector which corresponds to the eigenvalue $\lambda_1 = 2$. Thus, one solution of the system (5.27) is

$$\mathbf{x}_1(t) = e^{2t} \begin{pmatrix} 1 \\ 1 \\ 1 \end{pmatrix}.$$

Since A has only one independent eigenvector which corresponds to the eigenvalue λ_1 of multiplicity 3, a second, independent solution of the system must be sought in the form

$$\mathbf{x}_2(t) = e^{2t}(t\mathbf{u}_0 + \mathbf{u}_1),$$

where $\mathbf{u}_0 = \mathbf{v}_1$ is an eigenvector corresponding to λ_1 and $\mathbf{u}_1$ is a solution of the algebraic system $(A - \lambda_1 I)\mathbf{u}_1 = \mathbf{u}_0$, i.e., a generalized eigenvector. With $\mathbf{u}_1 = \begin{pmatrix} a \\ b \\ c \end{pmatrix}$,

$(A - \lambda_1 I)\mathbf{u}_1 = \mathbf{u}_0 \Rightarrow$

$$\begin{pmatrix} -1 & 2 & -1 \\ -1 & 2 & -1 \\ 0 & 1 & -1 \end{pmatrix} \begin{pmatrix} a \\ b \\ c \end{pmatrix} = \begin{pmatrix} 1 \\ 1 \\ 1 \end{pmatrix}$$

$\Rightarrow -a + 2b - c = 1$ and $b - c = 1$, and $c = 0 \Rightarrow b = 1$ and $a = 1 \Rightarrow \mathbf{u}_1 = \begin{pmatrix} 1 \\ 1 \\ 0 \end{pmatrix} \Rightarrow$

$$\mathbf{x}_2(t) = e^{2t} \left[t \begin{pmatrix} 1 \\ 1 \\ 1 \end{pmatrix} + \begin{pmatrix} 1 \\ 1 \\ 0 \end{pmatrix} \right] = e^{2t} \begin{pmatrix} t+1 \\ t+1 \\ t \end{pmatrix}.$$

A third, independent solution must be sought in the form

$$\mathbf{x}_3(t) = e^{2t} \left(\frac{1}{2}t^2 \mathbf{u}_0 + t\mathbf{u}_1 + \mathbf{u}_2 \right),$$

where $\mathbf{u}_0 = \mathbf{v}_1 = \begin{pmatrix} 1 \\ 1 \\ 1 \end{pmatrix}$ and $\mathbf{u}_1 = \begin{pmatrix} 1 \\ 1 \\ 0 \end{pmatrix}$ are as above, and $\mathbf{u}_2$ is a solution of the

algebraic system $(A - \lambda_1 I)\mathbf{u}_2 = \mathbf{u}_1$. With $\mathbf{u}_2 = \begin{pmatrix} a \\ b \\ c \end{pmatrix}$, $(A - \lambda_1 I)\mathbf{u}_2 = \mathbf{u}_1 \Rightarrow$

$$\begin{pmatrix} -1 & 2 & -1 \\ -1 & 2 & -1 \\ 0 & 1 & -1 \end{pmatrix} \begin{pmatrix} a \\ b \\ c \end{pmatrix} = \begin{pmatrix} 1 \\ 1 \\ 0 \end{pmatrix}$$

$\Rightarrow b - c = 0$ and $-a + 2b - c = 1 \Rightarrow b = c$, and $c = 1 \Rightarrow b = 1$ and $a = 0 \Rightarrow$

$\mathbf{u}_2 = \begin{pmatrix} 0 \\ 1 \\ 1 \end{pmatrix} \Rightarrow$

$$\mathbf{x}_3(t) = e^{2t} \left[\frac{1}{2}t^2 \begin{pmatrix} 1 \\ 1 \\ 1 \end{pmatrix} + t \begin{pmatrix} 1 \\ 1 \\ 0 \end{pmatrix} + \begin{pmatrix} 0 \\ 1 \\ 1 \end{pmatrix} \right] = e^{2t} \begin{pmatrix} \frac{1}{2}t^2 + t \\ \frac{1}{2}t^2 + t + 1 \\ \frac{1}{2}t^2 + 1 \end{pmatrix}.$$

Thus, three independent solutions of the system (5.27) are given by

$$\mathbf{x}_1(t) = e^{2t} \begin{pmatrix} 1 \\ 1 \\ 1 \end{pmatrix}, \quad \mathbf{x}_2(t) = e^{2t} \begin{pmatrix} t+1 \\ t+1 \\ t \end{pmatrix} \quad \text{and} \quad \mathbf{x}_3(t) = e^{2t} \begin{pmatrix} \frac{1}{2}t^2 + t \\ \frac{1}{2}t^2 + t + 1 \\ \frac{1}{2}t^2 + 1 \end{pmatrix},$$

and

$$X(t) = (\mathbf{x}_1(t)\ \mathbf{x}_2(t)\ \mathbf{x}_3(t)) = e^{2t} \begin{pmatrix} 1 & t+1 & \frac{1}{2}t^2 + t \\ 1 & t+1 & \frac{1}{2}t^2 + t + 1 \\ 1 & t & \frac{1}{2}t^2 + 1 \end{pmatrix}$$

is a fundamental matrix. The general solution is

$$\begin{aligned} \mathbf{x}(t) &= c_1\mathbf{x}_1(t) + c_2\mathbf{x}_2(t) + c_3\mathbf{x}_3(t) = X(t)\mathbf{c} \\ &= e^{2t} \begin{pmatrix} 1 & t+1 & \frac{1}{2}t^2 + t \\ 1 & t+1 & \frac{1}{2}t^2 + t + 1 \\ 1 & t & \frac{1}{2}t^2 + 1 \end{pmatrix} \begin{pmatrix} c_1 \\ c_2 \\ c_3 \end{pmatrix} \\ &= e^{2t} \begin{pmatrix} c_1 + c_2(t+1) + c_3(\frac{1}{2}t^2 + t) \\ c_1 + c_2(t+1) + c_3(\frac{1}{2}t^2 + t + 1) \\ c_1 + c_2 t + c_3(\frac{1}{2}t^2 + 1) \end{pmatrix}, \end{aligned}$$

i.e.,

$$x(t) = \left[c_1 + c_2(t+1) + c_3 \left(\frac{1}{2}t^2 + t \right) \right] e^{2t},$$

$$y(t) = \left[c_1 + c_2(t+1) + c_3 \left(\frac{1}{2}t^2 + t + 1 \right) \right] e^{2t},$$

$$z(t) = \left[c_1 + c_2 t + c_3 \left(\frac{1}{2}t^2 + 1 \right) \right] e^{2t}.$$

Example 5.18. Consider the system

$$\begin{cases} x' = -5x + 2y - 3z \\ y' = -7x + 3y - 8z \\ z' = -x + y - 4z \end{cases}. \tag{5.28}$$

This system may be expressed in matrix form as $\mathbf{x}' = A\mathbf{x}$, where

$$\mathbf{x} = \begin{pmatrix} x \\ y \\ z \end{pmatrix} \quad \text{and} \quad A = \begin{pmatrix} -5 & 2 & -3 \\ -7 & 3 & -8 \\ -1 & 1 & -4 \end{pmatrix}.$$

Then

$$\begin{aligned} \det(\lambda I - A) &= \begin{vmatrix} \lambda + 5 & -2 & 3 \\ 7 & \lambda - 3 & 8 \\ 1 & -1 & \lambda + 4 \end{vmatrix} \\ &= (\lambda + 5)[(\lambda - 3)(\lambda + 4) + 8] + 2[7(\lambda + 4) - 8] + 3[-7 - (\lambda - 3)] \\ &= (\lambda + 5)(\lambda^2 + \lambda - 4) + 11\lambda + 28 \\ &= (\lambda^3 + 6\lambda^2 + \lambda - 20) + 11\lambda + 28 \\ &= \lambda^3 + 6\lambda^2 + 12\lambda + 8 \\ &= (\lambda + 2)^3 = 0 \end{aligned}$$

$\Rightarrow \lambda_1 = -2$ is the only eigenvalue of A, of multiplicity 3.

For $\lambda_1 = -2$, $(\lambda_1 I - A)\mathbf{v} = \mathbf{0}$ with $\mathbf{v} = \begin{pmatrix} a \\ b \\ c \end{pmatrix} \Rightarrow$

$$\begin{pmatrix} 3 & -2 & 3 \\ 7 & -5 & 8 \\ 1 & -1 & 2 \end{pmatrix} \begin{pmatrix} a \\ b \\ c \end{pmatrix} = \begin{pmatrix} 0 \\ 0 \\ 0 \end{pmatrix} \Rightarrow \begin{pmatrix} 3 & -2 & 3 \\ 0 & 2 & -6 \\ 0 & 1 & -3 \end{pmatrix} \begin{pmatrix} a \\ b \\ c \end{pmatrix} = \begin{pmatrix} 0 \\ 0 \\ 0 \end{pmatrix}$$

$\Rightarrow b - 3c = 0$ and $3a - 2b + 3c = 0 \Rightarrow b = 3c$ and $a = c$, and $c = 1 \Rightarrow \mathbf{v} = \mathbf{v}_1 = \begin{pmatrix} 1 \\ 3 \\ 1 \end{pmatrix}$ is

the only independent eigenvector which corresponds to the eigenvalue $\lambda_1 = -2$. Thus, one solution of the system (5.28) is

$$\mathbf{x}_1(t) = e^{-2t} \begin{pmatrix} 1 \\ 3 \\ 1 \end{pmatrix}.$$

Since A has only one independent eigenvector which corresponds to the eigenvalue λ_1 of multiplicity 3, a second, independent solution of the system must be sought in the form

$$\mathbf{x}_2(t) = e^{-2t}(t\mathbf{u}_0 + \mathbf{u}_1),$$

where $\mathbf{u}_0 = \mathbf{v}_1$ is an eigenvector corresponding to λ_1 and $\mathbf{u}_1$ is a solution of the algebraic system $(A - \lambda_1 I)\mathbf{u}_1 = \mathbf{u}_0$, i.e., a generalized eigenvector. With $\mathbf{u}_1 = \begin{pmatrix} a \\ b \\ c \end{pmatrix}$,

$(A - \lambda_1 I)\mathbf{u}_1 = \mathbf{u}_0 \Rightarrow$

$$\begin{pmatrix} -3 & 2 & -3 \\ -7 & 5 & -8 \\ -1 & 1 & -2 \end{pmatrix} \begin{pmatrix} a \\ b \\ c \end{pmatrix} = \begin{pmatrix} 1 \\ 3 \\ 1 \end{pmatrix} \Rightarrow \begin{pmatrix} -3 & 2 & -3 \\ 0 & -2 & 6 \\ 0 & -1 & 3 \end{pmatrix} \begin{pmatrix} a \\ b \\ c \end{pmatrix} = \begin{pmatrix} 1 \\ -4 \\ -2 \end{pmatrix}$$

$\Rightarrow -b + 3c = -2$ and $-3a + 2b - 3c = 1$, and $c = 0 \Rightarrow b = 2$ and $a = 1 \Rightarrow \mathbf{u}_1 = \begin{pmatrix} 1 \\ 2 \\ 0 \end{pmatrix}$

$$\Rightarrow \quad \mathbf{x}_2(t) = e^{-2t} \left[t \begin{pmatrix} 1 \\ 3 \\ 1 \end{pmatrix} + \begin{pmatrix} 1 \\ 2 \\ 0 \end{pmatrix} \right] = e^{-2t} \begin{pmatrix} t+1 \\ 3t+2 \\ t \end{pmatrix}.$$

A third, independent solution must be sought in the form

$$\mathbf{x}_3(t) = e^{-2t} \left(\frac{1}{2}t^2\mathbf{u}_0 + t\mathbf{u}_1 + \mathbf{u}_2 \right),$$

where $\mathbf{u}_0 = \mathbf{v}_1 = \begin{pmatrix} 1 \\ 3 \\ 1 \end{pmatrix}$ and $\mathbf{u}_1 = \begin{pmatrix} 1 \\ 2 \\ 0 \end{pmatrix}$ are as above, and $\mathbf{u}_2$ is a solution of the

algebraic system $(A - \lambda_1 I)\mathbf{u}_2 = \mathbf{u}_1$. With $\mathbf{u}_2 = \begin{pmatrix} a \\ b \\ c \end{pmatrix}$, $(A - \lambda_1 I)\mathbf{u}_2 = \mathbf{u}_1 \Rightarrow$

$$\begin{pmatrix} -3 & 2 & -3 \\ -7 & 5 & -8 \\ -1 & 1 & -2 \end{pmatrix} \begin{pmatrix} a \\ b \\ c \end{pmatrix} = \begin{pmatrix} 1 \\ 2 \\ 0 \end{pmatrix} \Rightarrow \begin{pmatrix} -3 & 2 & -3 \\ 0 & -2 & 6 \\ 0 & -1 & 3 \end{pmatrix} \begin{pmatrix} a \\ b \\ c \end{pmatrix} = \begin{pmatrix} 1 \\ 2 \\ 1 \end{pmatrix}$$

$\Rightarrow -b + 3c = 1$ and $-3a + 2b - 3c = 1$, and $a = 0 \Rightarrow b = 2$ and $c = 1 \Rightarrow \mathbf{u}_2 = \begin{pmatrix} 0 \\ 2 \\ 1 \end{pmatrix}$

$$\Rightarrow \quad \mathbf{x}_3(t) = e^{-2t} \left[\frac{1}{2}t^2 \begin{pmatrix} 1 \\ 3 \\ 1 \end{pmatrix} + t \begin{pmatrix} 1 \\ 2 \\ 0 \end{pmatrix} + \begin{pmatrix} 0 \\ 2 \\ 1 \end{pmatrix} \right] = e^{-2t} \begin{pmatrix} \frac{1}{2}t^2 + t \\ \frac{3}{2}t^2 + 2t + 2 \\ \frac{1}{2}t^2 + 1 \end{pmatrix}.$$

Thus, three independent solutions of the system (5.28) are given by

$$\mathbf{x}_1(t) = e^{-2t} \begin{pmatrix} 1 \\ 3 \\ 1 \end{pmatrix}, \quad \mathbf{x}_2(t) = e^{-2t} \begin{pmatrix} t+1 \\ 3t+2 \\ t \end{pmatrix} \text{ and } \mathbf{x}_3(t) = e^{-2t} \begin{pmatrix} \frac{1}{2}t^2 + t \\ \frac{3}{2}t^2 + 2t + 2 \\ \frac{1}{2}t^2 + 1 \end{pmatrix},$$

and

$$X(t) = (\mathbf{x}_1(t)\ \mathbf{x}_2(t)\ \mathbf{x}_3(t)) = e^{-2t} \begin{pmatrix} 1 & t+1 & \frac{1}{2}t^2 + t \\ 3 & 3t+2 & \frac{3}{2}t^2 + 2t + 2 \\ 1 & t & \frac{1}{2}t^2 + 1 \end{pmatrix}$$

is a fundamental matrix. The general solution is

$$\begin{aligned} \mathbf{x}(t) &= c_1\mathbf{x}_1(t) + c_2\mathbf{x}_2(t) + c_3\mathbf{x}_3(t) = X(t)\mathbf{c} \\ &= e^{-2t} \begin{pmatrix} 1 & t+1 & \frac{1}{2}t^2 + t \\ 3 & 3t+2 & \frac{3}{2}t^2 + 2t + 2 \\ 1 & t & \frac{1}{2}t^2 + 1 \end{pmatrix} \begin{pmatrix} c_1 \\ c_2 \\ c_3 \end{pmatrix} \\ &= e^{-2t} \begin{pmatrix} c_1 + c_2(t+1) + c_3(\frac{1}{2}t^2 + t) \\ 3c_1 + c_2(3t+2) + c_3(\frac{3}{2}t^2 + 2t + 2) \\ c_1 + c_2 t + c_3(\frac{1}{2}t^2 + 1) \end{pmatrix}, \end{aligned}$$

i.e.,

$$\begin{aligned} x(t) &= \left[c_1 + c_2(t+1) + c_3 \left(\frac{1}{2}t^2 + t \right) \right] e^{-2t}, \\ y(t) &= \left[3c_1 + c_2(3t+2) + c_3 \left(\frac{3}{2}t^2 + 2t + 2 \right) \right] e^{-2t}, \\ z(t) &= \left[c_1 + c_2 t + c_3 \left(\frac{1}{2}t^2 + 1 \right) \right] e^{-2t}. \end{aligned}$$

Let A be a 4×4 matrix which has only one pair of complex-conjugate eigenvalues λ_1 and $\overline{\lambda}_1$ of multiplicity 2, and with only one pair of independent eigenvectors $\mathbf{v}_1$ and $\overline{\mathbf{v}}_1$, corresponding to λ_1 and $\overline{\lambda}_1$, respectively. Then two complex-conjugate solutions of the system $\mathbf{x}' = A\mathbf{x}$ are given by

$$\mathbf{z}_1(t) = e^{\lambda_1 t}\mathbf{v}_1 \quad \text{and} \quad \overline{\mathbf{z}}_1(t) = e^{\overline{\lambda}_1 t}\overline{\mathbf{v}}_1,$$

from which two real, independent solutions can be obtained as

$$\mathbf{x}_1(t) = \Re(\mathbf{z}_1(t)) = \frac{1}{2}[\mathbf{z}_1(t) + \overline{\mathbf{z}}_1(t)] \ \text{ and } \ \mathbf{x}_2(t) = \Im(\mathbf{z}_1(t)) = \frac{1}{2i}[\mathbf{z}_1(t) - \overline{\mathbf{z}}_1(t)],$$

as demonstrated earlier. In the present case, it is necessary to obtain two additional real, independent solutions. Hence, a second pair of complex-conjugate solutions is required, and they are obtained by means of complex generalized eigenvectors. Thus, seek a complex solution in the form

$$\mathbf{z}_2(t) = e^{\lambda_1 t}(t\mathbf{u}_0 + \mathbf{u}_1),$$

where, as before, $\mathbf{u}_0$ is an eigenvector and $\mathbf{u}_1$ is a solution of the algebraic system $(A - \lambda_1 I)\mathbf{u}_1 = \mathbf{u}_0$, i.e., a generalized eigenvector. Then $\mathbf{z}_2$ and $\overline{\mathbf{z}}_2$ are two complex solutions, and provide the two additional real, independent solutions

$$\mathbf{x}_3(t) = \Re(\mathbf{z}_2(t)) = \frac{1}{2}[\mathbf{z}_2(t) + \overline{\mathbf{z}}_2(t)] \ \text{ and } \ \mathbf{x}_4(t) = \Im(\mathbf{z}_2(t)) = \frac{1}{2i}[\mathbf{z}_2(t) - \overline{\mathbf{z}}_2(t)],$$

for a total of four real, independent solutions.

Example 5.19. Conside the system

$$\left\{ \begin{array}{rcrcrcr} x' & = & & -y & + & z & \\ y' & = & x & & + & & w \\ z' & = & & & & & -w \\ w' & = & & & & z & \end{array} \right\}. \tag{5.29}$$

This system may be expressed in matrix form as $\mathbf{x}' = A\mathbf{x}$, where

$$\mathbf{x} = \begin{pmatrix} x \\ y \\ z \\ w \end{pmatrix} \ \text{ and } \ A = \begin{pmatrix} 0 & -1 & 1 & 0 \\ 1 & 0 & 0 & 1 \\ 0 & 0 & 0 & -1 \\ 0 & 0 & 1 & 0 \end{pmatrix}.$$

Then, expanding the 4×4 determinant along the fourth row, we obtain

$$\begin{aligned} \det(\lambda I - A) & = \begin{vmatrix} \lambda & 1 & -1 & 0 \\ -1 & \lambda & 0 & -1 \\ 0 & 0 & \lambda & 1 \\ 0 & 0 & -1 & \lambda \end{vmatrix} \\ & = \begin{vmatrix} \lambda & 1 & 0 \\ -1 & \lambda & -1 \\ 0 & 0 & 1 \end{vmatrix} + \lambda \begin{vmatrix} \lambda & 1 & -1 \\ -1 & \lambda & 0 \\ 0 & 0 & \lambda \end{vmatrix} \\ & = (\lambda^2 + 1) + \lambda[\lambda(\lambda^2 + 1)] \\ & = (\lambda^2 + 1)^2 = 0 \end{aligned}$$

$\Rightarrow \lambda_1 = i$ and $\overline{\lambda}_1 = -i$ are the only eigenvalues of A, of multiplicity 2.

For $\lambda_1 = i$, $(\lambda_1 I - A)\mathbf{v} = \mathbf{0}$ with $\mathbf{v} = \begin{pmatrix} a \\ b \\ c \\ d \end{pmatrix} \Rightarrow$

$$\begin{pmatrix} i & 1 & -1 & 0 \\ -1 & i & 0 & -1 \\ 0 & 0 & i & 1 \\ 0 & 0 & -1 & i \end{pmatrix} \begin{pmatrix} a \\ b \\ c \\ d \end{pmatrix} = \begin{pmatrix} 0 \\ 0 \\ 0 \\ 0 \end{pmatrix}.$$

Row reduction of the coefficient matrix gives

$$\begin{pmatrix} i & 1 & -1 & 0 \\ -1 & i & 0 & -1 \\ 0 & 0 & i & 1 \\ 0 & 0 & -1 & i \end{pmatrix} \rightarrow \begin{pmatrix} i & 1 & -1 & 0 \\ 0 & 0 & -1 & -i \\ 0 & 0 & i & 1 \\ 0 & 0 & 0 & 0 \end{pmatrix} \rightarrow \begin{pmatrix} i & 1 & -1 & 0 \\ 0 & 0 & -1 & -i \\ 0 & 0 & 0 & 2 \\ 0 & 0 & 0 & 0 \end{pmatrix}$$

$\Rightarrow d = 0 \Rightarrow c = 0$ and $ia + b = 0$, and $a = i \Rightarrow b = 1 \Rightarrow$

$$\mathbf{v} = \mathbf{v}_1 = \begin{pmatrix} i \\ 1 \\ 0 \\ 0 \end{pmatrix} = \begin{pmatrix} 0 \\ 1 \\ 0 \\ 0 \end{pmatrix} + i \begin{pmatrix} 1 \\ 0 \\ 0 \\ 0 \end{pmatrix}$$

is an eigenvector which corresponds to the eigenvalue λ_1. Then

$$\begin{aligned}
\mathbf{z}_1(t) &= [\cos(t) + i\sin(t)] \left[\begin{pmatrix} 0 \\ 1 \\ 0 \\ 0 \end{pmatrix} + i \begin{pmatrix} 1 \\ 0 \\ 0 \\ 0 \end{pmatrix} \right] \\
&= \left[\cos(t) \begin{pmatrix} 0 \\ 1 \\ 0 \\ 0 \end{pmatrix} - \sin(t) \begin{pmatrix} 1 \\ 0 \\ 0 \\ 0 \end{pmatrix} \right] + i \left[\sin(t) \begin{pmatrix} 0 \\ 1 \\ 0 \\ 0 \end{pmatrix} + \cos(t) \begin{pmatrix} 1 \\ 0 \\ 0 \\ 0 \end{pmatrix} \right] \\
&= \begin{pmatrix} -\sin(t) \\ \cos(t) \\ 0 \\ 0 \end{pmatrix} + i \begin{pmatrix} \cos(t) \\ \sin(t) \\ 0 \\ 0 \end{pmatrix}, \\
\overline{\mathbf{z}}_1(t) &= \begin{pmatrix} -\sin(t) \\ \cos(t) \\ 0 \\ 0 \end{pmatrix} - i \begin{pmatrix} \cos(t) \\ \sin(t) \\ 0 \\ 0 \end{pmatrix}
\end{aligned}$$

are two complex-conjugate solutions and, hence,

$$\mathbf{x}_1(t) = \Re(\mathbf{z}_1(t)) = \begin{pmatrix} -\sin(t) \\ \cos(t) \\ 0 \\ 0 \end{pmatrix} \quad \text{and} \quad \mathbf{x}_2(t) = \Im(\mathbf{z}_1(t)) = \begin{pmatrix} \cos(t) \\ \sin(t) \\ 0 \\ 0 \end{pmatrix}$$

are two real, independent solutions of the system (5.29).

A generalized eigenvector corresponding to λ_1 is a solution $\mathbf{u}_1$ of the algebraic system $(A - \lambda_1 I)\mathbf{u}_1 = \mathbf{u}_0 = \mathbf{v}_1$, i.e., with $\mathbf{u}_1 = \begin{pmatrix} a \\ b \\ c \\ d \end{pmatrix}$,

$$\begin{pmatrix} -i & -1 & 1 & 0 \\ 1 & -i & 0 & 1 \\ 0 & 0 & -i & -1 \\ 0 & 0 & 1 & -i \end{pmatrix} \begin{pmatrix} a \\ b \\ c \\ d \end{pmatrix} = \begin{pmatrix} i \\ 1 \\ 0 \\ 0 \end{pmatrix}.$$

Row reduction of the augmented matrix gives

$$\begin{pmatrix} -i & -1 & 1 & 0 & | & i \\ 1 & -i & 0 & 1 & | & 1 \\ 0 & 0 & -i & -1 & | & 0 \\ 0 & 0 & 1 & -i & | & 0 \end{pmatrix} \rightarrow \begin{pmatrix} -i & -1 & 1 & 0 & | & i \\ 0 & 0 & 1 & i & | & 2i \\ 0 & 0 & -i & -1 & | & 0 \\ 0 & 0 & 0 & 0 & | & 0 \end{pmatrix} \rightarrow$$

$$\begin{pmatrix} -i & -1 & 1 & 0 & | & i \\ 0 & 0 & 1 & i & | & 2i \\ 0 & 0 & 0 & -2 & | & -2 \\ 0 & 0 & 0 & 0 & | & 0 \end{pmatrix}$$

$\Rightarrow d = 1,\ c + id = 2i$ and $-ia - b + c = i \Rightarrow c = i$ and $ia + b = 0$, and $b = 0 \Rightarrow a = 0$

$$\Rightarrow \mathbf{u}_1 = \begin{pmatrix} 0 \\ 0 \\ i \\ 1 \end{pmatrix} \text{ is a generalized eigenvector, and}$$

$$
\begin{aligned}
\mathbf{z}_2(t) &= [\cos(t) + i\sin(t)] \left[t \begin{pmatrix} i \\ 1 \\ 0 \\ 0 \end{pmatrix} + \begin{pmatrix} 0 \\ 0 \\ i \\ 1 \end{pmatrix} \right] \\
&= [\cos(t) + i\sin(t)] \left[\begin{pmatrix} 0 \\ t \\ 0 \\ 1 \end{pmatrix} + i \begin{pmatrix} t \\ 0 \\ 1 \\ 0 \end{pmatrix} \right] \\
&= \left[\cos(t) \begin{pmatrix} 0 \\ t \\ 0 \\ 1 \end{pmatrix} - \sin(t) \begin{pmatrix} t \\ 0 \\ 1 \\ 0 \end{pmatrix} \right] + i \left[\sin(t) \begin{pmatrix} 0 \\ t \\ 0 \\ 1 \end{pmatrix} + \cos(t) \begin{pmatrix} t \\ 0 \\ 1 \\ 0 \end{pmatrix} \right]
\end{aligned}
$$

and $\overline{\mathbf{z}}_2(t)$ are two additional complex-conjugate solutions. Hence,

$$
\begin{aligned}
\mathbf{x}_3(t) &= \Re(\mathbf{z}_2(t)) = \left[\cos(t) \begin{pmatrix} 0 \\ t \\ 0 \\ 1 \end{pmatrix} - \sin(t) \begin{pmatrix} t \\ 0 \\ 1 \\ 0 \end{pmatrix} \right] = \begin{pmatrix} -t\sin(t) \\ t\cos(t) \\ -\sin(t) \\ \cos(t) \end{pmatrix}, \\
\mathbf{x}_4(t) &= \Im(\mathbf{z}_2(t)) = \left[\sin(t) \begin{pmatrix} 0 \\ t \\ 0 \\ 1 \end{pmatrix} + \cos(t) \begin{pmatrix} t \\ 0 \\ 1 \\ 0 \end{pmatrix} \right] = \begin{pmatrix} t\cos(t) \\ t\sin(t) \\ \cos(t) \\ \sin(t) \end{pmatrix}
\end{aligned}
$$

are two additional real, independent solutions of the system (5.29),

$$
X(t) = (\mathbf{x}_1(t)\ \mathbf{x}_2(t)\ \mathbf{x}_3(t)\ \mathbf{x}_4(t)) = \begin{pmatrix} -\sin(t) & \cos(t) & -t\sin(t) & t\cos(t) \\ \cos(t) & \sin(t) & t\cos(t) & t\sin(t) \\ 0 & 0 & -\sin(t) & \cos(t) \\ 0 & 0 & \cos(t) & \sin(t) \end{pmatrix}
$$

is a fundamental matrix, and

$$
\begin{aligned}
\mathbf{x}(t) &= c_1\mathbf{x}_1(t) + c_2\mathbf{x}_2(t) + c_3\mathbf{x}_3(t) + c_4\mathbf{x}_4(t) \\
&= X(t)\mathbf{c} \\
&= \begin{pmatrix} -\sin(t) & \cos(t) & -t\sin(t) & t\cos(t) \\ \cos(t) & \sin(t) & t\cos(t) & t\sin(t) \\ 0 & 0 & -\sin(t) & \cos(t) \\ 0 & 0 & \cos(t) & \sin(t) \end{pmatrix} \begin{pmatrix} c_1 \\ c_2 \\ c_3 \\ c_4 \end{pmatrix} \\
&= \begin{pmatrix} -c_1\sin(t) + c_2\cos(t) - c_3t\sin(t) + c_4t\cos(t) \\ c_1\cos(t) + c_2\sin(t) + c_3t\cos(t) + c_4t\sin(t) \\ -c_3\sin(t) + c_4\cos(t) \\ c_3\cos(t) + c_4\sin(t) \end{pmatrix},
\end{aligned}
$$

i.e.,

$$
\begin{aligned}
x(t) &= -c_1\sin(t) + c_2\cos(t) - c_3t\sin(t) + c_4t\cos(t), \\
y(t) &= c_1\cos(t) + c_2\sin(t) + c_3t\cos(t) + c_4t\sin(t), \\
z(t) &= -c_3\sin(t) + c_4\cos(t), \\
w(t) &= c_3\cos(t) + c_4\sin(t)
\end{aligned}
$$

is the general solution.

Exercises 5.1

1. Find the general solution of the system $\left\{ \begin{array}{l} x' = -5x + 6y \\ y' = -3x + 4y \end{array} \right\}$.

2. Find the general solution of the system $\left\{ \begin{array}{l} x' = 3x + y \\ y' = -2x \end{array} \right\}$.

3. Find the general solution of the system $\mathbf{x}' = A\mathbf{x}$, where $A = \begin{pmatrix} 1 & 1 \\ 0 & 2 \end{pmatrix}$.

4. Find a fundamental matrix for the system $\mathbf{x}' = A\mathbf{x}$, where $A = \begin{pmatrix} 1 & 0 \\ 1 & 2 \end{pmatrix}$.

5. Find a fundamental matrix for the system $\mathbf{x}' = A\mathbf{x}$, where $A = \begin{pmatrix} 2 & 0 \\ 0 & 2 \end{pmatrix}$.

6. Solve the initial-value problem $\left\{ \begin{array}{l} x' = x - y \\ y' = 2x + 4y \end{array} \right\}$, $x(0) = 2$, $y(0) = 1$.

7. Find a fundamental matrix for the system $\mathbf{x}' = A\mathbf{x}$, where $A = \begin{pmatrix} 1 & 3 \\ -1 & -3 \end{pmatrix}$.

8. Find the general solution of the system $\left\{ \begin{array}{l} x' = 2y \\ y' = 2x \end{array} \right\}$.

9. Find the general solution of the system $\left\{ \begin{array}{l} x' = x \\ y' = -2x + 3y \\ z' = -x + y + 2z \end{array} \right\}$.

10. Find a fundamental matrix for the system $\mathbf{x}' = A\mathbf{x}$, where $A = \begin{pmatrix} 1 & -3 & 3 \\ -4 & -2 & 4 \\ -1 & -3 & 5 \end{pmatrix}$.

11. Find a fundamental matrix for the system $\mathbf{x}' = A\mathbf{x}$, where $A = \begin{pmatrix} -1 & 0 & 2 \\ -2 & 1 & 2 \\ 0 & 0 & 1 \end{pmatrix}$.

12. Find the general solution of the system $\left\{ \begin{array}{l} x' = -3x + y \\ y' = -4x - 3y \end{array} \right\}$.

13. Find the general solution of the system $\mathbf{x}' = A\mathbf{x}$, where $A = \begin{pmatrix} 0 & -1 \\ 13 & -6 \end{pmatrix}$.

14. Find a fundamental matrix for the system $\mathbf{x}' = A\mathbf{x}$, where $A = \begin{pmatrix} 2 & -2 \\ 1 & 0 \end{pmatrix}$.

15. Solve the initial-value problem $\mathbf{x}' = A\mathbf{x}$, $\mathbf{x}(0) = \mathbf{x}_0$, where $\mathbf{x}_0 = \begin{pmatrix} 2 \\ -1 \end{pmatrix}$ and
    $A = \begin{pmatrix} 1 & -1 \\ 1 & 1 \end{pmatrix}$.

16. Find the general solution of the system $\left\{ \begin{array}{l} x' = x \\ y' = 2x + 2y - 2z \\ z' = x + y \end{array} \right\}$.

17. Find the general solution of the system $\mathbf{x}' = A\mathbf{x}$, where $A = \begin{pmatrix} 0 & 0 & 1 \\ 0 & 1 & 0 \\ -1 & 2 & 0 \end{pmatrix}$.

18. Find a fundamental matrix for the system $\mathbf{x}' = A\mathbf{x}$, where
    $A = \begin{pmatrix} 0 & 0 & 0 & 1 \\ 0 & 1 & -1 & 0 \\ 0 & 1 & 1 & 0 \\ -1 & 0 & 0 & 0 \end{pmatrix}$.

19. Find the general solution of the system $\left\{ \begin{array}{l} x' = x + 3y \\ y' = y \end{array} \right\}$.

20. Find the general solution of the system $\mathbf{x}' = A\mathbf{x}$, where $A = \begin{pmatrix} -4 & 9 \\ -1 & 2 \end{pmatrix}$.

21. Find a fundamental matrix for the system $\mathbf{x}' = A\mathbf{x}$, where $A = \begin{pmatrix} 2 & 0 \\ 2 & 2 \end{pmatrix}$.

22. Find the general solution of the system $\left\{ \begin{array}{l} x' = 3x - y \\ y' = x + 2y - z \\ z' = 3y - z \end{array} \right\}$.

23. Find the general solution of the system $\mathbf{x}' = A\mathbf{x}$, where $A = \begin{pmatrix} 4 & 2 & 1 \\ 0 & 4 & 0 \\ 0 & 0 & 6 \end{pmatrix}$.

24. Find a fundamental matrix for the system $\mathbf{x}' = A\mathbf{x}$, where
$A = \begin{pmatrix} -3 & 1 & -2 \\ -3 & 1 & -6 \\ -1 & 1 & -4 \end{pmatrix}$.

25. Find a fundamental matrix for the system $\mathbf{x}' = A\mathbf{x}$, where
$A = \begin{pmatrix} 7 & -3 & -15 \\ 2 & 0 & -5 \\ 2 & -1 & -4 \end{pmatrix}$.

26. Find the general solution of the system $\begin{pmatrix} x' \\ y' \\ z' \end{pmatrix} = \begin{pmatrix} -2 & 1 & 0 \\ -1 & 0 & 0 \\ 0 & 0 & -1 \end{pmatrix} \begin{pmatrix} x \\ y \\ z \end{pmatrix}$.

27. Find the general solution of the system $\mathbf{x}' = A\mathbf{x}$, where $A = \begin{pmatrix} -2 & 0 & 1 \\ 1 & -1 & 0 \\ -1 & 0 & 0 \end{pmatrix}$.

28. Find the general solution of the system $\mathbf{x}' = A\mathbf{x}$, where $A = \begin{pmatrix} 2 & -1 & 1 \\ 1 & 0 & 1 \\ -1 & 1 & 1 \end{pmatrix}$.

29. Find the general solution of the system $\mathbf{x}' = A\mathbf{x}$, where
$A = \begin{pmatrix} 1 & 1 & 0 & 1 \\ -1 & 1 & -1 & 0 \\ 0 & 0 & 1 & 1 \\ 0 & 0 & -1 & 1 \end{pmatrix}$.

5.2   Nonhomogeneous Systems

Theorem 5.6. The general solution of the nonhomogeneous system

$$\mathbf{x}' = A(t)\mathbf{x} + \mathbf{f}(t) \tag{5.30}$$

is $\mathbf{x}(t) = \mathbf{x}_p(t) + \mathbf{x}_h(t)$, where $\mathbf{x}_p(t)$ is any particular solution of (5.30), and $\mathbf{x}_h(t)$ is the general solution of the *associated homogeneous system*

$$\mathbf{x}' = A(t)\mathbf{x}, \tag{5.31}$$

i.e.,

$$\mathbf{x}_h(t) = c_1\mathbf{x}_1(t) + c_2\mathbf{x}_2(t) + \cdots + c_n\mathbf{x}_n(t),$$

where $\mathbf{x}_1(t)$, $\mathbf{x}_2(t)$, $\cdots$, $\mathbf{x}_n(t)$ are n independent solutions of (5.31).

Proof. $\mathbf{x}(t) = \mathbf{x}_p(t) + \mathbf{x}_h(t)$ is a solution of the system (5.30) because

$$
\begin{aligned}
\mathbf{x}'(t) &= [\mathbf{x}_p(t) + \mathbf{x}_h(t)]' \\
&= \mathbf{x}_p'(t) + \mathbf{x}_h'(t) \\
&= A(t)\mathbf{x}_p(t) + \mathbf{f}(t) + A(t)\mathbf{x}_h(t) \\
&= A(t)[\mathbf{x}_p(t) + \mathbf{x}_h(t)] + \mathbf{f}(t) \\
&= A(t)\mathbf{x}(t) + \mathbf{f}(t).
\end{aligned}
$$

Since $\mathbf{x}(t)$ contains n arbitrary constants, it is the general solution of (5.30).

Let $X(t)$ be a fundamental matrix for the homogeneous system (5.31), and seek a particular solution of the nonhomogeneous system (5.30) in the form

$$\mathbf{x}_p(t) = X(t)\mathbf{u}(t), \tag{5.32}$$

where $\mathbf{u}(t)$ is a vector function to be determined. Then

$$\mathbf{x}_p'(t) = X'(t)\mathbf{u}(t) + X(t)\mathbf{u}'(t),$$

and, hence, (5.32) is a solution of (5.30) if and only if

$$X'(t)\mathbf{u}(t) + X(t)\mathbf{u}'(t) = A(t)X(t)\mathbf{u}(t) + \mathbf{f}(t). \tag{5.33}$$

Since $X'(t) = A(t)X(t)$ by Theorem 5.3 in Section 5.1.1, (5.33) is equivalent to

$$A(t)X(t)\mathbf{u}(t) + X(t)\mathbf{u}'(t) = A(t)X(t)\mathbf{u}(t) + \mathbf{f}(t),$$

i.e.,

$$X(t)\mathbf{u}'(t) = \mathbf{f}(t),$$

left multiplication of which by $X(t)^{-1}$ gives $\mathbf{u}'(t) = X(t)^{-1}\mathbf{f}(t)$ and, hence,

$$\mathbf{u}(t) = \int X(t)^{-1}\mathbf{f}(t)\,dt. \tag{5.34}$$

Thus, Equation (5.32), with $\mathbf{u}(t)$ defined by (5.34), gives

$$\mathbf{x}_p(t) = X(t) \int X(t)^{-1}\mathbf{f}(t)\,dt, \tag{5.35}$$

and determines a particular solution $\mathbf{x}_p(t)$ for the nonhomogeneous system (5.30). Analogous to single nonhomogeneous equations, this method is called *variation of parameters for systems*.

Note that the integrand in (5.35) is an n-vector. The integral of a vector-valued function $\mathbf{v}(t)$ is defined as the vector-valued function the components of which are the integrals of the components of $\mathbf{v}(t)$, i.e.,

$$\mathbf{v}(t) = \begin{pmatrix} v_1(t) \\ v_2(t) \\ \vdots \\ v_n(t) \end{pmatrix} \quad \Rightarrow \quad \int \mathbf{v}(t)\,dt = \begin{pmatrix} \int v_1(t)\,dt \\ \int v_2(t)\,dt \\ \vdots \\ \int v_n(t)\,dt \end{pmatrix}.$$

The general solution of the nonhomogeneous system $\mathbf{x}' = A(t)\mathbf{x} + \mathbf{f}(t)$ is then

$$\begin{aligned} \mathbf{x}(t) &= \mathbf{x}_h(t) + \mathbf{x}_p(t) \\ &= X(t)\mathbf{c} + X(t) \int X(t)^{-1}\mathbf{f}(t)\,dt \\ &= X(t)\left[\mathbf{c} + \int X(t)^{-1}\mathbf{f}(t)\,dt\right]. \end{aligned}$$

As in variation of parameters for single equations, the addition of arbitrary constants of integration is not necessary, since they may be incorporated into the arbitrary constant vector $\mathbf{c}$.

Example 5.20.   Consider the nonhomogeneous system

$$\left\{ \begin{aligned} x' &= -5x &+ 4y &+ 2t \\ y' &= -4x &+ 5y &+ t \end{aligned} \right\}. \tag{5.36}$$

This system may be expressed in matrix form as $\mathbf{x}' = A\mathbf{x} + \mathbf{f}(t)$, where

$$\mathbf{x} = \begin{pmatrix} x \\ y \end{pmatrix}, \quad A = \begin{pmatrix} -5 & 4 \\ -4 & 5 \end{pmatrix} \quad \text{and} \quad \mathbf{f}(t) = \begin{pmatrix} 2t \\ t \end{pmatrix}.$$

For the associated homogeneous system $\mathbf{x}' = A\mathbf{x}$,

$$
\begin{aligned}
\det(\lambda I - A) &= \begin{vmatrix} \lambda + 5 & -4 \\ 4 & \lambda - 5 \end{vmatrix} = (\lambda + 5)(\lambda - 5) + 16 = \lambda^2 - 9 \\
&= (\lambda - 3)(\lambda + 3) = 0
\end{aligned}
$$

$\Rightarrow \lambda_1 = 3$ and $\lambda_2 = -3$ are the eigenvalues of A.

For $\lambda_1 = 3$, $(\lambda_1 I - A)\mathbf{v} = \mathbf{0}$ with $\mathbf{v} = \begin{pmatrix} a \\ b \end{pmatrix} \Rightarrow$

$$
\begin{pmatrix} 8 & -4 \\ 4 & -2 \end{pmatrix} \begin{pmatrix} a \\ b \end{pmatrix} = \begin{pmatrix} 0 \\ 0 \end{pmatrix}
$$

$\Rightarrow 2a - b = 0$, and $a = 1 \Rightarrow \mathbf{v} = \mathbf{v}_1 = \begin{pmatrix} 1 \\ 2 \end{pmatrix}$ is an eigenvector which corresponds to the eigenvalue $\lambda_1 = 3$.

For $\lambda_2 = -3$, $(\lambda_2 I - A)\mathbf{v} = \mathbf{0}$ with $\mathbf{v} = \begin{pmatrix} a \\ b \end{pmatrix} \Rightarrow$

$$
\begin{pmatrix} 2 & -4 \\ 4 & -8 \end{pmatrix} \begin{pmatrix} a \\ b \end{pmatrix} = \begin{pmatrix} 0 \\ 0 \end{pmatrix}
$$

$\Rightarrow a - 2b = 0$, and $b = 1 \Rightarrow \mathbf{v} = \mathbf{v}_2 = \begin{pmatrix} 2 \\ 1 \end{pmatrix}$ is an eigenvector which corresponds to the eigenvalue $\lambda_2 = -3$.

Hence, two independent solutions of the homogeneous system are given by

$$
\mathbf{x}_1(t) = e^{3t} \begin{pmatrix} 1 \\ 2 \end{pmatrix} = \begin{pmatrix} e^{3t} \\ 2e^{3t} \end{pmatrix} \quad \text{and} \quad \mathbf{x}_2(t) = e^{-3t} \begin{pmatrix} 2 \\ 1 \end{pmatrix} = \begin{pmatrix} 2e^{-3t} \\ e^{-3t} \end{pmatrix},
$$

and

$$
X(t) = (\mathbf{x}_1(t) \; \mathbf{x}_2(t)) = \begin{pmatrix} e^{3t} & 2e^{-3t} \\ 2e^{3t} & e^{-3t} \end{pmatrix}
$$

is a fundamental matrix. Then

$$
\begin{aligned}
X(t)^{-1} &= -\frac{1}{3} \begin{pmatrix} e^{-3t} & -2e^{-3t} \\ -2e^{3t} & e^{3t} \end{pmatrix} = \frac{1}{3} \begin{pmatrix} -e^{-3t} & 2e^{-3t} \\ 2e^{3t} & -e^{3t} \end{pmatrix}, \\
X(t)^{-1}\mathbf{f}(t) &= \frac{1}{3} \begin{pmatrix} -e^{-3t} & 2e^{-3t} \\ 2e^{3t} & -e^{3t} \end{pmatrix} \begin{pmatrix} 2t \\ t \end{pmatrix} = \begin{pmatrix} 0 \\ te^{3t} \end{pmatrix}, \\
\int X(t)^{-1}\mathbf{f}(t)\,dt &= \int \begin{pmatrix} 0 \\ te^{3t} \end{pmatrix} dt = \begin{pmatrix} 0 \\ \frac{1}{3}te^{3t} - \frac{1}{9}e^{3t} \end{pmatrix} = \frac{1}{9}e^{3t} \begin{pmatrix} 0 \\ 3t - 1 \end{pmatrix} \\
\Rightarrow \quad \mathbf{x}_p(t) &= X(t) \int X(t)^{-1}\mathbf{f}(t)\,dt = \begin{pmatrix} e^{3t} & 2e^{-3t} \\ 2e^{3t} & e^{-3t} \end{pmatrix} \frac{1}{9}e^{3t} \begin{pmatrix} 0 \\ 3t - 1 \end{pmatrix} \\
&= \frac{1}{9}e^{3t} \begin{pmatrix} 2(3t - 1)e^{-3t} \\ (3t - 1)e^{-3t} \end{pmatrix} = \frac{1}{9} \begin{pmatrix} 6t - 2 \\ 3t - 1 \end{pmatrix},
\end{aligned}
$$

and the general solution of the nonhomogeneous system (5.36) is

$$
\begin{aligned}
\mathbf{x}(t) &= \mathbf{x}_h(t) + \mathbf{x}_p(t) = X(t)\mathbf{c} + \mathbf{x}_p(t) \\
&= \begin{pmatrix} e^{3t} & 2e^{-3t} \\ 2e^{3t} & e^{-3t} \end{pmatrix} \begin{pmatrix} c_1 \\ c_2 \end{pmatrix} + \frac{1}{9} \begin{pmatrix} 6t-2 \\ 3t-1 \end{pmatrix},
\end{aligned}
$$

i.e.,

$$
\begin{aligned}
x(t) &= c_1 e^{3t} + 2c_2 e^{-3t} + \frac{2}{9}(3t-1), \\
y(t) &= 2c_1 e^{3t} + c_2 e^{-3t} + \frac{1}{9}(3t-1).
\end{aligned}
$$

Example 5.21. Consider the nonhomogeneous system

$$
\left\{ \begin{aligned} x' &= x - 2y + e^t \cos(2t) \\ y' &= 2x + y + e^t \sin(2t) \end{aligned} \right\}. \tag{5.37}
$$

This system may be expressed in matrix form as $\mathbf{x}' = A\mathbf{x} + \mathbf{f}(t)$, where

$$
\mathbf{x} = \begin{pmatrix} x \\ y \end{pmatrix}, \quad A = \begin{pmatrix} 1 & -2 \\ 2 & 1 \end{pmatrix} \quad \text{and} \quad \mathbf{f}(t) = e^t \begin{pmatrix} \cos(2t) \\ \sin(2t) \end{pmatrix}.
$$

For the associated homogeneous system $\mathbf{x}' = A\mathbf{x}$,

$$
\begin{aligned}
\det(\lambda I - A) &= \begin{vmatrix} \lambda - 1 & 2 \\ -2 & \lambda - 1 \end{vmatrix} = (\lambda - 1)^2 + 4 \\
&= \lambda^2 - 2\lambda + 5 = 0
\end{aligned}
$$

$$
\Rightarrow \lambda, \overline{\lambda} = \frac{2 \pm \sqrt{-16}}{2} = 1 \pm 2i \text{ are the eigenvalues of } A.
$$

For $\lambda = 1 + 2i$, $(\lambda_1 I - A)\mathbf{v} = \mathbf{0}$ with $\mathbf{v} = \begin{pmatrix} a \\ b \end{pmatrix} \Rightarrow$

$$
\begin{pmatrix} 2i & 2 \\ -2 & 2i \end{pmatrix} \begin{pmatrix} a \\ b \end{pmatrix} = \begin{pmatrix} 0 \\ 0 \end{pmatrix}
$$

$\Rightarrow ia + b = 0$, and $a = 1 \Rightarrow \mathbf{v} = \begin{pmatrix} 1 \\ -i \end{pmatrix}$ is an eigenvector which corresponds to the eigenvalue $\lambda = 1 + 2i$.

Hence, a complex solution of the homogeneous system is given by

$$
z(t) = e^t[\cos(2t) + i\sin(2t)] \left[\begin{pmatrix} 1 \\ 0 \end{pmatrix} + i \begin{pmatrix} 0 \\ -1 \end{pmatrix} \right],
$$

two real, independent solutions are given by

$$\mathbf{x}_1(t) = e^t \left[\cos(2t) \begin{pmatrix} 1 \\ 0 \end{pmatrix} - \sin(2t) \begin{pmatrix} 0 \\ -1 \end{pmatrix} \right] = e^t \begin{pmatrix} \cos(2t) \\ \sin(2t) \end{pmatrix},$$

$$\mathbf{x}_2(t) = e^t \left[\sin(2t) \begin{pmatrix} 1 \\ 0 \end{pmatrix} + \cos(2t) \begin{pmatrix} 0 \\ -1 \end{pmatrix} \right] = e^t \begin{pmatrix} \sin(2t) \\ -\cos(2t) \end{pmatrix},$$

and

$$X(t) = (\mathbf{x}_1(t) \ \mathbf{x}_2(t)) = e^t \begin{pmatrix} \cos(2t) & \sin(2t) \\ \sin(2t) & -\cos(2t) \end{pmatrix}$$

is a fundamental matrix. Then

$$X(t)^{-1} = -e^{-t} \begin{pmatrix} -\cos(2t) & -\sin(2t) \\ -\sin(2t) & \cos(2t) \end{pmatrix} = e^{-t} \begin{pmatrix} \cos(2t) & \sin(2t) \\ \sin(2t) & -\cos(2t) \end{pmatrix},$$

$$X(t)^{-1}\mathbf{f}(t) = e^{-t} \begin{pmatrix} \cos(2t) & \sin(2t) \\ \sin(2t) & -\cos(2t) \end{pmatrix} e^t \begin{pmatrix} \cos(2t) \\ \sin(2t) \end{pmatrix} = \begin{pmatrix} 1 \\ 0 \end{pmatrix},$$

$$\int X(t)^{-1}\mathbf{f}(t)\,dt = \int \begin{pmatrix} 1 \\ 0 \end{pmatrix} dt = \begin{pmatrix} t \\ 0 \end{pmatrix}$$

$$\Rightarrow \quad \mathbf{x}_p(t) = X(t) \int X(t)^{-1}\mathbf{f}(t)\,dt = e^t \begin{pmatrix} \cos(2t) & \sin(2t) \\ \sin(2t) & -\cos(2t) \end{pmatrix} \begin{pmatrix} t \\ 0 \end{pmatrix}$$

$$= e^t \begin{pmatrix} t\cos(2t) \\ t\sin(2t) \end{pmatrix},$$

and the general solution of the nonhomogeneous system (5.37) is

$$\mathbf{x}(t) = \mathbf{x}_h(t) + \mathbf{x}_p(t) = X(t)\mathbf{c} + \mathbf{x}_p(t)$$

$$= e^t \begin{pmatrix} \cos(2t) & \sin(2t) \\ \sin(2t) & -\cos(2t) \end{pmatrix} \begin{pmatrix} c_1 \\ c_2 \end{pmatrix} + te^t \begin{pmatrix} \cos(2t) \\ \sin(2t) \end{pmatrix},$$

i.e.,

$$x(t) = e^t[c_1\cos(2t) + c_2\sin(2t) + t\cos(2t)],$$
$$y(t) = e^t[c_1\sin(2t) - c_2\cos(2t) + t\sin(2t)].$$

Example 5.22. Consider the nonhomogeneous system

$$\left\{ \begin{array}{rcl} x' & = & -5x + 9y + e^t \\ y' & = & -4x + 7y + e^t \end{array} \right\}. \tag{5.38}$$

This system may be expressed in matrix form as $\mathbf{x}' = A\mathbf{x} + \mathbf{f}(t)$, where

$$\mathbf{x} = \begin{pmatrix} x \\ y \end{pmatrix}, \quad A = \begin{pmatrix} -5 & 9 \\ -4 & 7 \end{pmatrix} \quad \text{and} \quad \mathbf{f}(t) = e^t \begin{pmatrix} 1 \\ 1 \end{pmatrix}.$$

For the associated homogeneous system $\mathbf{x}' = A\mathbf{x}$,

$$\det(\lambda I - A) = \begin{vmatrix} \lambda + 5 & -9 \\ 4 & \lambda - 7 \end{vmatrix} = (\lambda + 5)(\lambda - 7) + 36 = \lambda^2 - 2\lambda + 1$$

$$= (\lambda - 1)^2 = 0$$

$\Rightarrow \lambda_1 = 1$ is the only eigenvalue of A, of multiplicity $m_1 = 2$.

For $\lambda_1 = 1$, $(\lambda_1 I - A)\mathbf{v} = \mathbf{0}$ with $\mathbf{v} = \begin{pmatrix} a \\ b \end{pmatrix} \Rightarrow$

$$\begin{pmatrix} 6 & -9 \\ 4 & -6 \end{pmatrix} \begin{pmatrix} a \\ b \end{pmatrix} = \begin{pmatrix} 0 \\ 0 \end{pmatrix}$$

$\Rightarrow 2a - 3b = 0$, and $a = 3 \Rightarrow \mathbf{v} = \mathbf{v}_1 = \begin{pmatrix} 3 \\ 2 \end{pmatrix}$ is an eigenvector which corresponds to the eigenvalue $\lambda_1 = 1$.

Hence, one solution of the homogeneous system is given by

$$\mathbf{x}_1(t) = e^t \begin{pmatrix} 3 \\ 2 \end{pmatrix}.$$

A second, independent solution takes the form

$$\mathbf{x}_2(t) = e^t(t\mathbf{u}_0 + \mathbf{u}_1),$$

where $\mathbf{u}_0 = \mathbf{v}_1$ is an eigenvector which corresponds to λ_1, and $\mathbf{u}_1$ is a solution of the algebraic system $(A - \lambda_1 I)\mathbf{u}_1 = \mathbf{u}_0$. With $\mathbf{u}_1 = \begin{pmatrix} a \\ b \end{pmatrix}$, $(A - \lambda_1 I)\mathbf{u}_1 = \mathbf{u}_0 \Rightarrow$

$$\begin{pmatrix} -6 & 9 \\ -4 & 6 \end{pmatrix} \begin{pmatrix} a \\ b \end{pmatrix} = \begin{pmatrix} 3 \\ 2 \end{pmatrix}$$

$\Rightarrow 3b - 2a = 1$, and $a = 1 \Rightarrow \mathbf{u}_1 = \begin{pmatrix} 1 \\ 1 \end{pmatrix} \Rightarrow$

$$\mathbf{x}_2(t) = e^t \left[t \begin{pmatrix} 3 \\ 2 \end{pmatrix} + \begin{pmatrix} 1 \\ 1 \end{pmatrix} \right] = e^t \begin{pmatrix} 3t + 1 \\ 2t + 1 \end{pmatrix},$$

and

$$X(t) = (\mathbf{x}_1(t) \ \mathbf{x}_2(t)) = e^t \begin{pmatrix} 3 & 3t + 1 \\ 2 & 2t + 1 \end{pmatrix}$$

is a fundamental matrix. Then

$$X(t)^{-1} = e^{-t} \begin{pmatrix} 2t+1 & -(3t+1) \\ -2 & 3 \end{pmatrix},$$

$$X(t)^{-1}\mathbf{f}(t) = \begin{pmatrix} 2t+1 & -(3t+1) \\ -2 & 3 \end{pmatrix} \begin{pmatrix} 1 \\ 1 \end{pmatrix} = \begin{pmatrix} -t \\ 1 \end{pmatrix},$$

$$\int X(t)^{-1}\mathbf{f}(t)\,dt = \int \begin{pmatrix} -t \\ 1 \end{pmatrix} dt = \begin{pmatrix} -\frac{1}{2}t^2 \\ t \end{pmatrix}$$

$$\Rightarrow \quad \mathbf{x}_p(t) = X(t) \int X(t)^{-1}\mathbf{f}(t)\,dt = e^t \begin{pmatrix} 3 & 3t+1 \\ 2 & 2t+1 \end{pmatrix} \begin{pmatrix} -\frac{1}{2}t^2 \\ t \end{pmatrix}$$

$$= e^t \begin{pmatrix} \frac{3}{2}t^2 + t \\ t^2 + t \end{pmatrix},$$

and the general solution of the nonhomogeneous system (5.38) is

$$\mathbf{x}(t) = \mathbf{x}_h(t) + \mathbf{x}_p(t) = X(t)\mathbf{c} + \mathbf{x}_p(t)$$

$$= e^t \begin{pmatrix} 3 & 3t+1 \\ 2 & 2t+1 \end{pmatrix} \begin{pmatrix} c_1 \\ c_2 \end{pmatrix} + e^t \begin{pmatrix} \frac{3}{2}t^2 + t \\ t^2 + t \end{pmatrix},$$

i.e.,

$$x(t) = e^t \left[3c_1 + c_2(3t+1) + \frac{3}{2}t^2 + t \right],$$

$$y(t) = e^t \left[2c_1 + c_2(2t+1) + t^2 + t \right].$$

Definition 5.7. An *initial-value problem* for a nonhomogeneous system consists of a system $\mathbf{x}' = A(t)\mathbf{x} + \mathbf{f}(t)$, together with an *initial condition* $\mathbf{x}(t_0) = \mathbf{x}_0$, which requires that the solution $\mathbf{x}(t)$ be equal to $\mathbf{x}_0$ at $t = t_0$, and determines the arbitrary constant vector $\mathbf{c}$.

Theorem 5.7. Let $A(t)$ and $\mathbf{f}(t)$ be continuous on an interval I containing the point t_0 in its interior. The solution of the initial-value problem

$$\mathbf{x}' = A(t)\mathbf{x} + \mathbf{f}(t), \quad \mathbf{x}(t_0) = \mathbf{x}_0,$$

is given by

$$\mathbf{x}(t) = X(t)X(t_0)^{-1}\mathbf{x}_0 + X(t)\int_{t_0}^t X(s)^{-1}\mathbf{f}(s)\,ds$$

$$= X(t)\left[X(t_0)^{-1}\mathbf{x}_0 + \int_{t_0}^t X(s)^{-1}\mathbf{f}(s)\,ds \right],$$

where $X(t)$ is a fundamental matrix for the associated homogeneous system.

Proof. The general solution of the nonhomogeneous system may be expressed in terms of a definite integral as

$$\mathbf{x}(t) = X(t)\mathbf{c} + X(t) \int_{t_0}^t X(s)^{-1}\mathbf{f}(s)\, ds.$$

Then $\mathbf{x}(t_0) = \mathbf{x}_0 \Rightarrow \mathbf{x}_0 = X(t_0)\mathbf{c} \Rightarrow \mathbf{c} = X(t_0)^{-1}\mathbf{x}_0$.

Note that the definite integral of a vector-valued function is defined in a manner analogous to the definition of the indefinite integral:

$$\mathbf{v}(t) = \begin{pmatrix} v_1(t) \\ v_2(t) \\ \vdots \\ v_n(t) \end{pmatrix} \quad \Rightarrow \quad \int_a^b \mathbf{v}(s)\, ds = \begin{pmatrix} \int_a^b v_1(s)\, ds \\ \int_a^b v_2(s)\, ds \\ \vdots \\ \int_a^b v_n(s)\, ds \end{pmatrix}.$$

Example 5.23.   Consider the initial-value problem

$$\left\{ \begin{array}{rcl} x' & = & -x \;+\; 2y \;+\; e^t \\ y' & = & \qquad\;\; y \;+\; e^t \end{array} \right\}, \quad x(0) = 2, \;\; y(0) = 1. \tag{5.39}$$

This problem may be expressed in matrix form as $\mathbf{x}' = A\mathbf{x} + \mathbf{f}(t)$, $\mathbf{x}(0) = \mathbf{x}_0$, where

$$\mathbf{x} = \begin{pmatrix} x \\ y \end{pmatrix}, \quad A = \begin{pmatrix} -1 & 2 \\ 0 & 1 \end{pmatrix}, \quad \mathbf{f}(t) = e^t \begin{pmatrix} 1 \\ 1 \end{pmatrix} \quad \text{and} \quad \mathbf{x}_0 = \begin{pmatrix} 2 \\ 1 \end{pmatrix}.$$

For the associated homogeneous system $\mathbf{x}' = A\mathbf{x}$,

$$\det(\lambda I - A) = \begin{vmatrix} \lambda + 1 & -2 \\ 0 & \lambda - 1 \end{vmatrix} = (\lambda + 1)(\lambda - 1) = 0$$

$\Rightarrow \lambda_1 = 1$ and $\lambda_2 = -1$ are the eigenvalues of A.

For $\lambda_1 = 1$, $(\lambda_1 I - A)\mathbf{v} = \mathbf{0}$ with $\mathbf{v} = \begin{pmatrix} a \\ b \end{pmatrix} \Rightarrow$

$$\begin{pmatrix} 2 & -2 \\ 0 & 0 \end{pmatrix} \begin{pmatrix} a \\ b \end{pmatrix} = \begin{pmatrix} 0 \\ 0 \end{pmatrix}$$

$\Rightarrow a = b$, and $a = 1 \Rightarrow \mathbf{v} = \mathbf{v}_1 = \begin{pmatrix} 1 \\ 1 \end{pmatrix}$ is an eigenvector which corresponds to the eigenvalue $\lambda_1 = 1$.

For $\lambda_2 = -1$, $(\lambda_2 I - A)\mathbf{v} = \mathbf{0}$ with $\mathbf{v} = \begin{pmatrix} a \\ b \end{pmatrix} \Rightarrow$

$$\begin{pmatrix} 0 & -2 \\ 0 & -2 \end{pmatrix} \begin{pmatrix} a \\ b \end{pmatrix} = \begin{pmatrix} 0 \\ 0 \end{pmatrix}$$

$\Rightarrow b = 0$, and $a = 1 \Rightarrow \mathbf{v} = \mathbf{v}_2 = \begin{pmatrix} 1 \\ 0 \end{pmatrix}$ is an eigenvector which corresponds to the eigenvalue $\lambda_2 = -1$.

Hence, two independent solutions of the homogeneous system are given by

$$\mathbf{x}_1(t) = e^t \begin{pmatrix} 1 \\ 1 \end{pmatrix} = \begin{pmatrix} e^t \\ e^t \end{pmatrix} \quad \text{and} \quad \mathbf{x}_2(t) = e^{-t} \begin{pmatrix} 1 \\ 0 \end{pmatrix} = \begin{pmatrix} e^{-t} \\ 0 \end{pmatrix},$$

and

$$X(t) = (\mathbf{x}_1(t)\ \mathbf{x}_2(t)) = \begin{pmatrix} e^t & e^{-t} \\ e^t & 0 \end{pmatrix}$$

is a fundamental matrix. Then

$$X(t)^{-1} = -\begin{pmatrix} 0 & -e^{-t} \\ -e^t & e^t \end{pmatrix} = \begin{pmatrix} 0 & e^{-t} \\ e^t & -e^t \end{pmatrix},$$

$$X(t)^{-1}\mathbf{f}(t) = \begin{pmatrix} 0 & e^{-t} \\ e^t & -e^t \end{pmatrix} \begin{pmatrix} e^t \\ e^t \end{pmatrix} = \begin{pmatrix} 1 \\ 0 \end{pmatrix},$$

$$\int_0^t X(s)^{-1}\mathbf{f}(s)\,ds = \int_0^t \begin{pmatrix} 1 \\ 0 \end{pmatrix} ds = \begin{pmatrix} s \\ 0 \end{pmatrix}\Big|_0^t = \begin{pmatrix} t \\ 0 \end{pmatrix},$$

$$X(0)^{-1}\mathbf{x}(0) = \begin{pmatrix} 0 & 1 \\ 1 & -1 \end{pmatrix} \begin{pmatrix} 2 \\ 1 \end{pmatrix} = \begin{pmatrix} 1 \\ 1 \end{pmatrix},$$

$$X(0)^{-1}\mathbf{x}(0) + \int_0^t X(s)^{-1}\mathbf{f}(s)\,ds = \begin{pmatrix} 1 \\ 1 \end{pmatrix} + \begin{pmatrix} t \\ 0 \end{pmatrix} = \begin{pmatrix} t+1 \\ 1 \end{pmatrix}$$

$$\Rightarrow \mathbf{x}(t) = X(t)\left[X(0)^{-1}\mathbf{x}(0) + \int_0^t X(s)^{-1}\mathbf{f}(s)\,ds\right]$$

$$= \begin{pmatrix} e^t & e^{-t} \\ e^t & 0 \end{pmatrix} \begin{pmatrix} t+1 \\ 1 \end{pmatrix}$$

$$= \begin{pmatrix} (t+1)e^t + e^{-t} \\ (t+1)e^t \end{pmatrix},$$

i.e., $x(t) = (t+1)e^t + e^{-t}$, $y(t) = (t+1)e^t$ is the solution of the initial-value problem (5.39).

Example 5.24. Consider the initial-value problem

$$\left\{ \begin{array}{rcrcrcr} x' & = & -2x & + & 4y & + & 4e^{-2t} \\ y' & = & -x & - & 2y & + & 2e^{-2t} \end{array} \right\}, \quad x(0) = 2, \quad y(0) = -1. \quad (5.40)$$

This problem may be expressed in matrix form as $\mathbf{x}' = A\mathbf{x} + \mathbf{f}(t)$, $\mathbf{x}(0) = \mathbf{x}_0$, where

$$\mathbf{x} = \begin{pmatrix} x \\ y \end{pmatrix}, \quad A = \begin{pmatrix} -2 & 4 \\ -1 & -2 \end{pmatrix}, \quad \mathbf{f}(t) = e^{-2t} \begin{pmatrix} 4 \\ 2 \end{pmatrix} \quad \text{and} \quad \mathbf{x}_0 = \begin{pmatrix} 2 \\ -1 \end{pmatrix}.$$

For the associated homogeneous system $\mathbf{x}' = A\mathbf{x}$,

$$\det(\lambda I - A) = \begin{vmatrix} \lambda + 2 & -4 \\ 1 & \lambda + 2 \end{vmatrix} = (\lambda + 2)^2 + 4 = \lambda^2 + 4\lambda + 8 = 0$$

$$\Rightarrow \lambda, \overline{\lambda} = \frac{-4 \pm \sqrt{-16}}{2} = -2 \pm 2i \text{ are the eigenvalues of } A.$$

For $\lambda = -2 + 2i$, $(\lambda I - A)\mathbf{v} = \mathbf{0}$ with $\mathbf{v} = \begin{pmatrix} a \\ b \end{pmatrix} \Rightarrow$

$$\begin{pmatrix} 2i & -4 \\ 1 & 2i \end{pmatrix} \begin{pmatrix} a \\ b \end{pmatrix} = \begin{pmatrix} 0 \\ 0 \end{pmatrix}$$

$\Rightarrow a + 2ib = 0$, and $b = i \Rightarrow \mathbf{v} = \begin{pmatrix} 2 \\ i \end{pmatrix}$ is an eigenvector which corresponds to the eigenvalue $\lambda = -2 + 2i$.

Hence, a complex solution of the homogeneous system is given by

$$\mathbf{z}(t) = e^{-2t}[\cos(2t) + i\sin(2t)] \left[\begin{pmatrix} 2 \\ 0 \end{pmatrix} + i \begin{pmatrix} 0 \\ 1 \end{pmatrix} \right],$$

$$\begin{aligned} \mathbf{x}_1(t) &= e^{-2t} \left[\cos(2t) \begin{pmatrix} 2 \\ 0 \end{pmatrix} - \sin(2t) \begin{pmatrix} 0 \\ 1 \end{pmatrix} \right] = e^{-2t} \begin{pmatrix} 2\cos(2t) \\ -\sin(2t) \end{pmatrix}, \\ \mathbf{x}_2(t) &= e^{-2t} \left[\sin(2t) \begin{pmatrix} 2 \\ 0 \end{pmatrix} + \cos(2t) \begin{pmatrix} 0 \\ 1 \end{pmatrix} \right] = e^{-2t} \begin{pmatrix} 2\sin(2t) \\ \cos(2t) \end{pmatrix} \end{aligned}$$

are two real, independent solutions, and

$$X(t) = (\mathbf{x}_1(t) \ \mathbf{x}_2(t)) = e^{-2t} \begin{pmatrix} 2\cos(2t) & 2\sin(2t) \\ -\sin(2t) & \cos(2t) \end{pmatrix}$$

is a fundamental matrix. Then

$$X(t)^{-1} = \frac{1}{2}e^{2t}\begin{pmatrix} \cos(2t) & -2\sin(2t) \\ \sin(2t) & 2\cos(2t) \end{pmatrix},$$

$$X(t)^{-1}\mathbf{f}(t) = \frac{1}{2}e^{2t}\begin{pmatrix} \cos(2t) & -2\sin(2t) \\ \sin(2t) & 2\cos(2t) \end{pmatrix}e^{-2t}\begin{pmatrix} 4 \\ 2 \end{pmatrix}$$

$$= \begin{pmatrix} 2\cos(2t) - 2\sin(2t) \\ 2\sin(2t) + 2\cos(2t) \end{pmatrix},$$

$$\int_0^t X(s)^{-1}\mathbf{f}(s)\,ds = \int_0^t \begin{pmatrix} 2\cos(2s) - 2\sin(2s) \\ 2\sin(2s) + 2\cos(2s) \end{pmatrix} ds$$

$$= \begin{pmatrix} \sin(2s) + \cos(2s) \\ -\cos(2s) + \sin(2s) \end{pmatrix}\Bigg|_0^t$$

$$= \begin{pmatrix} \sin(2t) + \cos(2t) - 1 \\ -\cos(2t) + \sin(2t) + 1 \end{pmatrix},$$

$$X(0)^{-1}\mathbf{x}(0) = \frac{1}{2}\begin{pmatrix} 1 & 0 \\ 0 & 2 \end{pmatrix}\begin{pmatrix} 2 \\ -1 \end{pmatrix} = \begin{pmatrix} 1 \\ -1 \end{pmatrix},$$

$$X(0)^{-1}\mathbf{x}(0) + \int_0^t X(s)^{-1}\mathbf{f}(s)\,ds = \begin{pmatrix} 1 \\ -1 \end{pmatrix} + \begin{pmatrix} \sin(2t) + \cos(2t) - 1 \\ -\cos(2t) + \sin(2t) + 1 \end{pmatrix}$$

$$= \begin{pmatrix} \sin(2t) + \cos(2t) \\ -\cos(2t) + \sin(2t) \end{pmatrix}$$

$$\Rightarrow \quad \mathbf{x}(t) = X(t)\left[X(0)^{-1}\mathbf{x}(0) + \int_0^t X(s)^{-1}\mathbf{f}(s)\,ds\right]$$

$$= e^{-2t}\begin{pmatrix} 2\cos(2t) & 2\sin(2t) \\ -\sin(2t) & \cos(2t) \end{pmatrix}\begin{pmatrix} \sin(2t) + \cos(2t) \\ -\cos(2t) + \sin(2t) \end{pmatrix}$$

$$= e^{-2t}\begin{pmatrix} 2 \\ -1 \end{pmatrix}$$

i.e., $x(t) = 2e^{-2t}$, $y(t) = -e^{-2t}$ is the solution of the initial-value problem (5.40).

Example 5.25. Consider the initial-value problem

$$\left\{\begin{array}{rcrcrr} x' & = & & -y & + & 2 \\ y' & = & x & - & 2y & + & t \end{array}\right\}, \quad x(0) = 3, \quad y(0) = 2. \tag{5.41}$$

This problem may be expressed in matrix form as $\mathbf{x}' = A\mathbf{x} + \mathbf{f}(t)$, $\mathbf{x}(0) = \mathbf{x}_0$, where

$$\mathbf{x} = \begin{pmatrix} x \\ y \end{pmatrix}, \quad A = \begin{pmatrix} 0 & -1 \\ 1 & -2 \end{pmatrix}, \quad \mathbf{f}(t) = \begin{pmatrix} 2 \\ t \end{pmatrix} \quad \text{and} \quad \mathbf{x}_0 = \begin{pmatrix} 3 \\ 2 \end{pmatrix}.$$

For the associated homogeneous system $\mathbf{x}' = A\mathbf{x}$,

$$\det(\lambda I - A) = \begin{vmatrix} \lambda & 1 \\ -1 & \lambda + 2 \end{vmatrix} = \lambda(\lambda + 2) + 1 = \lambda^2 + 2\lambda + 1$$
$$= (\lambda + 1)^2 = 0$$

$\Rightarrow \lambda_1 = -1$ is the only eigenvalue of A, of multiplicity $m_1 = 2$.

For $\lambda_1 = -1$, $(\lambda_1 I - A)\mathbf{v} = \mathbf{0}$ with $\mathbf{v} = \begin{pmatrix} a \\ b \end{pmatrix} \Rightarrow$

$$\begin{pmatrix} -1 & 1 \\ -1 & 1 \end{pmatrix} \begin{pmatrix} a \\ b \end{pmatrix} = \begin{pmatrix} 0 \\ 0 \end{pmatrix}$$

$\Rightarrow a = b$, and $a = 1 \Rightarrow \mathbf{v} = \mathbf{v}_1 = \begin{pmatrix} 1 \\ 1 \end{pmatrix}$ is an eigenvector which corresponds to the eigenvalue $\lambda_1 = -1$.

Hence, one solution of the homogeneous system is given by

$$\mathbf{x}_1(t) = e^{-t} \begin{pmatrix} 1 \\ 1 \end{pmatrix}.$$

A second, independent solution takes the form

$$\mathbf{x}_2(t) = e^{-t}(t\mathbf{u}_0 + \mathbf{u}_1),$$

where $\mathbf{u}_0 = \mathbf{v}_1$ is an eigenvector which corresponds to λ_1, and $\mathbf{u}_1$ is a solution of the algebraic system $(A - \lambda_1 I)\mathbf{u}_1 = \mathbf{u}_0$. With $\mathbf{u}_1 = \begin{pmatrix} a \\ b \end{pmatrix}$, $(A - \lambda_1 I)\mathbf{u}_1 = \mathbf{u}_0 \Rightarrow$

$$\begin{pmatrix} 1 & -1 \\ 1 & -1 \end{pmatrix} \begin{pmatrix} a \\ b \end{pmatrix} = \begin{pmatrix} 1 \\ 1 \end{pmatrix}$$

$\Rightarrow a - b = 1$, and $b = 0 \Rightarrow \mathbf{u}_1 = \begin{pmatrix} 1 \\ 0 \end{pmatrix} \Rightarrow$

$$\mathbf{x}_2(t) = e^{-t} \left[t \begin{pmatrix} 1 \\ 1 \end{pmatrix} + \begin{pmatrix} 1 \\ 0 \end{pmatrix} \right] = e^{-t} \begin{pmatrix} t + 1 \\ t \end{pmatrix},$$

and

$$X(t) = (\mathbf{x}_1(t)\ \mathbf{x}_2(t)) = e^{-t} \begin{pmatrix} 1 & t + 1 \\ 1 & t \end{pmatrix}$$

is a fundamental matrix. Then

$$X(t)^{-1} = -e^t \begin{pmatrix} t & -t-1 \\ -1 & 1 \end{pmatrix} = e^t \begin{pmatrix} -t & t+1 \\ 1 & -1 \end{pmatrix},$$

$$X(t)^{-1}\mathbf{f}(t) = e^t \begin{pmatrix} -t & t+1 \\ 1 & -1 \end{pmatrix}\begin{pmatrix} 2 \\ t \end{pmatrix} = e^t \begin{pmatrix} t^2 - t \\ 2 - t \end{pmatrix},$$

$$\int_0^t (s^2 - s)e^s \, ds = (s^2 - s)e^s \Big|_0^t - \int_0^t (2s - 1)e^s \, ds$$

$$= (t^2 - t)e^t - (2s - 1)e^s \Big|_0^t + 2\int_0^t e^s \, ds$$

$$= (t^2 - t)e^t - (2t - 1)e^t - 1 + 2e^s \Big|_0^t$$

$$= (t^2 - t)e^t - (2t - 1)e^t - 1 + 2e^t - 2$$

$$= (t^2 - 3t + 3)e^t - 3,$$

$$\int_0^t (2 - s)e^s \, ds = (2 - s)e^s \Big|_0^t + \int_0^t e^s \, ds$$

$$= (2 - t)e^t - 2 + e^t - 1$$

$$= (3 - t)e^t - 3,$$

$$\int_0^t X(s)^{-1}\mathbf{f}(s) \, ds = \int_0^t e^s \begin{pmatrix} s^2 - s \\ 2 - s \end{pmatrix} ds$$

$$= \begin{pmatrix} (t^2 - 3t + 3)e^t - 3 \\ (3 - t)e^t - 3 \end{pmatrix},$$

$$X(0)^{-1}\mathbf{x}(0) = \begin{pmatrix} 0 & 1 \\ 1 & -1 \end{pmatrix}\begin{pmatrix} 3 \\ 2 \end{pmatrix} = \begin{pmatrix} 2 \\ 1 \end{pmatrix},$$

$$X(0)^{-1}\mathbf{x}(0) + \int_0^t X(s)^{-1}\mathbf{f}(s) \, ds = \begin{pmatrix} 2 \\ 1 \end{pmatrix} + \begin{pmatrix} (t^2 - 3t + 3)e^t - 3 \\ (3 - t)e^t - 3 \end{pmatrix}$$

$$= \begin{pmatrix} (t^2 - 3t + 3)e^t - 1 \\ (3 - t)e^t - 2 \end{pmatrix}$$

$$\Rightarrow \mathbf{x}(t) = X(t)\left[X(0)^{-1}\mathbf{x}(0) + \int_0^t X(s)^{-1}\mathbf{f}(s) \, ds\right]$$

$$= e^{-t} \begin{pmatrix} 1 & t+1 \\ 1 & t \end{pmatrix}\begin{pmatrix} (t^2 - 3t + 3)e^t - 1 \\ (3 - t)e^t - 2 \end{pmatrix}$$

$$= \begin{pmatrix} 6 - t - 3e^{-t} - 2te^{-t} \\ 3 - e^{-t} - 2te^{-t} \end{pmatrix}$$

i.e, $x(t) = 6 - t - 3e^{-t} - 2te^{-t}$, $y(t) = 3 - e^{-t} - 2te^{-t}$ is the solution of the initial-value problem (5.41).

Example 5.26. Consider the initial-value problem

$$\begin{cases} x' = x \\ y' = 3x \quad - z + t\cos(t) \\ z' = -x + y \quad + t\sin(t) \end{cases}, \; x(0) = 1, \; y(0) = 2, \; z(0) = 1. \quad (5.42)$$

This problem may be expressed in matrix form as $\mathbf{x}' = A\mathbf{x} + \mathbf{f}(t)$, $\mathbf{x}(0) = \mathbf{x}_0$, where

$$\mathbf{x} = \begin{pmatrix} x \\ y \\ z \end{pmatrix}, \quad A = \begin{pmatrix} 1 & 0 & 0 \\ 3 & 0 & -1 \\ -1 & 1 & 0 \end{pmatrix}, \quad \mathbf{f}(t) = \begin{pmatrix} 0 \\ t\cos(t) \\ t\sin(t) \end{pmatrix} \quad \text{and} \quad \mathbf{x}_0 = \begin{pmatrix} 1 \\ 2 \\ 1 \end{pmatrix}.$$

For the associated homogeneous system $\mathbf{x}' = A\mathbf{x}$,

$$\det(\lambda I - A) = \begin{vmatrix} \lambda - 1 & 0 & 0 \\ -3 & \lambda & 1 \\ 1 & -1 & \lambda \end{vmatrix} = (\lambda - 1)(\lambda^2 + 1) = 0$$

$\Rightarrow \lambda_1 = 1$ and $\lambda_2, \overline{\lambda}_2 = \pm i$ are the eigenvalues of A.

For $\lambda_1 = 1$, $(\lambda_1 I - A)\mathbf{v} = \mathbf{0}$ with $\mathbf{v} = \begin{pmatrix} a \\ b \\ c \end{pmatrix} \Rightarrow$

$$\begin{pmatrix} 0 & 0 & 0 \\ -3 & 1 & 1 \\ 1 & -1 & 1 \end{pmatrix} \begin{pmatrix} a \\ b \\ c \end{pmatrix} = \begin{pmatrix} 0 \\ 0 \\ 0 \end{pmatrix} \Rightarrow \begin{pmatrix} 0 & 0 & 0 \\ -3 & 1 & 1 \\ 0 & -2 & 4 \end{pmatrix} \begin{pmatrix} a \\ b \\ c \end{pmatrix} = \begin{pmatrix} 0 \\ 0 \\ 0 \end{pmatrix}$$

$\Rightarrow b = 2c$ and $a = c$, and $c = 1 \Rightarrow \mathbf{v} = \mathbf{v}_1 = \begin{pmatrix} 1 \\ 2 \\ 1 \end{pmatrix} \Rightarrow$

$$\mathbf{x}_1(t) = e^t \begin{pmatrix} 1 \\ 2 \\ 1 \end{pmatrix}.$$

For $\lambda_2 = i$, $(\lambda_2 I - A)\mathbf{v} = \mathbf{0}$ with $\mathbf{v} = \begin{pmatrix} a \\ b \\ c \end{pmatrix} \Rightarrow$

$$\begin{pmatrix} i - 1 & 0 & 0 \\ -3 & i & 1 \\ 1 & -1 & i \end{pmatrix} \begin{pmatrix} a \\ b \\ c \end{pmatrix} = \begin{pmatrix} 0 \\ 0 \\ 0 \end{pmatrix}$$

$$\Rightarrow a = 0 \text{ and } b = ic, \text{ and } c = 1 \Rightarrow \mathbf{v} = \mathbf{v}_2 = \begin{pmatrix} 0 \\ i \\ 1 \end{pmatrix} \Rightarrow$$

$$\mathbf{z}(t) = [\cos(t) + i\sin(t)] \left[\begin{pmatrix} 0 \\ 0 \\ 1 \end{pmatrix} + i \begin{pmatrix} 0 \\ 1 \\ 0 \end{pmatrix} \right]$$

is a complex solution of the homogeneous system,

$$\mathbf{x}_2(t) = \cos(t) \begin{pmatrix} 0 \\ 0 \\ 1 \end{pmatrix} - \sin(t) \begin{pmatrix} 0 \\ 1 \\ 0 \end{pmatrix} = \begin{pmatrix} 0 \\ -\sin(t) \\ \cos(t) \end{pmatrix},$$

$$\mathbf{x}_3(t) = \sin(t) \begin{pmatrix} 0 \\ 0 \\ 1 \end{pmatrix} + \cos(t) \begin{pmatrix} 0 \\ 1 \\ 0 \end{pmatrix} = \begin{pmatrix} 0 \\ \cos(t) \\ \sin(t) \end{pmatrix}$$

are two real, independent solutions, and

$$X(t) = \begin{pmatrix} e^t & 0 & 0 \\ 2e^t & -\sin(t) & \cos(t) \\ e^t & \cos(t) & \sin(t) \end{pmatrix}$$

is a fundamental matrix. Then (see Appendix A.3 for inversion of matrices)

$$X(t)^{-1} = \begin{pmatrix} e^{-t} & 0 & 0 \\ 2\sin(t) - \cos(t) & -\sin(t) & \cos(t) \\ -\sin(t) - 2\cos(t) & \cos(t) & \sin(t) \end{pmatrix},$$

$$X(t)^{-1}\mathbf{f}(t) = \begin{pmatrix} e^{-t} & 0 & 0 \\ 2\sin(t) - \cos(t) & -\sin(t) & \cos(t) \\ -\sin(t) - 2\cos(t) & \cos(t) & \sin(t) \end{pmatrix} \begin{pmatrix} 0 \\ t\cos(t) \\ t\sin(t) \end{pmatrix} = \begin{pmatrix} 0 \\ 0 \\ t \end{pmatrix},$$

$$\int_0^t X(s)^{-1}\mathbf{f}(s)\,ds = \int_0^t \begin{pmatrix} 0 \\ 0 \\ s \end{pmatrix} ds = \begin{pmatrix} 0 \\ 0 \\ \frac{1}{2}t^2 \end{pmatrix},$$

$$X(0)^{-1}\mathbf{x}_0 = \begin{pmatrix} 1 & 0 & 0 \\ -1 & 0 & 1 \\ -2 & 1 & 0 \end{pmatrix} \begin{pmatrix} 1 \\ 2 \\ 1 \end{pmatrix} = \begin{pmatrix} 1 \\ 0 \\ 0 \end{pmatrix},$$

$$X(0)^{-1}\mathbf{x}_0 + \int_0^t X(s)^{-1}\mathbf{f}(s)\,ds = \begin{pmatrix} 1 \\ 0 \\ 0 \end{pmatrix} + \begin{pmatrix} 0 \\ 0 \\ \frac{1}{2}t^2 \end{pmatrix} = \begin{pmatrix} 1 \\ 0 \\ \frac{1}{2}t^2 \end{pmatrix}$$

$$\Rightarrow \quad \mathbf{x}(t) \;=\; X(t)\left[X(0)^{-1}\mathbf{x}_0 + \int_0^t X(s)^{-1}\mathbf{f}(s)\,ds\right]$$

$$= \begin{pmatrix} e^t & 0 & 0 \\ 2e^t & -\sin(t) & \cos(t) \\ e^t & \cos(t) & \sin(t) \end{pmatrix}\begin{pmatrix} 1 \\ 0 \\ \tfrac{1}{2}t^2 \end{pmatrix} = \begin{pmatrix} e^t \\ 2e^t + \tfrac{1}{2}t^2\cos(t) \\ e^t + \tfrac{1}{2}t^2\sin(t) \end{pmatrix},$$

i.e., $x(t) = e^t$, $y(t) = 2e^t + \dfrac{1}{2}t^2\cos(t)$, $z(t) = e^t + \dfrac{1}{2}t^2\sin(t)$ is the solution of the initial-value problem (5.42).

Exercises 5.2

1. Find the general solution of the system $\left\{ \begin{array}{l} x' = 2x + 3e^{2t} \\ y' = x - y + e^t \end{array} \right\}$.

2. Find the general solution of the system $\left\{ \begin{array}{l} x' = 4y + 4\cos(2t) \\ y' = -x - 2\sin(2t) \end{array} \right\}$.

3. Find the general solution of the system $\left\{ \begin{array}{l} x' = -x + 4y + t^2e^t \\ y' = -x + 3y + te^t \end{array} \right\}$.

4. Find the general solution of the system $\left\{ \begin{array}{l} x' = 2x - 2y \\ y' = x + 4y + 2 \end{array} \right\}$.

5. Solve the initial-value problem $\left\{ \begin{array}{l} x' = x + e^t \\ y' = 2y + 2e^{2t} \end{array} \right\}$, $x(0) = 3$, $y(0) = 2$.

6. Solve the initial-value problem $\left\{ \begin{array}{l} x' = -y + 1 \\ y' = x + 1 \end{array} \right\}$, $x(0) = 2$, $y(0) = 1$.

7. Solve the initial-value problem $\left\{ \begin{array}{l} x' = -2x - y + e^{-4t} \\ y' = 4x - 6y + 2e^{-4t} \end{array} \right\}$, $x(0) = 0$, $y(0) = 1$.

8. Solve the initial-value problem $\mathbf{x}' = A\mathbf{x} + \mathbf{f}(t)$, $\mathbf{x}(0) = \mathbf{x}_0$, where

$$\mathbf{x} = \begin{pmatrix} x \\ y \\ z \end{pmatrix},\ A = \begin{pmatrix} 1 & 0 & 0 \\ 4 & -1 & 0 \\ -1 & 0 & 2 \end{pmatrix},\ \mathbf{f}(t) = e^t\begin{pmatrix} 1 \\ 2 \\ -1 \end{pmatrix}\ \text{and}\ \mathbf{x}_0 = \begin{pmatrix} 1 \\ 3 \\ 1 \end{pmatrix}.$$

Chapter 5 Exercises

1. A differential equation of order $n \geq 2$ for the unknown function $y(t)$ can be transformed into a system of n first-order equations for the unknown functions $x_1(t)$, $x_2(t)$, $\cdots$, $x_n(t)$ by letting $x_1 = y$, $x_2 = y'$, $x_3 = y''$, $\cdots$, $x_n = y^{(n-1)}$. Consider the equation $y'' - 2y' + y = 0$.

(a) Find two independent solutions $y_1(t)$ and $y_2(t)$ of the equation, and the general solution $y(t)$.

(b) Transform the equation into a system of two first-order equations.

(c) Find two independent solutions $\mathbf{x}_1(t)$ and $\mathbf{x}_2(t)$ of the system in part (b), and the general solution $x_1(t)$, $x_2(t)$. Confirm that $x_1(t)$ is equivalent to $y(t)$.

(d) Compute the Wronskians $W[y_1(t)\ y_2(t)]$ and $W[\mathbf{x}_1(t)\ \mathbf{x}_2(t)]$ and compare the results.

2. Let $X(t)$ be a fundamental matrix for the system $\mathbf{x}' = A\mathbf{x}$.

(a) Find a fundamental matrix $Y(t)$ such that $Y(0) = I$, the identity matrix, and express the solution of the initial-value problem $\mathbf{x}' = A\mathbf{x}$, $\mathbf{x}(0) = \mathbf{x}_0$, in terms of $Y(t)$.

(b) Find a fundamental matrix $Z(t)$ such that $Z(t_0) = I$, where t_0 is a real number, and express the solution of the initial-value problem $\mathbf{x}' = A\mathbf{x}$, $\mathbf{x}(t_0) = \mathbf{x}_0$, in terms of $Z(t)$.

3. Consider the system $\left\{ \begin{array}{l} x' = 2x \\ y' = x - 2y \end{array} \right\}$.

(a) Find the general solution of the system.

(b) Solve the first equation in the system for $x(t)$, substitute into the second equation for x, and solve the second equation for $y(t)$. Confirm that your answer is equivalent to the one in part (a).

(c) Differentiate the second equation in the system and eliminate x and x' in order to obtain a second-order equation for $y(t)$.

(d) Solve the equation in part (c) for $y(t)$, determine $x(t)$, and confirm that your solution is equivalent to the one in part (a).

4. An $n \times n$ matrix A is *diagonalizable*, i.e., there exists a nonsingular matrix P such that $P^{-1}AP = D$ is a diagonal matrix, if and only if A admits n independent eigenvectors. Then D has the eigenvalues of A along its diagonal, and the columns of P are the eigenvectors of A. Consider the system $\mathbf{x}' = A\mathbf{x}$, where $A = \begin{pmatrix} -7 & 12 \\ -4 & 7 \end{pmatrix}$.

(a) Find the general solution.

(b) Determine a new unknown $\mathbf{y}$ in terms of $\mathbf{x}$ such that the system $\mathbf{x}' = A\mathbf{x}$ for $\mathbf{x}$ transforms into an equivalent system $\mathbf{y}' = D\mathbf{y}$ for $\mathbf{y}$.

(c) Solve the system in part (b) for $\mathbf{y}(t)$.

(d) Determine $\mathbf{x}(t)$ from $\mathbf{y}(t)$ in part (c) and confirm that your answer is equivalent to the one in part (a).

5. Find a fundamental matrix for the system $\mathbf{x}' = A\mathbf{x}$, where $A = \begin{pmatrix} 1 & 0 & 0 & 0 \\ 0 & 1 & 0 & 0 \\ 0 & 0 & 1 & 1 \\ 0 & 0 & 0 & 1 \end{pmatrix}$, by generalizing the method employed in Examples 5.15 and 5.16.

6. Find a fundamental matrix for the system $\mathbf{x}' = A\mathbf{x}$, where $A = \begin{pmatrix} 1 & 1 & 0 & 0 \\ 0 & 1 & 1 & 0 \\ 0 & 0 & 1 & 1 \\ 0 & 0 & 0 & 1 \end{pmatrix}$, by generalizing the method employed in Examples 5.17 and 5.18 and taking

$$\mathbf{x}_4(t) = e^{\lambda t} \left[\frac{1}{6} t^3 \mathbf{u}_0 + \frac{1}{2} t^2 \mathbf{u}_1 + t \mathbf{u}_2 + \mathbf{u}_3 \right].$$

In general, the subscripts of the vectors $\mathbf{u}_n$, from left to right, are $n = 0, 1, 2, 3, \cdots$, and their coefficients, from right to left, are $\dfrac{t^n}{n!}$, $n = 0, 1, 2, 3, \cdots$. The latter *sequence* of functions has a special significance, and will be encountered in Part II of this book.

7. Let $\lambda = \alpha + i\beta$ be a complex eigenvalue of an $n \times n$ matrix A, with the corresponding complex eigenvector $\mathbf{v} = \mathbf{a} + i\mathbf{b}$. Show that the corresponding two real solutions

$$\mathbf{x}_1(t) = e^{\alpha t}[\cos(\beta t)\mathbf{a} - \sin(\beta t)\mathbf{b}] \quad \text{and} \quad \mathbf{x}_2(t) = e^{\alpha t}[\sin(\beta t)\mathbf{a} + \cos(\beta t)\mathbf{b}]$$

are linearly independent.

Part II
Infinite Series

Chapter 6

Sequences and Series

Infinite sequences and series arise in such numerous applications that neither science nor engineering would be possible in its present form without them. Sequences and series are defined in the present chapter. More specialized forms of series and some of their applications will be discussed in subsequent chapters.

All of the linear differential equations solved in Part I of this book are equations with constant coefficients, with the exception of Cauchy-Euler equations, which are of such a special form that they can be transformed into equations with constant coefficients. In general, an equation with variable coefficients such as

$$y'' + xy' + y = 0 \tag{6.1}$$

can be solved only by means of infinite series. In the final chapter of this book, we shall have gathered sufficient knowledge to solve Equation (6.1).

6.1 Sequences

Definition 6.1. Let f be a real-valued function and k an integer. The *ordered set* of values of f at the integers k, $k+1$, $k+2$, $\cdots$, i.e.,

$$\{f(k),\ f(k+1),\ f(k+2),\ \cdots\},$$

is called a *sequence* of real numbers. The integer k is the *initial value* of n. It is customary to let $f(n) = a_n$ (or b_n or c_n), called the *general term* of the sequence, and to express the sequence as

$$\{a_k,\ a_{k+1},\ a_{k+2},\ \cdots\}$$

or, more concisely, as $\{a_n\}_{n=k}^{\infty}$.

Example 6.1. The ordered set of real numbers

$$\left\{1, \frac{1}{2}, \frac{1}{3}, \frac{1}{4}, \cdots\right\}$$

is a sequence with $a_n = \dfrac{1}{n}$ and $k = 1$. It may be expressed as $\left\{\dfrac{1}{n}\right\}_{n=1}^{\infty}$.

Example 6.2. The ordered set of real numbers

$$\left\{1, \frac{1}{2}, \frac{1}{4}, \frac{1}{8}, \frac{1}{16}, \cdots\right\}$$

is a sequence with $a_n = \dfrac{1}{2^n}$ and $k = 0$. It may be expressed as $\left\{\dfrac{1}{2^n}\right\}_{n=0}^{\infty}$.

Example 6.3. The ordered set of real numbers

$$\{-4, \ -2, \ 0, \ 2, \ 4, \ 6, \ \cdots\}$$

is a sequence with $a_n = 2n$ and $k = -2$. It may be expressed as $\{2n\}_{n=-2}^{\infty}$.

Example 6.4. The ordered set of real numbers

$$\{2, \ 3, \ 4, \ 5, \ \cdots\}$$

is a sequence with $a_n = n$ and $k = 2$, or $a_n = n + 1$ and $k = 1$, or $a_n = n + 2$ and $k = 0$. Thus, the representation of a sequence as $\{a_n\}_{n=k}^{\infty}$ is not unique. Hence,

$$\{2, \ 3, \ 4, \ 5, \ \cdots\} = \{n\}_{n=2}^{\infty} = \{n+1\}_{n=1}^{\infty} = \{n+2\}_{n=0}^{\infty},$$

but $\{n\}_{n=2}^{\infty}$ is the simplest.

Example 6.5. The ordered set of real numbers

$$\{1, \ -1, \ 1, \ -1, \ 1, \ -1, \ \cdots\}$$

is a sequence with $a_n = (-1)^n$ and $k = 0$, or $a_n = (-1)^n$ and $k = 2$, or $a_n = (-1)^{n-1}$ and $k = 1$.

Example 6.6. The sequence $\{a_n\}_{n=0}^{\infty}$, where $a_n = \dfrac{n}{\sqrt{n+1}}$, is

$$\left\{0, \ \frac{1}{\sqrt{2}}, \ \frac{2}{\sqrt{3}}, \ \frac{3}{2}, \ \frac{4}{\sqrt{5}}, \ \cdots\right\}.$$

Example 6.7. The *Fibonacci sequence* is defined by

$$a_1 = 1, \quad a_2 = 1, \quad \text{and} \quad a_n = a_{n-1} + a_{n-2} \quad \text{for} \quad n \geq 3.$$

The first few terms are

$$\{1, \ 1, \ 2, \ 3, \ 5, \ 8, \ 13, \ 21, \ 34, \ \cdots\}.$$

Such a sequence, where the terms are not given explicitly in terms of n, but in terms of preceding terms, is said to be defined *inductively*.

Given a sequence $\{a_n\}_{n=k}^{\infty}$, it is frequently the case that the initial value k of n is irrelevant. In that case, the sequence is expressed simply as $\{a_n\}$. One such instance is when it is necessary to determine whether or not the terms a_n approach a unique, finite number as n is increased indefinitely.

Definition 6.2. Given a sequence $\{a_n\}$,

$$\lim_{n \to \infty} a_n = L$$

means that, the absolute value of the difference (i.e., the distance) between a_n and L can be made arbitrarily close to 0 by taking n sufficiently large. More rigorously, for any $\varepsilon > 0$, however small, there exists an integer N, which depends upon ε, such that

$$n \geq N \quad \Rightarrow \quad |a_n - L| < \varepsilon.$$

If $\lim_{n \to \infty} a_n = L$, the sequence $\{a_n\}$ is said to *converge* to L, and L is called the *limit* of the sequence. The notation $a_n \to L$ as $n \to \infty$ is also employed. If no such L exists, then the sequence is said to *diverge*, and $\lim_{n \to \infty} a_n$ does not exist.

Example 6.8. It is clear that the number $\dfrac{1}{n}$ can be made arbitrarily close to 0 by taking n sufficiently large. For example, in order to make $\dfrac{1}{n} < 10^{-10}$, take $n > 10^{10}$. In order to make $\dfrac{1}{n} < 10^{-100}$, take $n > 10^{100}$, etc. Hence,

$$\lim_{n \to \infty} \frac{1}{n} = 0.$$

Formally, for any $\varepsilon > 0$, $\left|\dfrac{1}{n} - 0\right| = \dfrac{1}{n} < \varepsilon$ if and only if $n > \dfrac{1}{\varepsilon}$. Hence, it suffices to let N be any integer such that $N > \dfrac{1}{\varepsilon}$. Then

$$n \geq N \quad \Rightarrow \quad n > \frac{1}{\varepsilon} \quad \Rightarrow \quad \frac{1}{n} < \varepsilon \quad \Rightarrow \quad \left|\frac{1}{n} - 0\right| < \varepsilon,$$

which *proves* that the sequence $\left\{\dfrac{1}{n}\right\}$ converges to 0.

Notice the manner in which this proof would fail if we made the false assumption that $\lim\limits_{n\to\infty} a_n = L$ where $L \neq 0$. For example, if we take $L = 17$, then

$$\left|\frac{1}{n} - 17\right| \geq 16$$

for *all* $n \neq 0$, and, hence, $\left|\dfrac{1}{n} - 17\right| < \varepsilon$ is impossible for any $\varepsilon \leq 16$.

Example 6.9. Let c be a constant. In the present context, a *constant* is any number independent of the "variable" n. The sequence

$$\{c\} = \{c, \ c, \ c, \ \cdots\}$$

converges to c, i.e., $\lim\limits_{n\to\infty} c = c$ since, for any $\varepsilon > 0$, $|c - c| = 0 < \varepsilon$ for all $n \geq 1$.

Example 6.10. As in Example 6.8, the sequence $\left\{\dfrac{1}{n^2}\right\}$ converges to 0 since $\dfrac{1}{n^2}$ can be made arbitrarily close to 0 by taking n sufficiently large. More generally,

$$\lim_{n\to\infty} \frac{1}{n^p} = 0$$

for any real number $p > 0$ since, for any $\varepsilon > 0$, let $N > \dfrac{1}{\varepsilon^{1/p}}$. Then

$$n \geq N \quad \Rightarrow \quad n > \frac{1}{\varepsilon^{1/p}} \quad \Rightarrow \quad \frac{1}{n} < \varepsilon^{1/p} \quad \Rightarrow \quad \frac{1}{n^p} < \varepsilon \quad \Rightarrow \quad \left|\frac{1}{n^p} - 0\right| < \varepsilon.$$

If $p = 0$, then $\lim\limits_{n\to\infty} \dfrac{1}{n^p} = \lim\limits_{n\to\infty} 1 = 1$. If $p < 0$, then $\lim\limits_{n\to\infty} \dfrac{1}{n^p}$ does not exist because $\dfrac{1}{n^p} = n^{-p}$, with $-p > 0$, increases indefinitely as n increases indefinitely. Thus, the sequence $\left\{\dfrac{1}{n^p}\right\}$ converges for $p \geq 0$ and diverges for $p < 0$.

Example 6.11. Consider the sequence $\{(-1)^n\}$ of Example 6.5.

$$\lim_{n\to\infty} (-1)^n$$

does not exist because $a_n = (-1)^n$ takes both of the values 1 and -1 regardless of how large n is and, hence, the terms a_n do not approach a unique number. Thus, the sequence $\{(-1)^n\}$ diverges.

Example 6.12. $\lim\limits_{n\to\infty} \sin(n)$ does not exist because $\sin(n)$ oscillates and does not remain close to any one number regardless of how large n is. Hence, the sequence $\{\sin(n)\}$ diverges.

Example 6.13. The number $\dfrac{1}{2^n}$ can be made arbitrarily close to 0 by taking n sufficiently large. Hence,

$$\lim_{n\to\infty} \frac{1}{2^n} = 0,$$

i.e., the sequence $\left\{\dfrac{1}{2^n}\right\}$ converges to 0.

Example 6.14. Let r be a real number, and consider the sequence $\{r^n\}_{n=0}^{\infty}$. We shall determine those values of r for which the sequence converges, and find the limit.

If $r > 1$, then r^n increases indefinitely as n increases indefinitely; hence, the sequence $\{r^n\}$ diverges.

If $r = 1$, then $r^n = 1$ for all $n \geq 0$; hence, the sequence $\{r^n\}$ converges to 1.

If $|r| < 1$, i.e., $-1 < r < 1$, then r^n can be made arbitrarily close to 0 by taking n sufficiently large; hence, the sequence $\{r^n\}$ converges to 0.

If $r \leq -1$, then r^n alternates between positive and negative values, with $r^n \geq 1$ if n is even and $r^n \leq -1$ if n is odd; hence, the sequence $\{r^n\}$ diverges.

Theorem 6.1. Let $\{a_n\}$ and $\{b_n\}$ be convergent sequences, with $\lim\limits_{n\to\infty} a_n = L$ and $\lim\limits_{n\to\infty} b_n = M$. Then:

1. The sequence $\{a_n + b_n\}$ converges, and $\lim\limits_{n\to\infty} (a_n + b_n) = L + M$.

2. The sequence $\{ca_n\}$ converges for any constant c, and $\lim\limits_{n\to\infty} ca_n = cL$.

3. The sequence $\{a_n b_n\}$ converges, and $\lim\limits_{n\to\infty} a_n b_n = LM$.

4. The sequence $\left\{\dfrac{a_n}{b_n}\right\}$ converges if $M \neq 0$, and $\lim\limits_{n\to\infty} \dfrac{a_n}{b_n} = \dfrac{L}{M}$.

Example 6.15. By Example 6.10, $\lim\limits_{n\to\infty} \dfrac{1}{n^2} = 0$ and $\lim\limits_{n\to\infty} \dfrac{1}{n^3} = 0$. Hence, by item 2 of Theorem 6.1 with $c = -1$, $\lim\limits_{n\to\infty} \left(-\dfrac{1}{n^3}\right) = 0$ and, by item 1, $\lim\limits_{n\to\infty} \left(\dfrac{1}{n^2} - \dfrac{1}{n^3}\right) = 0$.

Example 6.16. Since the sequence $\left\{\dfrac{1}{n}\right\}$ converges to 0 by Example 6.8 and the sequence $\{1\}$ converges to 1 by Example 6.9 with $c = 1$, it follows by Theorem 6.1 that the sequence $\left\{1 - \dfrac{1}{n}\right\}$ converges to 1.

Example 6.17. If either $\{a_n\}$ or $\{b_n\}$ diverges, then Theorem 6.1 is not applicable, and sums, differences, products and quotients of such sequences may converge or may diverge, depending upon the particular sequences.

Both of the sequences $\{n^2\}$ and $\{n^3\}$ diverge because their terms increase indefinitely as n increases indefinitely, and $\{n^3 - n^2\}$ diverges. The limit is *not* 0.
Both of the sequences $\{\sqrt{n+1}\}$ and $\{\sqrt{n}\}$ diverge, but

$$\sqrt{n+1} - \sqrt{n} = \left(\sqrt{n+1} - \sqrt{n}\right)\frac{\sqrt{n+1} + \sqrt{n}}{\sqrt{n+1} + \sqrt{n}} = \frac{1}{\sqrt{n+1} + \sqrt{n}}$$

converges to 0 since the denominator can be made arbitrarily large and, hence, the fraction arbitrarily close to 0, by taking n sufficiently large.

The sequence $\left\{\dfrac{1}{n}\right\}$ converges to 0 and the sequence $\{n^2\}$ diverges. The product $\left\{\dfrac{1}{n}n^2\right\} = \{n\}$ diverges.

The sequence $\left\{\dfrac{1}{n^3}\right\}$ converges to 0 and the sequence $\{n^2\}$ diverges. The product $\left\{\dfrac{1}{n^3}n^2\right\} = \left\{\dfrac{1}{n}\right\}$ converges.

Example 6.18. Consider the sequence $\left\{\dfrac{n^3 - n^2 + 1}{2n^3 + n - 1}\right\}$. In order to determine the limit of such an expression, divide the numerator and the denominator by n^r, where r is the greatest exponent of n in the denominator. In the present case, $r = 3$, and

$$\frac{n^3 - n^2 + 1}{2n^3 + n - 1} = \frac{1 - \frac{1}{n} + \frac{1}{n^3}}{2 + \frac{1}{n^2} - \frac{1}{n^3}}.$$

Since $\lim\limits_{n\to\infty} \dfrac{1}{n} = 0$, $\lim\limits_{n\to\infty} \dfrac{1}{n^2} = 0$, $\lim\limits_{n\to\infty} \dfrac{1}{n^3} = 0$ and $\lim\limits_{n\to\infty} c = c$ for any constant c,

$$\lim_{n\to\infty}\left(1 - \frac{1}{n} + \frac{1}{n^3}\right) = 1 \quad \text{and} \quad \lim_{n\to\infty}\left(2 + \frac{1}{n^2} - \frac{1}{n^3}\right) = 2$$

by Theorem 6.1. Hence, $\lim\limits_{n\to\infty} \dfrac{n^3 - n^2 + 1}{2n^3 + n - 1} = \dfrac{1}{2}$.

Example 6.19. Consider the sequence $\left\{ \dfrac{2n+1}{\sqrt{3n^2+3n+5}} \right\}$. Divide the numerator and the denominator by $n = \sqrt{n^2}$ to obtain

$$\frac{2n+1}{\sqrt{3n^2+3n+5}} = \frac{2+\frac{1}{n}}{\sqrt{3+\frac{3}{n}+\frac{5}{n^2}}},$$

which converges to $\dfrac{2}{\sqrt{3}}$ as $n \to \infty$.

Definition 6.3. Given a sequence $\{a_n\}$,

$$\lim_{n\to\infty} a_n = \infty$$

means that a_n can be made arbitrarily large by taking n sufficiently large. More rigorously, for any $K > 0$, however large, there exists an integer N, which depends upon K, such that

$$n \geq N \quad \Rightarrow \quad a_n > K.$$

Similarly,

$$\lim_{n\to\infty} a_n = -\infty$$

means that $|a_n|$ can be made arbitrarily large with $a_n < 0$ by taking n sufficiently large. More rigorously, for any $K > 0$, however large, there exists an integer N, which depends upon K, such that

$$n \geq N \quad \Rightarrow \quad a_n < -K.$$

In either case, the sequence $\{a_n\}$ diverges.

Example 6.20. The terms of the sequence $\{n^3\}$ can be made arbitrarily large by taking n sufficiently large. Formally, for any $K > 0$, let $N > K^{1/3}$. Then

$$n \geq N \quad \Rightarrow \quad n > K^{1/3} \quad \Rightarrow \quad n^3 > K$$

$\Rightarrow \lim_{n\to\infty} n^3 = \infty$ and the sequence $\{n^3\}$ diverges. Similarly, $\lim_{n\to\infty} (-n^3) = -\infty$ and the sequence $\{-n^3\}$ diverges.

Definition 6.3 is useful in distinguishing sequences $\{a_n\}$ with $\lim_{n\to\infty} a_n = \pm\infty$ from other divergent sequences such as $\{\sin(n)\}$ and $\{(-1)^n\}$.

In general, it is difficult to determine the convergence or divergence of a sequence directly from first principles, especially for more complicated sequences, and several theorems are available in order to facilitate this task.

Theorem 6.2. For any sequence $\{a_n\}$,

$$\lim_{n\to\infty} a_n = 0 \quad \text{if and only if} \quad \lim_{n\to\infty} |a_n| = 0.$$

Proof. a_n is close to 0 if and only if $|a_n|$ is close to 0.

Example 6.21. Since

$$\lim_{n\to\infty} \left| \frac{(-1)^n}{n} \right| = \lim_{n\to\infty} \frac{1}{n} = 0,$$

it follows, by Theorem 6.2, that $\lim\limits_{n\to\infty} \dfrac{(-1)^n}{n} = 0$.

Theorem 6.3. Let f be a real-valued function and let $a_n = f(n)$. Then

$$\lim_{x\to\infty} f(x) = L \quad \Rightarrow \quad \lim_{n\to\infty} a_n = L.$$

In other words, if $\lim\limits_{x\to\infty} f(x) = L$, then it is also true that $\lim\limits_{n\to\infty} a_n = L$.

The converse of Theorem 6.3 is false, i.e., if $\lim\limits_{n\to\infty} a_n = L$, then it may or may not be true that $\lim\limits_{x\to\infty} f(x) = L$. For example, let $f(x) = \sin(\pi x)$. Then $a_n = \sin(\pi n) = 0$ for all n and, hence, $\lim\limits_{n\to\infty} a_n = 0$, but $\lim\limits_{x\to\infty} f(x)$ does not exist.

Example 6.22. Consider the sequence $\left\{ \dfrac{\ln(n)}{n} \right\}$. In order to determine the limit of the sequence, let $f(x) = \dfrac{\ln(x)}{x}$, and employ L'Hôpital's rule to determine $\lim\limits_{x\to\infty} f(x)$.

$$\lim_{x\to\infty} \frac{\ln(x)}{x} = \lim_{x\to\infty} \frac{\frac{1}{x}}{1} = 0 \quad \Rightarrow \quad \lim_{n\to\infty} \frac{\ln(n)}{n} = 0,$$

by Theorem 6.3.

Example 6.23. Consider the sequence $\left\{ \left(1 + \dfrac{1}{n} \right)^n \right\}$. In order to determine the limit of the sequence, let $f(x) = \left(1 + \dfrac{1}{x} \right)^x$, and employ the fact that

$$f(x) = e^{\ln[f(x)]} = e^{\ln\left[\left(1 + \frac{1}{x} \right)^x \right]} = e^{x \ln\left(1 + \frac{1}{x} \right)}.$$

Since the exponential function is continuous,

$$\lim_{x\to\infty} e^{x \ln\left(1 + \frac{1}{x} \right)} = e^{\lim\limits_{x\to\infty} \left[x \ln\left(1 + \frac{1}{x} \right) \right]},$$

and

$$\lim_{x \to \infty} x \ln\left(1 + \frac{1}{x}\right) = \lim_{x \to \infty} \frac{\ln\left(1 + \frac{1}{x}\right)}{\frac{1}{x}},$$

which is of the form $\frac{0}{0}$ and, hence, L'Hôpital's rule can be applied. Thus,

$$\lim_{x \to \infty} \frac{\ln(1 + \frac{1}{x})}{\frac{1}{x}} = \lim_{x \to \infty} \frac{\frac{1}{1 + \frac{1}{x}}\left(-\frac{1}{x^2}\right)}{-\frac{1}{x^2}} = \lim_{x \to \infty} \frac{1}{1 + \frac{1}{x}} = 1$$

$$\Rightarrow \lim_{x \to \infty} f(x) = e^1 = e \Rightarrow \lim_{n \to \infty} \left(1 + \frac{1}{n}\right)^n = e,$$

by Theorem 6.3.

Theorem 6.4. Let $\{a_n\}$, $\{b_n\}$ and $\{c_n\}$ be sequences, and suppose that

$$a_n \leq b_n \leq c_n \ \text{ for all } \ n \geq k,$$

where k is an integer. Then

$$\lim_{n \to \infty} a_n = \lim_{n \to \infty} c_n = L \ \Rightarrow \ \lim_{n \to \infty} b_n = L.$$

This theorem is called the *squeeze theorem* because the terms of the sequence $\{b_n\}$ are "squeezed" between the corresponding terms of the sequences $\{a_n\}$ and $\{b_n\}$.

Example 6.24. Consider the sequence $\left\{\dfrac{\sin(n)}{n}\right\}_{n=1}^{\infty}$. Since $-1 \leq \sin(n) \leq 1$, we obtain the inequalities

$$-\frac{1}{n} \leq \frac{\sin(n)}{n} \leq \frac{1}{n}.$$

By Theorem 6.4, $\lim_{n \to \infty}\left(-\frac{1}{n}\right) = 0$ and $\lim_{n \to \infty}\left(\frac{1}{n}\right) = 0 \Rightarrow \lim_{n \to \infty} \frac{\sin(n)}{n} = 0$.

Alternatively, since $0 \leq |\sin(n)| \leq 1$, we obtain the inequalities

$$0 \leq \left|\frac{\sin(n)}{n}\right| \leq \frac{1}{n}.$$

By Theorem 6.4, $\lim_{n \to \infty} 0 = 0$ and $\lim_{n \to \infty}\left(\frac{1}{n}\right) = 0 \Rightarrow \lim_{n \to \infty}\left|\frac{\sin(n)}{n}\right| = 0$ and, hence, $\lim_{n \to \infty} \frac{\sin(n)}{n} = 0$ by Theorem 6.2.

Example 6.25. Consider the sequence $\{a_n\}_{n=1}^{\infty}$, where $a_n = \dfrac{2^n}{n!}$. Then

$$a_n = \frac{2 \cdot 2 \cdot 2 \cdots 2 \cdot 2}{1 \cdot 2 \cdot 3 \cdots (n-1) \cdot n} = \frac{2}{1} \cdot \frac{2}{2} \cdot \frac{2}{3} \cdots \frac{2}{n-1} \cdot \frac{2}{n}.$$

If $n = 1$, then $a_1 = 2 \le \dfrac{4}{n}$. If $n = 2$, then $a_2 = 2 \le \dfrac{4}{n}$. If $n \ge 3$, then

$$\frac{2}{2} \cdot \frac{2}{3} \cdots \frac{2}{n-1} \le 1 \quad \Rightarrow \quad \frac{2}{1} \cdot \frac{2}{2} \cdot \frac{2}{3} \cdots \frac{2}{n-1} \le 2 \quad \Rightarrow \quad a_n \le \frac{4}{n}.$$

Hence,

$$0 \le a_n \le \frac{4}{n} \quad \text{for all} \ \ n \ge 1.$$

Since $\lim\limits_{n \to \infty} 0 = 0$ and $\lim\limits_{n \to \infty} \dfrac{4}{n} = 0$, it follows by Theorem 6.4 that $\lim\limits_{n \to \infty} a_n = 0$.

Example 6.26. Consider the sequence $\{a_n\}_{n=1}^{\infty}$, where $a_n = \dfrac{n!}{n^n}$. Then

$$a_n = \frac{1 \cdot 2 \cdot 3 \cdots (n-1) \cdot n}{n \cdot n \cdot n \cdots n \cdot n} = \frac{1}{n} \cdot \frac{2}{n} \cdot \frac{3}{n} \cdots \frac{n-1}{n} \cdot \frac{n}{n},$$

$a_1 = 1$ and, for $n \ge 2$,

$$\frac{2}{n} \cdot \frac{3}{n} \cdots \frac{n-1}{n} \cdot \frac{n}{n} \le 1 \quad \Rightarrow \quad a_n \le \frac{1}{n}.$$

Hence,

$$0 \le a_n \le \frac{1}{n} \quad \text{for all} \ \ n \ge 1.$$

Since $\lim\limits_{n \to \infty} 0 = 0$ and $\lim\limits_{n \to \infty} \dfrac{1}{n} = 0$, it follows by Theorem 6.4 that $\lim\limits_{n \to \infty} a_n = 0$.

Definition 6.4. A sequence $\{a_n\}$ is *increasing* for $n \ge N$, where N is an integer, if

$$a_{n+1} \ge a_n \quad \text{for all} \ \ n \ge N.$$

It is *decreasing* for $n \ge N$ if

$$a_{n+1} \le a_n \quad \text{for all} \ \ n \ge N.$$

A sequence which is either increasing or decreasing is called *monotone*.

Example 6.27. The sequence $\{a_n\} = \left\{ \dfrac{1}{n} \right\}$ is decreasing for $n \ge 1$ because

$$a_{n+1} = \frac{1}{n+1} < \frac{1}{n} = a_n \quad \text{for all} \ \ n \ge 1.$$

Example 6.28. The sequence $\{a_n\} = \left\{1 - \dfrac{1}{2^n}\right\}$ is increasing for $n \geq 0$ because

$$2^n < 2^{n+1} \quad \Rightarrow \quad \frac{1}{2^n} > \frac{1}{2^{n+1}} \quad \Rightarrow \quad -\frac{1}{2^n} < -\frac{1}{2^{n+1}} \quad \Rightarrow \quad 1 - \frac{1}{2^n} < 1 - \frac{1}{2^{n+1}},$$

i.e., $a_n < a_{n+1}$ for all $n \geq 0$.

Example 6.29. Consider the sequence $\{a_n\}_{n=1}^{\infty}$, where $a_n = ne^{-\frac{n^2}{8}}$. In order to determine whether or not this sequence is monotone, let $f(x) = xe^{-\frac{x^2}{8}}$. Then

$$f'(x) = e^{-\frac{x^2}{8}} + xe^{-\frac{x^2}{8}}\left(-\frac{x}{4}\right) = e^{-\frac{x^2}{8}}\left(1 - \frac{x^2}{4}\right) < 0 \quad \text{for} \quad x > 2.$$

It follows that the function f is decreasing for $x > 2$ and, hence, the sequence $\{a_n\}$ is decreasing for $n \geq 3 > 2$.

Example 6.30. The sequences $\{(-1)^n\}$ and $\{\sin(n)\}$ are not monotone because none of the inequalities in Definition 6.4 can hold for all $n \geq N$ for any integer N.

Definition 6.5. A sequence $\{a_n\}_{n=k}^{\infty}$ is *bounded above* if there exists a real number K such that $a_n \leq K$ for all $n \geq k$. It is *bounded below* if there exists a real number M such that $a_n \geq M$ for all $n \geq k$. It is *bounded* if it is bounded above and bounded below, i.e., there exist real numbers K and M such that $M \leq a_n \leq K$ for all $n \geq k$. A sequence which is not bounded is called *unbounded*. K is called an *upper bound*, and M a *lower bound* of the sequence.

Example 6.31. The sequence $\left\{\dfrac{n}{n+1}\right\}_{n=0}^{\infty}$ is bounded because

$$0 \leq \frac{n}{n+1} \leq 1 \quad \text{for all} \quad n \geq 0.$$

Here, $M = 0$ and $K = 1$. These numbers are not unique since any $M \leq 0$ and $K \geq 1$ are also lower and upper bounds of the sequence, respectively.

Example 6.32. The sequence $\{2^n\}_{n=1}^{\infty}$ is bounded below because

$$2^n \geq 2 \quad \text{for all} \quad n \geq 1.$$

It is not bounded above because $\lim\limits_{n \to \infty} 2^n = \infty$, i.e., 2^n can be made arbitrarily large by taking n sufficiently large and, hence, it is impossible to have $2^n \leq K$ for all $n \geq 1$, for any real number K. Thus, $\{2^n\}_{n=1}^{\infty}$ is unbounded.

Example 6.33. The sequence $\{1-n\}_{n=1}^{\infty}$ is bounded above because

$$n \geq 1 \quad \Rightarrow \quad -n \leq -1 \quad \Rightarrow \quad a_n = 1-n \leq 0.$$

It is not bounded below because $\lim_{n\to\infty}(1-n) = -\infty$. Thus, it is unbounded.

Theorem 6.5. A sequence $\{a_n\}_{n=k}^{\infty}$ is bounded if and only if the sequence $\{|a_n|\}_{n=k}^{\infty}$ is bounded above.

Proof. If $\{a_n\}_{n=k}^{\infty}$ is bounded, then there exist real numbers M and K such that $M \leq a_n \leq K$ for all $n \geq k$. Let $L = \max\{|M|, |K|\}$. Then

$$M \leq a_n \leq K \quad \Rightarrow \quad -L \leq a_n \leq L \quad \Rightarrow \quad |a_n| \leq L,$$

i.e., $\{|a_n|\}_{n=k}^{\infty}$ is bounded above. Conversely, if $\{|a_n|\}_{n=k}^{\infty}$ is bounded above, then there exists a real number K such that $|a_n| \leq K$ for all $n \geq k$, and

$$|a_n| \leq K \quad \Rightarrow \quad -K \leq a_n \leq K,$$

i.e., $\{a_n\}_{n=k}^{\infty}$ is bounded.

Example 6.34. The sequence $\{\sin(n)\}_{n=0}^{\infty}$ is bounded because $-1 \leq \sin(n) \leq 1$, which is equivalent to $|\sin(n)| \leq 1$, i.e., the sequence $\{|\sin(n)|\}_{n=0}^{\infty}$ is bounded above.

Theorem 6.6. If a sequence $\{a_n\}_{n=k}^{\infty}$ is increasing for $n \geq N$, where N is an integer, and bounded above, then it converges. If it is decreasing for $n \geq N$ and bounded below, then it converges. If it is monotone for $n \geq N$ and bounded, then it converges.

Example 6.35. The sequence $\left\{\dfrac{1}{n}\right\}_{n=1}^{\infty}$ is decreasing for $n \geq 1$ since $\dfrac{1}{n+1} < \dfrac{1}{n}$ for all $n \geq 1$, and it is bounded below since $\dfrac{1}{n} > 0$ for all $n \geq 1$. Hence, by Theorem 6.6, it converges, a result which has already been established in Example 6.8.

Example 6.36. The sequence $\left\{1-e^{-n}\right\}_{n=0}^{\infty}$ is increasing for $n \geq 0$ because

$$e^{n+1} > e^n \quad \Rightarrow \quad e^{-n} > e^{-(n+1)} \quad \Rightarrow \quad a_n = 1-e^{-n} < 1-e^{-(n+1)} = a_{n+1},$$

and it is bounded above since

$$e^{-n} > 0 \quad \Rightarrow \quad -e^{-n} < 0 \quad \Rightarrow \quad a_n = 1-e^{-n} < 1 \text{ for all } n \geq 0.$$

Hence, by Theorem 6.6, it converges. Note that the sequence $\left\{e^{-n}\right\}_{n=0}^{\infty}$ converges to 0 by Example 6.14 with $r = e^{-1}$. Hence, $\left\{1-e^{-n}\right\}_{n=0}^{\infty}$ converges to 1 by Theorem 6.1.

Theorem 6.7. Let $P(n)$ denote a statement or a formula which involves an integer n. If $P(1)$ is true and the *implication* $P(n) \Rightarrow P(n+1)$ is true for all $n \geq 1$, then $P(n)$ is true for all $n \geq 1$. More generally, if $P(k)$ is true, where k is an integer, and $P(n) \Rightarrow P(n+1)$ is true for all $n \geq k$, then $P(n)$ is true for all $n \geq k$. This is called the *principle of induction*.

In order to prove that the implication $P(n) \Rightarrow P(n+1)$ is true, assume $P(n)$ is true and employ $P(n)$ to show that $P(n+1)$ is also true. The assumption that $P(n)$ is true is called the *inductive hypothesis*.

Definition 6.6. Let a_1, a_2, $\cdots$, a_n be real numbers. The symbol $\sum_{i=1}^{n} a_i$, read "The sum of a_i as i ranges from 1 to n," is defined by

$$\sum_{i=1}^{n} a_i = a_1 + a_2 + a_3 + \cdots + a_{n-1} + a_n,$$

and is called *sigma notation*.

Example 6.37. Consider the sum

$$\sum_{i=1}^{n} i = 1 + 2 + 3 + \cdots + (n-1) + n.$$

We wish to prove the formula

$$\sum_{i=1}^{n} i = \frac{n(n+1)}{2} \tag{6.2}$$

for all $n \geq 1$. Let $P(n)$ denote the formula (6.2), and apply the principle of induction. If $n = 1$, then $P(1)$ states that $1 = 1$, which is true. In order to prove that the implication $P(n) \Rightarrow P(n+1)$ is true, assume $P(n)$ is true and employ $P(n)$ to show that $P(n+1)$ is also true. Thus,

$$\begin{aligned}
\sum_{i=1}^{n+1} i &= 1 + 2 + 3 + \cdots + n + (n+1) \\
&= \sum_{i=1}^{n} i + (n+1) \\
&= \frac{n(n+1)}{2} + (n+1) \quad \text{(by the inductive hypothesis)} \\
&= \frac{n(n+1)}{2} + \frac{2(n+1)}{2} \\
&= \frac{(n+1)(n+2)}{2},
\end{aligned}$$

which is $P(n + 1)$, i.e., (6.2) with n replaced by $n + 1$. Thus, the formula (6.2) has been proven by induction.

Example 6.38. Consider the sequence $\{a_n\}_{n=1}^{\infty}$, defined inductively by

$$a_1 = 1, \quad \text{and} \quad a_{n+1} = \sqrt{6 + a_n} \quad \text{for} \quad n \geq 1.$$

We shall employ induction to prove that the sequence is increasing for $n \geq 1$ and is bounded above, and, hence, that it converges, by Theorem 6.6.

The first four terms of the sequence are

$$a_1 = 1, \quad a_2 = \sqrt{7}, \quad a_3 = \sqrt{6 + \sqrt{7}}, \quad a_4 = \sqrt{6 + \sqrt{6 + \sqrt{7}}}.$$

Since $\sqrt{7} < 3$, we find that

$$a_1 = 1 < 3, \quad a_2 = \sqrt{7} < 3, \quad a_3 = \sqrt{6 + \sqrt{7}} < 3, \quad a_4 = \sqrt{6 + \sqrt{6 + \sqrt{7}}} < 3,$$

and it seems that $a_n < 3$ for every $n \geq 1$. In order to confirm this, we shall employ induction, where $P(n)$ is the statement "$a_n < 3$."

Since $a_1 < 3$, $P(1)$ is true. Assuming that $P(n)$ is true (the inductive hypothesis), i.e., $a_n < 3$, we obtain

$$a_n < 3 \quad \Rightarrow \quad 6 + a_n < 6 + 3 = 9 \quad \Rightarrow \quad a_{n+1} = \sqrt{6 + a_n} < \sqrt{9} = 3,$$

which is $P(n + 1)$. Thus, it is proved that $a_n < 3$ for all $n \geq 1$, and the sequence is bounded above.

Since $a_1 < a_2 < a_3 < a_4$, it seems that the sequence is increasing. Let $P(n)$ denote the statement "$a_n < a_{n+1}$."

Since $a_1 < a_2$, $P(1)$ is true. Assuming that $P(n)$ is true, i.e., $a_n < a_{n+1}$, we obtain

$$a_n < a_{n+1} \quad \Rightarrow \quad 6 + a_n < 6 + a_{n+1} \quad \Rightarrow \quad a_{n+1} = \sqrt{6 + a_n} < \sqrt{6 + a_{n+1}} = a_{n+2},$$

which is $P(n + 1)$. Thus, it is proved that $a_n < a_{n+1}$ for all $n \geq 1$, and the sequence is increasing.

By Theorem 6.6, the sequence converges. Let $L = \lim_{n \to \infty} a_n$. Then

$$a_{n+1} = \sqrt{6 + a_n} \quad \Rightarrow \quad \lim_{n \to \infty} a_{n+1} = \lim_{n \to \infty} \sqrt{6 + a_n} = \sqrt{6 + \lim_{n \to \infty} a_n},$$

where the last equality follows by the continuity of the function $g(x) = \sqrt{6 + x}$. Since $n \to \infty \Rightarrow n + 1 \to \infty$,

$$\lim_{n\to\infty} a_{n+1} = \lim_{n+1\to\infty} a_{n+1} = \lim_{n\to\infty} a_n = L.$$

Hence, $L = \sqrt{6 + L} \Rightarrow L^2 = 6 + L \Rightarrow L^2 - L - 6 = 0 \Rightarrow (L - 3)(L + 2) = 0 \Rightarrow L = 3$ or $L = -2$. Since $a_n > 0$ for all $n \geq 1$, $L \geq 0$ and, hence, $L = 3$.

Exercises 6.1

In Exercises 1–8, express the given sequence as $\{a_n\}_{n=k}^{\infty}$.

1. $\{5,\ 7,\ 9,\ 11,\ \cdots\}$

2. $\{-6,\ -3,\ 0,\ 3,\ \cdots\}$

3. $\left\{1,\ -\dfrac{1}{2},\ \dfrac{1}{3},\ -\dfrac{1}{4},\ \cdots\right\}$

4. $\left\{1,\ \dfrac{1}{4},\ \dfrac{1}{9},\ \dfrac{1}{16},\ \cdots\right\}$

5. $\left\{1,\ \dfrac{1}{3},\ \dfrac{1}{9},\ \dfrac{1}{27},\ \cdots\right\}$

6. $\left\{0,\ 1 - \dfrac{1}{2},\ 1 - \dfrac{1}{3},\ 1 - \dfrac{1}{4},\ \cdots\right\}$

7. $\left\{\dfrac{1}{2},\ \dfrac{2}{3},\ \dfrac{3}{4},\ \dfrac{4}{5},\ \cdots\right\}$

8. $\left\{1 - \dfrac{1}{2},\ \dfrac{1}{2} - \dfrac{2}{4},\ \dfrac{2}{4} - \dfrac{3}{8},\ \dfrac{3}{8} - \dfrac{4}{16},\ \cdots\right\}$

9. Write down the first five terms of the sequence $\left\{\dfrac{\sqrt{n^2 + 1}}{2n + 1}\right\}_{n=0}^{\infty}$.

10. Write down the first five terms of the inductively-defined sequence $a_1 = 2$, $a_2 = 3$, $a_n = a_{n-1} - a_{n-2}$ for $n \geq 3$.

11. Let $\{a_n\}_{n=0}^{\infty}$ and $\{b_n\}_{n=1}^{\infty}$ be sequences such that $b_n = a_{n+1} + \dfrac{n}{2^n}$ for all $n \geq 1$. Determine b_{n+1} for $n \geq 0$ and b_{n-1} for $n \geq 2$.

12. Express the sequence $\left\{\dfrac{1}{3},\ \dfrac{1}{5},\ \dfrac{1}{7},\ \dfrac{1}{9},\ \cdots\right\}$ as $\{a_n\}_{n=k}^{\infty}$ in three different ways.

In Exercises 13–48, determine whether or not the given sequence $\{a_n\}$ converges. If it converges, find the limit. If it diverges, determine whether or not $\lim\limits_{n\to\infty} a_n = \pm\infty$.

13. $a_n = \dfrac{1}{n^\pi}$

14. $a_n = \dfrac{-1}{n^{-3}}$

15. $a_n = \dfrac{1}{3^n}$

16. $a_n = 2^{-n}$

17. $a_n = \left(\dfrac{9}{10}\right)^n$

18. $a_n = \dfrac{(-2)^n}{3^n}$

19. $a_n = \dfrac{3^n}{(-2)^n}$

20. $a_n = \dfrac{3}{\sqrt{n}}$

21. $a_n = \dfrac{10^{1,000,000,000,000}}{n^{0.0000000001}}$

22. $a_n = 3 - \dfrac{2}{n^2} + \dfrac{5}{4^n}$

23. $a_n = n + \dfrac{1}{3^n}$

24. $a_n = \dfrac{3n^2 - 2n - 3}{2n^2 + 3n + 1}$

25. $a_n = \dfrac{3n^3 - 2n - 3}{4n^2 + n + 1}$

26. $a_n = \dfrac{3n^2 - 2n - 3}{2n^3 + 2n - 1}$

27. $a_n = \dfrac{3n^2 - 2n - 3}{\sqrt{2n^4 + 3n + 1}}$

28. $a_n = \dfrac{3n^2 - 2n - 3}{\sqrt{2n^5 - 2n + 1}}$

29. $a_n = \dfrac{3n^2 - 2n - 3}{\sqrt{2n^3 - n + 1}}$

30. $a_n = n^2 - 2\sqrt{n}$

31. $a_n = \sqrt{n^2 + n} - \sqrt{n^2 - n}$

32. $a_n = n - \sqrt{n^2 + n}$

33. $a_n = \sqrt{n^3 + 1} - n$

34. $a_n = \dfrac{(-2)^n}{3^n n^2}$

35. $a_n = \dfrac{(-1)^{n-1}}{n}$

36. $a_n = \dfrac{1 - (-1)^n}{n}$

37. $a_n = \dfrac{[\ln(n)]^2}{n}$

38. $a_n = \dfrac{n}{e^n}$

39. $a_n = \dfrac{n^3}{e^n}$

40. $a_n = \dfrac{[\ln(n)]^p}{n^q}, \; p > 0, \; q > 0$

41. $a_n = n^{1/n}$

42. $a_n = [\ln(n)]^{1/\ln(n)}$

43. $a_n = [\ln(n)]^{1/n}$

44. $a_n = n^{1/\ln(n)}$

45. $a_n = \dfrac{\cos(n)}{n}$

46. $a_n = \dfrac{\sin(n^2)}{\sqrt{n}}$

47. $a_n = \dfrac{e^n}{n!}$

48. $a_n = \dfrac{(2n)!}{2^n n^{2n}}$

In Exercises 49–54, determine whether or not the given sequence $\{a_n\}$ is increasing or decreasing for $n \geq N$.

49. $\left\{ \dfrac{3}{2^n} \right\}_{n=1}^{\infty}$

50. $\left\{ 2 - \dfrac{1}{n} \right\}_{n=1}^{\infty}$

51. $\left\{ \dfrac{-1}{1 - \frac{1}{n}} \right\}_{n=2}^{\infty}$

52. $\left\{ \dfrac{n}{\ln(n)} \right\}_{n=2}^{\infty}$

53. $\left\{ \dfrac{n \ln(n)}{e^n} \right\}_{n=1}^{\infty}$

54. $\left\{ \dfrac{\sin(n)}{n^2} \right\}_{n=1}^{\infty}$

In Exercises 55–58, determine whether or not the given sequence $\{a_n\}_{n=1}^{\infty}$ is bounded above $(a_n \leq K)$, bounded below $(a_n \geq M)$, or bounded $(M \leq a_n \leq K)$. In each case, determine K and/or M, if it exists (the bounds K and M are not unique).

55. $a_n = \dfrac{n}{\sqrt{n+1}}$

56. $a_n = \dfrac{1}{2^n} - \ln(n)$

57. $a_n = \dfrac{-1}{1 - \frac{1}{n+1}}$

58. $a_n = n^2 e^{-n}$

59. Prove, by induction, that $\displaystyle\sum_{i=1}^{n} i^2 = \dfrac{n(n+1)(2n+1)}{6}$.

60. Prove, by induction, that the sequence $\{a_n\}_{n=1}^{\infty}$, defined inductively by $a_1 = 1$ and $a_{n+1} = 1 + \sqrt{a_n}$ for $n \geq 1$, is increasing for $n \geq 1$ and bounded above, hence convergent, and find the limit.

61. Consider the sequence $\{a_n\}_{n=1}^{\infty}$, defined inductively by $a_1 = 1$ and $a_{n+1} = 1 - \dfrac{2}{a_n}$ for $n \geq 1$. Does the sequence converge? Justify your answer.

62. Consider the sequence $\{a_n\}_{n=1}^{\infty}$, defined inductively by $a_1 = 2$ and $a_{n+1} = 2 - \dfrac{1}{a_n}$ for $n \geq 1$. Prove, by induction, that $1 \leq a_n \leq 2$ and that $\{a_n\}_{n=1}^{\infty}$ is decreasing for $n \geq 1$, and find the limit.

6.2   Series

Definition 6.7. Let $\{a_n\}_{n=1}^{\infty}$ be a sequence. Define the sequence $\{s_n\}_{n=1}^{\infty}$ by

$$
\begin{aligned}
s_1 &= a_1 \\
s_2 &= a_1 + a_2 \\
s_2 &= a_1 + a_2 + a_3 \\
&\ \ \vdots \\
s_n &= a_1 + a_2 + a_3 + \cdots + a_n = \sum_{i=1}^{n} a_i.
\end{aligned}
$$

The sequence

$$
\begin{aligned}
\{s_n\}_{n=1}^{\infty} &= \{s_1,\ s_2,\ s_3,\ \cdots,\ s_n,\ \cdots\} \\
&= \left\{ a_1,\ a_1 + a_2,\ a_1 + a_2 + a_3,\ \cdots,\ \sum_{i=1}^{n} a_i, \cdots \right\}
\end{aligned}
$$

is denoted by the symbol

$$
\sum_{n=1}^{\infty} a_n = a_1 + a_2 + a_3 + \cdots \tag{6.3}
$$

and called an *infinite series*, or simply a *series*. The series $\displaystyle\sum_{n=1}^{\infty} a_n$ is said to *converge* if the sequence $\{s_n\}$ converges. Otherwise, the series *diverges*. If $\displaystyle\lim_{n\to\infty} s_n = s$, then s is called the *sum* of the series, and

$$
\sum_{n=1}^{\infty} a_n = \lim_{n\to\infty} s_n = \lim_{n\to\infty} \sum_{i=1}^{n} a_i = s.
$$

The number s_n is called the nth *partial sum* of the series $\displaystyle\sum_{n=1}^{\infty} a_n$.

Since it is impossible to perform an infinite number of additions, Definition 6.7 gives precise meaning to the concept of an "infinite sum" as the limit of a sequence of finite sums.

Note that the symbol n in (6.3) is a "dummy index," analogous to a "dummy variable" in a definite integral, and may be replaced by any other symbol whatsoever. Thus,

$$
\sum_{n=1}^{\infty} a_n = \sum_{i=1}^{\infty} a_i = \sum_{k=1}^{\infty} a_k = \sum_{\zeta=1}^{\infty} a_\zeta = a_1 + a_2 + a_3 + \cdots
$$

all represent one and the same series, determined entirely by the sequence $\{a_n\}_{n=1}^{\infty}$.

In Definition 6.7, the sequence $\{a_n\}$ was employed with $n = 1, 2, 3, \cdots$ for the sake of definiteness. More generally, if the initial value of n is k, then the corresponding series is

$$\sum_{n=k}^{\infty} a_n = a_k + a_{k+1} + a_{k+2} + \cdots .$$

For example,

$$\sum_{n=0}^{\infty} a_n = a_0 + a_1 + a_2 + \cdots , \quad \text{and} \quad \sum_{n=17}^{\infty} a_n = a_{17} + a_{18} + a_{19} + \cdots .$$

Since a series is a special type of sequence, the properties of sequences given by Theorem 6.1 in Section 6.1 are also shared by series. The first two are relevant for series:

Theorem 6.8. If $\displaystyle\sum_{n=1}^{\infty} a_n$ and $\displaystyle\sum_{n=1}^{\infty} b_n$ converge, with $\displaystyle\sum_{n=1}^{\infty} a_n = s$ and $\displaystyle\sum_{n=1}^{\infty} b_n = t$, then:

1. The series $\displaystyle\sum_{n=1}^{\infty} (a_n + b_n)$ converges, and $\displaystyle\sum_{n=1}^{\infty} (a_n + b_n) = s + t$.

2. The series $\displaystyle\sum_{n=1}^{\infty} ca_n$ converges for any constant c, and $\displaystyle\sum_{n=1}^{\infty} ca_n = c \sum_{n=1}^{\infty} a_n = cs$.

Note that, if $\displaystyle\sum_{n=1}^{\infty} a_n$ converges and $\displaystyle\sum_{n=1}^{\infty} b_n$ diverges, then $\displaystyle\sum_{n=1}^{\infty} (a_n + b_n)$ must diverge because, if $\displaystyle\sum_{n=1}^{\infty} (a_n + b_n)$ converges, then

$$\sum_{n=1}^{\infty} b_n = \sum_{n=1}^{\infty} [(a_n + b_n) - a_n] = \sum_{n=1}^{\infty} (a_n + b_n) - \sum_{n=1}^{\infty} a_n$$

converges, which is a contradiction.

Example 6.39. Let r be a real number, and consider the sequence $\{r^n\}_{n=0}^{\infty}$. The corresponding series is

$$\sum_{n=0}^{\infty} r^n,$$

called the *geometric series*. In order to determine the values of r for which the series converges and to find the sum, consider the nth partial sum

$$s_n = \sum_{i=0}^{n} r^i = 1 + r + r^2 + r^3 + \cdots + r^{n-1} + r^n.$$

Then

$$
\begin{aligned}
rs_n &= r\left(1 + r + r^2 + r^3 + \cdots + r^{n-1} + r^n\right) \\
&= r + r^2 + r^3 + \cdots + r^{n-1} + r^n + r^{n+1}
\end{aligned}
$$

and, hence,

$$
\begin{aligned}
s_n - rs_n &= 1 + r + r^2 + r^3 + \cdots + r^{n-1} + r^n \\
&\quad - r - r^2 - r^3 - \cdots - r^{n-1} - r^n - r^{n+1} \\
&= 1 - r^{n+1} \\
\Rightarrow (1-r)s_n &= 1 - r^{n+1}.
\end{aligned}
$$

If $r \neq 1$, then

$$s_n = \frac{1 - r^{n+1}}{1 - r}.$$

By Example 6.14 in Section 6.1, the sequence $\{r^n\}$ converges to 0 if $-1 < r < 1$ and diverges for $r \leq -1$ or $r > 1$. Hence,

$$\lim_{n\to\infty} s_n = \lim_{n\to\infty} \frac{1 - r^{n+1}}{1 - r} = \frac{1}{1 - r} \quad \text{if} \quad -1 < r < 1,$$

and $\{s_n\}$ diverges for $r \leq -1$ or $r > 1$. If $r = 1$, then $r^n = 1$ for all n, and

$$s_n = 1 + 1 + 1 + \cdots + 1 = n + 1$$

$\Rightarrow \{s_n\}$ diverges. In summary,

$$\sum_{n=0}^{\infty} r^n = \frac{1}{1 - r}, \quad |r| < 1,$$

and the series diverges for $|r| \geq 1$.

Example 6.40. Consider the series

$$\sum_{n=0}^{\infty} \frac{1}{2^n} = \sum_{n=0}^{\infty} \left(\frac{1}{2}\right)^n.$$

This series is geometric with $r = \frac{1}{2}$ and, since $\left|\frac{1}{2}\right| = \frac{1}{2} < 1$, the series converges and

$$\sum_{n=0}^{\infty} \frac{1}{2^n} = \frac{1}{1 - \frac{1}{2}} = 2.$$

Example 6.41. Consider the series

$$\sum_{n=0}^{\infty} \frac{2^n}{(-3)^n} = \sum_{n=0}^{\infty} \left(-\frac{2}{3}\right)^n.$$

This series is geometric with $r = -\frac{2}{3}$ and, since $\left|-\frac{2}{3}\right| = \frac{2}{3} < 1$, the series converges and

$$\sum_{n=0}^{\infty} \frac{2^n}{(-3)^n} = \frac{1}{1 + \frac{2}{3}} = \frac{3}{5}.$$

Example 6.42. Consider the series

$$\sum_{n=0}^{\infty} -2 \cdot 8^n \cdot 3^{-2n} = \sum_{n=0}^{\infty} -2 \left(\frac{8}{9}\right)^n = -2 \sum_{n=0}^{\infty} \left(\frac{8}{9}\right)^n,$$

where the last equality follows by item 2 of Theorem 6.8. This series is geometric with $r = \frac{8}{9}$ and, since $\left|\frac{8}{9}\right| = \frac{8}{9} < 1$, the series converges and

$$\sum_{n=0}^{\infty} -2 \cdot 8^n \cdot 3^{-2n} = -2 \frac{1}{1 - \frac{8}{9}} = -18.$$

Example 6.43. Consider the series

$$\sum_{n=0}^{\infty} 5 \cdot (-3)^{2n+1} 2^{-3n} = \sum_{n=0}^{\infty} -15 \left(\frac{9}{8}\right)^n = -15 \sum_{n=0}^{\infty} \left(\frac{9}{8}\right)^n.$$

This series is geometric with $r = \frac{9}{8}$ and, since $\left|\frac{9}{8}\right| = \frac{9}{8} \geq 1$, the series diverges.

Example 6.44. Consider the geometric series

$$\sum_{n=1}^{\infty} r^n, \quad |r| < 1,$$

where the initial value of n is 1 instead of 0. Then

$$\begin{aligned}
\sum_{n=1}^{\infty} r^n &= r + r^2 + r^3 + \cdots \\
&= -1 + \left(1 + r + r^2 + r^3 + \cdots\right) \\
&= -1 + \sum_{n=0}^{\infty} r^n \\
&= -1 + \frac{1}{1-r} \\
&= \frac{r}{1-r}.
\end{aligned}$$

More generally, for any $k \geq 1$,

$$
\begin{aligned}
\sum_{n=k}^{\infty} r^n &= r^k + r^{k+1} + \cdots \\
&= -1 - r - r^2 - \cdots - r^{k-1} + \left(1 + r + r^2 + \cdots + r^{k-1} + r^k + r^{k+1} + \cdots\right) \\
&= -\left(1 + r + r^2 + \cdots + r^{k-1}\right) + \left(1 + r + r^2 + \cdots\right) \\
&= -\sum_{n=0}^{k-1} r^n + \sum_{n=0}^{\infty} r^n \\
&= -\frac{1 - r^k}{1 - r} + \frac{1}{1 - r} \quad \text{(by Example 6.39)} \\
&= \frac{r^k}{1 - r}.
\end{aligned}
$$

For example,

$$
\sum_{n=1}^{\infty} 2\left(\frac{3}{4}\right)^n = 2\sum_{n=1}^{\infty} \left(\frac{3}{4}\right)^n = 2\frac{\frac{3}{4}}{1 - \frac{3}{4}} = 6,
$$

and

$$
\sum_{n=2}^{\infty} \frac{2}{(-5)^n} = 2\sum_{n=2}^{\infty} \left(-\frac{1}{5}\right)^n = 2\frac{(-\frac{1}{5})^2}{1 + \frac{1}{5}} = \frac{1}{15}.
$$

Example 6.45.   Consider the series

$$
\sum_{n=1}^{\infty} \frac{1}{n(n+1)} = \sum_{n=1}^{\infty} \left(\frac{1}{n} - \frac{1}{n+1}\right),
$$

where the right side is obtained from the left by partial fractions. Then the nth partial sum of the series is

$$
\begin{aligned}
s_n &= \sum_{k=1}^{n} \left(\frac{1}{k} - \frac{1}{k+1}\right) \\
&= \left(1 - \frac{1}{2}\right) + \left(\frac{1}{2} - \frac{1}{3}\right) + \left(\frac{1}{3} - \frac{1}{4}\right) + \cdots + \left(\frac{1}{n-1} - \frac{1}{n}\right) + \left(\frac{1}{n} - \frac{1}{n+1}\right) \\
&= 1 - \frac{1}{n+1}.
\end{aligned}
$$

Hence, $\lim_{n \to \infty} s_n = 1$, i.e., the series converges and

$$
\sum_{n=1}^{\infty} \frac{1}{n(n+1)} = 1.
$$

A series in which such cancellations occur in s_n is often called a *telescoping series*.

Example 6.46. Consider a series with only a finite number of nonzero terms, i.e.,

$$\sum_{n=1}^{\infty} a_n,$$

with $a_n = 0$ for $n > m \geq 0$. Then the partial sums s_n of the series are given by

$$
\begin{aligned}
s_1 &= a_1 \\
s_2 &= a_1 + a_2 \\
s_3 &= a_1 + a_2 + a_3 \\
&\vdots \\
s_m &= a_1 + a_2 + a_3 + \cdots + a_m = \sum_{k=1}^{m} a_k \\
s_{m+1} &= a_1 + a_2 + a_3 + \cdots + a_m + 0 = \sum_{k=1}^{m} a_k \\
s_{m+2} &= a_1 + a_2 + a_3 + \cdots + a_m + 0 + 0 = \sum_{k=1}^{m} a_k,
\end{aligned}
$$

etc., i.e., $s_n = \sum_{k=1}^{m} a_k$ for all $n \geq m$ and, hence, $\lim_{n\to\infty} s_n = \sum_{k=1}^{m} a_k$. Thus,

$$\sum_{k=1}^{\infty} a_k = \lim_{n\to\infty} s_n = \sum_{k=1}^{m} a_k,$$

i.e., the series reduces to an ordinary finite sum. Such a series is called a *finite series*.

The convergence or divergence of a geometric or a telescoping series and, in the case of convergence, the sum of the series, has been established without any great difficulty. For other types of series, these properties cannot, in general, be determined by first principles, and various theorems must be employed.

Theorem 6.9. If $\sum_{n=1}^{\infty} a_n$ converges, then $\lim_{n\to\infty} a_n = 0$. Equivalently, if $\lim_{n\to\infty} a_n \neq 0$, then $\sum_{n=1}^{\infty} a_n$ diverges. The latter version is often called the nth-*term test*.

Proof. Let $s = \sum_{n=1}^{\infty} a_n = \lim_{n\to\infty} s_n$, where $s_n = \sum_{k=1}^{n} a_k$ is the nth partial sum of the series.

Then

$$s_n = a_1 + a_2 + \cdots + a_{n-1} + a_n \quad \text{and}$$
$$s_{n-1} = a_1 + a_2 + \cdots + a_{n-1}$$
$$\Rightarrow \quad s_n - s_{n-1} = a_n.$$

Hence,

$$\lim_{n \to \infty} a_n = \lim_{n \to \infty} (s_n - s_{n-1}) = \lim_{n \to \infty} s_n - \lim_{n \to \infty} s_{n-1} = s - s = 0.$$

The second assertion in the theorem is the *contrapositive* of the first, and the two are logically equivalent.

Note that the proof fails if $\sum_{n=1}^{\infty} a_n$ diverges for, then, the number s does not exist, and the term $s - s$ has no meaning.

Example 6.47. The series $\sum_{n=1}^{\infty} \left(\frac{1}{3} \right)^n$ converges since it is geometric with $r = \frac{1}{3}$ and $\left| \frac{1}{3} \right| < 1$, and $\lim_{n \to \infty} \left(\frac{1}{3} \right)^n = 0$, as guaranteed by Theorem 6.9.

Example 6.48. Consider the series

$$\sum_{n=1}^{\infty} (-1)^{n-1},$$

with the nth partial sum

$$s_n = 1 - 1 + 1 - 1 + 1 - 1 + \cdots + (-1)^{n-1} = \left\{ \begin{array}{l} 0, \text{ if } n \text{ is even} \\ 1, \text{ if } n \text{ is odd} \end{array} \right\}.$$

Thus, $\{s_n\}_{n=1}^{\infty} = \{1, \ 0, \ 1, \ 0, \ 1, \ 0, \ \cdots\}$ diverges and, hence, the series diverges. This result can be established much more easily by means of Theorem 6.9. Since $\lim_{n \to \infty} (-1)^n$ does not exist, $\lim_{n \to \infty} (-1)^n \neq 0$ and, hence, the series diverges.

Example 6.49. Consider the series

$$\sum_{n=0}^{\infty} \frac{n}{\sqrt{n^2 + 1}}.$$

Since $\lim_{n \to \infty} \frac{n}{\sqrt{n^2 + 1}} = 1 \neq 0$, the series diverges by the nth-term test (Theorem 6.9).

The reader is warned that the *converse* of Theorem 6.9 is *false*, i.e., if $\lim_{n \to \infty} a_n = 0$, then there is no guarantee that the series $\sum_{n=1}^{\infty} a_n$ converges. It may converge, or it may diverge, depending upon the particular series. Examples of both will be given shortly.

6.2.1 The Integral Test

Let f be positive, continuous and decreasing for $x \geq 1$, and let $a_n = f(n)$.

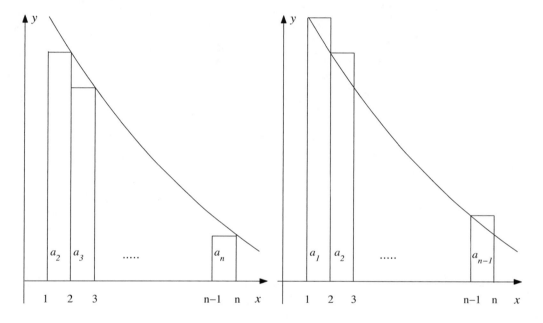

Figure 6.1: Rectangles of lesser area (left) and rectangles of greater area (right).

Since every rectangle has unit width, its area is equal to its height. Hence, the areas of the rectangles on the left are $a_2, a_3, \cdots, a_n$, and the areas of the ones on the right are $a_1, a_2, \cdots, a_{n-1}$, as depicted in Figure 6.1. Employing the fact that the area under each curve for $1 \leq x \leq n$ is $\int_1^n f(x)\,dx$, we obtain the inequalities

$$a_2 + a_3 + \cdots + a_n \leq \int_1^n f(x)\,dx \leq a_1 + a_2 + \cdots + a_{n-1}. \tag{6.4}$$

Consider the series $\sum_{n=1}^{\infty} a_n$, and let $\{s_n\}_{n=1}^{\infty}$ be its nth partial sum. From (6.4), we obtain the inequalites

$$s_n = a_1 + (a_2 + a_3 + \cdots + a_n) \le a_1 + \int_1^n f(x)\,dx, \qquad (6.5)$$

$$s_n = (a_1 + a_2 + a_3 + \cdots + a_{n-1}) + a_n \ge a_n + \int_1^n f(x)\,dx. \qquad (6.6)$$

Since $a_n \ge 0$ for $n \ge 1$, the sequence $\{s_n\}_{n=1}^\infty$ is increasing because

$$s_{n+1} = a_1 + a_2 + a_3 + \cdots + a_n + a_{n+1} \ge a_1 + a_2 + a_3 + \cdots + a_n = s_n.$$

If $\int_1^\infty f(x)\,dx < \infty$, then, by (6.5) and the fact that $f(x) > 0$ for $x \ge 1$,

$$s_n \le a_1 + \int_1^n f(x)\,dx \le a_1 + \int_1^\infty f(x)\,dx < \infty$$

$\Rightarrow \{s_n\}_{n=1}^\infty$ is bounded above and, hence, it converges by Theorem 6.6.

If $\int_1^\infty f(x)\,dx = \infty$, i.e., the improper integral diverges, then, by (6.6),

$$s_n \ge a_n + \int_1^n f(x)\,dx \ge \int_1^n f(x)\,dx$$

$$\Rightarrow \lim_{n\to\infty} s_n \ge \lim_{n\to\infty} \int_1^n f(x)\,dx = \int_1^\infty f(x)\,dx = \infty$$

$\Rightarrow \lim\limits_{n\to\infty} s_n = \infty$, i.e., the sequence $\{s_n\}_{n=1}^\infty$ and, hence, the series $\sum\limits_{n=1}^\infty a_n$, diverges.

In summary, we have derived the following:

Theorem 6.10. Let f be positive, continuous and decreasing for $x \ge 1$, and let $a_n = f(n)$. Then the series

$$\sum_{n=1}^\infty a_n$$

converges if and only if

$$\int_1^\infty f(x)\,dx < \infty.$$

More generally, if f is positive, continuous and decreasing for $x \ge k$ and $a_n = f(n)$, then the series

$$\sum_{n=k}^\infty a_n$$

converges if and only if

$$\int_k^\infty f(x)\,dx < \infty.$$

This theorem is known as the *integral test*.

Example 6.50. Consider the series

$$\sum_{n=1}^\infty \frac{1}{n^2},$$

and let $f(x) = \dfrac{1}{x^2}$. Since f is positive, continuous and decreasing for $x \geq 1$ and $a_n = f(n)$, the integral test applies. Thus,

$$\int_1^\infty \frac{1}{x^2}\,dx = -\frac{1}{x}\Big|_1^\infty = 1 < \infty \quad \Rightarrow \quad \sum_{n=1}^\infty \frac{1}{n^2}$$

converges by Theorem 6.10. We shall have to wait until Chapter 8 before we shall be able to determine the sum of this series.

Example 6.51. Consider the series

$$\sum_{n=1}^\infty \frac{1}{n},$$

and let $f(x) = \dfrac{1}{x}$. Since f is positive, continuous and decreasing for $x \geq 1$ and $a_n = f(n)$, the integral test applies. Thus,

$$\int_1^\infty \frac{1}{x}\,dx = \ln|x|\Big|_1^\infty = \infty \quad \Rightarrow \quad \sum_{n=1}^\infty \frac{1}{n}$$

diverges by Theorem 6.10.

Note that, in Example 6.50,

$$\lim_{n\to\infty} \frac{1}{n^2} = 0 \ \text{ and } \ \sum_{n=1}^\infty \frac{1}{n^2} \ \text{ converges,}$$

whereas in Example 6.51,

$$\lim_{n\to\infty} \frac{1}{n} = 0 \ \text{ and } \ \sum_{n=1}^\infty \frac{1}{n} \ \text{ diverges.}$$

Thus, as stated earlier following the nth-term test, $\lim\limits_{n\to\infty} a_n = 0$ does not guarantee the convergence of the series $\sum\limits_{n=1}^{\infty} a_n$. Comparing the two series above,

$$\sum_{n=1}^{\infty} \frac{1}{n^2} = 1 + \frac{1}{4} + \frac{1}{9} + \frac{1}{16} + \frac{1}{25} + \frac{1}{36} + \frac{1}{49} + \frac{1}{64} + \frac{1}{81} + \cdots, \qquad (6.7)$$

$$\sum_{n=1}^{\infty} \frac{1}{n} = 1 + \frac{1}{2} + \frac{1}{3} + \frac{1}{4} + \frac{1}{5} + \frac{1}{6} + \frac{1}{7} + \frac{1}{8} + \frac{1}{9} + \cdots, \qquad (6.8)$$

we find that, although the terms in (6.8) approach 0, they do so much more slowly than the ones in (6.7), and that is the reason for its divergence. Whereas the sum in (6.7) approaches a finite number, the sum in (6.8) increases indefinitely.

Example 6.52. Let p be a real number, and consider the *p-series*

$$\sum_{n=1}^{\infty} \frac{1}{n^p}.$$

If $p < 0$, then $-p > 0$ and $\lim\limits_{n\to\infty} \frac{1}{n^p} = \lim\limits_{n\to\infty} n^{-p} = \infty \neq 0$. Hence, the series diverges by the nth-term test.

If $p = 0$, then $\lim\limits_{n\to\infty} \frac{1}{n^p} = \lim\limits_{n\to\infty} 1 = 1 \neq 0$. Hence, the series diverges by the nth-term test.

If $p > 0$, let $f(x) = \frac{1}{x^p}$. Since f is positive, continuous and decreasing for $x \geq 1$ and $a_n = f(n)$, the integral test applies. The series diverges if $p = 1$ by Example 6.51 and, for $p \neq 1$,

$$\int_1^{\infty} \frac{1}{x^p}\,dx = \int_1^{\infty} x^{-p}\,dx = \left.\frac{x^{1-p}}{1-p}\right|_1^{\infty} = \left\{ \begin{array}{ll} \infty, & \text{if } p < 1 \\ \frac{1}{p-1}, & \text{if } p > 1 \end{array} \right\}.$$

Hence, the series converges for $p > 1$ and diverges for $p \leq 1$ by Theorem 6.10.

Example 6.53. Consider the series

$$\sum_{n=1}^{\infty} \frac{1}{\sqrt{n}}.$$

Since $\frac{1}{\sqrt{n}} = \frac{1}{n^{1/2}}$, this is a *p*-series with $p = \frac{1}{2}$ and, since $\frac{1}{2} \leq 1$, the series diverges by Example 6.52.

Example 6.54. Consider the series

$$\sum_{n=1}^{\infty} \frac{1}{n\sqrt{n}}.$$

Since $\dfrac{1}{n\sqrt{n}} = \dfrac{1}{n^{3/2}}$, this is a p-series with $p = \dfrac{3}{2}$ and, since $\dfrac{3}{2} > 1$, the series converges by Example 6.52.

Example 6.55. Consider the series

$$\sum_{n=2}^{\infty} \frac{1}{n \ln(n)}.$$

Let $f(x) = \dfrac{1}{x \ln(x)}$. Since f is positive, continuous and decreasing for $x \geq 2$ and $a_n = f(n)$, the integral test applies. Thus, making the substitution $u = \ln(x)$,

$$\int_{2}^{\infty} \frac{1}{x \ln(x)} \, dx = \int_{\ln(2)}^{\infty} \frac{1}{u} \, du = \ln |u| \Big|_{\ln(2)}^{\infty} = \infty.$$

Hence, the series diverges by Theorem 6.10.

Approximations of Series

Let $\displaystyle\sum_{n=1}^{\infty} a_n$ be a convergent series. If the sum s of the series cannot be determined, then it can be approximated. By definition of limit, since

$$s = \sum_{n=1}^{\infty} a_n = \lim_{n \to \infty} s_n = \lim_{n \to \infty} \sum_{k=1}^{n} a_k,$$

the terms s_n can be made arbitrarily close to s by taking n sufficiently large. Thus, s_n is approximately equal to s, written $s_n \approx s$, and the larger we take n, the better the approximation. Whenever an approximation is made, knowledge of the maximum possible error is essential. The error made in approximating s by s_n is

$$R_n = s - s_n = \sum_{n=1}^{\infty} a_n - \sum_{k=1}^{n} a_k = \sum_{k=n+1}^{\infty} a_k = a_{n+1} + a_{n+2} + a_{n+3} + \cdots,$$

called the *remainder* of the series.

In the present discussion, we restrict our attention to series $\sum\limits_{n=1}^{\infty} a_n$ where $a_n = f(n)$ and f is positive, continuous and decreasing for $x \geq 1$. In order to determine upper and lower bounds for R_n, we appeal to Figure 6.2.

From the graph on the left, we obtain

$$R_n = a_{n+1} + a_{n+2} + \cdots \leq \int_n^{\infty} f(x)\,dx, \qquad (6.9)$$

and, from the one on the right, we find

$$R_n = a_{n+1} + a_{n+2} + \cdots \geq \int_{n+1}^{\infty} f(x)\,dx. \qquad (6.10)$$

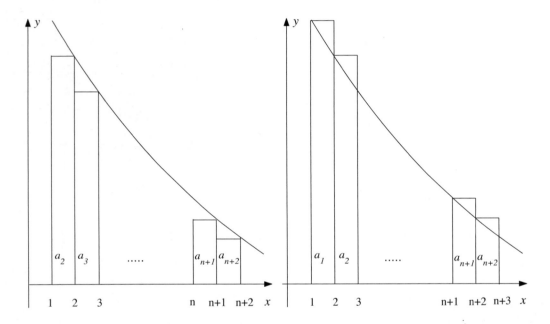

Figure 6.2: Upper and lower bounds for the remainder R_n.

Combining (6.9) and (6.10), we obtain the inequalities

$$\int_{n+1}^{\infty} f(x)\,dx \leq R_n \leq \int_n^{\infty} f(x)\,dx. \qquad (6.11)$$

Hence, the error in approximating s by s_n is at least $\int_{n+1}^{\infty} f(x)\,dx$ and at most $\int_n^{\infty} f(x)\,dx.$

Example 6.56. Consider the p-series

$$\sum_{n=1}^{\infty} \frac{2}{n^3}.$$

Since $p = 3 > 1$, the series converges by the integral test (Theorem 6.10). If the sum of the series is approximated by s_2, i.e., $n = 2$, then

$$s = \sum_{n=1}^{\infty} \frac{2}{n^3} \approx s_2 = \sum_{k=1}^{2} \frac{2}{k^3} = 2 + \frac{1}{4} = 2.25,$$

and

$$\int_3^{\infty} \frac{2}{x^3}\,dx \le R_2 \le \int_2^{\infty} \frac{2}{x^3}\,dx$$

$$\Rightarrow \quad -\frac{1}{x^2}\bigg|_3^{\infty} \le R_2 \le -\frac{1}{x^2}\bigg|_2^{\infty} \quad \Rightarrow \quad \frac{1}{9} \le R_2 \le \frac{1}{4}.$$

Thus, the minimum error is $\frac{1}{9} \approx 0.111$ and the maximum error is $\frac{1}{4} = 0.25$. If, instead, the sum is approximated by s_5, i.e., $n = 5$, then

$$s = \sum_{n=1}^{\infty} \frac{2}{n^3} \approx s_5 = \sum_{k=1}^{5} \frac{2}{k^3} = 2 + \frac{1}{4} + \frac{2}{27} + \frac{2}{64} + \frac{2}{125} = 2.37,$$

and

$$-\frac{1}{x^2}\bigg|_6^{\infty} \le R_5 \le -\frac{1}{x^2}\bigg|_5^{\infty} \quad \Rightarrow \quad \frac{1}{36} \le R_2 \le \frac{1}{25},$$

i.e., the minimum error is $\frac{1}{36} \approx 0.028$ and the maximum error is $\frac{1}{25} = 0.04$, with a much better approximation.

Example 6.57. Consider the series

$$\sum_{n=2}^{\infty} \frac{1}{n[\ln(n)]^2}.$$

Let $f(x) = \frac{1}{x[\ln(x)]^2}$. Since f is positive, continuous and decreasing for $x \ge 2$, the integral test applies, and the series converges because

$$\int_2^{\infty} \frac{1}{x[\ln(x)]^2}\,dx = -\frac{1}{\ln(x)}\bigg|_2^{\infty} = \frac{1}{\ln(2)} < \infty.$$

Suppose that an approximation of the sum s of the series is required such that the error is no greater than 0.1. How large must n be taken? Since

$$R_n \leq \int_n^\infty \frac{1}{x[\ln(x)]^2}\,dx = -\frac{1}{\ln(x)}\Big|_n^\infty = \frac{1}{\ln(n)},$$

the required precision is guaranteed if $\dfrac{1}{\ln(n)} \leq 0.1$, which requires that $\ln(n) \geq 10$, i.e., $n \geq e^{10} \approx 22{,}026.47$. Hence, $n \geq 22{,}027$.

Example 6.58.   Consider the series

$$\sum_{n=1}^\infty \frac{3n^2}{e^{n^3}}.$$

Let $f(x) = \dfrac{3x^2}{e^{x^3}} = 3x^2 e^{-x^3}$. Then f is positive and continuous for $x \geq 1$, and

$$f'(x) = 6xe^{-x^3} - 6x^4 e^{-x^3} = 6xe^{-x^3}(1 - x^3) < 0$$

for $x > 1 \Rightarrow f$ is deceasing for $x \geq 1$. Hence, the integral test applies, and the series converges because

$$\int_1^\infty \frac{3x^2}{e^{x^3}}\,dx = -\frac{1}{e^{x^3}}\Big|_1^\infty = \frac{1}{e} < \infty.$$

Suppose that an approximation of the sum s of the series is required which is correct to 4 decimal places. How large must n be taken? An approximation which is correct to 4 decimal places requires that $R_n < 0.0001$. Thus,

$$R_n \leq \int_n^\infty \frac{3x^2}{e^{x^3}}\,dx = -\frac{1}{e^{x^3}}\Big|_n^\infty = \frac{1}{e^{n^3}} < 0.0001$$

is achieved by taking n such that $e^{n^3} > 10{,}000$, i.e., $n > [\ln(10{,}000)]^{1/3} \approx 2.096$. Hence, $n \geq 3$.

Comparing the results of Examples 6.57 and 6.58, we notice that a large degree of accuracy is obtained in the latter by taking only 3 terms of the series, whereas fairly poor accuracy is obtained in the former by taking as many as $22{,}027$ terms. Such discrepancy is due to the fact that the terms of the series in Example 6.58 approach 0 much more rapidly than the ones in Example 6.57, and the addition of more terms has a small effect upon the final sum.

6.2.2   The Comparison Tests

It is frequently possible to determine whether a given series converges or diverges by comparing its terms to those of series the convergence or divergence of which is already known. Two such comparison tests are given in the present section.

Theorem 6.11. Let $\{a_n\}$ and $\{b_n\}$ be sequences, and suppose that

$$0 \le a_n \le b_n$$

for all $n \ge k$, where k is an integer. Then:

1. If $\displaystyle\sum_{n=1}^{\infty} b_n$ converges, then $\displaystyle\sum_{n=1}^{\infty} a_n$ also converges.

2. If $\displaystyle\sum_{n=1}^{\infty} a_n$ diverges, then $\displaystyle\sum_{n=1}^{\infty} b_n$ also diverges.

This theorem is known as the *comparison test.*

Note that the initial value of n is given as 1 for definiteness, and may be replaced by any other integer, and the initial values of n in the two series need not be the same. The reason is that, for any integer m,

$$\sum_{n=1}^{\infty} a_n = \sum_{n=1}^{m-1} a_n + \sum_{n=m}^{\infty} a_n,$$

and $\displaystyle\sum_{n=1}^{\infty} a_n$ converges if and only if $\displaystyle\sum_{n=m}^{\infty} a_n$ converges because a finite number of terms such as $\displaystyle\sum_{n=1}^{m-1} a_n$ do not affect convergence.

Example 6.59.   Consider the series

$$\sum_{n=0}^{\infty} \frac{1}{n^2 + 1}.$$

Since

$$0 \le \frac{1}{n^2 + 1} \le \frac{1}{n^2}$$

for all $n \ge 1$ and the series $\displaystyle\sum_{n=1}^{\infty} \frac{1}{n^2}$ is known to converge (it is a p-series with $p = 2 > 1$),

it follows by the comparison test (Theorem 6.11) with $a_n = \dfrac{1}{n^2 + 1}$ and $b_n = \dfrac{1}{n^2}$ that

$$\sum_{n=0}^{\infty} \frac{1}{n^2 + 1} \text{ converges.}$$

Example 6.60. Consider the series

$$\sum_{n=2}^{\infty} \frac{1}{n - 1}.$$

Since

$$0 \le \frac{1}{n} \le \frac{1}{n - 1}$$

for all $n \ge 2$ and the series $\sum_{n=1}^{\infty} \frac{1}{n}$ is known to diverge (it is a p-series with $p = 1 \le 1$),

it follows by the comparison test (Theorem 6.11) with $a_n = \frac{1}{n}$ and $b_n = \frac{1}{n - 1}$ that

$$\sum_{n=2}^{\infty} \frac{1}{n - 1} \text{ diverges.}$$

Example 6.61. Consider the series

$$\sum_{n=0}^{\infty} \frac{2^n}{3^n + 1}.$$

Since

$$0 \le \frac{2^n}{3^n + 1} \le \frac{2^n}{3^n} = \left(\frac{2}{3}\right)^n$$

for all $n \ge 0$ and the series $\sum_{n=0}^{\infty} \left(\frac{2}{3}\right)^n$ is known to converge (it is a geometric series

with $r = \frac{2}{3}$ and $\left|\frac{2}{3}\right| = \frac{2}{3} < 1$), it follows by the comparison test (Theorem 6.11) with

$a_n = \frac{2^n}{3^n + 1}$ and $b_n = \left(\frac{2}{3}\right)^n$ that $\sum_{n=0}^{\infty} \frac{2^n}{3^n + 1}$ converges.

Example 6.62. Consider the series

$$\sum_{n=2}^{\infty} \frac{3^n}{2^n - 3}.$$

Since

$$\frac{3^n}{2^n - 3} \ge \frac{3^n}{2^n} = \left(\frac{3}{2}\right)^n \ge 0$$

for all $n \geq 2$ and the series $\displaystyle\sum_{n=0}^{\infty} \left(\frac{3}{2}\right)^n$ is known to diverge (it is a geometric series

with $r = \dfrac{3}{2}$ and $\left|\dfrac{3}{2}\right| = \dfrac{3}{2} \geq 1$), it follows by the comparison test (Theorem 6.11) with

$a_n = \left(\dfrac{3}{2}\right)^n$ and $b_n = \dfrac{3^n}{2^n - 3}$ that $\displaystyle\sum_{n=2}^{\infty} \dfrac{3^n}{2^n - 3}$ diverges.

Example 6.63. Consider the series

$$\sum_{n=0}^{\infty} \frac{1}{n+1}.$$

The inequality

$$0 \leq \frac{1}{n+1} \leq \frac{1}{n}$$

for all $n \geq 1$ is of no use, because $\displaystyle\sum_{n=1}^{\infty} \dfrac{1}{n}$ diverges. Instead, employ the inequality

$$\frac{1}{n+1} \geq \frac{1}{n+n} = \frac{1}{2n} \geq 0$$

for all $n \geq 1$. Since $\displaystyle\sum_{n=1}^{\infty} \dfrac{1}{2n} = \dfrac{1}{2} \sum_{n=1}^{\infty} \dfrac{1}{n}$ diverges, $\displaystyle\sum_{n=0}^{\infty} \dfrac{1}{n+1}$ diverges by the comparison test.

Example 6.64. Consider the series

$$\sum_{n=1}^{\infty} \frac{\ln(1 + \frac{1}{n})}{n}.$$

In order to make use of the fact that $\displaystyle\lim_{n\to\infty} \left(1 + \frac{1}{n}\right)^n = e$, express the given series as

$$\sum_{n=1}^{\infty} \frac{\ln(1 + \frac{1}{n})}{n} = \sum_{n=1}^{\infty} \frac{n\ln(1 + \frac{1}{n})}{n^2} = \sum_{n=1}^{\infty} \frac{\ln[(1 + \frac{1}{n})^n]}{n^2}.$$

Since the logarithmic function is continuous,

$$\lim_{n\to\infty} \ln\left[\left(1 + \frac{1}{n}\right)^n\right] = \ln\left[\lim_{n\to\infty} \left(1 + \frac{1}{n}\right)^n\right] = \ln(e) = 1.$$

By definition of limit, the quantity $\ln\left[\left(1 + \dfrac{1}{n}\right)^n\right]$ can be made arbitrarily close to 1 and, hence, less than 2, by taking n sufficiently large. Thus, there exists an integer N such that

$$n \geq N \quad \Rightarrow \quad \ln\left[\left(1 + \frac{1}{n}\right)^n\right] \leq 2,$$

from which we obtain

$$\frac{\ln(1 + \frac{1}{n})}{n} = \frac{\ln[(1 + \frac{1}{n})^n]}{n^2} \leq \frac{2}{n^2}, \quad n \geq N.$$

Since $\displaystyle\sum_{n=1}^{\infty} \frac{2}{n^2} = 2 \sum_{n=1}^{\infty} \frac{1}{n^2}$ converges, it follows by the comparison test that $\displaystyle\sum_{n=1}^{\infty} \frac{\ln(1 + \frac{1}{n})}{n}$ converges.

Example 6.65. Consider the series

$$\sum_{n=1}^{\infty} \frac{[\ln(n)]^6}{n^2}.$$

Since $\displaystyle\lim_{x \to \infty} \frac{[\ln(x)]^p}{x^q} = 0$ for any $p > 0$, $q > 0$, by L'Hôpital's rule, $\displaystyle\lim_{n \to \infty} \frac{[\ln(n)]^p}{n^q} = 0$ by Theorem 6.3. Thus,

$$\frac{[\ln(n)]^6}{n^2} = \frac{[\ln(n)]^6}{n^{1/2}} \frac{1}{n^{3/2}},$$

and $\displaystyle\lim_{n \to \infty} \frac{[\ln(n)]^6}{n^{1/2}} = 0 \Rightarrow$ there exists an integer N such that

$$n \geq N \quad \Rightarrow \quad \frac{[\ln(n)]^6}{n^{1/2}} < 1 \quad \Rightarrow \quad 0 \leq \frac{[\ln(n)]^6}{n^2} \leq \frac{1}{n^{3/2}},$$

and, since $\displaystyle\sum_{n=1}^{\infty} \frac{1}{n^{3/2}}$ converges, $\displaystyle\sum_{n=1}^{\infty} \frac{[\ln(n)]^6}{n^2}$ converges by the comparison test.

Example 6.66. Consider the series

$$\sum_{n=1}^{\infty} a_n = \sum_{n=1}^{\infty} \frac{n + 5}{n^3 - n^2 + 2n + 3}.$$

In order to determine which inequalities to employ, it is necessary to deduce the "large-n behaviour" of a_n. In the limit as $n \to \infty$, $n + 5 \sim n$, read "$n + 5$ behaves as n," and $n^3 - n^2 + 2n + 3 \sim n^3$. The reason is that the term with the highest power of n dominates the expression for large n. Hence,

$$\frac{n + 5}{n^3 - n^2 + 2n + 3} \sim \frac{n}{n^3} = \frac{1}{n^2},$$

and, since $\sum_{n=1}^{\infty} \frac{1}{n^2}$ converges, we must show that $a_n \le \frac{c}{n^2}$ for all sufficiently large n, where c is a constant. Thus,

$$\frac{n+5}{n^3 - n^2 + 2n + 3} \le \frac{n+5}{n^3 - n^2} \le \frac{n+n}{n^3 - \frac{1}{2}n^3} = \frac{4}{n^2}, \quad n \ge 5,$$

since $n + 5 \le n + n$ for $n \ge 5$ and $-\frac{1}{2}n^3 \le -n^2$ for $n \ge 2$. Hence, $\sum_{n=1}^{\infty} a_n$ converges by the comparison test.

As seen in Example 6.66, certain of the inequalities required for the comparison test may become too tedious. An alternative test, which is especially suitable for series such as the one in Example 6.66, is given by the following:

Theorem 6.12. Let $\{a_n\}$ and $\{b_n\}$ be sequences with $a_n > 0$ and $b_n > 0$ for $n \ge k$, where k is an integer, and let

$$L = \lim_{n \to \infty} \frac{a_n}{b_n}.$$

1. If $0 < L < \infty$, then either both $\sum_{n=1}^{\infty} a_n$ and $\sum_{n=1}^{\infty} b_n$ converge, or they both diverge.

2. If $L = 0$ and $\sum_{n=1}^{\infty} b_n$ converges, then $\sum_{n=1}^{\infty} a_n$ converges.

3. If $L = \infty$ and $\sum_{n=1}^{\infty} b_n$ diverges, then $\sum_{n=1}^{\infty} a_n$ diverges.

As in the comparison test, the initial value 1 of n may be replaced by any other integer. This test is called the *limit comparison test..*

Example 6.67. Consider, once again, the series in Example 6.66,

$$\sum_{n=1}^{\infty} a_n = \sum_{n=1}^{\infty} \frac{n+5}{n^3 - n^2 + 2n + 3}.$$

Since we have deduced in Example 6.66 that $a_n \sim 4\frac{1}{n^2}$, let $b_n = \frac{1}{n^2}$. Then

$$L = \lim_{n \to \infty} \frac{a_n}{b_n} = \lim_{n \to \infty} \frac{n^3 + 5n^2}{n^3 - n^2 + 2n + 3} = 1$$

and, since $0 < 1 < \infty$ and $\displaystyle\sum_{n=1}^{\infty} b_n$ converges, $\displaystyle\sum_{n=1}^{\infty} a_n$ converges by the limit comparison test (Theorem 6.12).

Example 6.68. Consider the series

$$\sum_{n=1}^{\infty} a_n = \sum_{n=1}^{\infty} \frac{1}{n^{1+\frac{1}{n}}}.$$

Since $\lim\limits_{x\to\infty} x^{1/x} = 1$ by L'Hôpital's rule, $\lim\limits_{n\to\infty} n^{1/n} = 1$ by Theorem 6.3. Hence,

$$\frac{1}{n^{1+\frac{1}{n}}} = \frac{1}{n}\frac{1}{n^{1/n}} \sim \frac{1}{n}$$

for large n. Let $b_n = \dfrac{1}{n}$. Then

$$\lim_{n\to\infty} \frac{a_n}{b_n} = \lim_{n\to\infty} \frac{1}{n^{1/n}} = 1$$

and, since $0 < 1 < \infty$ and $\displaystyle\sum_{n=1}^{\infty} b_n$ diverges, $\displaystyle\sum_{n=1}^{\infty} a_n$ diverges by the limit comparison test (Theorem 6.12).

Example 6.69. Consider the series

$$\sum_{n=1}^{\infty} a_n = \sum_{n=1}^{\infty} \frac{n^2 - 2n + 1}{\sqrt[3]{n^{10} + 3n^2 + n}}.$$

Since, for large n,

$$\frac{n^2 - 2n + 1}{\sqrt[3]{n^{10} + 3n^2 + n}} \sim \frac{n^2}{\sqrt[3]{n^{10}}} = \frac{n^2}{n^{10/3}} = \frac{1}{n^{4/3}},$$

let $b_n = \dfrac{1}{n^{4/3}}$. Then

$$\lim_{n\to\infty} \frac{a_n}{b_n} = \lim_{n\to\infty} \frac{n^{10/3} - 2n^{7/3} + n^{4/3}}{\sqrt[3]{n^{10} + 3n^2 + n}} = \lim_{n\to\infty} \frac{1 - \frac{2}{n} + \frac{1}{n^2}}{\sqrt[3]{1 + \frac{3}{n^8} + \frac{1}{n^9}}} = 1$$

and, since $0 < 1 < \infty$ and $\displaystyle\sum_{n=1}^{\infty} b_n$ converges, $\displaystyle\sum_{n=1}^{\infty} a_n$ converges by the limit comparison test (Theorem 6.12).

Example 6.70. Consider the series

$$\sum_{n=1}^{\infty} a_n = \sum_{n=1}^{\infty} \frac{[\ln(n)]^2}{n^{3/2}}.$$

Since $\sum_{n=1}^{\infty} \frac{1}{n^p}$ converges for any $p > 1$ and $\lim_{n \to \infty} \frac{[\ln(n)]^2}{n^q} = 0$ for any $q > 0$, choose any $p > 1$ and $q > 0$ such that $p + q = \frac{3}{2}$, e.g., $p = \frac{5}{4}$ and $q = \frac{1}{4}$, and let $b_n = \frac{1}{n^{5/4}}$. Then

$$L = \lim_{n \to \infty} \frac{a_n}{b_n} = \lim_{n \to \infty} \frac{[\ln(n)]^2}{n^{1/4}} = 0$$

and, since $L = 0$ and $\sum_{n=1}^{\infty} b_n$ converges, $\sum_{n=1}^{\infty} a_n$ converges by the limit comparison test (Theorem 6.12).

Example 6.71. Consider the series

$$\sum_{n=3}^{\infty} a_n = \sum_{n=3}^{\infty} \frac{1}{\sqrt{n+1}\,[\ln(n-1)]^7},$$

and let $b_n = \frac{1}{n}$. Then

$$L = \lim_{n \to \infty} \frac{a_n}{b_n} = \lim_{n \to \infty} \frac{n}{\sqrt{n+1}[\ln(n-1)]^7} = \lim_{n \to \infty} \frac{n^{1/2}}{\sqrt{1 + \frac{1}{n}}\,[\ln(n-1)]^7} = \infty$$

because $\lim_{n \to \infty} \frac{[\ln(n-1)]^7}{n^{1/2}} = 0$. Since $L = \infty$ and $\sum_{n=1}^{\infty} b_n$ diverges, $\sum_{n=3}^{\infty} a_n$ diverges by the limit comparison test (Theorem 6.12).

6.2.3 Alternating Series

Definition 6.8. A series of the form

$$\sum_{n=0}^{\infty} (-1)^n b_n = b_0 - b_1 + b_2 - b_3 + b_4 - b_5 + \cdots,$$

where $b_n > 0$ for all $n \geq 0$, is called an *alternating series*. More generally, for any integers k and m,

$$\sum_{n=k}^{\infty} (-1)^{n+m} b_n,$$

with $b_n > 0$ for all $n \geq k$, is an alternating series.

Thus, an alternating series is one where the terms are alternately positive and negative.

Example 6.72. The series

$$\sum_{n=0}^{\infty} \frac{(-1)^n}{n+1} = 1 - \frac{1}{2} + \frac{1}{3} - \frac{1}{4} + \cdots$$

is an alternating series with $b_n = \dfrac{1}{n+1} > 0$ for $n \geq 0$.

Example 6.73. The series

$$\sum_{n=1}^{\infty} \frac{(-1)^{n-1}}{\sqrt{n}} = 1 - \frac{1}{\sqrt{2}} + \frac{1}{\sqrt{3}} - \frac{1}{2} + \cdots$$

is an alternating series with $b_n = \dfrac{1}{\sqrt{n}} > 0$ for $n \geq 1$.

Example 6.74. The series

$$\sum_{n=1}^{\infty} (-1)^n \sin(n)$$

is *not* an alternating series because there are values of n for which $b_n = \sin(n) \not> 0$.

Theorem 6.13. Consider the alternating series

$$\sum_{n=0}^{\infty} (-1)^n b_n.$$

If $\{b_n\}$ is decreasing for $n \geq k$, where k is an integer, and $\displaystyle \lim_{n \to \infty} b_n = 0$, then the series converges. This theorem is called the *alternating series test*.

Example 6.75. The alternating series

$$\sum_{n=1}^{\infty} \frac{(-1)^n}{n} = -1 + \frac{1}{2} - \frac{1}{3} + \frac{1}{4} - \cdots$$

converges by the alternating series test (Theorem 6.13) since $\left\{ \dfrac{1}{n} \right\}_{n=1}^{\infty}$ is decreasing for $n \geq 1$ and $\displaystyle \lim_{n \to \infty} \frac{1}{n} = 0$.

Example 6.76. Consider the alternating series

$$\sum_{n=2}^{\infty}(-1)^n\frac{\ln(n)}{n}.$$

Let $f(x) = \dfrac{\ln(x)}{x}$. Then $f'(x) = \dfrac{1 - \ln(x)}{x^2} < 0$ for $x > e \Rightarrow f$ is decreasing for $x \ge e$.

Hence, $\left\{\dfrac{\ln(n)}{n}\right\}_{n=2}^{\infty}$ is decreasing for $n \ge 3 > e$, and, since $\lim\limits_{n\to\infty}\dfrac{\ln(n)}{n} = 0$, the series converges by the alternating series test (Theorem 6.13).

Approximations of Alternating Series

Theorem 6.14. Suppose that $b_n > 0$ and $\{b_n\}$ is decreasing for $n \ge 0$, and that $\lim\limits_{n\to\infty} b_n = 0$, so that the alternating series

$$\sum_{n=0}^{\infty}(-1)^n b_n$$

converges by the alternating series test. If the sum

$$s = \sum_{n=0}^{\infty}(-1)^n b_n = b_0 - b_1 + b_2 - \cdots + (-1)^n b_n + (-1)^{n+1}b_{n+1} + (-1)^{n+2}b_{n+2}\cdots$$

is approximated by the nth partial sum

$$s_n = \sum_{k=0}^{n}(-1)^k b_k = b_0 - b_1 + b_2 - \cdots + (-1)^n b_n,$$

then the absolute value of the error is less than the absolute value b_{n+1} of the first neglected term (which is $\pm b_{n+1}$). In other words,

$$|R_n| = |s - s_n| < b_{n+1},$$

where $R_n = \sum_{k=n+1}^{\infty}(-1)^k b_k$ is the *remainder*, as defined in Section 6.2.1.

Proof.

$$
\begin{aligned}
s - s_n &= \sum_{k=n+1}^{\infty}(-1)^k b_k \\
&= (-1)^{n+1}b_{n+1} + (-1)^{n+2}b_{n+2} + (-1)^{n+3}b_{n+3} + (-1)^{n+4}b_{n+4} + \cdots \\
&= (-1)^{n+1}(b_{n+1} - b_{n+2} + b_{n+3} - b_{n+4} + b_{n+5} - \cdots) \\
\Rightarrow |s - s_n| &= b_{n+1} - b_{n+2} + b_{n+3} - b_{n+4} + b_{n+5} - \cdots \\
&= b_{n+1} - (b_{n+2} - b_{n+3}) - (b_{n+4} - b_{n+5}) - \cdots \\
&< b_{n+1}
\end{aligned}
$$

because $\{b_n\}$ is decreasing for $n \geq 0 \Rightarrow -(b_{n+m} - b_{n+m+1}) < 0$ for all $m \geq 0$.

Example 6.77. Consider the alternating series

$$\sum_{n=1}^{\infty} \frac{(-1)^{n-1}}{n^4}.$$

Since $\{b_n\} = \left\{\dfrac{1}{n^4}\right\}$ is decreasing and $b_n > 0$ for $n \geq 1$, and $\lim\limits_{n\to\infty} b_n = 0$, the series converges by the alternating series test (Theorem 6.13). Suppose that the sum s of the series is approximated by s_3, i.e.,

$$s = \sum_{n=1}^{\infty} \frac{(-1)^{n-1}}{n^4} \approx s_3 = \sum_{k=1}^{3} \frac{(-1)^{k-1}}{k^4} = 1 - \frac{1}{16} + \frac{1}{81} \approx 0.9498.$$

Then

$$|R_3| = |s - s_3| < \frac{1}{4^4} = \frac{1}{256} \approx 0.0039,$$

i.e., the error, in absolute value, is at most 0.0039.

Example 6.78. Consider the alternating series

$$\sum_{n=2}^{\infty} \frac{(-1)^n}{\ln(n)}.$$

Since $\{b_n\} = \left\{\dfrac{1}{\ln(n)}\right\}$ is decreasing and $b_n > 0$ for $n \geq 2$, and $\lim\limits_{n\to\infty} b_n = 0$, the series converges by the alternating series test (Theorem 6.13). How large must n be in order that the approximation of s by s_n be correct to four decimal places?

In order to ensure four decimal place accuracy, we require that

$$|\text{error}| = |R_n| = |s - s_n| < b_{n+1} \leq 0.0001.$$

Thus,

$$b_{n+1} = \frac{1}{\ln(n+1)} \leq 0.0001$$

if and only if

$$\ln(n+1) \geq 10,000$$

if and only if

$$n \geq e^{10,000} - 1,$$

which is an astronomically large number. The reason is that the terms $\dfrac{1}{\ln(n)} \to 0$ far too slowly compared to, say, $\dfrac{1}{n^4}$, and so many terms are required in order for the finite sum s_n to become sufficiently close to the infinite sum s.

6.2.4 Absolute and Conditional Convergence

Theorem 6.15. If $\displaystyle\sum_{n=1}^{\infty} |a_n|$ converges, then $\displaystyle\sum_{n=1}^{\infty} a_n$ converges. Equivalently, if $\displaystyle\sum_{n=1}^{\infty} a_n$ diverges, then $\displaystyle\sum_{n=1}^{\infty} |a_n|$ diverges.

Proof. Since $|a_n| = \pm a_n$, $a_n = \pm|a_n|$ and, hence, $-|a_n| \le a_n \le |a_n|$, which gives

$$0 \le a_n + |a_n| \le 2|a_n|.$$

If $\displaystyle\sum_{n=1}^{\infty} |a_n|$ converges, then $\displaystyle\sum_{n=1}^{\infty} 2|a_n| = 2\sum_{n=1}^{\infty} |a_n|$ converges and, by the comparison test, $\displaystyle\sum_{n=1}^{\infty} (a_n + |a_n|)$ converges. Hence,

$$\sum_{n=1}^{\infty} a_n = \sum_{n=1}^{\infty} [(a_n + |a_n|) - |a_n|]$$

converges by Theorem 6.8. The second statement is the *contrapositive* of the first, and is logically equivalent to it.

Example 6.79. Since $\displaystyle\sum_{n=1}^{\infty} \frac{1}{n^2}$ converges (it is a p-series with $p = 2 > 1$) and

$$\sum_{n=1}^{\infty} \left|\frac{(-1)^n}{n^2}\right| = \sum_{n=1}^{\infty} \frac{1}{n^2},$$

it follows by Theorem 6.15 that $\displaystyle\sum_{n=1}^{\infty} \frac{(-1)^n}{n^2}$ converges. Of course, this result can also be established independently by the alternating series test.

Example 6.80. The series $\displaystyle\sum_{n=1}^{\infty} \frac{(-1)^n}{n}$ converges by the alternating series test, but the series

$$\sum_{n=1}^{\infty} \left|\frac{(-1)^n}{n}\right| = \sum_{n=1}^{\infty} \frac{1}{n}$$

diverges (it is a p-series with $p = 1 \le 1$).

Examples 6.79 and 6.80 demonstrate that, for certain series, both $\displaystyle\sum_{n=1}^{\infty} a_n$ and $\displaystyle\sum_{n=1}^{\infty} |a_n|$ converge, whereas for others, $\displaystyle\sum_{n=1}^{\infty} a_n$ converges but $\displaystyle\sum_{n=1}^{\infty} |a_n|$ diverges. Of course, if $\displaystyle\sum_{n=1}^{\infty} |a_n|$ converges, then $\displaystyle\sum_{n=1}^{\infty} a_n$ converges by Theorem 6.15.

Definition 6.9. A series $\displaystyle\sum_{n=1}^{\infty} a_n$ *converges absolutely* if both

$$\sum_{n=1}^{\infty} a_n \quad \text{and} \quad \sum_{n=1}^{\infty} |a_n|$$

converge. If $\displaystyle\sum_{n=1}^{\infty} a_n$ converges but $\displaystyle\sum_{n=1}^{\infty} |a_n|$ diverges, then the series $\displaystyle\sum_{n=1}^{\infty} a_n$ *converges conditionally.*

If $a_n \geq 0$ for all $n \geq 1$, then $|a_n| = a_n$ and, hence, $\displaystyle\sum_{n=1}^{\infty} a_n$ converges if and only if it converges absolutely. Thus, there is a difference between absolute and conditional convergence only for series $\displaystyle\sum_{n=1}^{\infty} a_n$ where the a_n take both positive and negative values.

It must be emphasized that, whether $\displaystyle\sum_{n=1}^{\infty} a_n$ converges absolutely or conditionally, it converges. The distinction between absolute and conditional convergence pertains only to whether or not the series $\displaystyle\sum_{n=1}^{\infty} |a_n|$ converges.

Example 6.81. By Example 6.79, the series $\displaystyle\sum_{n=1}^{\infty} \frac{(-1)^n}{n^2}$ converges absolutely and, by Example 6.80, the series $\displaystyle\sum_{n=1}^{\infty} \frac{(-1)^n}{n}$ converges conditionally. Note that both series converge. The distinction arises because, in the former,

$$\sum_{n=1}^{\infty} \left| \frac{(-1)^n}{n^2} \right| = \sum_{n=1}^{\infty} \frac{1}{n^2}$$

converges, whereas in the latter,

$$\sum_{n=1}^{\infty} \left| \frac{(-1)^n}{n} \right| = \sum_{n=1}^{\infty} \frac{1}{n}$$

diverges.

Example 6.82. Consider the series

$$\sum_{n=2}^{\infty} \frac{(-1)^n}{n \ln(n)}.$$

This series converges by the alternating series test. However,

$$\sum_{n=2}^{\infty} \left| \frac{(-1)^n}{n \ln(n)} \right| = \sum_{n=2}^{\infty} \frac{1}{n \ln(n)}$$

diverges by the integral test. Hence, $\displaystyle\sum_{n=2}^{\infty} \frac{(-1)^n}{n \ln(n)}$ converges conditionally.

Example 6.83. Consider the series

$$\sum_{n=0}^{\infty} \frac{(-2)^n}{5^n}.$$

The series

$$\sum_{n=0}^{\infty} \left| \frac{(-2)^n}{5^n} \right| = \sum_{n=0}^{\infty} \frac{2^n}{5^n} = \sum_{n=0}^{\infty} \left(\frac{2}{5} \right)^n$$

converges since it is geometric with $|r| < 1$. Hence, $\displaystyle\sum_{n=0}^{\infty} \frac{(-2)^n}{5^n}$ converges absolutely.

Example 6.84. The series

$$\sum_{n=0}^{\infty} \frac{(-1)^n \sqrt{n^2 + 1}}{n + 1}$$

diverges by the nth-term test because $\displaystyle\lim_{n \to \infty} \frac{(-1)^n \sqrt{n^2 + 1}}{n + 1} \neq 0$ (the limit does not exist). It follows by Theorem 6.15 that

$$\sum_{n=0}^{\infty} \left| \frac{(-1)^n \sqrt{n^2 + 1}}{n + 1} \right| = \sum_{n=0}^{\infty} \frac{\sqrt{n^2 + 1}}{n + 1}$$

diverges, a result which can be established independently since $\displaystyle\lim_{n \to \infty} \frac{\sqrt{n^2 + 1}}{n + 1} = 1 \neq 0.$

Theorem 6.16. Let $\{a_n\}$ be a sequence and suppose that

$$L = \lim_{n \to \infty} \left| \frac{a_{n+1}}{a_n} \right|$$

exists. Then:

1. If $L < 1$, then $\displaystyle\sum_{n=0}^{\infty} a_n$ converges absolutely.

2. If $L > 1$, then $\displaystyle\sum_{n=0}^{\infty} a_n$ diverges.

3. If $L = 1$, then no conclusions can be made regarding convergence.

As usual, with regard to convergence, the initial value 0 of n can be replaced by any other integer. This theorem is called the *ratio test*.

Note that, since the ratio test involves $|a_n|$ and not a_n, it cannot be employed as a test for conditional convergence.

Example 6.85. Consider the series

$$\sum_{n=0}^{\infty} a_n = \sum_{n=0}^{\infty} \frac{(-1)^n n^3}{2^n}.$$

$$|a_n| = \left| \frac{(-1)^n n^3}{2^n} \right| = \frac{n^3}{2^n} \text{ and } |a_{n+1}| = \frac{(n+1)^3}{2^{n+1}} \Rightarrow$$

$$L = \lim_{n \to \infty} \left| \frac{a_{n+1}}{a_n} \right| = \lim_{n \to \infty} \frac{(n+1)^3}{2^{n+1}} \frac{2^n}{n^3} = \frac{1}{2} \lim_{n \to \infty} \frac{(n+1)^3}{n^3} = \frac{1}{2} < 1$$

$\Rightarrow \displaystyle\sum_{n=0}^{\infty} a_n$ converges absolutely by the ratio test (Theorem 6.16). Thus, both

$$\sum_{n=0}^{\infty} a_n = \sum_{n=0}^{\infty} \frac{(-1)^n n^3}{2^n} \text{ and } \sum_{n=0}^{\infty} |a_n| = \sum_{n=0}^{\infty} \frac{n^3}{2^n}$$

converge.

Example 6.86. Consider the series

$$\sum_{n=0}^{\infty} a_n = \sum_{n=0}^{\infty} \frac{(-3)^n}{n^4 + 1}.$$

$$|a_n| = \left| \frac{(-3)^n}{n^4 + 1} \right| = \frac{3^n}{n^4 + 1} \text{ and } |a_{n+1}| = \frac{3^{n+1}}{(n+1)^4 + 1} \Rightarrow$$

$$L = \lim_{n \to \infty} \left| \frac{a_{n+1}}{a_n} \right| = \lim_{n \to \infty} \frac{3^{n+1}}{(n+1)^4 + 1} \frac{n^4 + 1}{3^n} = 3 \lim_{n \to \infty} \frac{n^4 + 1}{(n+1)^4 + 1} = 3 > 1$$

$$\Rightarrow \sum_{n=0}^{\infty} a_n \text{ diverges by the ratio test (Theorem 6.16). Thus, both}$$

$$\sum_{n=0}^{\infty} a_n = \sum_{n=0}^{\infty} \frac{(-3)^n}{n^4 + 1} \quad \text{and} \quad \sum_{n=0}^{\infty} |a_n| = \sum_{n=0}^{\infty} \frac{3^n}{n^4 + 1}$$

diverge.

Example 6.87. For the series

$$\sum_{n=1}^{\infty} a_n = \sum_{n=1}^{\infty} \frac{1}{n},$$

which diverges,

$$L = \lim_{n \to \infty} \left| \frac{a_{n+1}}{a_n} \right| = \lim_{n \to \infty} \frac{n}{n+1} = 1$$

and, for the series

$$\sum_{n=1}^{\infty} a_n = \sum_{n=1}^{\infty} \frac{1}{n^2},$$

which converges,

$$L = \lim_{n \to \infty} \left| \frac{a_{n+1}}{a_n} \right| = \lim_{n \to \infty} \frac{n^2}{(n+1)^2} = 1.$$

Thus, convergence or divergence cannot be determined by the ratio test if $L = 1$.

Example 6.88. Consider the series

$$\sum_{n=1}^{\infty} a_n = \sum_{n=1}^{\infty} \frac{n!}{n^n}.$$

Since $a_n > 0$, $|a_n| = a_n = \dfrac{n!}{n^n}$ and $|a_{n+1}| = \dfrac{(n+1)!}{(n+1)^{n+1}} \Rightarrow$

$$
\begin{aligned}
L &= \lim_{n\to\infty} \left| \frac{a_{n+1}}{a_n} \right| = \lim_{n\to\infty} \frac{(n+1)!}{(n+1)^{n+1}} \frac{n^n}{n!} = \lim_{n\to\infty} \frac{(n+1)n^n}{(n+1)^{n+1}} = \lim_{n\to\infty} \frac{n^n}{(n+1)^n} \\
&= \lim_{n\to\infty} \left(\frac{n}{n+1} \right)^n = \lim_{n\to\infty} \frac{1}{\left(\frac{n+1}{n}\right)^n} = \lim_{n\to\infty} \frac{1}{\left(1+\frac{1}{n}\right)^n} = \frac{1}{e} < 1.
\end{aligned}
$$

Hence, $\displaystyle\sum_{n=1}^{\infty} a_n$ converges by the ratio test. Since $a_n > 0$, convergence and absolute convergence are synonymous.

Example 6.89.   Consider the series

$$
\sum_{n=0}^{\infty} a_n = \sum_{n=0}^{\infty} \frac{(2n)!}{2^n (n!)^2}.
$$

$$
\begin{aligned}
\left| \frac{a_{n+1}}{a_n} \right| &= \frac{(2n+2)!}{2^{n+1}[(n+1)!]^2} \frac{2^n (n!)^2}{(2n)!} = \frac{(2n+2)(2n+1)}{2} \left[\frac{n!}{(n+1)!} \right]^2 \\
&= (n+1)(2n+1) \left(\frac{1}{n+1} \right)^2 = \frac{2n+1}{n+1} \\
\Rightarrow \quad L &= \lim_{n\to\infty} \left| \frac{a_{n+1}}{a_n} \right| = \lim_{n\to\infty} \frac{2n+1}{n+1} = 2 > 1.
\end{aligned}
$$

Hence, $\displaystyle\sum_{n=0}^{\infty} a_n$ diverges by the ratio test.

Example 6.90.   Consider the series

$$
\sum_{n=0}^{\infty} a_n = \sum_{n=0}^{\infty} \frac{1 \cdot 3 \cdot 5 \cdots (2n+1)}{3^n n!}.
$$

$$
\begin{aligned}
\left| \frac{a_{n+1}}{a_n} \right| &= \frac{1 \cdot 3 \cdot 5 \cdots (2n+1)(2n+3)}{3^{n+1}(n+1)!} \frac{3^n n!}{1 \cdot 3 \cdot 5 \cdots (2n+1)} = \frac{2n+3}{3(n+1)} \\
\Rightarrow \quad L &= \lim_{n\to\infty} \left| \frac{a_{n+1}}{a_n} \right| = \lim_{n\to\infty} \frac{2n+3}{3(n+1)} = \frac{2}{3} < 1.
\end{aligned}
$$

Hence, $\displaystyle\sum_{n=0}^{\infty} a_n$ converges by the ratio test.

Theorem 6.17. Let $\{a_n\}$ be a sequence and suppose that

$$L = \lim_{n \to \infty} |a_n|^{1/n}$$

exists. Then:

1. If $L < 1$, then $\displaystyle\sum_{n=0}^{\infty} a_n$ converges absolutely.

2. If $L > 1$, then $\displaystyle\sum_{n=0}^{\infty} a_n$ diverges.

3. If $L = 1$, then no conclusions can be made regarding convergence.

Again, the initial value 0 of n can be replaced by any other integer. This theorem is called the *root test*.

As for the ratio test, the root test cannot be employed as a test for conditional convergence.

Example 6.91. Consider the series

$$\sum_{n=1}^{\infty} a_n = \sum_{n=1}^{\infty} \frac{[\ln(n)]^{5n}}{n^{3n}}.$$

Since

$$L = \lim_{n \to \infty} |a_n|^{1/n} = \lim_{n \to \infty} \frac{[\ln(n)]^5}{n^3} = 0 < 1,$$

$\displaystyle\sum_{n=1}^{\infty} a_n$ converges by the root test (Theorem 6.17).

Example 6.92. Consider the series

$$\sum_{n=1}^{\infty} a_n = \sum_{n=1}^{\infty} \left(1 + \frac{1}{n}\right)^{n^2}.$$

Since

$$L = \lim_{n \to \infty} |a_n|^{1/n} = \lim_{n \to \infty} \left(1 + \frac{1}{n}\right)^n = e > 1,$$

$\displaystyle\sum_{n=1}^{\infty} a_n$ diverges by the root test (Theorem 6.17).

Exercises 6.2

1. Write down the nth partial sum s_n of the series $\displaystyle\sum_{n=0}^{\infty} \frac{1}{2^n}$ for $n = 0, 1, \cdots, 4$.

2. Write down the nth partial sum s_n of the series $\displaystyle\sum_{n=1}^{\infty} \frac{1}{n}$ for $n = 1, 2, \cdots, 5$.

3. Let $\{s_n\}_{n=1}^{\infty}$ denote the sequence of partial sums of the series $\displaystyle\sum_{n=1}^{\infty} a_n$. Determine the sum s of the series if $s_n = \dfrac{3n-1}{2n+1}$ for $n \geq 1$.

In Exercises 4–11, determine the sum of the given series.

4. $\displaystyle\sum_{n=0}^{\infty} \frac{1}{5^n}$

5. $\displaystyle\sum_{n=0}^{\infty} \frac{2^n}{(-5)^n}$

6. $\displaystyle\sum_{n=1}^{\infty} \frac{2 \cdot 3^n}{5^n}$

7. $\displaystyle\sum_{n=2}^{\infty} \frac{1}{3^n}$

8. $\displaystyle\sum_{n=0}^{\infty} 5 \cdot 2^{3n} 3^{-2n}$

9. $\displaystyle\sum_{n=1}^{\infty} 5 \cdot 3^{2n} 2^{-4n}$

10. $\displaystyle\sum_{n=2}^{\infty} 5^n (-2)^{-3n}$

11. $\displaystyle\sum_{n=0}^{\infty} \frac{2}{4n^2 + 8n + 3}$

In Exercises 12–23, determine whether the given series converges or diverges.

12. $\displaystyle\sum_{n=1}^{\infty} \frac{2\sqrt{n^2+3}}{n}$

13. $\displaystyle\sum_{n=0}^{\infty} \frac{\cos(n)}{2 + \sin^2(n)}$

14. $\displaystyle\sum_{n=0}^{\infty} [1 - (-1)^n]$

15. $\displaystyle\sum_{n=0}^{\infty} \frac{n^3 + 2n^2 - 1}{n^2 + n + 1}$

16. $\displaystyle\sum_{n=1}^{\infty} \frac{1}{n^2\sqrt{n}}$

17. $\displaystyle\sum_{n=1}^{\infty} \frac{\sqrt{n}}{n^2}$

18. $\displaystyle\sum_{n=1}^{\infty} \frac{1}{n^{r+1}}, \; r > 0$

19. $\displaystyle\sum_{n=1}^{\infty} n^{r-1}, \; r \geq 0$

20. $\displaystyle\sum_{n=1}^{\infty}\frac{1}{2n-1}$

21. $\displaystyle\sum_{n=1}^{\infty}2ne^{-n^2}$

22. $\displaystyle\sum_{n=2}^{\infty}\frac{1}{n[\ln(n)]^p}, \ p<1$

23. $\displaystyle\sum_{n=2}^{\infty}\frac{1}{n[\ln(n)]^p}, \ p>1$

24. Consider the series $\displaystyle\sum_{n=1}^{\infty}\frac{3}{n^4}$.

   (a) Approximate the sum s of the series by s_2 and determine lower and upper bounds for the error R_2.

   (b) How large must n be taken in order that s_n approximate s with error no greater that 0.001?

25. Consider the series $\displaystyle\sum_{n=1}^{\infty}\frac{1}{n\sqrt{n}}$.

   (a) Approximate the sum s of the series by s_3 and determine lower and upper bounds for the error R_3.

   (b) How large must n be taken in order that s_n approximate s with error no greater that 0.0001?

In Exercises 26–45, determine whether the given series converges or diverges.

26. $\displaystyle\sum_{n=0}^{\infty}\frac{1}{n\sqrt{n}+3}$

27. $\displaystyle\sum_{n=2}^{\infty}\frac{1}{\sqrt{n}-1}$

28. $\displaystyle\sum_{n=0}^{\infty}\frac{3^n}{4^n+1}$

29. $\displaystyle\sum_{n=0}^{\infty}\frac{3}{2n^2-3}$

30. $\displaystyle\sum_{n=0}^{\infty}\frac{2^n+1}{3^n}$

31. $\displaystyle\sum_{n=0}^{\infty}\frac{2^n+n}{e^n}$

32. $\displaystyle\sum_{n=1}^{\infty}\frac{1}{\sqrt{n}+n}$

33. $\displaystyle\sum_{n=1}^{\infty}\frac{\sqrt{n}-1}{n+1}$

34. $\displaystyle\sum_{n=0}^{\infty}\frac{n^3+2n-1}{n^4+n^3+2}$

35. $\displaystyle\sum_{n=1}^{\infty}\frac{\sqrt[3]{n^2+1}}{n^2+n-1}$

36. $\displaystyle\sum_{n=2}^{\infty} \frac{1}{n^{2/3}\ln(n)}$

37. $\displaystyle\sum_{n=2}^{\infty} \frac{\ln(n)}{n^2}$

38. $\displaystyle\sum_{n=1}^{\infty} \frac{\ln(1+\frac{1}{n})}{\sqrt{n}}$

39. $\displaystyle\sum_{n=2}^{\infty} \frac{[\ln(n)]^3}{n\sqrt{n}}$

40. $\displaystyle\sum_{n=1}^{\infty} \frac{(-1)^n}{n^{2/3}}$

41. $\displaystyle\sum_{n=0}^{\infty} \frac{(-1)^n}{2+\sin(n)}$

42. $\displaystyle\sum_{n=2}^{\infty} \frac{(-1)^n}{\sqrt{\ln(n)}}$

43. $\displaystyle\sum_{n=2}^{\infty} \frac{(-1)^n\, n}{e^n \ln(n)}$

44. $\displaystyle\sum_{n=1}^{\infty} \frac{(-1)^n - 1}{n}$

45. $\displaystyle\sum_{n=1}^{\infty} \frac{1+(-1)^n\, n}{n^2}$

46. Consider the series $\displaystyle\sum_{n=1}^{\infty} \frac{(-1)^{n-1}}{n^2}$.

   (a) Approximate the sum s of the series by s_3 and determine an upper bound for $|R_n|$.

   (b) How large must n be taken in order that s_n approximate s correct to 4 decimal places?

47. Consider the series $\displaystyle\sum_{n=0}^{\infty} \frac{(-1)^n}{n^3+1}$.

   (a) Approximate the sum s of the series by s_2 and determine an upper bound for $|R_n|$.

   (b) How large must n be taken in order that s_n approximate s with a maximum error of $\pm\dfrac{1}{1,001}$?

In Exercises 48–53, determine whether the given series converges absolutely, converges conditionally, or diverges.

48. $\displaystyle\sum_{n=2}^{\infty} \frac{(-1)^n}{n-1}$

49. $\displaystyle\sum_{n=1}^{\infty} \frac{(-1)^{n+1}}{n\sqrt{n}}$

50. $\displaystyle\sum_{n=0}^{\infty} \frac{(-1)^n \sqrt{n}}{n+1}$

51. $\displaystyle\sum_{n=1}^{\infty} \frac{(-2)^n}{n^2}$

52. $\displaystyle\sum_{n=2}^{\infty} \frac{(-1)^n [\ln(n)]^2}{n}$

53. $\displaystyle\sum_{n=1}^{\infty} \frac{(-2)^n}{3^n - 1}$

In Exercises 54–63, determine whether the given series converges or diverges.

54. $\displaystyle\sum_{n=1}^{\infty} \frac{2^n (n+1)^3}{3^n \, n^2}$

55. $\displaystyle\sum_{n=0}^{\infty} \frac{3^{n-1} \, n^2}{2^{n+1} (n+1)^4}$

56. $\displaystyle\sum_{n=0}^{\infty} \frac{n^3 + 2n^2 - 1}{n!}$

57. $\displaystyle\sum_{n=0}^{\infty} \frac{2n}{(n+1)!}$

58. $\displaystyle\sum_{n=1}^{\infty} \frac{(n!)^2}{n^2 (2n)!}$

59. $\displaystyle\sum_{n=1}^{\infty} \frac{n!}{3 \cdot 6 \cdot 9 \cdots (3n)}$

60. $\displaystyle\sum_{n=0}^{\infty} \frac{(2n+1)!}{n!(n+1)!}$

61. $\displaystyle\sum_{n=0}^{\infty} \frac{n!(n+3)!}{(2n+3)!}$

62. $\displaystyle\sum_{n=2}^{\infty} \frac{(-n)^n}{[\ln(n)]^{2n}}$

63. $\displaystyle\sum_{n=0}^{\infty} \frac{(-1)^n n^{2n}}{2^n (n^2 + 1)^n}$

Chapter 6 Exercises

1. Prove, by induction, the formula $s_n = \dfrac{1 - r^{n+1}}{1 - r}$ for the nth partial sum of the geometric series $\displaystyle\sum_{n=0}^{\infty} r^n$.

2. Prove that $\displaystyle\sum_{n=1}^{\infty} a_n$ converges if and only if $\displaystyle\sum_{n=m}^{\infty} a_n$ converges for every integer $m \geq 1$.

3. Determine whether or not the series $\displaystyle\sum_{n=16}^{\infty} \frac{1}{n \ln(n) \{\ln[\ln(n)]\}}$ converges.

4. Determine whether or not the series $\displaystyle\sum_{n=1}^{\infty} \frac{1}{1+2+3+\cdots+n}$ converges.

5. Determine whether or not the series $\displaystyle\sum_{n=1}^{\infty} \frac{n}{1+4+9+\cdots+n^2}$ converges.

6. Prove that every finite series converges absolutely.

7. Consider the Fibonacci sequence $a_1 = a_2 = 1$ and $a_n = a_{n-1} + a_{n-2}$ for $n \geq 3$. The latter relation is called a *difference equation*, which is the discrete version of a differential equation. Find two solutions in the form $a_n = r^n$, take a linear combination, and impose the "initial conditions" $a_1 = a_2 = 1$ to determine a_n explicitly in terms of n for every $n \geq 1$.

Chapter 7

Taylor Series

The subject of Chapter 6 has been the study of sequences and series of numbers. The topic of the present chapter is the study of series which contain a variable x, i.e., series of *functions*. Thus, the convergence or divergence of the series, as well as its sum, will depend upon the value of x, making the infinite series a function of x.

7.1 Power Series

Definition 7.1. Let a be a real number. A series of the form

$$\sum_{n=0}^{\infty} c_n(x-a)^n = c_0 + c_1(x-a) + c_2(x-a)^2 + c_3(x-a)^3 + \cdots \qquad (7.1)$$

is called a *power series about a* or *centred at a*, and the numbers c_n, $n = 1, 2, 3, \cdots$ are called the *coefficients* of the power series. In the special case where $a = 0$, the series reduces to

$$\sum_{n=0}^{\infty} c_n x^n = c_0 + c_1 x + c_2 x^2 + c_3 x^3 + \cdots,$$

i.e., a power series about 0.

Note that, at $x = a$, the power series (7.1) reduces to the single term c_0 and, hence, converges absolutely. However, only those power series which converge for all x in an interval are of any practical use.

Example 7.1. The power series

$$\sum_{n=0}^{\infty} n^n x^n$$

is centred at 0 and has the coefficients $c_n = n^n$. By the root test (Theorem 6.17), the series converges absolutely if

$$\lim_{n \to \infty} |a_n|^{1/n} = \lim_{n \to \infty} |n^n x^n|^{1/n} = \lim_{n \to \infty} n|x| < 1,$$

which is possible only if $x = 0$. Thus, this series converges only at $x = 0$.

Example 7.2. The geometric series (with $r = x$)

$$\sum_{n=0}^{\infty} x^n$$

is a power series about 0 with the coefficients $c_n = 1$, $n \geq 0$. It converges to $\dfrac{1}{1-x}$ for $|x| < 1$ and diverges for $|x| \geq 1$, as demonstrated in Section 6.2, Example 6.39. For $|x| < 1$, it converges absolutely because

$$\sum_{n=0}^{\infty} |x^n| = \sum_{n=0}^{\infty} |x|^n$$

and $||x|| = |x| < 1$.

Example 7.3. Consider the power series

$$\sum_{n=0}^{\infty} \frac{1}{n!} x^n$$

about 0 with the coefficients $c_n = \dfrac{1}{n!}$, and let $a_n = \dfrac{x^n}{n!}$. Since

$$\lim_{n \to \infty} \left| \frac{a_{n+1}}{a_n} \right| = \lim_{n \to \infty} \left| \frac{x^{n+1}}{(n+1)!} \frac{n!}{x^n} \right| = \lim_{n \to \infty} \frac{|x|}{n+1} = 0 < 1$$

for all x, the series converges absolutely for all x by the ratio test (Theorem 6.16).

The preceding three examples indicate that, given a power series about a, the series may converge only at a, it may converge for all x in a finite interval, or it may converge for all real x.

Definition 7.2. If the power series

$$\sum_{n=0}^{\infty} c_n (x - a)^n$$

converges absolutely for $|x - a| < R$ and diverges for $|x - a| > R$, then R is called the *radius of convergence* of the power series. If the series converges only at $x = a$, then $R = 0$. If the series converges absolutely for all real x, then $R = \infty$.

Note that $|x - a|$ is the distance between x and a, and $|x - a| < R$ is the interval of all points x such that $-R < x - a < R$, i.e., $a - R < x < a + R$. The term "radius" is employed because, in the event that x be a complex number, the set $|x - a| < R$ is a disc of radius R centred at a. We shall, however, restrict our attention to real numbers.

The endpoints of the interval $|x - a| < R$ are the two points $|x - a| = R$, i.e., $x = a \pm R$. At these values of x, the series may converge absolutely, it may converge conditionally, or it may diverge. The interval I on which the series converges, either absolutely or conditionally, may therefore be any one of

$$[a - R, a + R], \quad [a - R, a + R), \quad (a - R, a + R] \quad \text{and} \quad (a - R, a + R),$$

and is called the *interval of convergence* of the power series.

In Example 7.1, $R = 0$ and $I = [0, 0]$, in Example 7.2, $R = 1$ and $I = (-1, 1)$, and, in Example 7.3, $R = \infty$ and $I = (-\infty, \infty)$.

Theorem 7.1. The radius of convergence of the power series

$$\sum_{n=0}^{\infty} c_n (x - a)^n$$

is given by

$$R = \lim_{n \to \infty} \left| \frac{c_n}{c_{n+1}} \right|,$$

provided that the limit exists.

Proof. Let $a_n = c_n(x - a)^n$. By the ratio test (Theorem 6.16), the series converges absolutely if

$$\lim_{n \to \infty} \left| \frac{a_{n+1}}{a_n} \right| = |x - a| \lim_{n \to \infty} \left| \frac{c_{n+1}}{c_n} \right| < 1,$$

i.e.,

$$|x - a| < \frac{1}{\lim\limits_{n \to \infty} \left| \frac{c_{n+1}}{c_n} \right|} = \lim_{n \to \infty} \left| \frac{c_n}{c_{n+1}} \right|,$$

and diverges if

$$|x - a| > \lim_{n \to \infty} \left| \frac{c_n}{c_{n+1}} \right|.$$

Hence,

$$R = \lim_{n \to \infty} \left| \frac{c_n}{c_{n+1}} \right|$$

is the radius of convergence.

Once R has been determined, the series converges absolutely at least for

$$a - R < x < a + R.$$

In order to determine convergence or divergence at the two endpoints $|x - a| = R$, and, hence, the entire interval of convergence, a test other than the ratio test must be employed.

Example 7.4. Consider the power series

$$\sum_{n=0}^{\infty} \frac{x^n}{n+1}$$

about 0 with the coefficients $c_n = \dfrac{1}{n+1}$. The radius of convergence is

$$R = \lim_{n \to \infty} \left| \frac{c_n}{c_{n+1}} \right| = \lim_{n \to \infty} \frac{n+2}{n+1} = 1.$$

Hence, the series converges absolutely for $|x| < 1$, i.e., $-1 < x < 1$.

At $x = 1$, the series becomes $\displaystyle\sum_{n=0}^{\infty} \frac{1}{n+1}$, which diverges.

At $x = -1$, the series becomes $\displaystyle\sum_{n=0}^{\infty} \frac{(-1)^n}{n+1}$, which converges conditionally. Thus, the interval of convergence is $I = [-1, 1)$.

Example 7.5. Consider the power series

$$\sum_{n=1}^{\infty} \frac{(x-3)^n}{n}$$

about 3 with the coefficients $c_n = \dfrac{1}{n}$, $n \geq 1$. This is a power series with $c_0 = 0$. The radius of convergence is

$$R = \lim_{n \to \infty} \left| \frac{c_n}{c_{n+1}} \right| = \lim_{n \to \infty} \frac{n+1}{n} = 1.$$

Hence, the series converges absolutely for $|x-3| < 1$, i.e., $-1 < x-3 < 1$, or $2 < x < 4$.

At $x = 2$, the series becomes $\sum_{n=1}^{\infty} \frac{(-1)^n}{n}$, which converges conditionally.

At $x = 4$, the series becomes $\sum_{n=1}^{\infty} \frac{1}{n}$, which diverges. Thus, the interval of convergence is $I = [2, 4)$.

Example 7.6. Consider the power series

$$\sum_{n=2}^{\infty} \frac{(3 - 2x)^n}{n - 1}.$$

Before the point a at which the series is centred, as well as its coefficients c_n, can be determined, the series must be placed in the standard power series form

$$\sum_{n=2}^{\infty} \frac{(3 - 2x)^n}{n - 1} = \sum_{n=2}^{\infty} \frac{(-2)^n}{n - 1} \left(x - \frac{3}{2}\right)^n,$$

from which we find $a = \frac{3}{2}$ and $c_n = \frac{(-2)^n}{n - 1}$, $n \geq 2$. This power series has $c_0 = c_1 = 0$. The radius of convergence is

$$R = \lim_{n \to \infty} \left|\frac{c_n}{c_{n+1}}\right| = \lim_{n \to \infty} \frac{2^n}{n - 1} \frac{n}{2^{n+1}} = \frac{1}{2}.$$

Hence, the series converges absolutely for

$$\left|x - \frac{3}{2}\right| < \frac{1}{2}, \quad \text{i.e.,} \quad -\frac{1}{2} < x - \frac{3}{2} < \frac{1}{2}, \quad \text{or} \quad 1 < x < 2.$$

At $x = 1$, the series becomes $\sum_{n=2}^{\infty} \frac{1}{n - 1}$, which diverges.

At $x = 2$, the series becomes $\sum_{n=2}^{\infty} \frac{(-1)^n}{n - 1}$, which converges conditionally. Thus, the interval of convergence is $I = (1, 2]$.

Example 7.7. Consider the power series

$$\sum_{n=0}^{\infty} \frac{(-3)^n (2x + 4)^n}{\sqrt{n + 1}} = \sum_{n=0}^{\infty} \frac{(-6)^n}{\sqrt{n + 1}} (x + 2)^n$$

centred at $a = -2$ with the coefficients $\dfrac{(-6)^n}{\sqrt{n+1}}$. The radius of convergence is

$$R = \lim_{n \to \infty} \left| \frac{c_n}{c_{n+1}} \right| = \lim_{n \to \infty} \frac{6^n}{\sqrt{n+1}} \frac{\sqrt{n+2}}{6^{n+1}} = \frac{1}{6}.$$

Hence, the series converges absolutely for

$$|x + 2| < \frac{1}{6}, \quad \text{i.e.,} \quad -\frac{1}{6} < x + 2 < \frac{1}{6}, \quad \text{or} \quad -\frac{13}{6} < x < -\frac{11}{6}.$$

At $x = -\dfrac{13}{6}$, the series becomes $\displaystyle\sum_{n=0}^{\infty} \frac{1}{\sqrt{n+1}}$, which diverges.

At $x = -\dfrac{11}{6}$, the series becomes $\displaystyle\sum_{n=0}^{\infty} \frac{(-1)^n}{\sqrt{n+1}}$, which converges conditionally. Thus, the interval of convergence is $I = \left(-\dfrac{13}{6}, -\dfrac{11}{6} \right]$.

Example 7.8.   Consider the power series

$$\sum_{n=0}^{\infty} 2^n (x - 1)^{2n}$$

centred at 1. Since only even powers of $x - 1$ are present, the coefficient of every odd power of $x - 1$ is 0, i.e., the coefficient of $(x - 1)^{2n+1}$ is $c_{2n+1} = 0$ for $n \geq 0$, and the coefficient of $(x - 1)^{2n}$ is $c_{2n} = 2^n$.

In such a power series, where every second term is 0, Theorem 7.1 cannot be applied since the expression $\left| \dfrac{c_n}{c_{n+1}} \right|$ is undefined whenever n is even. In this case, the radius of convergence can be found directly by the ratio test. Thus, with $a_n = 2^n (x - 1)^{2n}$,

$$\lim_{n \to \infty} \left| \frac{a_{n+1}}{a_n} \right| = \lim_{n \to \infty} \left| \frac{2^{n+1} (x - 1)^{2n+2}}{2^n (x - 1)^{2n}} \right| = \lim_{n \to \infty} 2|x - 1|^2 = 2|x - 1|^2 < 1$$

for $|x - 1| < \dfrac{1}{\sqrt{2}}$. The radius of convergence is therefore $R = \dfrac{1}{\sqrt{2}}$, and the series converges absolutely for

$$-\frac{1}{\sqrt{2}} < x - 1 < \frac{1}{\sqrt{2}}, \quad \text{i.e.,} \quad 1 - \frac{1}{\sqrt{2}} < x < 1 + \frac{1}{\sqrt{2}}.$$

At the endpoints $x = 1 \pm \dfrac{1}{\sqrt{2}}$, the series becomes $\displaystyle\sum_{n=0}^{\infty} 1$, and diverges. Thus, the interval of convergence is $I = \left(1 - \dfrac{1}{\sqrt{2}}, 1 + \dfrac{1}{\sqrt{2}} \right)$.

Exercises 7.1

In Exercises 1–6, write down the first 5 terms of the given power series.

1. $\displaystyle\sum_{n=0}^{\infty} \frac{x^n}{4^n}$

2. $\displaystyle\sum_{n=0}^{\infty} \frac{(x-2)^n}{\sqrt{n+1}}$

3. $\displaystyle\sum_{n=0}^{\infty} \frac{(x+1)^n}{(-3)^n}$

4. $\displaystyle\sum_{n=1}^{\infty} \frac{(x+2)^n}{n^2}$

5. $\displaystyle\sum_{n=0}^{\infty} \frac{x^{2n}}{\sqrt{n+1}}$

6. $\displaystyle\sum_{n=1}^{\infty} \frac{(x-3)^{3n}}{n\sqrt{n}}$

7. Determine c_n, $n \geq 0$, if $\displaystyle\sum_{n=0}^{\infty} 2^n (x-1)^n + \sum_{n=0}^{\infty} \frac{1}{n+1}(x-1)^n = \sum_{n=0}^{\infty} c_n(x-1)^n$.

8. Determine c_n, $n \geq 0$, if $\displaystyle\alpha \sum_{n=0}^{\infty} a_n(x-a)^n + \beta \sum_{n=0}^{\infty} b_n(x-a)^n = \sum_{n=0}^{\infty} c_n(x-a)^n$.

9. Determine c_n, $n \geq 0$, if $\displaystyle 3 + 2x - 5x^2 + \sum_{n=0}^{\infty} b_n x^n = \sum_{n=0}^{\infty} c_n x^n$.

10. Determine c_n, $n \geq 0$, if $\displaystyle 2 + (x-3) - (x-3)^4 + \sum_{n=0}^{\infty} b_n(x-3)^n = \sum_{n=0}^{\infty} c_n(x-3)^n$.

11. Express $\displaystyle\sum_{n=0}^{\infty} c_n x^n$ as a sum of two power series, one of which contains only even powers of x, and the other only odd.

In Exercises 12-23, find the radius and interval of convergence of the given power series.

12. $\displaystyle\sum_{n=0}^{\infty} \frac{2^n x^n}{n+1}$

13. $\displaystyle\sum_{n=0}^{\infty} \frac{x^n}{n^2+1}$

14. $\displaystyle\sum_{n=0}^{\infty} \frac{\sqrt{n}(x-6)^n}{n^3+1}$

15. $\displaystyle\sum_{n=0}^{\infty} \frac{(-1)^n(x-1)^n}{2n+1}$

16. $\displaystyle\sum_{n=0}^{\infty} \frac{(x+1)^n}{2^n}$

17. $\displaystyle\sum_{n=0}^{\infty} \frac{2^n(2x-4)^n}{\sqrt{n+1}}$

18. $\displaystyle\sum_{n=0}^{\infty} \frac{2^n (6 - 3x)^n}{n + 1}$ 19. $\displaystyle\sum_{n=0}^{\infty} \frac{(x - 3)^{2n}}{2^n}$

20. $\displaystyle\sum_{n=0}^{\infty} \frac{x^{3n}}{\sqrt{n^2 + 1}}$ 21. $\displaystyle\sum_{n=0}^{\infty} (3x - 2)^{2n}$

22. $\displaystyle\sum_{n=1}^{\infty} \frac{3^{n+1}(n^2 + 1)}{2^n \sqrt{n}}(x + 2)^n$ 23. $\displaystyle\sum_{n=0}^{\infty} \frac{2^{2n}(x - 3)^n}{n!}$

In Exercises 24 and 25, determine the radius of convergence of the given series.

24. $\displaystyle\sum_{n=0}^{\infty} \frac{(2n)!}{(n!)^2} x^n$ 25. $\displaystyle\sum_{n=1}^{\infty} \frac{[(n - 1)!]^2}{(2n)!}(x - 1)^{2n}$

26. (a) Determine c_n, $n \geq 0$, if $\left(\displaystyle\sum_{n=0}^{\infty} a_n x^n\right)\left(\displaystyle\sum_{n=0}^{\infty} b_n x^n\right) = \displaystyle\sum_{n=0}^{\infty} c_n x^n$.

  (b) Determine c_n, $n \geq 0$, if

$$\left[\sum_{n=0}^{\infty} a_n(x - a)^n\right]\left[\sum_{n=0}^{\infty} b_n(x - a)^n\right] = \sum_{n=0}^{\infty} c_n(x - a)^n.$$

7.2   Representations of Functions by Power Series

As seen earlier, the geometric series $\displaystyle\sum_{n=0}^{\infty} x^n$ converges for $|x| < 1$, and the sum of the series is $\dfrac{1}{1 - x}$, i.e.,

$$\sum_{n=0}^{\infty} x^n = \frac{1}{1 - x}, \quad |x| < 1.$$

This equation also shows that the function $f(x) = \dfrac{1}{1 - x}$ can be expressed as a power series about 0 for $|x| < 1$, i.e.,

$$f(x) = \frac{1}{1 - x} = \sum_{n=0}^{\infty} x^n, \quad |x| < 1. \tag{7.2}$$

In numerous problems, it is necessary to express a given function $f(x)$ as a power series about a given point a,

$$f(x) = \sum_{n=0}^{\infty} c_n(x - a)^n, \quad |x - a| < R,$$

where R is the radius of convergence of the series. The solution of a problem often appears as a power series, and it is then necessary to identify the function which is represented by that series. The study of such issues is the content of the present section.

Example 7.9. Consider the function

$$f(x) = \frac{3x^2}{1 + x}.$$

In order to express $f(x)$ as a power series about 0, employ the geometric series,

$$\frac{1}{1 - t} = \sum_{n=0}^{\infty} t^n, \quad |t| < 1,$$

with $t = -x$. Then

$$f(x) = \frac{3x^2}{1 + x} = 3x^2 \sum_{n=0}^{\infty} (-x)^n = \sum_{n=0}^{\infty} 3(-1)^n x^{n+2}, \quad |x| = |t| < 1.$$

Example 7.10. Consider the function

$$f(x) = \frac{1}{3 - x}.$$

In order to express $f(x)$ as a power series about 0, we may write $f(x)$ as

$$f(x) = \frac{1}{3 - x} = \frac{1}{3} \frac{1}{1 - \frac{x}{3}} = \frac{1}{3} \frac{1}{1 - t},$$

where $t = \dfrac{x}{3}$. Employing (7.2) in the variable t, we obtain

$$f(x) = \frac{1}{3} \frac{1}{1 - t} = \frac{1}{3} \sum_{n=0}^{\infty} t^n = \frac{1}{3} \sum_{n=0}^{\infty} \left(\frac{x}{3}\right)^n = \sum_{n=0}^{\infty} \frac{1}{3^{n+1}} x^n.$$

Since the geometric series in the variable t converges absolutely for $|t| < 1$, the above series representation of $f(x)$ converges absolutely for $\left|\dfrac{x}{3}\right| = |t| < 1$, i.e., for $|x| < 3$. Thus, the radius of convergence of the series is $R = 3$.

Example 7.11. Consider, again, the function

$$f(x) = \frac{1}{3 - x}.$$

In order to express $f(x)$ as a power series about 2, $f(x)$ must first be expressed as a function of $x - 2$, since the power series must contain powers of $x - 2$. Thus,

$$f(x) = \frac{1}{3 - x} = \frac{1}{3 - (x - 2) - 2} = \frac{1}{1 - (x - 2)} = \frac{1}{1 - t},$$

where $t = x - 2$. Employing the geometric series in the variable t for $|t| < 1$, we obtain

$$f(x) = \frac{1}{1 - t} = \sum_{n=0}^{\infty} t^n = \sum_{n=0}^{\infty} (x - 2)^n,$$

which converges absolutely for $|x - 2| = |t| < 1$. The radius of convergence of the series is therefore $R = 1$.

Example 7.12. Consider the function

$$f(x) = \frac{1}{8 - 2x}.$$

In order to express $f(x)$ as a power series about 2, write $f(x)$ as

$$f(x) = \frac{1}{8 - 2x} = \frac{1}{8 - 2(x - 2) - 4} = \frac{1}{4 - 2(x - 2)} = \frac{1}{4} \frac{1}{1 - \frac{x-2}{2}} = \frac{1}{4} \frac{1}{1 - t},$$

where $t = \dfrac{x - 2}{2}$. Then

$$f(x) = \frac{1}{4} \frac{1}{1 - t} = \frac{1}{4} \sum_{n=0}^{\infty} t^n = \frac{1}{4} \sum_{n=0}^{\infty} \left(\frac{x - 2}{2} \right)^n = \sum_{n=0}^{\infty} \frac{1}{2^{n+2}} (x - 2)^n,$$

which converges absolutely for $\left| \dfrac{x - 2}{2} \right| = |t| < 1$, i.e., for $|x - 2| < 2$. The radius of convergence of the series is therefore $R = 2$.

Example 7.13. Consider the function

$$f(x) = \frac{4}{4 + x^2}.$$

In order to express $f(x)$ as a power series about 0, write $f(x)$ as

$$f(x) = \frac{4}{4 + x^2} = \frac{1}{1 + \frac{x^2}{4}} = \frac{1}{1 - t},$$

where $t = -\dfrac{x^2}{4}$. Then

$$f(x) = \frac{1}{1-t} = \sum_{n=0}^{\infty} t^n = \sum_{n=0}^{\infty} \left(-\frac{x^2}{4}\right)^n = \sum_{n=0}^{\infty} \frac{(-1)^n}{4^n} x^{2n}.$$

The series converges absolutely for $\left|-\dfrac{x^2}{4}\right| = |t| < 1$, i.e., $|x| < 2$. Thus, the radius of convergence of the series is $R = 2$.

Example 7.14. Consider the function

$$f(x) = \frac{1}{1+x} + \frac{1}{1-2x}.$$

With $t = -x$,

$$\frac{1}{1+x} = \frac{1}{1-t} = \sum_{n=0}^{\infty} t^n = \sum_{n=0}^{\infty} (-1)^n x^n, \quad |x| = |t| < 1,$$

with radius of convergence $R_1 = 1$, and, with $t = 2x$,

$$\frac{1}{1-2x} = \frac{1}{1-t} = \sum_{n=0}^{\infty} t^n = \sum_{n=0}^{\infty} 2^n x^n, \quad |2x| = |t| < 1 \;\Rightarrow\; |x| < \frac{1}{2},$$

with radius of convergence $R_2 = \dfrac{1}{2}$. It follows that

$$f(x) = \frac{1}{1+x} + \frac{1}{1-2x} = \sum_{n=0}^{\infty} (-1)^n x^n + \sum_{n=0}^{\infty} 2^n x^n = \sum_{n=0}^{\infty} [(-1)^n + 2^n] x^n.$$

The radius of convergence is

$$R = \lim_{n \to \infty} \left| \frac{c_n}{c_{n+1}} \right| = \lim_{n \to \infty} \frac{(-1)^n + 2^n}{(-1)^{n+1} + 2^{n+1}} = \frac{1}{2},$$

which is the smaller of $R_1 = 1$ and $R_2 = \dfrac{1}{2}$. It can be shown that, in general, the radius of convergence R of a linear combination of two series is at least the minimum of the radii of convergence of the two series.

Theorem 7.2. Suppose that

$$f(x) = \sum_{n=0}^{\infty} c_n (x-a)^n, \quad |x-a| < R,$$

with the radius of convergence $R > 0$. Then the derivative of the series can be obtained by term-by-term differentiation of the series, i.e.,

$$f'(x) = \frac{d}{dx} \sum_{n=0}^{\infty} c_n(x-a)^n = \sum_{n=0}^{\infty} \frac{d}{dx}[c_n(x-a)^n] = \sum_{n=0}^{\infty} nc_n(x-a)^{n-1}, \qquad (7.3)$$

with radius of convergence R. Since the first term ($n = 0$) in the series on the right of (7.3) is 0, the series may be expressed as

$$\sum_{n=0}^{\infty} nc_n(x-a)^{n-1} = \sum_{n=1}^{\infty} nc_n(x-a)^{n-1}$$

and, making the *change of index* $k = n - 1$, we obtain

$$\sum_{n=1}^{\infty} nc_n(x-a)^{n-1} = \sum_{k=0}^{\infty} (k+1)c_{k+1}(x-a)^k,$$

which is the more standard form of a power series.

Example 7.15. Consider the function

$$f(x) = \frac{1}{(1-x)^2}.$$

Since $f(x)$ is the derivative of $\dfrac{1}{1-x}$, we obtain, by Theorem 7.2,

$$\frac{1}{(1-x)^2} = \frac{d}{dx}\frac{1}{1-x} = \frac{d}{dx}\sum_{n=0}^{\infty} x^n = \sum_{n=0}^{\infty} nx^{n-1} = \sum_{n=1}^{\infty} nx^{n-1} = \sum_{k=0}^{\infty}(k+1)x^k,$$

where $k = n - 1$, with radius of convergence $R = 1$.

Theorem 7.3. Suppose that

$$f(x) = \sum_{n=0}^{\infty} c_n(x-a)^n, \quad |x-a| < R,$$

with the radius of convergence $R > 0$. Then the integral of the series can be obtained by term-by-term integration of the series, i.e.,

$$\int f(x)\,dx = \int \sum_{n=0}^{\infty} c_n(x-a)^n \, dx = \sum_{n=0}^{\infty} \int [c_n(x-a)^n]\,dx = \sum_{n=0}^{\infty} \frac{c_n(x-a)^{n+1}}{n+1} + C,$$

$$(7.4)$$

with radius of convergence R. Making the change of index $k = n + 1$ in the series on the right of (7.4), the series may be expressed as

$$\sum_{n=0}^{\infty} \frac{c_n(x-a)^{n+1}}{n+1} + C = \sum_{k=1}^{\infty} \frac{c_{k-1}(x-a)^k}{k} + C,$$

where C is an arbitrary constant of integration.

Example 7.16. Consider the function

$$f(x) = \ln(1-x), \quad x < 1.$$

Since $f(x)$ is an antiderivative of $-\dfrac{1}{1-x}$, we obtain, by Theorem 7.3,

$$
\begin{aligned}
\ln(1-x) &= -\int \frac{1}{1-x}\, dx = -\int \sum_{n=0}^{\infty} x^n\, dx = -\sum_{n=0}^{\infty} \frac{x^{n+1}}{n+1} + C \\
&= C - \sum_{k=1}^{\infty} \frac{x^k}{k},
\end{aligned}
$$

where $k = n + 1$. Since both the series and $\ln(1-x)$ have the value 0 at $x = 0$, $C = 0$ and, hence,

$$\ln(1-x) = \sum_{k=1}^{\infty} \frac{-1}{k} x^k, \tag{7.5}$$

with radius of convergence $R = 1$. Since the series converges for any x with $|x| < 1$, and $|-x| = |x|$, replacing x by $-x$ in (7.5) gives

$$\ln(1+x) = \sum_{k=1}^{\infty} \frac{-1}{k}(-x)^k = \sum_{k=1}^{\infty} \frac{-(-1)^k}{k} x^k = \sum_{k=1}^{\infty} \frac{(-1)^{k-1}}{k} x^k \tag{7.6}$$

as the power series representation of $f(x) = \ln(1+x)$ about 0 with $R = 1$.

In all of the preceding examples, the representation of $f(x)$ as a power series has relied upon manipulations of the geometric series, i.e., Equation (7.2). This is not always adequate, and more general methods are required.

Theorem 7.4. If

$$f(x) = \sum_{n=0}^{\infty} c_n(x-a)^n, \quad |x-a| < R,$$

with the radius of convergence $R > 0$, then the coefficients c_n are given by

$$c_n = \frac{f^{(n)}(a)}{n!}, \quad n \geq 0. \tag{7.7}$$

Proof. By Theorem 7.2, the power series may be differentiated term-by-term. Thus,

$$
\begin{aligned}
f(x) &= c_0 + c_1(x-a) + c_2(x-a)^2 + c_3(x-a)^3 + c_4(x-a)^4 + c_5(x-a)^5 + \cdots, \\
f'(x) &= c_1 + 2c_2(x-a) + 3c_3(x-a)^2 + 4c_4(x-a)^3 + 5c_5(x-a)^4 + \cdots, \\
f''(x) &= 2c_2 + 2\cdot 3c_3(x-a) + 3\cdot 4c_4(x-a)^2 + 4\cdot 5c_5(x-a)^3 + \cdots, \\
f'''(x) &= 2\cdot 3c_3 + 2\cdot 3\cdot 4c_4(x-a) + 3\cdot 4\cdot 5c_5(x-a)^2 + \cdots, \\
f^{(4)}(x) &= 2\cdot 3\cdot 4c_4 + 2\cdot 3\cdot 4\cdot 5c_5(x-a) + \cdots,
\end{aligned}
$$

etc. It follows that

$$
f(a) = c_0, \quad f'(a) = c_1, \quad f''(a) = 2c_2, \quad f'''(a) = 3!c_3, \quad f^{(4)}(a) = 4!c_4,
$$

etc., and, hence,

$$
c_0 = f(a) = \frac{f^{(0)}(a)}{0!}, \quad c_1 = f'(a) = \frac{f'(a)}{1!}, \quad c_2 = \frac{f''(a)}{2!}, \quad c_3 = \frac{f'''(a)}{3!}, \quad c_4 = \frac{f^{(4)}(a)}{4!},
$$

and, in general, $c_n = \dfrac{f^{(n)}(a)}{n!}$ for all $n \geq 0$.

Example 7.17. Let us confirm the formula (7.7) for the geometric series

$$
f(x) = \frac{1}{1-x} = \sum_{n=0}^{\infty} x^n
$$

about $a = 0$, which has $c_n = 1$ for all $n \geq 0$.

$$
\begin{aligned}
f(x) &= \frac{1}{1-x} & \Rightarrow \quad f(0) &= 1 = 0!, \\
f'(x) &= \frac{1}{(1-x)^2} & \Rightarrow \quad f'(0) &= 1 = 1!, \\
f''(x) &= \frac{2}{(1-x)^3} & \Rightarrow \quad f''(0) &= 2 = 2!, \\
f'''(x) &= \frac{2\cdot 3}{(1-x)^4} & \Rightarrow \quad f'''(0) &= 3!, \\
f^{(4)}(x) &= \frac{2\cdot 3\cdot 4}{(1-x)^5} & \Rightarrow \quad f^{(4)}(0) &= 4!,
\end{aligned}
$$

etc., and, in general, $f^{(n)}(0) = n!$. Hence, $c_n = \dfrac{f^{(n)}(0)}{n!} = 1$, as expected.

Definition 7.3. Given a function f, the series

$$
T(x) = \sum_{n=0}^{\infty} c_n(x-a)^n, \quad \text{with} \quad c_n = \frac{f^{(n)}(a)}{n!},
$$

is called the *Taylor series* of f *about* a or *centred at* a. In the special case where $a = 0$, the Taylor series of f about 0 is also called the *Maclaurin series* of f.

By Theorem 7.4 and Definition 7.3, the power series which represents a function about a point a is its Taylor series about a. A distinction between the two arises, however, due to the fact that there are functions f for which the Taylor series $T(x)$ is not equal to $f(x)$ on an interval $|x - a| < R$, $R > 0$, and is therefore not a power series representation of $f(x)$. We shall see later how to prove that $T(x) = f(x)$ for functions for which it is true.

It follows by Theorem 7.4 that the power series representation of a function f about a point a is *unique*, i.e., if

$$f(x) = \sum_{n=0}^{\infty} c_n(x - a)^n = \sum_{n=0}^{\infty} d_n(x - a)^n, \quad |x - a| < R, \quad R > 0,$$

then $c_n = \dfrac{f^{(n)}(a)}{n!} = d_n$, $n \geq 0$. Thus, as observed in Example 7.17, different methods of computing the series representation of a function must yield identical results.

It follows also by Theorem 7.4 that if

$$f(x) = \sum_{n=0}^{\infty} c_n(x - a)^n \equiv 0,$$

then $c_n = 0$ for all $n \geq 0$. This fact is essential in the solution of differential equations by infinite series.

Example 7.18. Let $f(x) = e^x$ and $a = 0$. Then

$$f^{(n)}(x) = e^x \text{ for all } n \geq 0 \implies c_n = \frac{f^{(n)}(0)}{n!} = \frac{1}{n!}$$

and, hence, the Taylor series of e^x about 0, i.e., its Maclaurin series, is

$$T(x) = \sum_{n=0}^{\infty} \frac{1}{n!} x^n,$$

with the radius of convergence

$$R = \lim_{n \to \infty} \left| \frac{c_n}{c_{n+1}} \right| = \lim_{n \to \infty} \frac{(n + 1)!}{n!} = \lim_{n \to \infty} (n + 1) = \infty.$$

Thus, the series converges absolutely for all x. We shall prove later, but assume for the present, that $T(x) = f(x) = e^x$ for all x, i.e.,

$$e^x = \sum_{n=0}^{\infty} \frac{1}{n!} x^n \text{ for all } x.$$

Example 7.19. Let $f(x) = e^{2x}$ and $a = 0$. Since $e^x = \sum_{n=0}^{\infty} \frac{1}{n!} x^n$ for all x, replacing x by $2x$ gives

$$e^{2x} = \sum_{n=0}^{\infty} \frac{1}{n!} (2x)^n = \sum_{n=0}^{\infty} \frac{2^n}{n!} x^n \text{ for all } x.$$

Notice that $c_n = \dfrac{2^n}{n!} = \dfrac{f^{(n)}(0)}{n!}$, in accord with Theorem 7.4.

Example 7.20. Let $f(x) = e^x$ and $a = 3$. Then $f^{(n)}(x) = e^x$ for all $n \geq 0$ and, hence,

$$c_n = \frac{f^{(n)}(3)}{n!} = \frac{e^3}{n!} \text{ and } T(x) = \sum_{n=0}^{\infty} \frac{e^3}{n!} (x-3)^n$$

is the Taylor series of e^x about 3. An alternative is to employ $e^x = \sum_{n=0}^{\infty} \frac{1}{n!} x^n$ for all x and to replace x by $x - 3$ to obtain

$$e^x = e^3 e^{x-3} = e^3 \sum_{n=0}^{\infty} \frac{1}{n!} (x-3)^n = \sum_{n=0}^{\infty} \frac{e^3}{n!} (x-3)^n,$$

which is the power series representation of e^x about 3 and, hence, its Taylor series about 3, as above.

Example 7.21. Let $f(x) = \tan^{-1}(x)$, $-\dfrac{\pi}{2} < \tan^{-1}(x) < \dfrac{\pi}{2}$. Since $f'(x) = \dfrac{1}{1 + x^2}$ and $f''(x) = \dfrac{-2x}{(1 + x^2)^2}$, the computation of $f^{(n)}(x)$ for every $n \geq 0$ is tedious. A much better alternative is to employ the geometric series (once again!) and Theorem 7.3. Thus,

$$\frac{1}{1-t} = \sum_{n=0}^{\infty} t^n, \quad |t| < 1,$$

$$\Rightarrow \frac{1}{1+x^2} = \sum_{n=0}^{\infty} (-x^2)^n = \sum_{n=0}^{\infty} (-1)^n x^{2n}, \quad |x| < 1,$$

$$\Rightarrow \tan^{-1}(x) = \int \frac{1}{1+x^2}\, dx = \int \sum_{n=0}^{\infty} (-1)^n x^{2n} = C + \sum_{n=0}^{\infty} \frac{(-1)^n}{2n+1} x^{2n+1}, \quad |x| < 1.$$

Since both the series and $f(x)$ have the value 0 at $x = 0$, $C = 0$. Hence,

$$\tan^{-1}(x) = \sum_{n=0}^{\infty} \frac{(-1)^n}{2n+1} x^{2n+1}, \quad |x| < 1,$$

is the power series representation of f about 0, and the series on the right is its Taylor series about 0. This alternative derivation of $T(x)$ automatically shows that $T(x) = f(x)$ for $|x| < 1$.

Note, in Example 7.21, the restriction $-\frac{\pi}{2} < \tan^{-1}(x) < \frac{\pi}{2}$ on the range (i.e., set of values) of $f(x) = \tan^{-1}(x)$. Without such a restriction, the inverse tangent would be multi-valued, and not a proper function. Had a different "branch" of the inverse tangent been chosen, e.g., $\frac{\pi}{2} < \tan^{-1}(x) < \frac{3\pi}{2}$, the value of the constant C would have been different ($C = \tan^{-1}(0) = \pi$ for the latter choice).

Example 7.22. Let $f(x) = \ln(x)$, $x > 0$, and $a = 1$. Then $f(1) = 0$,

$$f'(x) = \frac{1}{x}, \quad f''(x) = -\frac{1}{x^2}, \quad f'''(x) = \frac{2}{x^3}, \quad f^{(4)}(x) = -\frac{2 \cdot 3}{x^4}, \quad f^{(5)}(x) = \frac{2 \cdot 3 \cdot 4}{x^5},$$

and, in general, $f^{(n)}(x) = \dfrac{(-1)^{n-1}(n-1)!}{x^n}$ for $n \geq 1$. Hence, the Taylor coefficients of f are given by

$$c_0 = 0 \quad \text{and} \quad c_n = \frac{f^{(n)}(1)}{n!} = \frac{(-1)^{n-1}(n-1)!}{n!} = \frac{(-1)^{n-1}}{n}, \quad n \geq 1,$$

and its Taylor series about 1 is

$$T(x) = \sum_{n=1}^{\infty} \frac{(-1)^{n-1}}{n}(x-1)^n.$$

Alternatively, employing (7.5) in Example 7.16, i.e.,

$$\ln(1-x) = \sum_{n=1}^{\infty} \frac{-1}{n} x^n, \quad |x| < 1,$$

and, replacing x by $1 - x$, we obtain, for $|x-1| = |1-x| < 1$, the power series representation of $\ln(x)$ about 1, i.e.,

$$\ln(x) = \ln[1-(1-x)] = \sum_{n=1}^{\infty} \frac{-1}{n}(1-x)^n = \sum_{n=1}^{\infty} \frac{-(-1)^n}{n}(x-1)^n = \sum_{n=1}^{\infty} \frac{(-1)^{n-1}}{n}(x-1)^n,$$

and the series on the right is the Taylor series of $\ln(x)$ about 1. This alternative derivation of $T(x)$ automatically shows that $T(x) = f(x)$ for $|x-1| < 1$.

Example 7.23. Let $f(x) = \sin(x)$ and $a = 0$. Then

$$f'(x) = \cos(x), \quad f''(x) = -\sin(x), \quad f'''(x) = -\cos(x), \quad f^{(4)}(x) = \sin(x) = f(x)$$

$$\Rightarrow \ f(0) = 0, \quad f'(0) = 1, \quad f''(0) = 0, \quad f'''(0) = -1, \quad f^{(4)}(0) = 0,$$

and, in general,

$$f^{(2k)}(0) = 0 \ \text{ and } \ f^{(2k+1)}(0) = (-1)^k, \quad k \geq 0.$$

Hence, the Taylor coefficients of $\sin(x)$ about 0 are given by

$$c_{2k} = \frac{f^{(2k)}(0)}{(2k)!} = 0 \ \text{ and } \ c_{2k+1} = \frac{f^{(2k+1)}(0)}{(2k+1)!} = \frac{(-1)^k}{(2k+1)!}, \quad k \geq 0.$$

The Taylor series of $\sin(x)$ about 0 is therefore

$$T(x) = \sum_{n=0}^{\infty} c_n x^n = \sum_{k=0}^{\infty} c_{2k} x^{2k} + \sum_{k=0}^{\infty} c_{2k+1} x^{2k+1} = \sum_{k=0}^{\infty} \frac{(-1)^k}{(2k+1)!} x^{2k+1}.$$

The radius of convergence can be determined by the ratio test. With $a_k = \dfrac{(-1)^k x^{2k+1}}{(2k+1)!}$,

$$\lim_{k\to\infty} \left| \frac{a_{k+1}}{a_k} \right| = \lim_{k\to\infty} \left| \frac{x^{2k+3}}{(2k+3)!} \frac{(2k+1)!}{x^{2k+1}} \right| = \lim_{k\to\infty} \frac{|x|^2}{(2k+3)(2k+2)} = 0 < 1$$

for all x. Hence, $R = \infty$, i.e., the series converges absolutely for all x. We shall prove later, but assume for the present, that $T(x) = \sin(x)$ for all x. Thus,

$$\sin(x) = \sum_{k=0}^{\infty} \frac{(-1)^k}{(2k+1)!} x^{2k+1} = x - \frac{x^3}{3!} + \frac{x^5}{5!} - \frac{x^7}{7!} + \cdots$$

for all x.

Example 7.24. Let $f(x) = \cos(x)$ and $a = 0$. In order to determine the Taylor series of f about a, the procedure employed in Example 7.23 can be repeated. However, a more efficient method is to employ Theorem 7.2 and the result of Example 7.23. Thus,

$$\cos(x) = \frac{d}{dx}\sin(x) = \frac{d}{dx}\sum_{k=0}^{\infty} \frac{(-1)^k}{(2k+1)!} x^{2k+1} = \sum_{k=0}^{\infty} \frac{(-1)^k (2k+1)}{(2k+1)!} x^{2k}$$

$$= \sum_{k=0}^{\infty} \frac{(-1)^k}{(2k)!} x^{2k} = 1 - \frac{x^2}{2!} + \frac{x^4}{4!} - \frac{x^6}{6!} + \cdots$$

for all x.

Example 7.25. Let $f(x) = \sin(x)$ and $a = \dfrac{\pi}{2}$. In order to determine the Taylor series of f about a, the procedure employed in Example 7.23 can be repeated. However, a more efficient method is to employ the result of Example 7.24 and the fact that $\sin(x) = \cos\left(x - \dfrac{\pi}{2}\right)$. Thus, replacing x by $x - \dfrac{\pi}{2}$ in

$$\cos(x) = \sum_{k=0}^{\infty} \frac{(-1)^k}{(2k)!} x^{2k}$$

gives

$$\sin(x) = \cos\left(x - \frac{\pi}{2}\right) = \sum_{k=0}^{\infty} \frac{(-1)^k}{(2k)!} \left(x - \frac{\pi}{2}\right)^{2k}$$

for all x.

The Binomial Series

The *binomial theorem* states that, for any two real numbers a and b, and any integer $n \geq 0$,

$$(a + b)^n = \sum_{k=0}^{n} \binom{n}{k} a^k b^{n-k} = \sum_{k=0}^{n} \binom{n}{k} a^{n-k} b^k,$$

where

$$\binom{n}{k} = \frac{n!}{k!(n-k)!}$$

is read "n choose k," and is the number of different ways in which k objects can be selected from a set of n objects. Since

$$(a + b)^n = a^n \left(1 + \frac{b}{a}\right)^n,$$

it suffices to consider the simpler case where $a = 1$ and $b = x$, i.e.,

$$(1 + x)^n = \sum_{k=0}^{n} \binom{n}{k} x^k,$$

from which the more general formula can be reconstructed, if required.

Our goal at present is to develop a binomial theorem for

$$f(x) = (1 + x)^{\alpha},$$

where α is any real number, and not necessarily a nonnegative integer. This will, of course, involve an infinite power series rather than a finite sum. The advantage of determining a representation of f for general α is that the functions

$$f(x) = \sqrt{1+x}, \quad f(x) = \frac{1}{\sqrt{1+x}}, \quad f(x) = (1+x)^{3/2},$$

among numerous others, have the form $f(x) = (1+x)^\alpha$, and having a general formula for all α eliminates the necessity of finding the Taylor series of every such function separately. Thus,

$$
\begin{aligned}
f(x) &= (1+x)^\alpha, \\
f'(x) &= \alpha(1+x)^{\alpha-1}, \\
f''(x) &= \alpha(\alpha-1)(1+x)^{\alpha-2}, \\
f'''(x) &= \alpha(\alpha-1)(\alpha-2)(1+x)^{\alpha-3}, \\
&\vdots \\
f^{(k)}(x) &= \alpha(\alpha-1)(\alpha-2)\cdots(\alpha-k+1)(1+x)^{\alpha-k},
\end{aligned}
$$

and, hence,

$$f(0) = 1, \quad f'(0) = \alpha, \quad f''(0) = \alpha(\alpha-1), \quad f'''(0) = \alpha(\alpha-1)(\alpha-2), \quad \cdots,$$

$$f^{(k)}(0) = \alpha(\alpha-1)(\alpha-2)\cdots(\alpha-k+1).$$

The Taylor coefficients of f about 0 are therefore given by

$$
\begin{aligned}
c_0 &= f(0) = 1, \\
c_k &= \frac{f^{(k)}(0)}{k!} = \frac{\alpha(\alpha-1)(\alpha-2)\cdots(\alpha-k+1)}{k!}, \quad k \geq 1.
\end{aligned}
$$

Define the symbol $\binom{\alpha}{k}$ by

$$\binom{\alpha}{0} = 1 \quad \text{and} \quad \binom{\alpha}{k} = \frac{\alpha(\alpha-1)(\alpha-2)\cdots(\alpha-k+1)}{k!} \quad \text{for} \quad k \geq 1.$$

Then the Taylor series of f about 0 is

$$
\begin{aligned}
T(x) &= \sum_{k=0}^{\infty} \binom{\alpha}{k} x^k = 1 + \sum_{k=1}^{\infty} \frac{\alpha(\alpha-1)(\alpha-2)\cdots(\alpha-k+1)}{k!} x^k \\
&= 1 + \alpha x + \frac{\alpha(\alpha-1)}{2!} x^2 + \frac{\alpha(\alpha-1)(\alpha-2)}{3!} x^3 + \frac{\alpha(\alpha-1)(\alpha-2)(\alpha-3)}{4!} x^4 \\
&\quad + \cdots,
\end{aligned}
$$

with radius of convergence

$$
\begin{aligned}
R &= \lim_{k \to \infty} \left| \frac{c_k}{c_{k+1}} \right| \\
&= \lim_{k \to \infty} \left| \frac{\alpha(\alpha-1)(\alpha-2)\cdots(\alpha-k+1)}{k!} \frac{(k+1)!}{\alpha(\alpha-1)(\alpha-2)\cdots(\alpha-k+1)(\alpha-k)} \right| \\
&= \lim_{k \to \infty} \left| \frac{k+1}{\alpha-k} \right| = \lim_{k \to \infty} \frac{k+1}{k-\alpha} = 1
\end{aligned}
$$

since $|\alpha - k| = k - \alpha$ for all $k \geq \alpha$. It can be shown that $T(x) = f(x)$ for $|x| < 1$. Thus,

$$
(1+x)^{\alpha} = \sum_{k=0}^{\infty} \binom{\alpha}{k} x^k, \quad |x| < 1. \tag{7.8}
$$

The series on the right of (7.8) is called the *binomial series*, and this result is also called the *binomial theorem*.

Note that, in the special case where $\alpha = n \geq 0$ is an integer,

$$
f^{(k)}(x) = n(n-1)(n-2)\cdots(n-k+1)(1+x)^{n-k} = n!
$$

is a constant when $k = n$ and, hence, $f^{(k)}(x) = 0$ for all $k \geq n+1$, in which case, the binomial series reduces to the finite series

$$
(1+x)^n = \sum_{k=0}^{n} \binom{n}{k} x^k,
$$

with

$$
\binom{n}{k} = \frac{n(n-1)(n-2)\cdots(n-k+1)}{k!} \frac{(n-k)!}{(n-k)!} = \frac{n!}{k!(n-k)!},
$$

as in the binomial theorem.

Example 7.26. The Taylor series of $f(x) = \dfrac{1}{1+x}$ about 0 can be obtained by means of the geometric series,

$$
\frac{1}{1-t} = \sum_{n=0}^{\infty} t^n \quad \Rightarrow \quad \frac{1}{1+x} = \sum_{n=0}^{\infty} (-x)^n = \sum_{n=0}^{\infty} (-1)^n x^n, \quad |x| < 1.
$$

Alternatively, since $\dfrac{1}{1+x} = (1+x)^{-1}$, we may also employ the binomial series with $\alpha = -1$. Thus, with $\alpha = -1$, $\dbinom{\alpha}{0} = 1$ and, for $k \geq 1$,

$$
\begin{aligned}
\binom{\alpha}{k} &= \frac{\alpha(\alpha-1)(\alpha-2)(\alpha-3)\cdots(\alpha-k+1)}{k!} \\
&= \frac{(-1)(-2)(-3)\cdots(-k)}{k!} = \frac{(-1)^k k!}{k!} = (-1)^k.
\end{aligned}
$$

Hence,

$$\frac{1}{1+x} = \sum_{k=0}^{\infty} \binom{\alpha}{k} x^k = 1 + \sum_{k=1}^{\infty} (-1)^k x^k = \sum_{k=0}^{\infty} (-1)^k x^k, \quad |x| < 1,$$

as above.

Example 7.27. Consider the function $f(x) = \dfrac{1}{(1-x)^3} = (1-x)^{-3}$. Its Taylor series about 0 (Maclaurin series) is the binomial series with $\alpha = -3$ and with x replaced by $-x$. Thus, with $\alpha = -3$, $\binom{\alpha}{0} = 1$ and, for $k \geq 1$,

$$
\begin{aligned}
\binom{\alpha}{k} &= \frac{\alpha(\alpha-1)(\alpha-2)(\alpha-3)\cdots(\alpha-k+1)}{k!} \\
&= \frac{(-3)(-4)(-5)(-6)\cdots(-k-2)}{k!} \\
&= \frac{(-1)^k \cdot 3 \cdot 4 \cdot 5 \cdot 6 \cdots (k+2)}{k!}.
\end{aligned}
$$

In order to place the last expression into a more concise form, multiply and divide by 2. Then

$$
\begin{aligned}
\binom{\alpha}{k} &= \frac{(-1)^k \cdot 3 \cdot 4 \cdot 5 \cdot 6 \cdots (k+2)}{k!} \frac{2}{2} \\
&= \frac{(-1)^k (k+2)!}{2k!} \\
&= \frac{(-1)^k (k+1)(k+2)}{2}.
\end{aligned}
$$

Hence,

$$
\begin{aligned}
\frac{1}{(1-x)^3} &= \sum_{k=0}^{\infty} \binom{\alpha}{k} (-x)^k \\
&= 1 + \sum_{k=1}^{\infty} \frac{(-1)^k (k+1)(k+2)}{2} (-1)^k x^k \\
&= \sum_{k=0}^{\infty} \frac{(k+1)(k+2)}{2} x^k, \quad |x| < 1,
\end{aligned}
$$

since $\dfrac{(k+1)(k+2)}{2} = 1$ when $k = 0$.

Alternatively, employing the geometric series and Theorem 7.2,

$$\frac{1}{1-x} = \sum_{k=0}^{\infty} x^k$$

$$\Rightarrow \frac{1}{(1-x)^2} = \frac{d}{dx}\frac{1}{1-x} = \frac{d}{dx}\sum_{k=0}^{\infty} x^k = \sum_{k=0}^{\infty} kx^{k-1}$$

$$\Rightarrow \frac{2}{(1-x)^3} = \frac{d}{dx}\frac{1}{(1-x)^2} = \frac{d}{dx}\sum_{k=0}^{\infty} kx^{k-1} = \sum_{k=0}^{\infty} k(k-1)x^{k-2} = \sum_{k=2}^{\infty} k(k-1)x^{k-2}$$

since $k(k-1) = 0$ when $k = 0$ and $k = 1$. Making the change of index $n = k - 2$, we obtain

$$\frac{1}{(1-x)^3} = \sum_{n=0}^{\infty} \frac{(n+2)(n+1)}{2} x^n, \quad |x| < 1,$$

as above.

Example 7.28. Consider the function $f(x) = \dfrac{1}{\sqrt{1+x}} = (1+x)^{-\frac{1}{2}}$. Its Taylor series about 0 (Maclaurin series) is the binomial series with $\alpha = -\dfrac{1}{2}$. Thus, with $\alpha = -\dfrac{1}{2}$, $\dbinom{\alpha}{0} = 1$ and, for $k \geq 1$,

$$\begin{aligned}
\binom{\alpha}{k} &= \frac{\alpha(\alpha-1)(\alpha-2)(\alpha-3)\cdots(\alpha-k+1)}{k!} \\
&= \frac{(-\frac{1}{2})(-\frac{3}{2})(-\frac{5}{2})(-\frac{7}{2})\cdots(-\frac{2k-1}{2})}{k!} \\
&= \frac{(-1)^k \cdot 1 \cdot 3 \cdot 5 \cdot 7 \cdots (2k-1)}{2^k k!}.
\end{aligned}$$

In order to place the last expression into a more concise form, multiply and divide by $2 \cdot 4 \cdot 6 \cdots (2k)$. Then

$$\begin{aligned}
\binom{\alpha}{k} &= \frac{(-1)^k \cdot 1 \cdot 3 \cdot 5 \cdot 7 \cdots (2k-1)}{2^k k!} \frac{2 \cdot 4 \cdot 6 \cdots (2k)}{2 \cdot 4 \cdot 6 \cdots (2k)} \\
&= \frac{(-1)^k (2k)!}{2^k k!} \frac{1}{2^k \cdot 1 \cdot 2 \cdot 3 \cdots k} \\
&= \frac{(-1)^k (2k)!}{2^{2k} (k!)^2}.
\end{aligned}$$

Hence,

$$\frac{1}{\sqrt{1+x}} = \sum_{k=0}^{\infty} \binom{\alpha}{k} x^k = 1 + \sum_{k=1}^{\infty} \frac{(-1)^k (2k)!}{2^{2k}(k!)^2} x^k = \sum_{k=0}^{\infty} \frac{(-1)^k (2k)!}{2^{2k}(k!)^2} x^k, \quad |x| < 1,$$

since $\dfrac{(-1)^k (2k)!}{2^{2k} (k!)^2} = 1$ when $k = 0$.

Example 7.29. Consider the function $f(x) = \dfrac{x}{\sqrt[3]{8 + x^2}}$. In order to employ the binomial series, express $f(x)$ as

$$f(x) = \frac{x}{\sqrt[3]{8 + x^2}} = \frac{x}{2 \sqrt[3]{1 + \frac{x^2}{8}}} = \frac{x}{2} \left(1 + \frac{x^2}{8} \right)^{-\frac{1}{3}}.$$

The Taylor series of f about 0 is then the binomial series of $(1 + t)^\alpha$ with $t = \dfrac{x^2}{8}$ and $\alpha = -\dfrac{1}{3}$, multiplied by $\dfrac{x}{2}$. Thus, with $\alpha = -\dfrac{1}{3}$, $\dbinom{\alpha}{0} = 1$ and, for $k \geq 1$,

$$
\begin{aligned}
\binom{\alpha}{k} &= \frac{\alpha(\alpha - 1)(\alpha - 2)(\alpha - 3) \cdots (\alpha - k + 1)}{k!} \\
&= \frac{(-\frac{1}{3})(-\frac{4}{3})(-\frac{7}{3})(-\frac{10}{3}) \cdots (-\frac{3k-2}{3})}{k!} \\
&= \frac{(-1)^k \cdot 1 \cdot 4 \cdot 7 \cdot 10 \cdots (3k - 2)}{3^k k!}.
\end{aligned}
$$

Hence,

$$(1 + t)^{-\frac{1}{3}} = \sum_{k=0}^{\infty} \binom{\alpha}{k} x^k = 1 + \sum_{k=1}^{\infty} \frac{(-1)^k \cdot 1 \cdot 4 \cdot 7 \cdot 10 \cdots (3k - 2)}{3^k k!} t^k, \quad |t| < 1$$

$$
\begin{aligned}
\Rightarrow \quad \frac{x}{\sqrt[3]{8 + x^2}} &= \frac{x}{2} \left[1 + \sum_{k=1}^{\infty} \frac{(-1)^k \cdot 1 \cdot 4 \cdot 7 \cdot 10 \cdots (3k - 2)}{3^k k!} \left(\frac{x^2}{8} \right)^k \right] \\
&= \frac{x}{2} + \sum_{k=1}^{\infty} \frac{(-1)^k \cdot 1 \cdot 4 \cdot 7 \cdot 10 \cdots (3k - 2)}{2^{3k+1} 3^k k!} x^{2k+1},
\end{aligned}
$$

valid for $\left| \dfrac{x^2}{8} \right| = |t| < 1$, i.e., $|x| < 2\sqrt{2}$.

Example 7.30. Consider the function $f(x) = \sqrt{1 + x} = (1 + x)^{\frac{1}{2}}$. Its Taylor series about 0 is the binomial series with $\alpha = \dfrac{1}{2}$. Thus, with $\alpha = \dfrac{1}{2}$, $\dbinom{\alpha}{0} = 1$ and, for $k \geq 1$,

$$
\begin{aligned}
\binom{\alpha}{k} &= \frac{\alpha(\alpha - 1)(\alpha - 2)(\alpha - 3) \cdots (\alpha - k + 1)}{k!} \\
&= \frac{(\frac{1}{2})(-\frac{1}{2})(-\frac{3}{2})(-\frac{5}{2}) \cdots (-\frac{2k-3}{2})}{k!} \\
&= \frac{(-1)^{k-1} \cdot 1 \cdot 3 \cdot 5 \cdots (2k - 3)}{2^k k!} \quad \text{for} \quad k \geq 2,
\end{aligned}
$$

noting that there are k factors in the numerator, only $k - 1$ of which have minus signs, and $\binom{\alpha}{1} = \dfrac{1}{2}$. Multiplying and dividing by $2 \cdot 4 \cdot 6 \cdots (2k - 2)$, we obtain

$$
\begin{aligned}
\binom{\alpha}{k} &= \frac{(-1)^{k-1} \cdot 1 \cdot 3 \cdot 5 \cdots (2k-3)}{2^k k!} \frac{2 \cdot 4 \cdot 6 \cdots (2k-2)}{2 \cdot 4 \cdot 6 \cdots (2k-2)} \\
&= \frac{(-1)^{k-1}(2k-2)!}{2^k k!} \frac{1}{2^{k-1} \cdot 1 \cdot 2 \cdot 3 \cdots (k-1)} \\
&= \frac{(-1)^{k-1}(2k-2)!}{2^{2k-1} k!(k-1)!}, \quad k \geq 1.
\end{aligned}
$$

Hence,

$$
\sqrt{1 + x} = \sum_{k=0}^{\infty} \binom{\alpha}{k} x^k = 1 + \sum_{k=1}^{\infty} \frac{(-1)^{k-1}(2k-2)!}{2^{2k-1} k!(k-1)!} x^k, \quad |x| < 1.
$$

Taylor Polynomials and Approximations

Definition 7.4. Consider the Taylor series of a function f about a point a, i.e.,

$$
T(x) = \sum_{n=0}^{\infty} \frac{f^{(n)}(a)}{n!}(x - a)^n.
$$

The nth partial sum $T_n(x)$ of the Taylor series is

$$
\begin{aligned}
T_n(x) &= \sum_{k=0}^{n} \frac{f^{(k)}(a)}{k!}(x - a)^k \\
&= f(a) + f'(a)(x - a) + \frac{f''(a)}{2!}(x - a)^2 + \frac{f'''(a)}{3!}(x - a)^3 \\
&\quad + \cdots + \frac{f^{(n)}(a)}{n!}(x - a)^n,
\end{aligned}
$$

and is a polynomial of degree n, called the nth-*degree Taylor polynomial of f about a*. If the Taylor series of a function converges to the function on an interval, i.e., $T(x) = f(x)$ for $|x - a| < R$ and $R > 0$, then $f(x)$ can be approximated by its Taylor polynomial $T_n(x)$, and the error is

$$
R_n(x) = f(x) - T_n(x) = \sum_{k=n+1}^{\infty} \frac{f^{(k)}(a)}{k!}(x - a)^k,
$$

called the *remainder*.

The product of two Taylor series, or their quotient, about the same point a, is again a Taylor series about a, but the formula for the coefficients of the product is complicated (see Exercise 26 in Section 7.1), and none exists for the quotient. In such cases, their Taylor polynomials may still furnish useful information.

Example 7.31. Consider the function $f(x) = e^x \cos(x)$. In order to determine its 4th-degree Taylor polynomial about 0, the Taylor polynomials of suitably high degree of the functions e^x and $\cos(x)$ must be multiplied. Since

$$e^x = 1 + x + \frac{1}{2}x^2 + \frac{1}{6}x^3 + \frac{1}{24}x^4 + \cdots$$

and

$$\cos(x) = 1 - \frac{1}{2}x^2 + \frac{1}{24}x^4 + \cdots \,,$$

and the product is required only up to the fourth power of x, the terms x^k for $k \geq 5$ are neglected. Thus,

$$
\begin{aligned}
e^x \cos(x) &= \left(1 + x + \frac{1}{2}x^2 + \frac{1}{6}x^3 + \frac{1}{24}x^4\right)\left(1 - \frac{1}{2}x^2 + \frac{1}{24}x^4\right) \\
&= 1 + x - \frac{1}{3}x^3 - \frac{1}{6}x^4 + \cdots .
\end{aligned}
$$

Hence, $T_4(x) = 1 + x - \frac{1}{3}x^3 - \frac{1}{6}x^4$ for $f(x) = e^x \cos(x)$ about 0.

Example 7.32. Consider the function $f(x) = \tan(x)$. In order to determine its 5th-degree Taylor polynomial about 0, the Taylor polynomial of suitably high degree of the function $\sin(x)$ must be divided by that of $\cos(x)$. Thus,

$$\sin(x) = x - \frac{1}{6}x^3 + \frac{1}{120}x^5 + \cdots$$

and

$$\cos(x) = 1 - \frac{1}{2}x^2 + \frac{1}{24}x^4 + \cdots \,,$$

and, dividing the former by the latter and neglecting the terms x^k for $k \geq 6$, we obtain

$$
\begin{aligned}
\frac{\sin(x)}{\cos(x)} &= \frac{x - \frac{1}{6}x^3 + \frac{1}{120}x^5}{1 - \frac{1}{2}x^2 + \frac{1}{24}x^4} \\
&= x + \frac{1}{3}x^3 + \frac{2}{15}x^5 + \cdots .
\end{aligned}
$$

Hence, $T_5(x) = x + \frac{1}{3}x^3 + \frac{2}{15}x^5$ for $\tan(x)$ about 0.

Example 7.33. Consider the function $f(x) = (x^2 - 1)\ln(x)$. Its Taylor series about 1 can be determined by multiplying the Taylor series of $\ln(x)$ about 1 by the Taylor series of $x^2 - 1$ about 1. Since $x^2 - 1$ is a polynomial of degree 2, its Taylor series is also a polynomial of degree 2, and the multiplication can be performed without great difficulty.

By Example 7.22,

$$\ln(x) = \sum_{n=1}^{\infty} \frac{(-1)^{n-1}}{n}(x-1)^n, \quad |x-1| < 1.$$

The Taylor series of $g(x) = x^2 - 1$ about 1 can be obtained by Equation (7.7). Thus,

$$g'(x) = 2x, \quad g''(x) = 2, \quad \text{and} \quad g^{(n)}(x) = 0 \quad \text{for} \quad n \geq 3 \quad \Rightarrow$$

$$c_0 = g(1) = 0, \quad c_1 = g'(1) = 2, \quad c_2 = \frac{g''(1)}{2} = 1, \quad \text{and} \quad c_n = \frac{g^{(n)}(1)}{n!} = 0 \quad \text{for} \quad n \geq 3,$$

and the Taylor series of $x^2 - 1$ about 1 is $T(x) = 2(x-1) + (x-1)^2$. As can be readily verified,

$$T(x) = 2(x-1) + (x-1)^2 = x^2 - 1 \quad \text{for all} \quad x.$$

Then the product is

$$
\begin{aligned}
(x^2 - 1)\ln(x) &= [2(x-1) + (x-1)^2] \sum_{n=1}^{\infty} \frac{(-1)^{n-1}}{n}(x-1)^n \\
&= \sum_{n=1}^{\infty} \frac{2(-1)^{n-1}}{n}(x-1)^{n+1} + \sum_{n=1}^{\infty} \frac{(-1)^{n-1}}{n}(x-1)^{n+2} \\
&= 2(x-1)^2 + \sum_{n=2}^{\infty} \frac{2(-1)^{n-1}}{n}(x-1)^{n+1} + \sum_{n=1}^{\infty} \frac{(-1)^{n-1}}{n}(x-1)^{n+2}.
\end{aligned}
$$

Making the change of index $n \to n+1$ in the first series on the right, we obtain

$$
\begin{aligned}
(x^2 - 1)\ln(x) &= 2(x-1)^2 + \sum_{n=1}^{\infty} \frac{2(-1)^n}{n+1}(x-1)^{n+2} + \sum_{n=1}^{\infty} \frac{(-1)^{n-1}}{n}(x-1)^{n+2} \\
&= 2(x-1)^2 + \sum_{n=1}^{\infty} \left[\frac{2(-1)^n}{n+1} + \frac{(-1)^{n-1}}{n}\right](x-1)^{n+2} \\
&= 2(x-1)^2 + \sum_{n=1}^{\infty} \left[\frac{2(-1)^n}{n+1} - \frac{(-1)^n}{n}\right](x-1)^{n+2} \\
&= 2(x-1)^2 + \sum_{n=1}^{\infty} \left[\frac{(-1)^n(n-1)}{n(n+1)}\right](x-1)^{n+2} \\
&= 2(x-1)^2 + \sum_{n=2}^{\infty} \left[\frac{(-1)^n(n-1)}{n(n+1)}\right](x-1)^{n+2}, \quad |x-1| < 1.
\end{aligned}
$$

The last series on the right begins at $n = 2$ because $n - 1 = 0$ when $n = 1$. The series converges absolutely for $|x - 1| < 1$ since the Taylor series of $\ln(x)$ converges absolutely for $|x - 1| < 1$. Truncation of the series by neglecting the terms beyond $(x - 1)^n$ yields

$$2(x - 1)^2 + \sum_{k=2}^{n-2} \left[\frac{(-1)^k(k - 1)}{k(k + 1)} \right] (x - 1)^{k+2},$$

i.e., the Taylor polynomial $T_n(x)$ of degree n.

Example 7.34. Consider the function $f(x) = e^{-x^2}$. Assuming that the Taylor series of e^x converges to e^x for all x, we obtain

$$e^x = \sum_{n=0}^{\infty} \frac{x^n}{n!} \quad \Rightarrow \quad e^{-x^2} = \sum_{n=0}^{\infty} \frac{(-x^2)^n}{n!} = \sum_{n=0}^{\infty} \frac{(-1)^n x^{2n}}{n!}.$$

Since this is an alternating series for $x \neq 0$, if $f(x)$ is approximated by its nth-degree Taylor polynomial $T_n(x)$, the error, in absolute value, will be less than the absolute value of the first neglected term. Thus, with $b_n(x) = \dfrac{x^{2n}}{n!}$,

$$|R_n(x)| = |f(x) - T_n(x)| < b_{n+1}(x) = \frac{x^{2n+2}}{(n + 1)!}.$$

If, for instance, $f\left(\dfrac{1}{2}\right) = e^{-\frac{1}{4}}$ is approximated by $T_2\left(\dfrac{1}{2}\right)$, then

$$\left| R_2\left(\frac{1}{2}\right) \right| < \frac{1}{2^6 3!} = \frac{1}{384} \approx 0.0026,$$

and

$$e^{-\frac{1}{4}} \approx T_2\left(\frac{1}{2}\right) = \sum_{k=0}^{2} \frac{(-1)^k(\frac{1}{2})^{2k}}{k!} = 1 - \left(\frac{1}{2}\right)^2 + \frac{1}{2}\left(\frac{1}{2}\right)^4 = \frac{25}{32} = 0.78125.$$

The value of $e^{-\frac{1}{4}}$ to 4 decimal places obtained by calculator is 0.7788. The difference between the exact value and the approximate value is -0.00245, and

$$|-0.00245| = 0.00245 < 0.0026,$$

as guaranteed by the general theory. The difference between the exact value and the approximate value is negative because the first neglected term is negative and, hence, the approximate value is greater than the exact value.

Example 7.35. Consider the definite integral

$$\int_0^{\frac{1}{2}} e^{-x^2} \, dx.$$

Since $f(x) = e^{-x^2}$ does not have an elementary function as an antiderivative, we must appeal to infinite series. Employing the Taylor series of e^{-x^2} in Example 7.34 and Theorem 7.3, we obtain

$$\int_0^{\frac{1}{2}} e^{-x^2} \, dx = \int_0^{\frac{1}{2}} \sum_{n=0}^{\infty} \frac{(-1)^n x^{2n}}{n!} \, dx = \sum_{n=0}^{\infty} \frac{(-1)^n x^{2n+1}}{(2n+1)n!} \Big|_0^{\frac{1}{2}} = \sum_{n=0}^{\infty} \frac{(-1)^n}{2^{2n+1}(2n+1)n!}.$$

The sum s of the alternating series $\sum_{n=0}^{\infty} (-1)^n b_n$ on the right is the exact value of the integral. If the series is approximated by its nth partial sum s_n, then

$$|R_n| = |s - s_n| < b_{n+1} = \frac{1}{2^{2n+3}(2n+3)(n+1)!}.$$

If, for instance, the value of the integral is required to be correct to 2 decimal places, then n must be sufficiently large in order that $|R_n| < 0.01$. With $n = 1$,

$$|R_1| < b_2 = \frac{1}{2^5 \cdot 5 \cdot 2} = \frac{1}{320} \approx 0.003 < 0.01,$$

and

$$\int_0^{\frac{1}{2}} e^{-x^2} \, dx \approx s_1 = \frac{1}{2} - \frac{1}{2^3 \cdot 3} = \frac{11}{24} \approx 0.4583,$$

correct to 2 decimal places.

Example 7.36. Consider the definite integral

$$\int_0^{\frac{1}{4}} \frac{1}{\sqrt{1 + x^6}} \, dx.$$

By Example 7.28 with x replaced by x^6, we obtain

$$\frac{1}{\sqrt{1 + x^6}} = \sum_{k=0}^{\infty} \frac{(-1)^k (2k)!}{2^{2k}(k!)^2} x^{6k}, \quad |x| < 1.$$

Hence, by Theorem 7.3,

$$
\begin{aligned}
\int_0^{\frac{1}{4}} \frac{1}{\sqrt{1+x^6}} \, dx &= \int_0^{\frac{1}{4}} \sum_{k=0}^{\infty} \frac{(-1)^k (2k)!}{2^{2k}(k!)^2} x^{6k} \, dx = \sum_{k=0}^{\infty} \frac{(-1)^k (2k)! x^{6k+1}}{2^{2k}(k!)^2(6k+1)} \Big|_0^{\frac{1}{4}} \\
&= \sum_{k=0}^{\infty} \frac{(-1)^k (2k)!}{2^{2k}(k!)^2(6k+1)4^{6k+1}} \\
&= \sum_{k=0}^{\infty} \frac{(-1)^k (2k)!}{(k!)^2(6k+1)4^{7k+1}} \\
&= \sum_{k=0}^{\infty} (-1)^k b_k
\end{aligned}
$$

is an alternating series, and

$$
|R_k| < b_{k+1} = \frac{(2k+2)!}{[(k+1)!]^2(6k+7)4^{7k+8}}.
$$

If $k = 0$, then $|R_0| < b_1 = \dfrac{2}{7 \cdot 4^8} = \dfrac{1}{7 \cdot 2^{15}} = \dfrac{1}{229,376} = 0.000004359$. Hence,

$$
\int_0^{\frac{1}{4}} \frac{1}{\sqrt{1+x^6}} \, dx \approx s_0 = \frac{1}{4} = 0.25,
$$

correct to 5 decimal places.

Taylor polynomials can be employed in the evaluation of limits where either L'Hôpital's rule is inapplicable, or too tedious to be applied.

Example 7.37. Consider the limit

$$
\lim_{x \to 0} \frac{(2x^2+3)\sin^2(x)}{x^2 \cos(x)}.
$$

Employing the Taylor series of $\sin(x)$ and $\cos(x)$ about 0 and retaining only the first two terms, we obtain

$$
\begin{aligned}
\lim_{x \to 0} \frac{(2x^2+3)\sin^2(x)}{x^2 \cos(x)} &= \lim_{x \to 0} \frac{(2x^2+3)(x - \frac{1}{6}x^3 + \cdots)^2}{x^2(1 - \frac{1}{2}x^2 + \cdots)} \\
&= \lim_{x \to 0} \frac{(2x^2+3)x^2(1 - \frac{1}{6}x^2 + \cdots)^2}{x^2(1 - \frac{1}{2}x^2 + \cdots)} \\
&= \lim_{x \to 0} \frac{(2x^2+3)(1 - \frac{1}{6}x^2 + \cdots)^2}{(1 - \frac{1}{2}x^2 + \cdots)} \\
&= 3
\end{aligned}
$$

since $x^k \to 0$ for all $k \geq 1$ as $x \to 0$.

Example 7.38. Consider the limit

$$\lim_{x \to 0} \frac{(e^x - x - 1)\cos(x)}{\sin^2(x)}.$$

Since $e^x = 1 + x + \dfrac{x^2}{2} + \dfrac{x^3}{6} + \cdots$,

$$
\begin{aligned}
\lim_{x \to 0} \frac{(e^x - x - 1)\cos(x)}{\sin^2(x)} &= \lim_{x \to 0} \frac{(\frac{x^2}{2} + \frac{x^3}{6} + \cdots)(1 - \frac{1}{2}x^2 + \cdots)}{(x - \frac{1}{6}x^3 + \cdots)^2} \\
&= \lim_{x \to 0} \frac{x^2(\frac{1}{2} + \frac{x}{6} + \cdots)(1 - \frac{1}{2}x^2 + \cdots)}{x^2(1 - \frac{1}{6}x^2 + \cdots)^2} \\
&= \lim_{x \to 0} \frac{(\frac{1}{2} + \frac{x}{6} + \cdots)(1 - \frac{1}{2}x^2 + \cdots)}{(1 - \frac{1}{6}x^2 + \cdots)^2} \\
&= \frac{1}{2}.
\end{aligned}
$$

Example 7.39. Consider the one-sided limit

$$\lim_{x \to 0-} \frac{e^x \sin(x)}{\sqrt{2x^2 + x^3}\cos^2(x)},$$

i.e., $x \to 0$ with $x < 0$. Then

$$
\begin{aligned}
\lim_{x \to 0-} \frac{e^x \sin(x)}{\sqrt{2x^2 + x^3}\cos^2(x)} &= \lim_{x \to 0-} \frac{(1 + x + \cdots)(x - \frac{1}{6}x^3 + \cdots)}{|x|\sqrt{2 + x}\,(1 - \frac{1}{2}x^2 + \cdots)^2} \\
&= \lim_{x \to 0-} \frac{x}{|x|} \frac{(1 + x + \cdots)(1 - \frac{1}{6}x^2 + \cdots)}{\sqrt{2 + x}\,(1 - \frac{1}{2}x^2 + \cdots)^2} \\
&= \lim_{x \to 0-} -\frac{(1 + x + \cdots)(1 - \frac{1}{6}x^2 + \cdots)}{\sqrt{2 + x}\,(1 - \frac{1}{2}x^2 + \cdots)^2} \\
&= -\frac{1}{\sqrt{2}}
\end{aligned}
$$

since $\sqrt{x^2} = |x| = -x$ for $x < 0$.

Theorem 7.5. Suppose that the function f has the Taylor series

$$T(x) = \sum_{n=0}^{\infty} \frac{f^{(n)}(a)}{n!}(x - a)^n$$

about the point a, and let

$$T_n(x) = \sum_{k=0}^{n} \frac{f^{(k)}(a)}{k!}(x-a)^k$$

be its nth-degree Taylor polynomial. Then the remainder $R_n(x) = f(x) - T_n(x)$ is given by

$$R_n(x) = \frac{f^{(n+1)}(z)}{(n+1)!}(x-a)^{n+1}, \tag{7.9}$$

where z is a number between a and x. Equation (7.9) is known as *Taylor's remainder formula*.

Example 7.40. Consider the function $f(x) = e^x$. By Example 7.18, its Taylor series about 0 is

$$T(x) = \sum_{n=0}^{\infty} \frac{1}{n!}x^n$$

and converges absolutely for all x. If e^x is approximated by its nth-degree Taylor polynomial

$$T_n(x) = \sum_{k=0}^{n} \frac{1}{k!}x^k,$$

then, employing Theorem 7.5 and the fact that $f^{(n+1)}(z) = e^z$ for all $n \geq 0$, we obtain

$$R_n(x) = \frac{e^z}{(n+1)!}x^{n+1}$$

and, hence,

$$|R_n(x)| = \frac{e^z}{(n+1)!}|x|^{n+1}.$$

Suppose that we wish to approximate $\sqrt{e} = e^{1/2}$ correct to 3 decimal places. Since $x = \frac{1}{2}$ and z is between $a = 0$ and $x = \frac{1}{2}$, $0 \leq z \leq \frac{1}{2} < 1$. Then

$$\left|R_n\left(\frac{1}{2}\right)\right| = \frac{e^z}{(n+1)!}\left(\frac{1}{2}\right)^{n+1} < \frac{e}{(n+1)!\,2^{n+1}} \leq 0.001$$

if $(n+1)!\,2^{n+1} \geq 1000e \approx 2718.28$, which is satisfied for $n \geq 4$. Taking $n = 4$, we obtain

$$\sqrt{e} \approx \sum_{k=0}^{4} \frac{1}{k!\,2^k} = 1 + \frac{1}{2} + \frac{1}{8} + \frac{1}{48} + \frac{1}{384} \approx 1.6484.$$

The value of $\sqrt{e}$ obtained by calculator is approximately 1.6487, with a difference of $0.0003 < 0.001$, as expected.

Theorem 7.6. Suppose that the function f has the Taylor series

$$T(x) = \sum_{n=0}^{\infty} \frac{f^{(n)}(a)}{n!}(x-a)^n$$

about the point a, with radius of convergence $R > 0$. Let

$$T_n(x) = \sum_{k=0}^{n} \frac{f^{(k)}(a)}{k!}(x-a)^k$$

be its nth-degree Taylor polynomial, and let $R_n(x) = f(x) - T_n(x)$ be the remainder. Then $T(x) = f(x)$ for $|x-a| < R$ if and only if

$$\lim_{n\to\infty} R_n(x) = 0, \quad |x-a| < R.$$

Proof. $T(x) = f(x)$ if and only if $f(x) - T(x) = 0$ if and only if

$$R_n(x) = f(x) - T_n(x) \to 0 \quad \text{as} \quad n \to \infty$$

since $\lim_{n\to\infty} T_n(x) = T(x)$.

Example 7.41. In order to prove that the Taylor series of $f(x) = e^x$ about 0 converges to e^x for all x, it must be shown that

$$T(x) = \sum_{n=0}^{\infty} \frac{1}{n!}x^n = e^x = f(x).$$

By Theorem 7.6, it suffices to show that $R_n(x) = f(x) - T_n(x) \to 0$ as $n \to \infty$. By Theorem 7.5,

$$R_n(x) = \frac{f^{(n+1)}(z)}{(n+1)!}x^{n+1} = \frac{e^z}{(n+1)!}x^{n+1},$$

where z is a number between 0 and x.

If $x \geq 0$, then $0 \leq z \leq x \Rightarrow 1 \leq e^z \leq e^x \Rightarrow$

$$0 \leq |R_n(x)| = \frac{e^z}{(n+1)!}|x|^{n+1} \leq \frac{e^x}{(n+1)!}|x|^{n+1}.$$

Since

$$\sum_{n=0}^{\infty} \frac{e^x}{(n+1)!}x^{n+1} = e^x \sum_{n=0}^{\infty} \frac{1}{(n+1)!}x^{n+1}$$

converges absolutely by the ratio test, $\lim_{n\to\infty} \frac{e^x}{(n+1)!}x^{n+1} = 0$ by the nth-term test. Hence, $\lim_{n\to\infty} |R_n(x)| = 0$ by Theorem 6.4 and, by Theorem 6.2, $\lim_{n\to\infty} R_n(x) = 0$.

Similarly, if $x < 0$, then $x \leq z \leq 0 \Rightarrow e^x \leq e^z \leq 1 \Rightarrow$

$$0 \leq |R_n(x)| = \frac{e^z}{(n+1)!}|x|^{n+1} \leq \frac{1}{(n+1)!}|x|^{n+1} \to 0$$

$\Rightarrow \lim\limits_{n\to\infty} R_n(x) = 0$. Thus, $e^x = \sum\limits_{n=0}^{\infty} \frac{1}{n!}x^n$ for all x.

More generally, for any real number a,

$$e^x = e^a e^{x-a} = e^a \sum_{n=0}^{\infty} \frac{1}{n!}(x-a)^n = \sum_{n=0}^{\infty} \frac{e^a}{n!}(x-a)^n,$$

i.e., the Taylor series of e^x about any real number a converges to e^x for all x.

Example 7.42. In order to prove that the Taylor series of $f(x) = \sin(x)$ about 0 converges to $\sin(x)$ for all x, it must be shown that

$$T(x) = \sum_{k=0}^{\infty} \frac{(-1)^k}{(2k+1)!}x^{2k+1} = \sin(x) = f(x).$$

By Theorem 7.6, it suffices to show that $R_n(x) = f(x) - T_n(x) \to 0$ as $n \to \infty$. By Theorem 7.5,

$$R_n(x) = \frac{f^{(n+1)}(z)}{(n+1)!}x^{n+1},$$

where z is a number between 0 and x.

Since $f^{(n+1)}(z) = \pm\sin(z)$ or $\pm\cos(z)$, $|f^{(n+1)}(z)| \leq 1$ for all real z and $n \geq 0$. Hence,

$$0 \leq |R_n(x)| = \frac{|f^{(n+1)}(z)|}{(n+1)!}|x|^{n+1} \leq \frac{1}{(n+1)!}|x|^{n+1} \to 0$$

$\Rightarrow \lim\limits_{n\to\infty} R_n(x) = 0$. Thus, $\sin(x) = \sum\limits_{k=0}^{\infty} \frac{(-1)^k}{(2k+1)!}x^{2k+1}$ for all x.

It follows by Example 7.24 that $\cos(x) = \sum\limits_{k=0}^{\infty} \frac{(-1)^k}{(2k)!}x^{2k}$ for all x.

Definition 7.5. Let f be a function and a a real number. The function f is *analytic at a* if f has a Taylor series $T(x)$ about a, with radius of convergence $R > 0$, and the Taylor series converges to $f(x)$, i.e., $T(x) = f(x)$, for all x with $|x - a| < R$. If f does not have a Taylor series about a, or if the Taylor series does not converge to $f(x)$ for all x with $|x - a| < R$, then the point a is called a *singularity* or *singular point* of the function f.

Example 7.43. The function $f(x) = e^x$ is analytic at a for every real number a, as shown by Example 7.41.

Example 7.44. The functions $\sin(x)$ and $\cos(x)$ are analytic at 0, as shown by Example 7.42.

Example 7.45. The function

$$f(x) = \frac{1}{1-x} = \sum_{n=0}^{\infty} x^n, \quad |x| < 1,$$

is analytic at 0. However, it is not analytic at 1 because $f(1)$ is undefined and, hence, f does not have a Taylor series about 1. Thus, 1 is a singularity of f.

For any $a \neq 1$, f is analytic at a because

$$\frac{1}{1-x} = \frac{1}{1-(x-a)-a} = \frac{1}{1-\frac{x-a}{1-a}} = \sum_{n=0}^{\infty} \left(\frac{x-a}{1-a}\right)^n, \quad |x-a| < |1-a|.$$

Example 7.46. The function $f(x) = \sqrt{x} = x^{1/2}$ is not analytic at 0 because $f'(x) = \frac{1}{2\sqrt{x}} \Rightarrow f'(0)$ is undefined and, hence, f does not have a Taylor series about 0. Thus, 0 is a singular point of f.

Theorem 7.7. Suppose that f and g are analytic at a. Then

1. $c_1 f(x) + c_2 g(x)$ is analytic at a for any constants c_1 and c_2.

2. $f(x)g(x)$ is analytic at a.

3. $\dfrac{f(x)}{g(x)}$ is analytic at a provided that $g(a) \neq 0$.

The concept of analytic function is required in the solution of differential equations with variable coefficients by infinite series, as will be seen in Chapter 9.

Exercises 7.2

In Exercises 1–10, express the given function f as a power series about 0 and determine its radius of convergence.

1. $f(x) = \dfrac{1}{1+2x}$

2. $f(x) = \dfrac{6}{2 - x}$

3. $f(x) = \dfrac{1}{3 + x}$

4. $f(x) = \dfrac{2x}{4 - x}$

5. $f(x) = \dfrac{1}{6 + 2x}$

6. $f(x) = \dfrac{1}{1 - x^2}$

7. $f(x) = \dfrac{1}{2 + x^3}$

8. $f(x) = \dfrac{1}{1 - x} - \dfrac{1}{1 - 3x}$

9. $f(x) = \dfrac{1}{2 + x} + \dfrac{1}{3 - 2x}$

10. $f(x) = \dfrac{x^2 + 1}{x^2 - 1}$

In Exercises 11–28, find the Taylor series of the given function f about the given point a and determine its radius of convergence.

11. $f(x) = e^{-x}$, $a = 0$

12. $f(x) = e^{-3x}$, $a = 0$

13. $f(x) = e^x$, $a = 2$

14. $f(x) = e^x$, $a = -2$

15. $f(x) = e^{-3x^2}$, $a = 0$

16. $f(x) = e^{-3x}$, $a = 1$

17. $f(x) = \sin(2x)$, $a = 0$

18. $f(x) = \cos(3x)$, $a = 0$

19. $f(x) = \sin(x)$, $a = \pi$

20. $f(x) = \cos(x)$, $a = \pi$

21. $f(x) = \tan^{-1}(2x)$, $-\dfrac{\pi}{2} < \tan^{-1}(x) < \dfrac{\pi}{2}$, $a = 0$

22. $f(x) = \ln(x-1)$, $a = 2$

23. $f(x) = \ln(x)$, $a = 2$

24. $f(x) = \tan^{-1}(x-2)$, $-\dfrac{\pi}{2} < \tan^{-1}(x) < \dfrac{\pi}{2}$, $a = 2$

25. $f(x) = \dfrac{4}{\sqrt{4+x}}$, $a = 0$

26. $f(x) = \dfrac{x^2}{\sqrt[3]{1+x}}$, $a = 0$

27. $f(x) = x\sqrt{1+x^2}$, $a = 0$

28. $f(x) = \dfrac{x}{(1-x^3)^{3/2}}$, $a = 0$

29. Find the 4th-degree Taylor polynomial of $f(x) = e^x \sin(x)$ about 0.

30. Find the 4th-degree Taylor polynomial of $f(x) = \dfrac{\cos(x)}{1+\sin(x)}$ about 0.

31. Find the 4th-degree Taylor polynomial of $f(x) = (x^2+1)\cos(x)$ about 0.

32. Find the 4th-degree Taylor polynomial of $f(x) = \frac{x\ln(x)}{2-x}$ about 1.

33. Approximate $\sin\left(\dfrac{1}{2}\right)$ correct to 3 decimal places and confirm your answer with a calculator.

34. Approximate $\displaystyle\int_0^1 \cos(\sqrt{x})\,dx$ correct to 3 decimal places.

35. Approximate $\displaystyle\int_0^{\frac{1}{2}} \dfrac{1}{\sqrt{1+x^8}}\,dx$ correct to 3 decimal places.

36. Evaluate $\displaystyle\lim_{x\to 0} \dfrac{x(e^{3x}-1)^2\cos^2(x)}{\sin^3(x)}$.

37. Evaluate $\displaystyle\lim_{x\to 0} \dfrac{(x^2-1)(e^{-x}+x-1)\cos(x)}{x\sin(3x)}$.

38. Evaluate $\displaystyle\lim_{x\to 0} \dfrac{(x+2)^3\ln(1-x)}{\sin(2x)\cos(3x)}$.

39. Evaluate $\displaystyle\lim_{x\to 0-} \dfrac{x\sqrt{4x^4-x^5}}{\tan^3(2x)\cos^2(3x^2)}$.

40. Determine how large n must be taken in order to approximate $\sqrt[3]{e} = e^{1/3}$ by the Taylor polynomial of e^x about 0 at $x = \dfrac{1}{3}$ correct to 4 decimal places, and give the approximate value. Confirm your answer with a calculator.

41. Determine how large n must be taken in order to approximate $\ln(0.9)$ by the Taylor polynomial of $\ln(1 - x)$ about 0 at $x = 0.1$ correct to 3 decimal places, and give the approximate value. Confirm your answer with a calculator.

42. Show that $f(x) = \sin(x)$ is analytic at every real number a.

43. Show that $f(x) = \cos(x)$ is analytic at every real number a.

44. Employ power series to prove Euler's identity: $e^{ix} = \cos(x) + i \sin(x)$.

45. (a) Show that, for any two real numbers a and b, $ab \le |a||b|$.

(b) Show that, for any two real numbers a and b, $|a + b| \le |a| + |b|$. This inequality is known as the *triangle inequality*.

(c) Show that, if

$$f(x) = \sum_{n=0}^{\infty} a_n x^n \quad \text{and} \quad g(x) = \sum_{n=0}^{\infty} b_n x^n$$

have radii of convergence $R_1 > 0$ and $R_2 > 0$, respectively, then the radius of convergence R of

$$f(x) + g(x) = \sum_{n=0}^{\infty} (a_n + b_n) x^n$$

is at least the lesser of R_1 and R_2.

Chapter 8

Fourier Series

The topic of Chapter 7 was the representation of functions by power series. Various problems require the representation of functions by series which contain trigonometric functions. The content of the present chapter is the study of such series.

8.1   Fourier Series of Periodic Functions

Definition 8.1. A function f is *periodic* if there exists $T > 0$ such that

$$f(x + T) = f(x) \quad \text{for all real } x.$$

Such a function f is said to have *period* T (or to be *T-periodic*). The least (positive) period of f is called its *fundamental period*.

Example 8.1. The function $f(x) = \sin(x)$ is periodic with period $T = 2n\pi$ for any integer $n \geq 1$ since $\sin(x + 2n\pi) = \sin(x)$ for all x. The fundamental period of $\sin(x)$ is 2π.

Let f be periodic with period $T = 2L$, $L > 0$, and suppose that f is represented by a *trigonometric series*, i.e.,

$$f(x) = \frac{a_0}{2} + \sum_{n=1}^{\infty} \left[a_n \cos\left(\frac{n\pi x}{L}\right) + b_n \sin\left(\frac{n\pi x}{L}\right) \right], \tag{8.1}$$

where a_n, $n \geq 0$, and b_n, $n \geq 1$, are constants. The first term in the series, which corresponds to $n = 0$, is denoted by $\dfrac{a_0}{2}$ instead of a_0 merely for convenience, in order that a_0 and a_n for $n \geq 1$ can be defined by a single formula instead of two separate ones.

Given that Equation (8.1) holds, the coefficients a_n, $n \geq 0$, and b_n, $n \geq 1$, will be determined *formally*, i.e., without justification of the procedures employed in their derivation. Subsequently, the conditions under which and the values of x for which such a series converges to $f(x)$ will be given.

In order to determine the coefficients a_n, $n \geq 0$, let $m \geq 0$ be any integer, multiply Equation (8.1) by $\cos \left(\dfrac{m\pi x}{L} \right)$, and integrate from $-L$ to L to obtain

$$\int_{-L}^{L} f(x) \cos \left(\frac{m\pi x}{L} \right) dx = \int_{-L}^{L} \frac{a_0}{2} \cos \left(\frac{m\pi x}{L} \right) dx +$$

$$\int_{-L}^{L} \sum_{n=1}^{\infty} \left[a_n \cos \left(\frac{n\pi x}{L} \right) \cos \left(\frac{m\pi x}{L} \right) dx + b_n \sin \left(\frac{n\pi x}{L} \right) \cos \left(\frac{m\pi x}{L} \right) \right] dx.$$

Reverse the order of integration and summation to obtain

$$\int_{-L}^{L} f(x) \cos \left(\frac{m\pi x}{L} \right) dx = \frac{a_0}{2} \int_{-L}^{L} \cos \left(\frac{m\pi x}{L} \right) dx +$$

$$\sum_{n=1}^{\infty} \left[a_n \int_{-L}^{L} \cos \left(\frac{n\pi x}{L} \right) \cos \left(\frac{m\pi x}{L} \right) dx + b_n \int_{-L}^{L} \sin \left(\frac{n\pi x}{L} \right) \cos \left(\frac{m\pi x}{L} \right) dx \right].$$

If $m = 0$, then $\displaystyle\int_{-L}^{L} \cos \left(\frac{m\pi x}{L} \right) dx = \int_{-L}^{L} 1 \, dx = 2L,$

$$\int_{-L}^{L} \cos \left(\frac{n\pi x}{L} \right) \cos \left(\frac{m\pi x}{L} \right) dx = \int_{-L}^{L} \cos \left(\frac{n\pi x}{L} \right) dx = \frac{L}{n\pi} \sin \left(\frac{n\pi x}{L} \right) \Bigg|_{-L}^{L} = 0,$$

and

$$\int_{-L}^{L} \sin \left(\frac{n\pi x}{L} \right) \cos \left(\frac{m\pi x}{L} \right) dx = \int_{-L}^{L} \sin \left(\frac{n\pi x}{L} \right) dx = -\frac{L}{n\pi} \cos \left(\frac{n\pi x}{L} \right) \Bigg|_{-L}^{L} = 0.$$

Hence, $\displaystyle\int_{-L}^{L} f(x) \, dx = \frac{a_0}{2} 2L = a_0 L,$ from which it follows that

$$a_0 = \frac{1}{L} \int_{-L}^{L} f(x) \, dx. \tag{8.2}$$

If $m \geq 1$, then

$$\int_{-L}^{L} \cos \left(\frac{m\pi x}{L} \right) dx = \frac{L}{m\pi} \sin \left(\frac{m\pi x}{L} \right) \Bigg|_{-L}^{L} = 0.$$

Employing the trigonometric identities

$$\left\{ \begin{array}{l} \cos(a+b) = \cos(a)\cos(b) - \sin(a)\sin(b) \\ \cos(a-b) = \cos(a)\cos(b) + \sin(a)\sin(b) \end{array} \right\} \Rightarrow$$

$$\cos(a)\cos(b) = \frac{1}{2}\left[\cos(a-b) + \cos(a+b)\right]$$

with $a = \dfrac{n\pi x}{L}$ and $b = \dfrac{m\pi x}{L}$, we obtain

$$\int_{-L}^{L} \cos\left(\frac{n\pi x}{L}\right) \cos\left(\frac{m\pi x}{L}\right) dx$$

$$= \frac{1}{2}\int_{-L}^{L} \left\{ \cos\left[\frac{(n-m)\pi x}{L}\right] + \cos\left[\frac{(n+m)\pi x}{L}\right] \right\} dx$$

$$= \left\{ \begin{array}{ll} 0, & n \neq m \\ L, & n = m \end{array} \right\}$$

since, for any integer $k \neq 0$,

$$\int_{-L}^{L} \cos\left(\frac{k\pi x}{L}\right) dx = \frac{L}{k\pi}\sin\left(\frac{k\pi x}{L}\right)\Bigg|_{-L}^{L} = 0.$$

Employing the trigonometric identities

$$\left\{ \begin{array}{l} \sin(a+b) = \sin(a)\cos(b) + \cos(a)\sin(b) \\ \sin(a-b) = \sin(a)\cos(b) - \cos(a)\sin(b) \end{array} \right\} \Rightarrow$$

$$\sin(a)\cos(b) = \frac{1}{2}\left[\sin(a-b) + \sin(a+b)\right]$$

with $a = \dfrac{n\pi x}{L}$ and $b = \dfrac{m\pi x}{L}$, we obtain

$$\int_{-L}^{L} \sin\left(\frac{n\pi x}{L}\right) \cos\left(\frac{m\pi x}{L}\right) dx$$

$$= \frac{1}{2}\int_{-L}^{L} \left\{ \sin\left[\frac{(n-m)\pi x}{L}\right] + \sin\left[\frac{(n+m)\pi x}{L}\right] \right\} dx$$

$$= 0$$

since, for any integer $k \neq 0$,

$$\int_{-L}^{L} \sin\left(\frac{k\pi x}{L}\right) dx = -\frac{L}{k\pi}\cos\left(\frac{k\pi x}{L}\right)\Bigg|_{-L}^{L} = 0,$$

and, if $k = 0$, then $\displaystyle\int_{-L}^{L} \sin\left(\frac{k\pi x}{L}\right) dx = \int_{-L}^{L} 0\, dx = 0$. Thus, for any $m \geq 1$,

$$\int_{-L}^{L} f(x) \cos\left(\frac{m\pi x}{L}\right) dx = a_m L, \quad \text{i.e.,} \quad a_m = \frac{1}{L}\int_{-L}^{L} f(x) \cos\left(\frac{m\pi x}{L}\right) dx. \qquad (8.3)$$

Combining Equations (8.2) and (8.3), we obtain

$$a_m = \frac{1}{L}\int_{-L}^{L} f(x) \cos\left(\frac{m\pi x}{L}\right) dx, \quad m \geq 0. \qquad (8.4)$$

Similarly, multiplication of Equation (8.1) by $\sin\left(\frac{m\pi x}{L}\right)$, $m \geq 1$, and integration from $-L$ to L yields

$$b_m = \frac{1}{L}\int_{-L}^{L} f(x) \sin\left(\frac{m\pi x}{L}\right) dx, \quad m \geq 1. \qquad (8.5)$$

Definition 8.2. Suppose that f is periodic with period $T = 2L$. The trigonometric series

$$\frac{a_0}{2} + \sum_{n=1}^{\infty} \left[a_n \cos\left(\frac{n\pi x}{L}\right) + b_n \sin\left(\frac{n\pi x}{L}\right) \right],$$

with a_n, $n \geq 0$, and b_n, $n \geq 1$, defined by Equations (8.4) and (8.5), respectively, is called the *Fourier series of f*. The coefficients a_n, $n \geq 0$, are called the *Fourier cosine coefficients*, and b_n, $n \geq 1$, the *Fourier sine coefficients of f*. The integral formulas (8.4) and (8.5) which define the coefficients a_n and b_n are called the *Euler-Fourier formulas*.

Since f has period $2L$, the above integrals can be evaluated on *any interval of length $2L$*, and one should select the interval on which an explicit formula for $f(x)$ is available.

Example 8.2. Consider the function defined by

$$f(x) = x^2 + x, \quad -1 \leq x < 1, \quad f(x+2) = f(x) \quad \text{for all} \quad x.$$

Then f is periodic with period $T = 2$ and, with $L = \dfrac{T}{2} = 1$, its Fourier series takes the form

$$\frac{a_0}{2} + \sum_{n=1}^{\infty} \left[a_n \cos(n\pi x) + b_n \sin(n\pi x) \right].$$

Note that the formula $f(x) = x^2 + x$ is valid *only* for x in the interval $[-1, 1)$. For

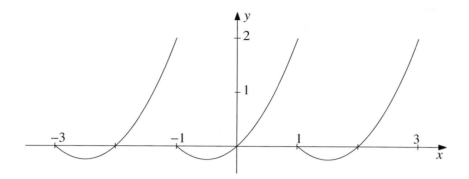

Figure 8.1: The graph of f in Example 8.2.

any x outside the interval $[-1, 1)$, the 2-periodicity of f must be employed in order to determine the value $f(x)$. The graph of f is depicted by Figure 8.1, where three periods are displayed. The curve from -1 to 1 repeats over the entire real line.

By Equations (8.4) and (8.5), the coefficients a_n, $n \geq 0$, and b_n, $n \geq 1$, are given by

$$
a_0 = \int_{-1}^{1} (x^2 + x) \, dx = \left(\frac{x^3}{3} + \frac{x^2}{2} \right) \Big|_{-1}^{1} = \frac{2}{3},
$$

$$
\begin{aligned}
a_n &= \int_{-1}^{1} (x^2 + x) \cos(n\pi x) \, dx \\
&= \frac{1}{n\pi} (x^2 + x) \sin(n\pi x) \Big|_{-1}^{1} - \frac{1}{n\pi} \int_{-1}^{1} (2x + 1) \sin(n\pi x) \, dx \\
&= \frac{1}{n^2\pi^2} (2x + 1) \cos(n\pi x) \Big|_{-1}^{1} - \frac{1}{n^2\pi^2} \int_{-1}^{1} 2 \cos(n\pi x) \, dx \\
&= \frac{4(-1)^n}{n^2\pi^2}, \quad n \geq 1,
\end{aligned}
$$

$$
\begin{aligned}
b_n &= \int_{-1}^{1} (x^2 + x) \sin(n\pi x) \, dx \\
&= -\frac{1}{n\pi} (x^2 + x) \cos(n\pi x) \Big|_{-1}^{1} + \frac{1}{n\pi} \int_{-1}^{1} (2x + 1) \cos(n\pi x) \, dx \\
&= -\frac{2(-1)^n}{n\pi} + \frac{1}{n^2\pi^2} (2x + 1) \sin(n\pi x) \Big|_{-1}^{1} - \frac{1}{n^2\pi^2} \int_{-1}^{1} 2 \sin(n\pi x) \, dx \\
&= \frac{2(-1)^{n-1}}{n\pi} + \frac{2}{n^3\pi^3} \cos(n\pi x) \Big|_{-1}^{1} \\
&= \frac{2(-1)^{n-1}}{n\pi}, \quad n \geq 1.
\end{aligned}
$$

Thus, the Fourier series of f is

$$\frac{1}{3} + \sum_{n=1}^{\infty} \left[\frac{4(-1)^n}{n^2\pi^2} \cos(n\pi x) + \frac{2(-1)^{n-1}}{n\pi} \sin(n\pi x) \right].$$

The following two definitions are required in order to state a convergence theorem for Fourier series.

Definition 8.3. A function f is *piecewise continuous on an interval* $[\alpha, \beta]$ if $[\alpha, \beta]$ can be partitioned into a finite number of subintervals such that f is continuous on each open subinterval and approaches a finite limit as x approaches an endpoint of any of the subintervals. A function is *piecewise continuous* if it is piecewise continuous on *every* finite interval.

Thus, a piecewise continuous function may have finite jump discontinuities on $[\alpha, \beta]$, but no other types of discontinuity. The graph of a typical piecewise continuous function on $[\alpha, \beta]$ is displayed in Figure 8.2.

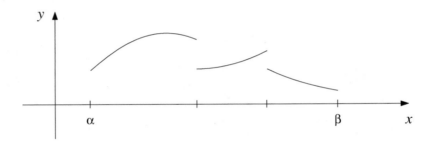

Figure 8.2: The graph of a piecewise continuous function on $[\alpha, \beta]$.

Definition 8.4. The *left-hand limit* $f(x-)$ of a function f at x is defined by

$$f(x-) = \lim_{y \to x-} f(y).$$

The *right-hand limit* $f(x+)$ of a function f at x is defined by

$$f(x+) = \lim_{y \to x+} f(y).$$

The *average value* of f at x is defined by

$$\frac{1}{2}[f(x-) + f(x+)].$$

If f is continuous at x, then $f(x-) = f(x+) = f(x)$, and the average value of f at x is $f(x)$. The one-sided limits and the average value of f at x are useful notions if f has a jump discontinuity at x.

Example 8.3. The function f in Example 8.2 is piecewise continuous. It has jump discontinuities at every odd integer $x = 2n + 1$, where n is an integer. At $x = 1$,

$$f(1-) = 2, \quad f(1+) = 0, \quad \text{and} \quad \frac{1}{2}[f(1-) + f(1+)] = 1$$

is the average value.

Theorem 8.1. Suppose that f is periodic with period $T = 2L$ and that f and f' are piecewise continuous. Then, at any point x, the Fourier series of f converges to

$$\frac{1}{2}[f(x+) + f(x-)],$$

i.e., the average value of f at x. If f is continuous at x, then the Fourier series of f at x converges to $f(x)$. This theorem is called the *Fourier convergence theorem*.

In certain books, a discontinuous function is *redefined* at a point x of discontinuity by $f(x) = \frac{1}{2}[f(x+) + f(x-)]$, in which case, the Fourier series of f converges to $f(x)$ for all x.

Example 8.4. Let $f(x) = 1 - x$ for $0 \le x < 1$ and $f(x + 1) = f(x)$ for all x. The graph of f is displayed in Figure 8.3.

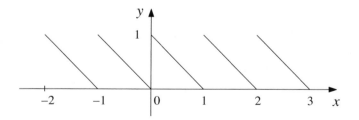

Figure 8.3: The graph of f in Example 8.4.

The function f has finite jump discontinuities at the integers, and no other types of discontinuity. Hence, f is piecewise continuous. Its derivative $f'(x) = -1$ everywhere except at the integers, where it is undefined, but $\lim_{x \to n\pm} f'(x) = -1$ is finite for every integer n. Hence, f' is piecewise continuous, and the Fourier convergence theorem (Theorem 8.1) applies.

Since f has period $T = 1$, $L = \dfrac{T}{2} = \dfrac{1}{2}$, and the Fourier series of f takes the form

$$\frac{a_0}{2} + \sum_{n=1}^{\infty} [a_n \cos(2n\pi x) + b_n \sin(2n\pi x)],$$

and, since an explicit formula for $f(x)$ is available on the interval $[0, 1)$, the integrals in Equations (8.4) and (8.5) must be evaluated from 0 to 1. Thus,

$$
\begin{aligned}
a_0 &= 2 \int_0^1 (1 - x)\, dx = \left. \left(2x - x^2 \right) \right|_0^1 = 1, \\[2mm]
a_n &= 2 \int_0^1 (1 - x) \cos(2n\pi x)\, dx \\[2mm]
&= \left. \frac{1}{n\pi} (1 - x) \sin(2n\pi x) \right|_0^1 + \frac{1}{n\pi} \int_0^1 \sin(2n\pi x)\, dx \\[2mm]
&= \left. -\frac{1}{2n^2\pi^2} \cos(2n\pi x) \right|_0^1 \\[2mm]
&= 0, \quad n \geq 1, \\[2mm]
b_n &= 2 \int_0^1 (1 - x) \sin(2n\pi x)\, dx \\[2mm]
&= \left. -\frac{1}{n\pi} (1 - x) \cos(2n\pi x) \right|_0^1 - \frac{1}{n\pi} \int_0^1 \cos(2n\pi x)\, dx \\[2mm]
&= \frac{1}{n\pi}, \quad n \geq 1.
\end{aligned}
$$

Hence, for all x except the integers,

$$f(x) = \frac{1}{2} + \sum_{n=1}^{\infty} \frac{1}{n\pi} \sin(2n\pi x).$$

At $x = m$, where m is an integer, the series converges to the average value $\dfrac{1}{2}$, as is evident from the series since $\sin(2n\pi m) = 0$ for every $n \geq 1$.

The number to which the series converges can be determined for any real number x. For example, at $x = \dfrac{3}{4}$, the series converges to $f\left(\dfrac{3}{4}\right) = \dfrac{1}{4}$. At $x = 731$, employing the 1-periodicity of f, the series converges to

$$\frac{1}{2}[f(731-) + f(731+)] = \frac{1}{2}[f(0-) + f(0+)] = \frac{1}{2},$$

and, at $x = 731.2$, the series converges to $f(731.2) = f(0.2) = 1 - 0.2 = 0.8$.

Example 8.5. Let $f(x) = \left\{ \begin{array}{ll} x, & 0 \leq x < 1 \\ 1, & 1 \leq x < 2 \end{array} \right\}$ and $f(x + 2) = f(x)$ for all x. The graph of f is displayed in Figure 8.4.

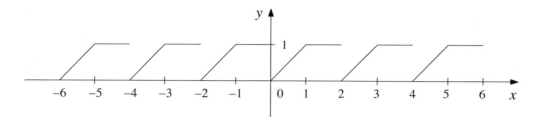

Figure 8.4: The graph of f in Example 8.5.

The function f is piecewise continuous, with discontinuities at the even integers $2m$, and f' is piecewise continuous, with discontinuities at all of the integers. The average value of f at an even integer is $\dfrac{1}{2}$. Thus, the Fourier series of f converges to $f(x)$ at every x except at $x = 2m$, where m is an integer.

Since f has period $T = 2$, $L = 1$ and the Fourier series of f takes the form

$$\frac{a_0}{2} + \sum_{n=1}^{\infty} [a_n \cos(n\pi x) + b_n \sin(n\pi x)],$$

with

$$
\begin{aligned}
a_0 &= \int_0^2 f(x)\, dx = \int_0^1 x\, dx + \int_1^2 1\, dx = \frac{1}{2} + 1 = \frac{3}{2}, \\
a_n &= \int_0^2 f(x) \cos(n\pi x)\, dx = \int_0^1 x \cos(n\pi x)\, dx + \int_1^2 \cos(n\pi x)\, dx \\
&= \frac{x}{n\pi} \sin(n\pi x) \Big|_0^1 - \frac{1}{n\pi} \int_0^1 \sin(n\pi x)\, dx + \frac{1}{n\pi} \sin(n\pi x) \Big|_1^2 \\
&= \frac{1}{n^2\pi^2} \cos(n\pi x) \Big|_0^1 = \frac{1}{n^2\pi^2} [(-1)^n - 1], \quad n \geq 1, \\
b_n &= \int_0^2 f(x) \sin(n\pi x)\, dx = \int_0^1 x \sin(n\pi x)\, dx + \int_1^2 \sin(n\pi x)\, dx \\
&= -\frac{x}{n\pi} \cos(n\pi x) \Big|_0^1 + \frac{1}{n\pi} \int_0^1 \cos(n\pi x)\, dx - \frac{1}{n\pi} \cos(n\pi x) \Big|_1^2 \\
&= -\frac{(-1)^n}{n\pi} + \frac{1}{n^2\pi^2} \sin(n\pi x) \Big|_0^1 - \frac{1}{n\pi} + \frac{(-1)^n}{n\pi} = -\frac{1}{n\pi}, \quad n \geq 1.
\end{aligned}
$$

Hence, for all x except the even integers,

$$f(x) = \frac{3}{4} + \sum_{n=1}^{\infty} \left\{ \frac{[(-1)^n - 1]}{n^2 \pi^2} \cos(n\pi x) - \frac{1}{n\pi} \sin(n\pi x) \right\}. \tag{8.6}$$

At every even integer $x = 2m$, the series converges to $\frac{1}{2}$.

The number to which the series converges can be determined for any real number x. For example, at $x = 1$, the series converges to $f(1) = 1$. At $x = 273$, employing the 2-periodicity of f, the series converges to $f(273) = f(1) = 1$. At $x = 28.3$, the series converges to $f(28.3) = f(0.3) = 0.3$.

An interesting result emerges at $x = 0$. Since the series converges to $\frac{1}{2}$ at $x = 0$, setting $x = 0$ in (8.6) gives

$$\frac{3}{4} + \sum_{n=1}^{\infty} \frac{[(-1)^n - 1]}{n^2 \pi^2} = \frac{1}{2}, \quad \text{i.e.,} \quad \sum_{n=1}^{\infty} \frac{[(-1)^n - 1]}{n^2 \pi^2} = -\frac{1}{4},$$

and, since $(-1)^n - 1 = 0$ for $n = 2k$ even and $(-1)^n - 1 = -2$ for $n = 2k + 1$ odd, we obtain

$$\sum_{k=0}^{\infty} \frac{-2}{(2k + 1)^2 \pi^2} = -\frac{1}{4}, \quad \text{i.e.,} \quad \sum_{k=0}^{\infty} \frac{1}{(2k + 1)^2} = \frac{\pi^2}{8}.$$

Thus, Fourier series can be employed to determine the exact sums of certain series.

Having completed a general discussion of Fourier series, we shall consider next certain important special cases.

Definition 8.5.   A function f defined on an interval I of the form $[-L, L]$ or $(-L, L)$, $L > 0$, is said to be *odd* if $f(-x) = -f(x)$ for all x in I.

Example 8.6.   For any $L > 0$, the function $f(x) = x^3$ is odd on $[-L, L]$ because $f(-x) = (-x)^3 = -x^3 = -f(x)$ for all x in $[-L, L]$.

Definition 8.6.   A function f defined on an interval I of the form $[-L, L]$ or $(-L, L)$, $L > 0$, is said to be *even* if $f(-x) = f(x)$ for all x in I.

Example 8.7.   For any $L > 0$, the function $f(x) = x^2$ is even on $(-L, L)$ because $f(-x) = (-x)^2 = x^2 = f(x)$ for all x in $(-L, L)$.

Example 8.8. The function $f(x) = e^x$ is neither even nor odd on any interval $I = [-L, L]$ since $f(-x) = e^{-x} \neq \pm e^x = \pm f(x)$, except at the single point $x = 0$.

Example 8.9. The function $f(x) = x^2$ is *not* even on $[0, 1]$ because $[0, 1]$ is not of the form $[-L, L]$ or $(-L, L)$.

Theorem 8.2. If f is odd on $[-L, L]$ or $(-L, L)$, then

$$\int_{-L}^{L} f(x)\,dx = 0.$$

Proof.

$$\int_{-L}^{L} f(x)\,dx = \int_{-L}^{0} f(x)\,dx + \int_{0}^{L} f(x)\,dx.$$

Let $y = -x$ in the first integral on the right to convert it into

$$\int_{L}^{0} f(-y)(-dy) = \int_{0}^{L} f(-y)\,dy = -\int_{0}^{L} f(y)\,dy$$

since $f(-y) = -f(y)$. Thus,

$$\int_{-L}^{L} f(x)\,dx = -\int_{0}^{L} f(y)\,dy + \int_{0}^{L} f(x)\,dx = 0.$$

Theorem 8.3. If f is even on $[-L, L]$ or $(-L, L)$, then

$$\int_{-L}^{L} f(x)\,dx = 2\int_{0}^{L} f(x)\,dx.$$

Proof:

$$\int_{-L}^{L} f(x)\,dx = \int_{-L}^{0} f(x)\,dx + \int_{0}^{L} f(x)\,dx.$$

Let $y = -x$ in the first integral on the right to convert it into

$$\int_{L}^{0} f(-y)(-dy) = \int_{0}^{L} f(-y)\,dy = \int_{0}^{L} f(y)\,dy$$

since $f(-y) = f(y)$. Thus,

$$\int_{-L}^{L} f(x)\,dx = \int_{0}^{L} f(y)\,dy + \int_{0}^{L} f(x)\,dx = 2\int_{0}^{L} f(x)\,dx.$$

Theorem 8.4. Suppose that f is a $2L$-periodic function. If f is odd, then the Fourier series of f reduces to

$$\sum_{n=1}^{\infty} b_n \sin\left(\frac{n\pi x}{L}\right),$$

with

$$b_n = \frac{2}{L} \int_0^L f(x) \sin\left(\frac{n\pi x}{L}\right) dx, \quad n \geq 1.$$

This series is called the *Fourier sine series* (or simply the *sine series*) of f.

Proof. The Fourier series of f is

$$\frac{a_0}{2} + \sum_{n=1}^{\infty} \left[a_n \cos\left(\frac{n\pi x}{L}\right) + b_n \sin\left(\frac{n\pi x}{L}\right) \right],$$

with

$$a_n = \frac{1}{L} \int_{-L}^{L} f(x) \cos\left(\frac{n\pi x}{L}\right) dx, \quad n \geq 0, \quad b_n = \frac{1}{L} \int_{-L}^{L} f(x) \sin\left(\frac{n\pi x}{L}\right) dx, \quad n \geq 1.$$

Since $\cos\left(\frac{n\pi x}{L}\right)$, $n \geq 0$, is an even function and f is an odd function, their product is an odd function and, hence, $a_n = 0$ for $n \geq 0$, by Theorem 8.2. Since $\sin\left(\frac{n\pi x}{L}\right)$, $n \geq 1$, is an odd function and f is an odd function, their product is an even function and, hence,

$$b_n = \frac{1}{L} \int_{-L}^{L} f(x) \sin\left(\frac{n\pi x}{L}\right) dx = \frac{2}{L} \int_0^L f(x) \sin\left(\frac{n\pi x}{L}\right) dx, \quad n \geq 1,$$

by Theorem 8.3.

Example 8.10. Let $f(x) = x$ on the interval $[-2, 2)$ and $f(x + 4) = f(x)$ for all x. This function is 4-periodic and odd. Hence, by Theorem 8.4 with $L = \frac{T}{2} = 2$, the Fourier series of f reduces to the sine series

$$\sum_{n=1}^{\infty} b_n \sin\left(\frac{n\pi x}{2}\right),$$

with

$$\begin{aligned}
b_n &= \frac{2}{2} \int_0^2 f(x) \sin\left(\frac{n\pi x}{2}\right) dx = \int_0^2 x \sin\left(\frac{n\pi x}{2}\right) dx \\
&= -\frac{2}{n\pi} x \cos\left(\frac{n\pi x}{2}\right) \Big|_0^2 + \frac{2}{n\pi} \int_0^2 \cos\left(\frac{n\pi x}{2}\right) dx \\
&= -\frac{4}{n\pi} \cos(n\pi) = \frac{4(-1)^{n-1}}{n\pi}, \quad n \geq 1.
\end{aligned}$$

Thus, the Fourier series of f is the sine series

$$\sum_{n=1}^{\infty} \frac{4(-1)^{n-1}}{n\pi} \sin\left(\frac{n\pi x}{2}\right),$$

and converges to $f(x)$ for all x except $x = \pm 2, \pm 6, \cdots$, where it converges to 0. The graph of f is displayed in Figure 8.5.

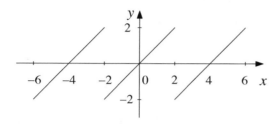

Figure 8.5: The graph of f in Example 8.10.

Theorem 8.5. Suppose that f is a $2L$-periodic function. If f is even, then the Fourier series of f reduces to

$$\frac{a_0}{2} + \sum_{n=1}^{\infty} a_n \cos\left(\frac{n\pi x}{L}\right),$$

with

$$a_n = \frac{2}{L} \int_0^L f(x) \cos\left(\frac{n\pi x}{L}\right) dx, \quad n \geq 0.$$

This series is called the *Fourier cosine series* (or simply the *cosine series*) of f.

Proof. The Fourier series of f is

$$\frac{a_0}{2} + \sum_{n=1}^{\infty} \left[a_n \cos\left(\frac{n\pi x}{L}\right) + b_n \sin\left(\frac{n\pi x}{L}\right)\right],$$

with

$$a_n = \frac{1}{L} \int_{-L}^{L} f(x) \cos\left(\frac{n\pi x}{L}\right) dx, \quad n \geq 0, \quad b_n = \frac{1}{L} \int_{-L}^{L} f(x) \sin\left(\frac{n\pi x}{L}\right) dx, \quad n \geq 1.$$

Since $\sin\left(\frac{n\pi x}{L}\right)$, $n \geq 1$, is an odd function and f is an even function, their product is an odd function and, hence, $b_n = 0$ for $n \geq 1$, by Theorem 8.2. Since $\cos\left(\frac{n\pi x}{L}\right)$, $n \geq 0$, and f are even functions, their product is an even function and, hence,

$$a_n = \frac{1}{L} \int_{-L}^{L} f(x) \cos\left(\frac{n\pi x}{L}\right) dx = \frac{2}{L} \int_0^L f(x) \cos\left(\frac{n\pi x}{L}\right) dx, \quad n \geq 0,$$

by Theorem 8.3.

Example 8.11. Let $f(x) = \left\{ \begin{array}{ll} 2, & -2 \leq x < -1 \\ 1, & -1 \leq x < 1 \\ 2, & 1 \leq x < 2 \end{array} \right\}$ on $[-2, 2)$ and $f(x+4) = f(x)$

for all x. The graph of f is displayed in Figure 8.6. This function has period $T = 4$

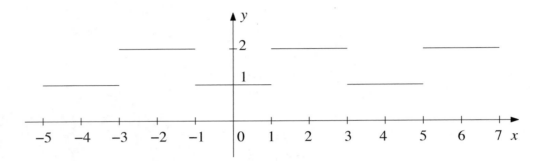

Figure 8.6: The graph of f in Example 8.11.

and is even. Hence, by Theorem 8.5 with $L = \dfrac{T}{2} = 2$, its Fourier series reduces to the cosine series

$$\frac{a_0}{2} + \sum_{n=1}^{\infty} a_n \cos\left(\frac{n\pi x}{2}\right),$$

with

$$a_n = \frac{2}{2} \int_0^2 f(x) \cos\left(\frac{n\pi x}{2}\right) dx$$

$$= \int_0^1 \cos\left(\frac{n\pi x}{2}\right) dx + \int_1^2 2\cos\left(\frac{n\pi x}{2}\right) dx, \quad n \geq 0,$$

from which we obtain

$$a_0 = \int_0^1 1 \, dx + \int_1^2 2 \, dx = 3,$$

$$a_n = \frac{2}{n\pi} \sin\left(\frac{n\pi x}{2}\right)\Big|_0^1 + \frac{4}{n\pi} \sin\left(\frac{n\pi x}{2}\right)\Big|_1^2 = \frac{2}{n\pi} \sin\left(\frac{n\pi}{2}\right) - \frac{4}{n\pi} \sin\left(\frac{n\pi}{2}\right)$$

$$= -\frac{2}{n\pi} \sin\left(\frac{n\pi}{2}\right), \quad n \geq 1.$$

Thus, the Fourier series of f is the cosine series

$$\frac{3}{2} + \sum_{n=1}^{\infty} -\frac{2}{n\pi} \sin\left(\frac{n\pi}{2}\right) \cos\left(\frac{n\pi x}{2}\right),$$

and converges to $f(x)$ at every x except the odd integers, where it converges to $\dfrac{3}{2}$.

Exercises 8.1

1. Show that if f is periodic with period T, then $f(x + nT) = f(x)$ for every integer n.

2. Let $f(x) = x^2 + 1$ for $-1 \le x < 2$ and $f(x + 3) = f(x)$ for all x. Determine the values $f(x)$ of f at $x = 5$, 7, -4, 783 and -291.

3. Let f be $2L$-periodic, and suppose that f is represented by a trigonometric series, i.e.,

$$f(x) = \frac{a_0}{2} + \sum_{n=1}^{\infty} \left[a_n \cos\left(\frac{n\pi x}{L}\right) + b_n \sin\left(\frac{n\pi x}{L}\right) \right].$$

The coefficients a_n have been determined in the text. In a similar way, show (formally) that $b_n = \dfrac{1}{L} \displaystyle\int_{-L}^{L} f(x) \sin\left(\dfrac{n\pi x}{L}\right) dx$ for every $n \ge 1$.

4. Let $f(x) = \left\{ \begin{array}{ll} 0, & -2 \le x < 0 \\ 1, & 0 \le x < 2 \end{array} \right\}$ and $f(x+4) = f(x)$ for all x. Find the Fourier series of f.

5. Let $f(x) = \left\{ \begin{array}{ll} 0, & 0 \le x < 1 \\ x, & 1 \le x < 2 \end{array} \right\}$ and $f(x + 2) = f(x)$ for all x. Find the Fourier series of f.

6. Let $f(x) = 2x - 3$ for $2 \le x < 5$ and $f(x+3) = f(x)$ for all x. Find the Fourier series of f.

7. Let $f(x) = \dfrac{1}{x}$ for $0 < x \le 1$ and $f(x + 1) = f(x)$ for all x. Is f piecewise continuous?

8. Let $f(x) = \left\{ \begin{array}{ll} 0, & -1 \le x < 0 \\ -x, & 0 \le x < 1 \end{array} \right\}$, and $f(x + 2) = f(x)$ for all x.

   (a) Find the Fourier series of f.

   (b) Sketch the graph of f.

   (c) Determine the numbers to which the series converges at $x = 0$, $\dfrac{1}{2}$, 1, 18, 18.5 and 19.

9. Let $f(x) = x^2$ for $0 \le x < 2$ and $f(x + 2) = f(x)$ for all x.

   (a) Find the Fourier series of f.

(b) Sketch the graph of f.

(c) Determine the numbers to which the Fourier series of f converges at $x = 3$, 8 and -10.

10. Let $f(x) = x^3$ for $-1 \le x < 1$ and $f(x + 2) = f(x)$ for all x. Find the Fourier series of f.

11. Let $f(x) = \left\{ \begin{array}{cc} -1, & -2 \le x < 0 \\ 1, & 0 \le x < 2 \end{array} \right\}$, and $f(x + 4) = f(x)$ for all x.

(a) Sketch the graph of f.

(b) Find the Fourier series of f.

12. Let $f(x) = x^2$ for $-1 \le x < 1$ and $f(x + 2) = f(x)$ for all x. Find the Fourier series of f.

13. Let $f(x) = \left\{ \begin{array}{cc} 1 - x^2, & 0 \le x \le 1 \\ 1 - (x - 2)^2, & 1 < x < 2 \end{array} \right\}$, and $f(x + 2) = f(x)$ for all x.

(a) Sketch the graph of f.

(b) Find the Fourier series of f. Determine the points x where the series converges to $f(x)$.

(c) Select a suitable value of x in order to deduce the sum of the series
$$\sum_{n=1}^{\infty} \frac{(-1)^{n-1}}{n^2}.$$

14. Consider the 3-periodic function f which has the graph depicted by Figure 8.7.

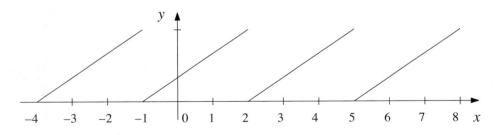

Figure 8.7: The graph of f.

(a) Explain why $\displaystyle\int_5^8 f(x)\, dx = \int_{-1}^2 f(x)\, dx$.

(b) Explain why $\displaystyle\int_{-1}^{2} f(x)\,dx = \int_{0}^{3} f(x)\,dx$.

15. Prove that if f is T-periodic, then, for any real number α,

$$\int_{\alpha}^{\alpha+T} f(x)\,dx = \int_{0}^{T} f(x)\,dx.$$

Hence, deduce that for any two real numbers α and β,

$$\int_{\alpha}^{\alpha+T} f(x)\,dx = \int_{\beta}^{\beta+T} f(x)\,dx.$$

Thus, the integral of a T-periodic function over any interval of length T is the same. (*Hint:* Write $\displaystyle\int_{\alpha}^{\alpha+T} f(x)\,dx = \int_{\alpha}^{0} f(x)\,dx + \int_{0}^{\alpha+T} f(x)\,dx$ and let $y = x + T$ in the first integral on the right.)

16. Let $f(x) = \left\{ \begin{array}{ll} -\cos(x), & -\pi \le x < 0 \\ \cos(x), & 0 \le x < \pi \end{array} \right\}$ and $f(x + 2\pi) = f(x)$ for all x. Find the Fourier series of f.

8.2 Fourier Series of Functions on Finite Intervals

Suppose that a function f is defined only on a finite interval $[a, b]$, and it is necessary to express $f(x)$ as a Fourier series, a sine series, or a cosine series for $a \le x \le b$. Such problems arise, for example, in the solution of ordinary and partial differential equations. The Fourier series, including the special cases of sine and cosine series, of such a function f are obtained as the Fourier series of certain periodic functions which are suitable extensions of f to the entire real line $\mathbb{R} = (-\infty, \infty)$.

Definition 8.7. Suppose that f is defined on an interval $[a, b]$, and let I be an interval containing $[a, b]$. A function $\tilde{f}$ defined on I is called an *extension* of f from $[a, b]$ to I if $\tilde{f}(x) = f(x)$ for all x in $[a, b]$.

Of course, $\tilde{f}$ can be defined in any manner whatsoever outside the interval $[a, b]$. The only restriction upon the function $\tilde{f}(x)$ is that it be equal to $f(x)$ for all x in $[a, b]$. Thus, there is an infinite number of possible extensions of a given function f from $[a, b]$ to I. However, only three very particular types of extension are important in the study of Fourier series.

Definition 8.8. Let f be defined on $[a, b]$ and let $T = b - a$. Define the function $\tilde{f}$ on $\mathbb{R}$ by

$$\tilde{f}(x) = f(x) \text{ for all } x \text{ in } [a, b] \text{ and } \tilde{f}(x + T) = \tilde{f}(x) \text{ for all } x.$$

The function $\tilde{f}$ is called the *T-periodic extension of f to* $\mathbb{R}$.

Example 8.12. Let $f(x) = 1 - x$ on $[0, 1]$. Then the 1-periodic extension $\tilde{f}$ of f to $\mathbb{R}$ is defined by $\tilde{f}(x) = f(x) = 1 - x$ for $0 \leq x \leq 1$ and $\tilde{f}(x+1) = \tilde{f}(x)$ for all x. The graph of $\tilde{f}$ is displayed in Figure 8.8.

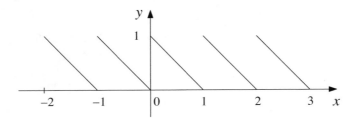

Figure 8.8: The graph of the 1-periodic extension $\tilde{f}$ of f to $\mathbb{R}$.

Note that, in Example 8.12, $\tilde{f}$ is not well defined at integral values of x since, on the one hand, $\tilde{f}(1) = f(1) = 0$ but, on the other hand, $\tilde{f}(1) = \tilde{f}(0) = f(0) = 1$. In general, if f is defined on a *closed* interval of the form $[a, b]$ and $T = b - a$, then the T-periodic extension of f to $\mathbb{R}$ is not well defined at the points nT, $n = 0, \pm 1, \pm 2, \cdots$, unless $f(a) = f(b)$. Such points, where an extension $\tilde{f}$ is not well defined, are points of discontinuity. In the study of Fourier series, the *value* of a function at a point x of discontinuity is irrelevant, because the Fourier series of $\tilde{f}$ converges to the average value of $\tilde{f}$ at x, regardless of how $\tilde{f}(x)$ is defined, and we shall pay no more heed to this matter.

Definition 8.9. Let f be defined on $[a, b]$, let $T = b - a$ and let $\tilde{f}$ be the T-periodic extension of f to $\mathbb{R}$. Then, with $L = \dfrac{T}{2}$, the *Fourier series of f on* $[a, b]$ is the Fourier series of $\tilde{f}$, i.e.,

$$\frac{a_0}{2} + \sum_{n=1}^{\infty} \left[a_n \cos\left(\frac{n\pi x}{L}\right) + b_n \sin\left(\frac{n\pi x}{L}\right) \right], \tag{8.7}$$

with

$$a_n = \frac{1}{L} \int_a^b \tilde{f}(x) \cos\left(\frac{n\pi x}{L}\right) dx = \frac{1}{L} \int_a^b f(x) \cos\left(\frac{n\pi x}{L}\right) dx, \quad n \geq 0, \tag{8.8}$$

$$b_n = \frac{1}{L} \int_a^b \tilde{f}(x) \sin\left(\frac{n\pi x}{L}\right) dx = \frac{1}{L} \int_a^b f(x) \sin\left(\frac{n\pi x}{L}\right) dx, \quad n \geq 1, \tag{8.9}$$

employing the fact that $\tilde{f}(x) = f(x)$ for all x in $[a, b]$.

The Fourier series of f can be determined directly by Equations (8.7), (8.8) and (8.9), without any reference to the extension $\tilde{f}$. Knowledge of $\tilde{f}$ is required only if the sum of the series at points $x \le a$ or $x \ge b$ needs to be determined.

Example 8.13. The function $\tilde{f}$ in Example 8.12 is the same as the periodic function f in Example 8.4 on page 289, where its Fourier series was derived. Since $\tilde{f}$ and $\tilde{f}'$ are piecewise continuous and $\tilde{f}$ is continuous for $0 < x < 1$, its Fourier series converges to $\tilde{f}(x) = f(x)$ for $0 < x < 1$. Thus,

$$1 - x = \frac{1}{2} + \sum_{n=1}^{\infty} \frac{1}{n\pi} \sin(2n\pi x), \quad 0 < x < 1,$$

and the series on the right (including the constant term) is the Fourier series of $f(x) = 1 - x$ on $[0, 1]$.

Example 8.14. Let $f(x) = x$ on $[0, 1]$. The graphs of f and its 1-periodic extension $\tilde{f}$ to $\mathbb{R}$ are displayed in Figure 8.9.

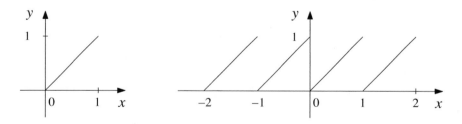

Figure 8.9: The graphs of $f(x) = x$ on $[0, 1]$ and its 1-periodic extension $\tilde{f}$ to $\mathbb{R}$.

The Fourier series of f on $[0, 1]$ is the Fourier series of the periodic function $\tilde{f}$ with $L = \frac{1}{2}$, i.e.,

$$\frac{a_0}{2} + \sum_{n=1}^{\infty} [a_n \cos(2n\pi x) + b_n \sin(2n\pi x)],$$

with

$$a_0 = 2 \int_0^1 x \, dx = 1,$$

and, for $n \geq 1$,

$$
\begin{aligned}
a_n &= 2 \int_0^1 x \cos(2n\pi x)\, dx = \frac{x}{n\pi} \sin(2n\pi x)\Big|_0^1 - \frac{1}{n\pi} \int_0^1 \sin(2n\pi x)\, dx = 0, \\
b_n &= 2 \int_0^1 x \sin(2n\pi x)\, dx = -\frac{x}{n\pi} \cos(2n\pi x)\Big|_0^1 + \frac{1}{n\pi} \int_0^1 \cos(2n\pi x)\, dx = -\frac{1}{n\pi}.
\end{aligned}
$$

Since $\tilde{f}$ and $\tilde{f}'$ are piecewise continuous and $\tilde{f}$ is continuous for $0 < x < 1$,

$$
x = \frac{1}{2} - \sum_{n=1}^{\infty} \frac{1}{n\pi} \sin(2n\pi x), \quad 0 < x < 1.
$$

Example 8.15. Let $f(x) = x + 1$ on $[-1, 2]$. The graph of the 3-periodic extension $\tilde{f}$ of f to $\mathbb{R}$ is displayed in Figure 8.10.

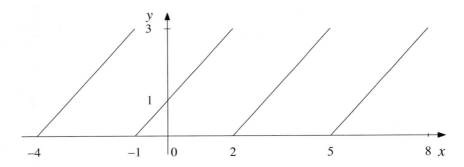

Figure 8.10: The graph of the 3-periodic extension $\tilde{f}$ of f to $\mathbb{R}$.

The Fourier series of f on $[-1, 2]$ is the Fourier series of the periodic function $\tilde{f}$ with $L = \frac{3}{2}$, i.e.,

$$
\frac{a_0}{2} + \sum_{n=1}^{\infty} \left[a_n \cos\left(\frac{2n\pi x}{3}\right) + b_n \sin\left(\frac{2n\pi x}{3}\right) \right],
$$

with

$$a_0 = \frac{2}{3} \int_{-1}^{2} (x+1)\, dx = \frac{2}{3}\left(\frac{x^2}{2} + x\right)\bigg|_{-1}^{2} = \frac{2}{3}\left(4 + \frac{1}{2}\right) = 3,$$

$$a_n = \frac{2}{3} \int_{-1}^{2} (x+1)\cos\left(\frac{2n\pi x}{3}\right) dx$$

$$= \frac{1}{n\pi}(x+1)\sin\left(\frac{2n\pi x}{3}\right)\bigg|_{-1}^{2} - \frac{1}{n\pi}\int_{-1}^{2} \sin\left(\frac{2n\pi x}{3}\right) dx$$

$$= \frac{3}{n\pi}\sin\left(\frac{4n\pi}{3}\right) + \frac{3}{2n^2\pi^2}\cos\left(\frac{2n\pi x}{3}\right)\bigg|_{-1}^{2}$$

$$= \frac{3}{n\pi}\sin\left(\frac{4n\pi}{3}\right) + \frac{3}{2n^2\pi^2}\left[\cos\left(\frac{4n\pi}{3}\right) - \cos\left(\frac{2n\pi}{3}\right)\right]$$

$$= \frac{3}{n\pi}\sin\left(\frac{4n\pi}{3}\right), \quad n \geq 1,$$

$$b_n = \frac{2}{3} \int_{-1}^{2} (x+1)\sin\left(\frac{2n\pi x}{3}\right) dx$$

$$= -\frac{1}{n\pi}(x+1)\cos\left(\frac{2n\pi x}{3}\right)\bigg|_{-1}^{2} + \frac{1}{n\pi}\int_{-1}^{2} \cos\left(\frac{2n\pi x}{3}\right) dx$$

$$= -\frac{3}{n\pi}\cos\left(\frac{4n\pi}{3}\right) + \frac{3}{2n^2\pi^2}\sin\left(\frac{2n\pi x}{3}\right)\bigg|_{-1}^{2}$$

$$= -\frac{3}{n\pi}\cos\left(\frac{4n\pi}{3}\right) + \frac{3}{2n^2\pi^2}\left[\sin\left(\frac{4n\pi}{3}\right) + \sin\left(\frac{2n\pi}{3}\right)\right]$$

$$= -\frac{3}{n\pi}\cos\left(\frac{4n\pi}{3}\right), \quad n \geq 1.$$

Thus,

$$x + 1 = \frac{3}{2} + \sum_{n=1}^{\infty}\left[\frac{3}{n\pi}\sin\left(\frac{4n\pi}{3}\right)\cos\left(\frac{2n\pi x}{3}\right) - \frac{3}{n\pi}\cos\left(\frac{4n\pi}{3}\right)\sin\left(\frac{2n\pi x}{3}\right)\right]$$

$$= \frac{3}{2} + \sum_{n=1}^{\infty} \frac{3}{n\pi}\sin\left(\frac{4n\pi - 2n\pi x}{3}\right)$$

$$= \frac{3}{2} - \sum_{n=1}^{\infty} \frac{3}{n\pi}\sin\left[\frac{2n\pi(x-2)}{3}\right]$$

$$= \frac{3}{2} - \sum_{n=1}^{\infty} \frac{3}{n\pi}\sin\left[\frac{2n\pi(x+1)}{3}\right], \quad -1 < x < 2.$$

Suppose that f is defined on an interval of the form $[0, L]$, $L > 0$, and that a Fourier sine series representation of f on $[0, L]$ is required. Since a sine series is the

Fourier series of an odd function, the extension $\tilde{f}$ of f to $\mathbb{R}$ must be an odd function.

Definition 8.10. Let f be defined on $[0, L]$, and let f_1 be an extension of f to $[-L, L]$. If f_1 is an odd function, then f_1 is called the *odd extension of f to $[-L, L]$*.

Definition 8.11. Let f be defined on $[0, L]$, let f_1 be the odd extension of f to $[-L, L]$, and let $\tilde{f}$ be the $2L$-periodic extension of f_1 to $\mathbb{R}$. Then $\tilde{f}$ is called the *odd, $2L$-periodic extension of f to $\mathbb{R}$*.

Example 8.16. Let $f(x) = 1 - x$ on $[0, 1]$. The graphs of the odd extension f_1 of f to $[-1, 1]$ and the odd, 2-periodic extension $\tilde{f}$ of f to $\mathbb{R}$ are displayed in Figures 8.11 and 8.12, respectively.

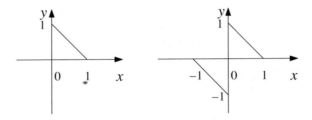

Figure 8.11: The graphs of f and its odd extension f_1 to $[-1, 1]$.

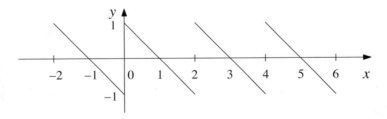

Figure 8.12: The graph of the odd, 2-periodic extension $\tilde{f}$ of f to $\mathbb{R}$.

The odd extension f_1 of f to $[-1, 1]$ is defined by

$$f_1(x) = \left\{ \begin{array}{ll} -1 - x, & -1 \leq x \leq 0 \\ 1 - x, & 0 \leq x \leq 1 \end{array} \right\},$$

with the understanding that f_1 is not well defined at $x = 0$.

Definition 8.12. Let f be defined on $[0, L]$. The *Fourier sine series of f on $[0, L]$* is the Fourier series of the odd, $2L$-periodic extension $\tilde{f}$ of f to $\mathbb{R}$, i.e.,

$$\sum_{n=1}^{\infty} b_n \sin\left(\frac{n\pi x}{L}\right), \tag{8.10}$$

with

$$b_n = \frac{2}{L} \int_0^L \tilde{f}(x) \sin\left(\frac{n\pi x}{L}\right) dx = \frac{2}{L} \int_0^L f(x) \sin\left(\frac{n\pi x}{L}\right) dx, \quad n \geq 1, \tag{8.11}$$

employing the fact that $\tilde{f}(x) = f(x)$ for $0 \leq x \leq L$.

The sine series of f on $[0, L]$ can be determined directly by Equations (8.10) and (8.11), without any reference to the extension $\tilde{f}$. Knowledge of $\tilde{f}$ is required only if the sum of the series at points $x \leq 0$ or $x \geq L$ needs to be determined.

Example 8.17. The sine series of $f(x) = 1 - x$ on $[0, 1]$ is

$$\sum_{n=1}^{\infty} b_n \sin(n\pi x),$$

with

$$
\begin{aligned}
b_n &= 2 \int_0^1 (1 - x) \sin(n\pi x)\, dx \\
&= -\frac{2}{n\pi}(1 - x) \cos(n\pi x)\Big|_0^1 - \frac{2}{n\pi} \int_0^1 \cos(n\pi x)\, dx \\
&= \frac{2}{n\pi}, \quad n \geq 1.
\end{aligned}
$$

Since f is continuous for $0 < x < 1$,

$$1 - x = \sum_{n=1}^{\infty} \frac{2}{n\pi} \sin(n\pi x), \quad 0 < x < 1,$$

and also at $x = 1$ since $f(1) = 0$, which is also the sum of the series at $x = 1$.

Example 8.18. The sine series of $f(x) = x$ on $[0, 1]$ is

$$\sum_{n=1}^{\infty} b_n \sin(n\pi x),$$

with

$$b_n = 2 \int_0^1 x \sin(n\pi x)\, dx = -\frac{2}{n\pi} x \cos(n\pi x) \Big|_0^1 + \frac{2}{n\pi} \int_0^1 \cos(n\pi x)\, dx$$

$$= \frac{2(-1)^{n-1}}{n\pi}, \quad n \geq 1.$$

Since f is continuous for $0 < x < 1$,

$$x = \sum_{n=1}^{\infty} \frac{2(-1)^{n-1}}{n\pi} \sin(n\pi x), \quad 0 < x < 1,$$

and also at $x = 0$ since $f(0) = 0$, which is also the sum of the series at $x = 0$. The graphs of the odd extension f_1 of f to $[-1, 1]$ and the odd, 2-periodic extension $\tilde{f}$ of f to $\mathbb{R}$ are displayed in Figures 8.13 and 8.14, respectively.

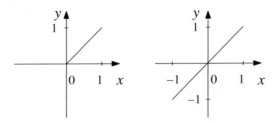

Figure 8.13: The graphs of $f(x) = x$ on $[0, 1]$ and its odd extension f_1 to $[-1, 1]$.

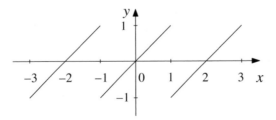

Figure 8.14: The graph of the odd, 2-periodic extension $\tilde{f}$ of f to $\mathbb{R}$.

The odd extension f_1 of f to $[-1, 1]$ is defined by $f_1(x) = x$.

Example 8.19. Let $f(x) = \left\{ \begin{array}{ll} 1, & 0 \leq x \leq 1 \\ 0, & 1 < x \leq 2 \end{array} \right\}$. The sine series of f on $[0, 2]$ is

$$\sum_{n=1}^{\infty} b_n \sin\left(\frac{n\pi x}{2}\right),$$

with

$$
\begin{aligned}
b_n &= \int_0^2 f(x) \sin\left(\frac{n\pi x}{2}\right) dx = \int_0^1 \sin\left(\frac{n\pi x}{2}\right) dx \\
&= \left. -\frac{2}{n\pi} \cos\left(\frac{n\pi x}{2}\right) \right|_0^1 \\
&= \frac{2}{n\pi}\left[1 - \cos\left(\frac{n\pi}{2}\right)\right], \quad n \geq 1.
\end{aligned}
$$

Since f is continuous for $0 < x < 2$ except at $x = 1$,

$$
f(x) = \sum_{n=1}^{\infty} \frac{2}{n\pi}\left[1 - \cos\left(\frac{n\pi}{2}\right)\right] \sin\left(\frac{n\pi x}{2}\right), \quad 0 < x < 2, \quad x \neq 1.
$$

At $x = 1$, the series converges to the average value $\frac{1}{2}$ of f.

Suppose that f is defined on an interval of the form $[0, L]$, $L > 0$, and that a Fourier cosine series representation of f on $[0, L]$ is required. Since a cosine series is the Fourier series of an even function, the extension $\tilde{f}$ of f to $\mathbb{R}$ must be an even function.

Definition 8.13. Let f be defined on $[0, L]$, and let f_1 be an extension of f to $[-L, L]$. If f_1 is an even function, then f_1 is called the *even extension of f to $[-L, L]$*.

Definition 8.14. Let f be defined on $[0, L]$, let f_1 be the even extension of f to $[-L, L]$, and let $\tilde{f}$ be the $2L$-periodic extension of f_1 to $\mathbb{R}$. Then $\tilde{f}$ is called the *even, $2L$-periodic extension of f to $\mathbb{R}$*.

Definition 8.15. Let f be defined on $[0, L]$. The *Fourier cosine series of f on $[0, L]$* is the Fourier series of the even, $2L$-periodic extension $\tilde{f}$ of f to $\mathbb{R}$, i.e.,

$$
\frac{a_0}{2} + \sum_{n=1}^{\infty} a_n \cos\left(\frac{n\pi x}{L}\right), \tag{8.12}
$$

with

$$
a_n = \frac{2}{L} \int_0^L \tilde{f}(x) \cos\left(\frac{n\pi x}{L}\right) dx = \frac{2}{L} \int_0^L f(x) \cos\left(\frac{n\pi x}{L}\right) dx, \quad n \geq 0, \tag{8.13}
$$

employing the fact that $\tilde{f}(x) = f(x)$ for $0 \leq x \leq L$.

The cosine series of f on $[0, L]$ can be determined directly by Equations (8.12) and (8.13), without any reference to the extension $\tilde{f}$. Knowledge of $\tilde{f}$ is required only if the sum of the series at points $x \leq 0$ or $x \geq L$ needs to be determined.

Example 8.20. Let $f(x) = 1 - x$ on $[0, 1]$. The graphs of the even extension f_1 of f to $[-1, 1]$ and the even, 2-periodic extension $\tilde{f}$ of f to $\mathbb{R}$ are displayed in Figures 8.15 and 8.16, respectively.

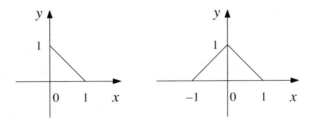

Figure 8.15: The graphs of f and its even extension f_1 to $[-1, 1]$.

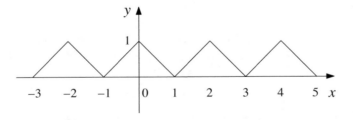

Figure 8.16: The graph of the even, 2-periodic extension $\tilde{f}$ of f to $\mathbb{R}$.

The even extension f_1 of f to $[-1, 1]$ is defined by $f_1(x) = \left\{ \begin{array}{ll} 1 + x, & -1 \leq x \leq 0 \\ 1 - x, & 0 \leq x \leq 1 \end{array} \right\}$.

The cosine series of f on $[0, 1]$ is

$$\frac{a_0}{2} + \sum_{n=1}^{\infty} a_n \cos(n\pi x),$$

with

$$
\begin{aligned}
a_0 &= 2\int_0^1 (1-x)\,dx = 1,\\[2mm]
a_n &= 2\int_0^1 (1-x)\cos(n\pi x)\,dx = \frac{2}{n\pi}(1-x)\sin(n\pi x)\Big|_0^1 + \frac{2}{n\pi}\int_0^1 \sin(n\pi x)\,dx\\[2mm]
&= -\frac{2}{n^2\pi^2}\cos(n\pi x)\Big|_0^1\\[2mm]
&= \frac{2}{n^2\pi^2}[1-(-1)^n],\quad n\geq 1.
\end{aligned}
$$

Since $\tilde{f}$ is continuous for $0\leq x\leq 1$,

$$
1-x = \frac{1}{2} + \sum_{n=1}^{\infty}\frac{2[1-(-1)^n]}{n^2\pi^2}\cos(n\pi x),\quad 0\leq x\leq 1.
$$

Example 8.21. Let $f(x) = x$ on $[0,1]$. The graphs of the even extension f_1 of f to $[-1,1]$ and the even, 2-periodic extension $\tilde{f}$ of f to $\mathbb{R}$ are displayed in Figures 8.17 and 8.18, respectively.

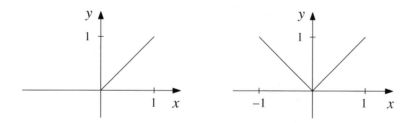

Figure 8.17: The graphs of $f(x) = x$ on $[0,1]$ and its even extension f_1 to $[-1,1]$.

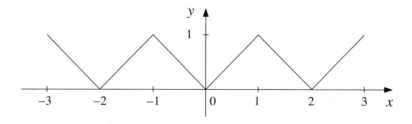

Figure 8.18: The graph of the even, 2-periodic extension $\tilde{f}$ of f to $\mathbb{R}$.

The even extension f_1 of f to $[-1, 1]$ is defined by $f_1(x) = |x|$.

The cosine series of f on $[0, 1]$ is

$$\frac{a_0}{2} + \sum_{n=1}^{\infty} a_n \cos(n\pi x),$$

with

$$a_0 = 2 \int_0^1 x \, dx = 1,$$

$$a_n = 2 \int_0^1 x \cos(n\pi x) \, dx = \frac{2}{n\pi} x \sin(n\pi x) \Big|_0^1 - \frac{2}{n\pi} \int_0^1 \sin(n\pi x) \, dx$$

$$= \frac{2}{n^2\pi^2} \cos(n\pi x) \Big|_0^1$$

$$= \frac{2}{n^2\pi^2} [(-1)^n - 1], \quad n \geq 1.$$

Since $\tilde{f}$ is continuous for $0 \leq x \leq 1$,

$$x = \frac{1}{2} + \sum_{n=1}^{\infty} \frac{2[(-1)^n - 1]}{n^2\pi^2} \cos(n\pi x), \quad 0 \leq x \leq 1.$$

Since $(-1)^n - 1 = 0$ if $n = 2k$ is even and $(-1)^n - 1 = -2$ if $n = 2k + 1$ is odd, the last equation becomes

$$x = \frac{1}{2} + \sum_{k=0}^{\infty} \frac{-4}{(2k+1)^2\pi^2} \cos[(2k+1)\pi x], \quad 0 \leq x \leq 1.$$

Setting $x = 1$ and employing the fact that $\cos[(2k+1)\pi] = -1$ for all $k \geq 0$, we obtain

$$1 = \frac{1}{2} + \sum_{k=0}^{\infty} \frac{4}{(2k+1)^2\pi^2},$$

which gives

$$\sum_{k=0}^{\infty} \frac{1}{(2k+1)^2} = \frac{\pi^2}{8}.$$

In addition, since

$$\sum_{n=1}^{\infty} \frac{1}{n^2} = \sum_{k=1}^{\infty} \frac{1}{(2k)^2} + \sum_{k=0}^{\infty} \frac{1}{(2k+1)^2} = \frac{1}{4} \sum_{k=1}^{\infty} \frac{1}{k^2} + \sum_{k=0}^{\infty} \frac{1}{(2k+1)^2},$$

we obtain

$$\frac{3}{4} \sum_{n=1}^{\infty} \frac{1}{n^2} = \frac{\pi^2}{8}, \quad \text{i.e.,} \quad \sum_{n=1}^{\infty} \frac{1}{n^2} = \frac{\pi^2}{6}.$$

Example 8.22. Let $f(x) = \left\{ \begin{array}{ll} 2, & 0 \le x < 1 \\ 1, & 1 \le x \le 2 \end{array} \right\}$. Its cosine series is

$$\frac{a_0}{2} + \sum_{n=1}^{\infty} a_n \cos\left(\frac{n\pi x}{2}\right),$$

with

$$
\begin{aligned}
a_0 &= \int_0^2 f(x)\, dx = \int_0^1 2\, dx + \int_1^2 1\, dx = 2 + 1 = 3, \\
a_n &= \int_0^2 f(x) \cos\left(\frac{n\pi x}{2}\right) dx = \int_0^1 2\cos\left(\frac{n\pi x}{2}\right) dx + \int_1^2 \cos\left(\frac{n\pi x}{2}\right) dx \\
&= \frac{4}{n\pi} \sin\left(\frac{n\pi x}{2}\right)\Big|_0^1 + \frac{2}{n\pi} \sin\left(\frac{n\pi x}{2}\right)\Big|_1^2 \\
&= \frac{4}{n\pi} \sin\left(\frac{n\pi}{2}\right) - \frac{2}{n\pi} \sin\left(\frac{n\pi}{2}\right) \\
&= \frac{2}{n\pi} \sin\left(\frac{n\pi}{2}\right), \quad n \ge 1.
\end{aligned}
$$

Since f is continuous on $[0,2]$ except at $x = 1$ and $\tilde{f}$ is an even extension, $\tilde{f}$ is continuous on $[0,2]$ except at $x = 1$. Hence,

$$f(x) = \frac{3}{2} + \sum_{n=1}^{\infty} \frac{2}{n\pi} \sin\left(\frac{n\pi}{2}\right) \cos\left(\frac{n\pi x}{2}\right), \quad 0 \le x \le 2, \quad x \ne 1.$$

At $x = 1$, the series converges to the average value $\dfrac{3}{2}$ of f. This is evident from the series, since

$$2 \sin\left(\frac{n\pi}{2}\right) \cos\left(\frac{n\pi}{2}\right) = \sin(n\pi) = 0.$$

Exercises 8.2

1. Suppose that the function f is defined on the interval $[0,6]$. Determine the form of its Fourier series.

2. Suppose that the function f is defined on the interval $[-3,5]$. Determine the form of its Fourier series.

3. Let $f(x) = \left\{ \begin{array}{ll} 1, & 0 \le x < 1 \\ 2, & 1 \le x \le 2 \end{array} \right\}$. Find the Fourier series of f.

4. Let $f(x) = \left\{ \begin{array}{ll} 2, & 0 \le x \le \pi \\ 0, & \pi < x \le 2\pi \end{array} \right\}$. Find the Fourier series of f.

5. Let $f(x) = x$ on $[2,4]$. Find the Fourier series of f.

6. Let $f(x) = x^3$ on $[1, 3]$. Find the Fourier series of f.

7. Suppose that the function f is defined on the interval $[0, 6]$. Determine the form of its Fourier sine series.

8. Let $f(x) = \left\{ \begin{array}{ll} x, & 0 \le x < 1 \\ 0, & 1 \le x \le 2 \end{array} \right\}$. Find the Fourier sine series of f.

9. Let $f(x) = \left\{ \begin{array}{ll} x, & 0 \le x < 1 \\ 2 - x, & 1 \le x \le 2 \end{array} \right\}$. Find the Fourier sine series of f.

10. Let $f(x) = x^2$ for $0 \le x \le 2$.

    (a) Find the Fourier sine series of f.

    (b) Sketch the graph of the odd, 4-periodic extension $\tilde{f}$ of f to $\mathbb{R}$.

    (c) Determine the points x in $[0, 2]$ where the series converges to $f(x)$.

    (d) Determine the numbers to which the sine series of f converges at $x = 3$, $x = 8$ and $x = -10$.

11. Suppose that the function f is defined on the interval $[0, 6]$. Determine the form of its Fourier cosine series.

12. Let $f(x) = \left\{ \begin{array}{ll} 1, & 0 \le x < \frac{1}{2} \\ 2, & \frac{1}{2} \le x \le 1 \end{array} \right\}$. Find the Fourier cosine series of f.

13. Let $f(x) = x^3$ on $[0, 1]$. Find the Fourier cosine series of f.

14. Let $f(x) = \sin(x)$ on $[0, 3]$. Find the Fourier cosine series of f.

15. Let $f(x) = x^2$ on $[-2, 2]$.

    (a) Sketch the graph of the 4-periodic extension $\tilde{f}$ of f to $\mathbb{R}$.

    (b) Determine all points x where the Fourier series of f converges to $\tilde{f}(x)$.

    (c) Find the Fourier series of f.

16. Let $f(x) = \left\{ \begin{array}{ll} x, & 0 \le x < 1 \\ 1, & 1 \le x \le 2 \end{array} \right\}$.

    (a) Sketch the graph of the odd, 4-periodic extension $\tilde{f}$ of f to $\mathbb{R}$.

    (b) Find the Fourier sine series of f. Determine the points x in $[0, 2]$ where the series converges to $f(x)$.

    (c) Determine the numbers to which the sine series of f converges at $x = 0$, $x = 1$, $x = 2$, $x = 78$ and $x = 79$.

    (d) Sketch the graph of the even, 4-periodic extension $\tilde{f}$ of f to $\mathbb{R}$.

(e) Find the Fourier cosine series of f. Determine the points x in $[0, 2]$ where the series converges to $f(x)$.

(f) Determine the numbers to which the cosine series of f converges at $x = 0$, $x = 1$, $x = 2$, $x = 78$ and $x = 79$.

17. Let f be defined on the interval $[0, \pi]$ by $f(x) = \left\{ \begin{array}{ll} 1, & 0 \leq x < \frac{\pi}{2} \\ 0, & \frac{\pi}{2} \leq x \leq \pi \end{array} \right\}$.

(a) Find the Fourier sine series of f. Determine the points x in $[0, \pi]$ where the series converges to $f(x)$.

(b) Find the Fourier cosine series of f. Determine the points x in $[0, \pi]$ where the series converges to $f(x)$.

(c) Find the Fourier series of f. Determine the points x in $[0, \pi]$ where the series converges to $f(x)$.

(d) Simplify the series in part (c) and select a suitable value of x in order to deduce the sum of the series $\displaystyle\sum_{k=0}^{\infty} \frac{(-1)^k}{2k + 1}$.

Chapter 8 Exercises

1. Let $f(x) = \left\{ \begin{array}{ll} x - 3, & 3 \leq x < 4 \\ 1, & 4 \leq x < 5 \\ 6 - x, & 5 \leq x \leq 6 \end{array} \right\}$.

(a) Sketch the graph of the 3-periodic extension $\tilde{f}$ of f to $\mathbb{R}$.

(b) Find the Fourier series of f.

(c) Determine all points x where the Fourier series of f converges to $\tilde{f}(x)$.

2. Suppose that f and f' are continuous on $[0, L]$, and let $F(x)$, $S(x)$ and $C(x)$ denote the Fourier series, the sine series and the cosine series of f, respectively. By analyzing the suitable extensions $\tilde{f}$ of f to $\mathbb{R}$ in each case, determine the conditions under which:

(a) $F(x) = f(x)$ at $x = 0$; $F(x) = f(x)$ at $x = L$.

(b) $S(x) = f(x)$ at $x = 0$; $S(x) = f(x)$ at $x = L$.

(c) $C(x) = f(x)$ at $x = 0$; $C(x) = f(x)$ at $x = L$.

3. (a) Let $L > 0$ and $y_n(x) = \sin\left(\frac{n\pi x}{L}\right)$, $n \geq 1$. Show that

$$\int_0^L y_n(x) y_m(x) \, dx = 0 \quad \text{if} \quad n \neq m.$$

In this case, the functions y_n and y_m with $n \neq m$ are said to be *orthogonal* on $[0, L]$, and the set of functions $\{y_n,\ n \geq 1\}$ is called an *orthogonal family* on $[0, L]$.

(b) Let $L > 0$ and $y_n(x) = \cos\left(\dfrac{n\pi x}{L}\right)$, $n \geq 0$. Show that the set of functions $\{y_n,\ n \geq 0\}$ is an orthogonal family on $[0, L]$.

(c) At the beginning of Section 8.1 and in Exercise 3 in Section 8.1, the Euler-Fourier formulas for the coefficients a_n and b_n of a Fourier series were determined by employing the fact that the set of functions

$$\left\{\cos\left(\frac{n\pi x}{L}\right),\ n \geq 0;\ \sin\left(\frac{m\pi x}{L}\right),\ m \geq 1\right\}$$

is an orthogonal family on $[-L, L]$. Employ part (a) to show (formally) that if

$$f(x) = \sum_{n=1}^{\infty} b_n \sin\left(\frac{n\pi x}{L}\right),$$

then

$$b_n = \frac{2}{L}\int_0^L f(x)\sin\left(\frac{n\pi x}{L}\right)dx, \quad n \geq 1.$$

(d) Similarly, employ part (b) to show that if

$$f(x) = \frac{a_0}{2} + \sum_{n=1}^{\infty} a_n \cos\left(\frac{n\pi x}{L}\right),$$

then

$$a_n = \frac{2}{L}\int_0^L f(x)\cos\left(\frac{n\pi x}{L}\right)dx, \quad n \geq 0.$$

4. Suppose that f and g are continuous and $2L$-periodic, and that f' and g' are piecewise continuous. Let

$$\frac{a_0}{2} + \sum_{n=1}^{\infty}\left[a_n \cos\left(\frac{n\pi x}{L}\right) + b_n \sin\left(\frac{n\pi x}{L}\right)\right]$$

be the Fourier series of f, and

$$\frac{c_0}{2} + \sum_{n=1}^{\infty}\left[c_n \cos\left(\frac{n\pi x}{L}\right) + d_n \sin\left(\frac{n\pi x}{L}\right)\right]$$

the Fourier series of g. Prove that if the two series are equal for all x, then $a_n = c_n$ for all $n \geq 0$ and $b_n = d_n$ for all $n \geq 1$. (The analogous results hold for sine series if f and g are odd, and for cosine series if they are even.)

5. (a) Let

$$f(x) = 2\sin\left(\frac{\pi x}{3}\right) - 3\sin\left(\frac{4\pi x}{3}\right) + 4\sin\left(\frac{5\pi x}{3}\right).$$

Determine the fundamental period of f and find its Fourier sine series by computing its sine coefficients, employing the appropriate Euler-Fourier formulas and Exercise 3(a). Find the sine series of f by employing the result of Exercise 4.

(b) Let

$$f(x) = 3 - \cos\left(\frac{3\pi x}{4}\right) + 2\cos\left(\frac{6\pi x}{4}\right) + 5\cos\left(\frac{7\pi x}{4}\right) + 3\cos(4\pi x).$$

Determine the fundamental period of f and find its Fourier cosine series.

(c) Let

$$f(x) = \frac{1}{2} - 2\cos\left(\frac{\pi x}{2}\right) + \cos\left(\frac{3\pi x}{2}\right) + 3\sin\left(\frac{7\pi x}{2}\right) - 5\sin\left(\frac{9\pi x}{2}\right).$$

Determine the fundamental period of f and find its Fourier series.

Chapter 9

Series Solutions of Differential Equations

9.1 Solutions About Ordinary Points

Definition 9.1. Consider the second-order, linear, homogeneous equation

$$y'' + p(x)y' + q(x)y = 0,$$

and let x_0 be a given point. If both of the functions p and q are analytic at x_0, then the point x_0 is called an *ordinary point* of the equation. If at least one of p and q is singular at x_0, then x_0 is called a *singular point* or *singularity* of the equation.

Example 9.1. Consider the equation

$$y'' - xy' + e^x y = 0,$$

with $p(x) = -x$ and $q(x) = e^x$. Since both p and q are analytic at every point x_0, every point is an ordinary point of the equation.

Example 9.2. Consider the equation

$$(x - 2)y'' + e^x y' - \frac{1}{x}y = 0.$$

In standard form, the equation becomes

$$y'' + \frac{e^x}{x - 2}y' - \frac{1}{x(x - 2)}y = 0,$$

with $p(x) = \dfrac{e^x}{x - 2}$ and $q(x) = -\dfrac{1}{x(x - 2)}$. Since p is analytic at every $x_0 \neq 2$, and q is analytic at every $x_0 \neq 0$ or 2, the points $x_0 = 0$ and $x_0 = 2$ are singular points, and all other points are ordinary.

317

Theorem 9.1. If x_0 is an ordinary point of the differential equation

$$y'' + p(x)y' + q(x)y = 0,$$

then the general solution is analytic at x_0, and is therefore given by

$$y = \sum_{n=0}^{\infty} a_n (x - x_0)^n, \quad |x - x_0| < R,$$

with two of the coefficients (usually a_0 and a_1) being arbitrary. Moreover, the radius of convergence R is at least as great as the distance from x_0 to the singular point x_1 of the equation which is closest to x_0. If the equation has no singular points, then $R = \infty$.

Example 9.3. The equation

$$y'' - 2y' + \frac{1}{x - 1} y = 0$$

has a singular point at $x_1 = 1$, and all other points are ordinary. The series solution

$$y = \sum_{n=0}^{\infty} a_n x^n$$

about $x_0 = 0$ has radius of convergence $R \geq 1$, the distance from the expansion point $x_0 = 0$ to the nearest singular point $x_1 = 1$, by the last part of Theorem 9.1. The series solution

$$y = \sum_{n=0}^{\infty} b_n \left(x - \frac{1}{4} \right)^n$$

about $x_0 = \frac{1}{4}$ has radius of convergence $R \geq \frac{3}{4}$, the distance from the expansion point $x_0 = \frac{1}{4}$ to the nearest singular point $x_1 = 1$.

Example 9.4. Complex singularities cannot be ignored. The equation

$$y'' + \frac{1}{x^2 + 1} y' + y = 0$$

has singular points at $x_1 = \pm i$. The series solution

$$\sum_{n=0}^{\infty} a_n x^n$$

about $x_0 = 0$ has radius of convergence $R \geq 1$, the distance from 0 to $\pm i$. The series solution

$$\sum_{n=0}^{\infty} a_n(x-2)^n$$

about $x_0 = 2$ has radius of convergence $R \geq \sqrt{5}$, the distance from 2 to $\pm i$. We *cannot* conclude that $R = \infty$ due to the absence of any real singularities.

Example 9.5. Consider the equation

$$y'' + xy' + y = 0.$$

Since $p(x) = x$ and $q(x) = 1$ are analytic at every point x_0 and, in particular, at $x_0 = 0$, the general solution can be expressed as

$$y(x) = \sum_{n=0}^{\infty} a_n x^n,$$

by Theorem 9.1. By Theorem 7.2, the derivatives of y may be obtained by termwise differentiation of the series, and substitution of y, y' and y'' into the differential equation will result in a relation amongst the coefficients a_n, $n \geq 0$, from which every a_n and, hence, y, may be determined. Thus,

$$y = \sum_{n=0}^{\infty} a_n x^n \quad \Rightarrow \quad y' = \sum_{n=0}^{\infty} n a_n x^{n-1} \quad \Rightarrow \quad y'' = \sum_{n=0}^{\infty} n(n-1) a_n x^{n-2},$$

and y is a solution of the differential equation if and only if

$$\sum_{n=0}^{\infty} n(n-1) a_n x^{n-2} + x \sum_{n=0}^{\infty} n a_n x^{n-1} + \sum_{n=0}^{\infty} a_n x^n = 0,$$

i.e.,

$$\sum_{n=0}^{\infty} n(n-1) a_n x^{n-2} + \sum_{n=0}^{\infty} n a_n x^n + \sum_{n=0}^{\infty} a_n x^n = 0. \tag{9.1}$$

In the first series, the term $n(n-1) = 0$ when $n = 0$ and when $n = 1$. Hence,

$$\sum_{n=0}^{\infty} n(n-1) a_n x^{n-2} = \sum_{n=2}^{\infty} n(n-1) a_n x^{n-2}.$$

Make the *change of index* $n \to n+2$ to obtain

$$\sum_{n=2}^{\infty} n(n-1) a_n x^{n-2} = \sum_{n+2=2}^{\infty} (n+2)(n+1) a_{n+2} x^n = \sum_{n=0}^{\infty} (n+2)(n+1) a_{n+2} x^n.$$

Condition (9.1) then becomes

$$\sum_{n=0}^{\infty}(n+2)(n+1)a_{n+2}x^n + \sum_{n=0}^{\infty} na_n x^n + \sum_{n=0}^{\infty} a_n x^n = 0.$$

Since all three series now have precisely the same form (i.e., they have the same power of x and the same initial value of n), they may be combined into a single series by adding their coefficients. Thus,

$$\sum_{n=0}^{\infty}(n+2)(n+1)a_{n+2}x^n + \sum_{n=0}^{\infty} na_n x^n + \sum_{n=0}^{\infty} a_n x^n$$

$$= \sum_{n=0}^{\infty}\left[(n+2)(n+1)a_{n+2} + (n+1)a_n\right]x^n = 0.$$

By the statement preceding Example 7.18 on page 259, it follows that

$$(n+2)(n+1)a_{n+2} + (n+1)a_n = 0$$

for all $n \geq 0$. Dividing by $n + 1 \neq 0$ and solving for a_{n+2} in terms of a_n, we obtain

$$a_{n+2} = -\frac{a_n}{n+2}, \quad n \geq 0,$$

called the *coefficient recursion* (or *recurrence*) *relation*. This relation must be solved in order to determine every a_n explicitly in terms of n. The form of the relation shows that the a_n with n even are determined by a_0, and the ones with n odd are determined by a_1. For the coefficients a_n with $n = 2k$ even,

$$n = 0 \quad \Rightarrow \quad a_2 = -\frac{a_0}{2},$$

$$n = 2 \quad \Rightarrow \quad a_4 = -\frac{a_2}{4} = \frac{a_0}{2\cdot 4} = \frac{a_0}{2^2(1\cdot 2)},$$

$$n = 4 \quad \Rightarrow \quad a_6 = -\frac{a_4}{6} = -\frac{a_0}{2\cdot 4\cdot 6} = -\frac{a_0}{2^3(1\cdot 2\cdot 3)},$$

$$n = 6 \quad \Rightarrow \quad a_8 = -\frac{a_6}{8} = \frac{a_0}{2\cdot 4\cdot 6\cdot 8} = \frac{a_0}{2^4(1\cdot 2\cdot 3\cdot 4)},$$

and the emerging pattern indicates that

$$a_{2k} = \frac{(-1)^k a_0}{2^k k!}, \quad k \geq 0.$$

For the coefficients a_n with $n = 2k + 1$ odd,

$$n = 1 \quad \Rightarrow \quad a_3 = -\frac{a_1}{3},$$

$$n = 3 \quad \Rightarrow \quad a_5 = -\frac{a_3}{5} = \frac{a_1}{3\cdot 5},$$

$$n = 5 \quad \Rightarrow \quad a_7 = -\frac{a_5}{7} = -\frac{a_1}{3\cdot 5\cdot 7},$$

and, in general,

$$a_{2k+1} = \frac{(-1)^k a_1}{3 \cdot 5 \cdot 7 \cdots (2k+1)}, \quad k \geq 1.$$

In order to express a_{2k+1} in a more concise form, multiply it by $\dfrac{2 \cdot 4 \cdot 6 \cdots (2k)}{2 \cdot 4 \cdot 6 \cdots (2k)} = 1$ to obtain

$$a_{2k+1} = \frac{(-1)^k a_1 \cdot 2 \cdot 4 \cdot 6 \cdots (2k)}{2 \cdot 3 \cdot 4 \cdot 5 \cdot 6 \cdot 7 \cdots (2k)(2k+1)} = \frac{(-1)^k 2^k k! \, a_1}{(2k+1)!}, \quad k \geq 0.$$

The solution is therefore given by

$$
\begin{aligned}
y(x) &= \sum_{n=0}^{\infty} a_n x^n = \sum_{k=0}^{\infty} a_{2k} x^{2k} + \sum_{k=0}^{\infty} a_{2k+1} x^{2k+1} \\
&= a_0 \sum_{k=0}^{\infty} \frac{(-1)^k}{2^k k!} x^{2k} + a_1 \sum_{k=0}^{\infty} \frac{(-1)^k 2^k k!}{(2k+1)!} x^{2k+1} \\
&= a_0 y_1(x) + a_1 y_2(x),
\end{aligned}
$$

where

$$y_1(x) = \sum_{k=0}^{\infty} \frac{(-1)^k}{2^k k!} x^{2k} \quad \text{and} \quad y_2(x) = \sum_{k=0}^{\infty} \frac{(-1)^k 2^k k!}{(2k+1)!} x^{2k+1}.$$

Since there are no restrictions upon the constants a_0 and a_1, they are both arbitrary. Setting $a_0 = 1$ and $a_1 = 0$ gives the solution $y = y_1$, and setting $a_0 = 0$ and $a_1 = 1$ gives the solution $y = y_2$. Moreover, since $y_1(0) = 1 \neq 0$ and $y_2(0) = 0$, y_1 and y_2 are linearly independent. Thus, $y = a_0 y_1 + a_1 y_2$ is the general solution, as guaranteed by Theorem 9.1. Since the equation has no singularities, $R = \infty$.

Note that the solution

$$y_1(x) = \sum_{k=0}^{\infty} \frac{(-1)^k}{2^k k!} x^{2k} = \sum_{k=0}^{\infty} \frac{1}{k!} \left(-\frac{x^2}{2} \right)^k = e^{-\frac{x^2}{2}}$$

is an *elementary function*, but y_2 is not.

Since

$$y = \sum_{n=0}^{\infty} a_n x^n,$$

it follows by Theorem 7.4 that

$$a_n = \frac{y^{(n)}(0)}{n!}, \quad n \geq 0.$$

In particular,
$$a_0 = y(0) \quad \text{and} \quad a_1 = y'(0).$$
Hence, if initial conditions are given, then a_0 and a_1 are determined.

For example, if $y(0) = 2$ and $y'(0) = 0$, then $a_0 = 2$ and $a_1 = 0$, from which it follows by the recursion relation that $a_{2k+1} = 0$ for all $k \geq 0$, and the solution of the initial-value problem is $y = 2y_1 = 2e^{-\frac{x^2}{2}}$.

Example 9.6.   Consider the equation
$$(x^2 + 1)y'' + xy' - 4y = 0.$$
Since
$$p(x) = \frac{x}{x^2 + 1} \quad \text{and} \quad q(x) = \frac{-4}{x^2 + 1}$$
are analytic at $x_0 = 0$, the point 0 is an ordinary point of the equation and, hence, Theorem 9.1 applies. Thus,
$$y = \sum_{n=0}^{\infty} a_n x^n \quad \Rightarrow \quad y' = \sum_{n=0}^{\infty} n a_n x^{n-1} \quad \Rightarrow \quad y'' = \sum_{n=0}^{\infty} n(n-1) a_n x^{n-2},$$
and y is a solution of the differential equation if and only if
$$(1 + x^2) \sum_{n=0}^{\infty} n(n-1) a_n x^{n-2} + x \sum_{n=0}^{\infty} n a_n x^{n-1} - 4 \sum_{n=0}^{\infty} a_n x^n = 0,$$
i.e.,
$$\sum_{n=0}^{\infty} n(n-1) a_n x^{n-2} + \sum_{n=0}^{\infty} n(n-1) a_n x^n + \sum_{n=0}^{\infty} n a_n x^n - \sum_{n=0}^{\infty} 4 a_n x^n = 0.$$
Combining the last three series, we obtain the condition
$$\sum_{n=0}^{\infty} n(n-1) a_n x^{n-2} + \sum_{n=0}^{\infty} (n^2 - 4) a_n x^n = 0,$$
and, making the change of index $n \to n + 2$ in the first series, we obtain
$$\sum_{n=0}^{\infty} (n+1)(n+2) a_{n+2} x^n + \sum_{n=0}^{\infty} (n^2 - 4) a_n x^n = 0,$$
i.e.,
$$\sum_{n=0}^{\infty} \left[(n+1)(n+2) a_{n+2} + (n-2)(n+2) a_n \right] x^n = 0.$$

The coefficient recursion relation is therefore

$$(n+1)(n+2)a_{n+2} + (n-2)(n+2)a_n = 0,$$

or, since $n + 2 \neq 0$ for $n \geq 0$,

$$a_{n+2} = -\frac{(n-2)a_n}{n+1} = \frac{(2-n)a_n}{n+1}, \quad n \geq 0.$$

For the coefficients a_n with n even,

$$n = 0 \;\Rightarrow\; a_2 = 2a_0,$$
$$n = 2 \;\Rightarrow\; a_4 = 0,$$
$$n = 4 \;\Rightarrow\; a_6 = 0,$$

etc.; hence, $a_{2k} = 0$ for $k \geq 2$.

For the coefficients a_n with n odd,

$$n = 1 \;\Rightarrow\; a_3 = \frac{a_1}{2},$$
$$n = 3 \;\Rightarrow\; a_5 = \frac{-a_3}{4} = \frac{-a_1}{2 \cdot 4},$$
$$n = 5 \;\Rightarrow\; a_7 = \frac{-3a_5}{6} = \frac{3a_1}{2 \cdot 4 \cdot 6},$$
$$n = 7 \;\Rightarrow\; a_9 = \frac{-5a_7}{8} = \frac{-3 \cdot 5a_1}{2 \cdot 4 \cdot 6 \cdot 8},$$
$$n = 9 \;\Rightarrow\; a_{11} = \frac{-7a_9}{10} = \frac{3 \cdot 5 \cdot 7a_1}{2 \cdot 4 \cdot 6 \cdot 8 \cdot 10},$$

etc., and, in general,

$$
\begin{aligned}
a_{2k+1} &= \frac{(-1)^{k-1}1 \cdot 3 \cdot 5 \cdot 7 \cdots (2k-3)a_1}{2 \cdot 4 \cdot 6 \cdot 8 \cdot 10 \cdots (2k)} \\
&= \frac{(-1)^{k-1}1 \cdot 3 \cdot 5 \cdot 7 \cdots (2k-3)a_1}{2^k k!} \\
&= \frac{(-1)^{k-1}1 \cdot 3 \cdot 5 \cdot 7 \cdots (2k-3)a_1}{2^k k!} \frac{2 \cdot 4 \cdot 6 \cdot 8 \cdot 10 \cdots (2k-2)}{2 \cdot 4 \cdot 6 \cdot 8 \cdot 10 \cdots (2k-2)} \\
&= \frac{(-1)^{k-1}(2k-2)!a_1}{2^{2k-1}k!(k-1)!}, \quad k \geq 1.
\end{aligned}
$$

Hence,

$$
\begin{aligned}
y &= \sum_{n=0}^{\infty} a_n x^n = \sum_{k=0}^{\infty} a_{2k} x^{2k} + \sum_{k=0}^{\infty} a_{2k+1} x^{2k+1} \\
&= a_0 + 2a_0 x^2 + a_1 x + \sum_{k=1}^{\infty} \frac{(-1)^{k-1}(2k-2)! a_1}{2^{2k-1} k! (k-1)!} x^{2k+1} \\
&= a_0(1 + 2x^2) + a_1 \left[x + \sum_{k=1}^{\infty} \frac{(-1)^{k-1}(2k-2)!}{2^{2k-1} k! (k-1)!} x^{2k+1} \right] \\
&= a_0 y_1 + a_1 y_2
\end{aligned}
$$

is the general solution, where

$$
y_1 = 1 + 2x^2 \quad \text{and} \quad y_2 = x + \sum_{k=1}^{\infty} \frac{(-1)^{k-1}(2k-2)!}{2^{2k-1} k! (k-1)!} x^{2k+1}.
$$

Thus, y_1 is an elementary function, but y_2 is not.

Suppose that the initial conditions $y(0) = -3$ and $y'(0) = 6$ are given. Since $y(0) = a_0$ and $y'(0) = a_1$, the solution of the initial-value problem is

$$
y = -3y_1 + 6y_2.
$$

Of course, if $y(0) = 0$, then $a_0 = 0$ and y_1 need not be computed, and if $y'(0) = 0$, then $a_1 = 0$ and y_2 need not be computed.

By Theorem 9.1, since the only singularities of the equation are $x_1 = \pm i$, and the distance from $x_0 = 0$ to $x_1 = \pm i$ is 1, the radius of convergence of the general solution, as well as that of any particular solution, is $R \geq 1$.

Since y_1 is a polynomial, i.e., a finite Taylor series, it radius of convergence is $R_1 = \infty$. In order to determine the precise value of the radius of convergence R_2 of y_2, we employ the ratio test. Thus, with $y_2(x) = x + \sum_{k=1}^{\infty} c_k(x)$,

$$
\begin{aligned}
\lim_{k \to \infty} \left| \frac{c_{k+1}(x)}{c_k(x)} \right| &= \lim_{k \to \infty} \left| \frac{(2k)! x^{2k+3}}{2^{2k+1}(k+1)! k!} \frac{2^{2k-1} k! (k-1)!}{(2k-2)! x^{2k+1}} \right| \\
&= |x|^2 \lim_{k \to \infty} \frac{(2k)(2k-1)}{2^2(k+1)k} \\
&= |x|^2 < 1
\end{aligned}
$$

if $|x| < 1$. Hence, the radius of convergence R_2 of y_2 is precisely 1.

In equations where the coefficient recursion relation cannot be solved explicitly for all $n \geq 0$, approximate solutions of the differential equation can be obtained by retaining a finite number of terms of the series.

Example 9.7. Consider the equation

$$y'' + \cos(x)y = 0,$$

with $p(x) \equiv 0$ and $q(x) = \cos(x)$. Since p and q are analytic at $x_0 = 0$, the general solution is given by

$$y = \sum_{n=0}^{\infty} a_n x^n.$$

Since

$$\cos(x) = \sum_{k=0}^{\infty} \frac{(-1)^k}{(2k)!} x^{2k} = 1 - \frac{x^2}{2!} + \frac{x^4}{4!} - \frac{x^6}{6!} + \cdots$$

is an infinite series and not a polynomial, we shall retain only the first six terms in y. Thus,

$$
\begin{aligned}
y &= a_0 + a_1 x + a_2 x^2 + a_3 x^3 + a_4 x^4 + a_5 x^5 + \cdots, \\
y' &= a_1 + 2a_2 x + 3a_3 x^2 + 4a_4 x^3 + 5a_5 x^4 + \cdots, \\
y'' &= 2a_2 + 6a_3 x + 12a_4 x^2 + 20a_5 x^3 + \cdots,
\end{aligned}
$$

and y is a solution of the equation if and only if

$$\left(2a_2 + 6a_3 x + 12a_4 x^2 + 20a_5 x^3 + \cdots\right) +$$
$$\left(1 - \frac{x^2}{2} + \frac{x^4}{24} - \cdots\right)\left(a_0 + a_1 x + a_2 x^2 + a_3 x^3 + a_4 x^4 + \cdots\right) = 0.$$

Performing the multiplication and collecting terms, we obtain the condition

$$(2a_2 + a_0) + (6a_3 + a_1)x + \left(12a_4 + a_2 - \frac{1}{2}a_0\right)x^2 + \left(20a_5 + a_3 - \frac{1}{2}a_1\right)x^3 + \cdots = 0,$$

which leads to the relations

$$2a_2 + a_0 = 0, \quad 6a_3 + a_1 = 0, \quad 12a_4 + a_2 - \frac{1}{2}a_0 = 0 \quad \text{and} \quad 20a_5 + a_3 - \frac{1}{2}a_1 = 0,$$

i.e., a partial set of recursion relations for the coefficients a_n. It follows that

$$a_2 = -\frac{a_0}{2}, \quad a_4 = \frac{1}{12}\left(\frac{1}{2}a_0 - a_2\right) = \frac{a_0}{12}, \quad a_3 = -\frac{a_1}{6}, \quad a_5 = \frac{1}{20}\left(\frac{1}{2}a_1 - a_3\right) = \frac{a_1}{30},$$

and a_0 and a_1 are arbitrary. Thus,

$$
\begin{aligned}
y &= a_0 + a_1 x + a_2 x^2 + a_3 x^3 + a_4 x^4 + a_5 x^5 + \cdots \\
&= a_0 + a_1 x - \frac{1}{2} a_0 x^2 - \frac{1}{6} a_1 x^3 + \frac{1}{12} a_0 x^4 + \frac{1}{30} a_1 x^5 + \cdots \\
&= a_0 \left(1 - \frac{1}{2} x^2 + \frac{1}{12} x^4 + \cdots \right) + a_1 \left(x - \frac{1}{6} x^3 + \frac{1}{30} x^5 + \cdots \right) \\
&= a_0 y_1 + a_1 y_2,
\end{aligned}
$$

where

$$
y_1 = 1 - \frac{1}{2} x^2 + \frac{1}{12} x^4 + \cdots \quad \text{and} \quad y_2 = x - \frac{1}{6} x^3 + \frac{1}{30} x^5 + \cdots
$$

are two linearly independent solutions.

If a solution of the equation

$$
y'' + p(x) y' + q(x) y = 0 \tag{9.2}
$$

is sought about an ordinary point $x_0 \neq 0$, then the change of variables

$$
t = x - x_0, \quad y(x) = z(t), \quad p(x) = P(t), \quad q(x) = Q(t),
$$

transforms the equation into the equivalent equation

$$
z'' + P(t) z' + Q(t) z = 0, \tag{9.3}
$$

with $t = t_0 = 0$ as the ordinary point corresponding to $x = x_0$. Once the solution $z(t)$ of Equation (9.3) is determined, the solution $y(x)$ of Equation (9.2) is obtained by $y(x) = z(t) = z(x - x_0)$.

If the solution of a differential equation is sought in a neighbourhood of a singular point x_1, then Theorem 9.1 does not apply and the methods employed in the foregoing examples fail. In order to obtain such a solution, a different procedure is required, called the *Frobenius method*, a topic which is beyond the scope of this book.

Exercises 9.1

1. Determine all points x_0 where the given function is analytic.

   (a) $f(x) = \dfrac{3}{x + 2}$

   (b) $f(x) = \dfrac{x^2 + 1}{x^2 - 4}$

   (c) $f(x) = \tan(x)$

(d) $f(x) = \dfrac{x+1}{e^x - 1}$

(e) $f(x) = \sqrt{x+2}, \; x \geq -2$

2. Compute the Taylor series of $f(x) = \dfrac{x^2 - x + 1}{x + 1}$ about $x_0 = 0$ by dividing $1 + x$ into $1 - x + x^2$.

3. Consider the series $\displaystyle\sum_{n=2}^{\infty} a_n x^n$.

   (a) Write down the first four terms.

   (b) Let $n = m + 2$ and express the series as one involving the index m. Write down the first four terms.

   (c) Replace m by n in the series obtained in part (b) and write down the first four terms.

   (d) Show that step (b) may be avoided simply by replacing n by $n + 2$ in the original series.

4. Determine a_n, $n \geq 0$, if $\displaystyle\sum_{n=0}^{\infty} n a_n x^n + \sum_{n=0}^{\infty} a_n x^{n+2} = 0$.

5. Consider the differential equation $y'' + xy' + 2y = 0$.

   (a) Find the coefficient recursion relation for the general series solution about $x_0 = 0$.

   (b) Solve the recursion relation, i.e, find a_n explicitly in terms of n, and thereby obtain the general solution and two linearly independent solutions.

   (c) Write down the first four terms of each one of the two series solutions.

   (d) Express one of the series solutions as an elementary function.

   (e) Deduce the radius of convergence of each series solution.

   (f) Solve the initial-value problem for the given equation if $y(0) = 0$ and $y'(0) = 2$.

6. Consider the differential equation $(1 + x^2)y'' - 4xy' + 6y = 0$.

   (a) Find the coefficient recursion relation for the general series solution about $x_0 = 0$.

   (b) Solve the recursion relation and thereby determine the general solution and two linearly independent solutions.

   (c) Find y satisfying the given equation if $y(0) = -3$ and $y'(0) = 1$.

7. Find two linearly independent solutions of the differential equation

$$y'' + xy' - 2y = 0.$$

8. Find two linearly independent solutions of the differential equation

$$(2 + x^2)y'' + 2xy' - 2y = 0.$$

9. Consider the equation
$$y'' + e^x y = 0.$$

   (a) Find the 5th-degree Taylor polynomial $T_5(x)$ of the general solution.

   (b) Find $T_5(x)$ for each one of two independent solutions.

10. Consider *Legendre's equation of order ν*,

$$(1 - x^2)y'' - 2xy' + \nu(\nu + 1)y = 0,$$

   where ν is a constant.

   (a) Find the coefficient recursion relation for the general series solution about $x_0 = 0$.

   (b) Deduce from the recursion relation that if $\nu = m$ is a nonnegative integer, then one of the two series solutions is a polynomial $P_m(x)$ of degree m (i.e., show that $a_{m+2} = a_{m+4} = a_{m+6} = \cdots = 0$).

   (c) Impose the condition $P_m(1) = 1$ (which specifies the arbitrary constant within the polynomial solution) and find $P_m(x)$ for $0 \le m \le 3$. The polynomials $P_m(x)$, with $P_m(1) = 1$, are called *Legendre polynomials*.

9.2   Periodic Solutions

Consider the nonhomogeneous equation

$$y'' + \lambda y = f(x), \quad -\infty < x < \infty, \tag{9.4}$$

where f is $2L$-periodic and continuous, f' is piecewise continuous, and λ is a real constant. Suppose that a $2L$-periodic solution y of equation (9.4) is sought. By the Fourier convergence theorem (Theorem 8.1),

$$f(x) = \frac{a_0}{2} + \sum_{n=1}^{\infty} \left[a_n \cos\left(\frac{n\pi x}{L}\right) + b_n \sin\left(\frac{n\pi x}{L}\right) \right], \quad -\infty < x < \infty,$$

where a_n and b_n are the Fourier cosine and sine coefficients of f, respectively. Given the form of f, a $2L$-periodic solution y is sought in the form of a $2L$-periodic Fourier series, i.e.,

$$y = \frac{c_0}{2} + \sum_{n=1}^{\infty} \left[c_n \cos\left(\frac{n\pi x}{L}\right) + d_n \sin\left(\frac{n\pi x}{L}\right) \right].$$

Once the coefficients c_n and d_n have been determined formally, it can be shown that the resulting series is the Fourier series of a function y, that y' and y'' can be determined by the termwise differentiation of the series, and that y, y' and y'' are continuous. Thus,

$$y'' = \sum_{n=1}^{\infty} \left[-\frac{n^2\pi^2}{L^2} c_n \cos\left(\frac{n\pi x}{L}\right) - \frac{n^2\pi^2}{L^2} d_n \sin\left(\frac{n\pi x}{L}\right) \right],$$

and $y'' + \lambda y = f(x)$ requires that

$$-\sum_{n=1}^{\infty} \left[\frac{n^2\pi^2}{L^2} c_n \cos\left(\frac{n\pi x}{L}\right) + \frac{n^2\pi^2}{L^2} d_n \sin\left(\frac{n\pi x}{L}\right) \right]$$

$$+\lambda \left\{ \frac{c_0}{2} + \sum_{n=1}^{\infty} \left[c_n \cos\left(\frac{n\pi x}{L}\right) + d_n \sin\left(\frac{n\pi x}{L}\right) \right] \right\}$$

$$= \frac{a_0}{2} + \sum_{n=1}^{\infty} \left[a_n \cos\left(\frac{n\pi x}{L}\right) + b_n \sin\left(\frac{n\pi x}{L}\right) \right],$$

which is satisfied if

$$\lambda c_0 = a_0, \quad \left(\lambda - \frac{n^2\pi^2}{L^2} \right) c_n = a_n, \quad \text{and} \quad \left(\lambda - \frac{n^2\pi^2}{L^2} \right) d_n = b_n, \quad n \geq 1.$$

If $\lambda \neq \dfrac{n^2\pi^2}{L^2}$ for any integer $n \geq 0$, then

$$c_n = \frac{a_n}{\lambda - \frac{n^2\pi^2}{L^2}}, \quad n \geq 0, \quad \text{and} \quad d_n = \frac{b_n}{\lambda - \frac{n^2\pi^2}{L^2}}, \quad n \geq 1,$$

and the solution y is determined.

If $\lambda = 0$, then there is no periodic solution unless

$$a_0 = \frac{1}{L} \int_{-L}^{L} f(x)\, dx = 0,$$

in which case, c_0 is arbitrary, and if $\lambda = \dfrac{k^2\pi^2}{L^2}$ for an integer $k \geq 1$, then there is no periodic solution unless

$$a_k = \frac{1}{L} \int_{-L}^{L} f(x) \cos\left(\frac{k\pi x}{L}\right) dx = 0 \quad \text{and} \quad b_k = \frac{1}{L} \int_{-L}^{L} f(x) \sin\left(\frac{k\pi x}{L}\right) dx = 0,$$

in which case, c_k and d_k are arbitrary. The case where no $2L$-periodic solution exists is one of *resonance*, which occurs if the forcing term f contains a term proportional to a periodic solution of the homogeneous equation $y'' + \lambda y = 0$. The solution in that case is not periodic, but contains a term proportional to x.

Example 9.8. Let $f(x) = x^3 - 2x^2 + 1$ on $[0, 2]$ and $f(x + 2) = f(x)$ for all x. Since f is continuous on $[0, 2]$ and $f(0) = 1 = f(2)$, f is continuous everywhere and f' is piecewise continuous. Hence,

$$f(x) = \frac{a_0}{2} + \sum_{n=1}^{\infty} [a_n \cos(n\pi x) + b_n \sin(n\pi x)], \quad -\infty < x < \infty.$$

A 2-periodic solution of the equation

$$y'' + 3y = f(x)$$

is therefore sought in the form

$$y = \frac{c_0}{2} + \sum_{n=1}^{\infty} [c_n \cos(n\pi x) + d_n \sin(n\pi x)], \quad -\infty < x < \infty.$$

Since $\lambda = 3 \neq n^2\pi^2$ for any integer $n \geq 0$, and $L = 1$,

$$c_n = \frac{a_n}{3 - n^2\pi^2}, \quad n \geq 0, \quad \text{and} \quad d_n = \frac{b_n}{3 - n^2\pi^2}, \quad n \geq 1,$$

and it remains to determine the Fourier coefficients of f. Thus,

$$a_0 = \int_0^2 (x^3 - 2x^2 + 1)\, dx = \left(\frac{1}{4}x^4 - \frac{2}{3}x^3 + x \right) \Big|_0^2 = \frac{2}{3},$$

$$a_n = \int_0^2 (x^3 - 2x^2 + 1) \cos(n\pi x)\, dx$$

$$= \frac{1}{n\pi}(x^3 - 2x^2 + 1)\sin(n\pi x) \Big|_0^2 - \frac{1}{n\pi}\int_0^2 (3x^2 - 4x)\sin(n\pi x)\, dx$$

$$= \frac{1}{n^2\pi^2}(3x^2 - 4x)\cos(n\pi x) \Big|_0^2 - \frac{1}{n^2\pi^2}\int_0^2 (6x - 4)\cos(n\pi x)\, dx$$

$$= \frac{4}{n^2\pi^2} - \frac{1}{n^3\pi^3}(6x - 4)\sin(n\pi x) \Big|_0^2 + \frac{6}{n^3\pi^3}\int_0^2 \sin(n\pi x)\, dx$$

$$= \frac{4}{n^2\pi^2} - \frac{6}{n^4\pi^4}\cos(n\pi x) \Big|_0^2 = \frac{4}{n^2\pi^2}, \quad n \geq 1,$$

$$
\begin{aligned}
b_n &= \int_0^2 (x^3 - 2x^2 + 1) \sin(n\pi x)\, dx \\
&= -\frac{1}{n\pi}(x^3 - 2x^2 + 1)\cos(n\pi x)\Big|_0^2 + \frac{1}{n\pi}\int_0^2 (3x^2 - 4x)\cos(n\pi x)\, dx \\
&= \frac{1}{n^2\pi^2}(3x^2 - 4x)\sin(n\pi x)\Big|_0^2 - \frac{1}{n^2\pi^2}\int_0^2 (6x - 4)\sin(n\pi x)\, dx \\
&= \frac{1}{n^3\pi^3}(6x - 4)\cos(n\pi x)\Big|_0^2 - \frac{6}{n^3\pi^3}\int_0^2 \cos(n\pi x)\, dx \\
&= \frac{12}{n^3\pi^3}, \quad n \geq 1.
\end{aligned}
$$

Hence,

$$
y = \frac{1}{9} + \sum_{n=1}^{\infty}\left[\frac{4\cos(n\pi x)}{n^2\pi^2(3 - n^2\pi^2)} + \frac{12\sin(n\pi x)}{n^3\pi^3(3 - n^2\pi^2)}\right], \quad -\infty < x < \infty.
$$

Example 9.9. Let f be an odd, 2-periodic function with $f(x) = x - x^2$ on $[0,1]$. Since f is continuous on $[0,1]$ and $f(0) = f(1) = 0$, f is continuous everywhere and f' is piecewise continuous. Hence,

$$
f(x) = \sum_{n=1}^{\infty} b_n \sin(n\pi x), \quad -\infty < x < \infty.
$$

A 2-periodic solution of the equation

$$
y'' + y = f(x)
$$

is therefore sought in the form

$$
y = \sum_{n=1}^{\infty} d_n \sin(n\pi x), \quad -\infty < x < \infty.
$$

Since $\lambda = 1 \neq n^2\pi^2$ for any integer $n \geq 0$, and $L = 1$,

$$
d_n = \frac{b_n}{1 - n^2\pi^2}, \quad n \geq 1.
$$

The Fourier sine coefficients of f are

$$
\begin{aligned}
b_n &= 2\int_0^1 (x - x^2)\sin(n\pi x)\, dx \\
&= -\frac{2}{n\pi}(x - x^2)\cos(n\pi x)\Big|_0^1 + \frac{2}{n\pi}\int_0^1 (1 - 2x)\cos(n\pi x)\, dx \\
&= \frac{2}{n^2\pi^2}(1 - 2x)\sin(n\pi x)\Big|_0^1 + \frac{4}{n^2\pi^2}\int_0^1 \sin(n\pi x)\, dx \\
&= -\frac{4}{n^3\pi^3}\cos(n\pi x)\Big|_0^1 = \frac{4}{n^3\pi^3}[1 - (-1)^n], \quad n \geq 1.
\end{aligned}
$$

Hence,

$$y = \sum_{n=1}^{\infty} \frac{4\left[1 - (-1)^n\right]}{n^3 \pi^3 \left(1 - n^2\pi^2\right)} \sin(n\pi x), \quad -\infty < x < \infty.$$

Example 9.10. Let f be even and 2-periodic, with $f(x) = x$ on $[0, 1]$. Since f is continuous on $[0, 1]$ and f is even, it is continuous everywhere and f' is piecewise continuous. Hence,

$$f(x) = \frac{a_0}{2} + \sum_{n=1}^{\infty} a_n \cos(n\pi x), \quad -\infty < x < \infty.$$

A 2-periodic solution of the equation

$$y'' + y = f(x)$$

is therefore sought in the form

$$y = \frac{c_0}{2} + \sum_{n=1}^{\infty} c_n \cos(n\pi x), \quad -\infty < x < \infty.$$

Since $\lambda = 1 \neq n^2\pi^2$ for any integer $n \geq 0$, and $L = 1$,

$$c_0 = a_0 \quad \text{and} \quad c_n = \frac{a_n}{1 - n^2\pi^2}, \quad n \geq 1.$$

The Fourier cosine coefficients of f are

$$a_0 = 2\int_0^1 x\,dx = 1,$$

$$a_n = 2\int_0^1 x\cos(n\pi x)\,dx = \frac{2}{n\pi}x\sin(n\pi x)\Big|_0^1 - \frac{2}{n\pi}\int_0^1 \sin(n\pi x)\,dx$$

$$= \frac{2}{n^2\pi^2}\cos(n\pi x)\Big|_0^1 = \frac{2}{n^2\pi^2}\left[(-1)^n - 1\right], \quad n \geq 1.$$

Hence,

$$y = \frac{1}{2} + \sum_{n=1}^{\infty} \frac{2\left[(-1)^n - 1\right]}{n^2\pi^2(1 - n^2\pi^2)} \cos(n\pi x), \quad -\infty < x < \infty.$$

Exercises 9.2

1. Let $f(x) = x^2 - x + 2$ on $[0, 2]$ and $f(x+2) = f(x)$ for all x. Find a 2-periodic solution of the equation $y'' + 3y = f(x)$.

2. Let $f(x) = x^2 - 2x$ on $[-1, 3]$ and $f(x+4) = f(x)$ for all x. Find a 4-periodic solution of the equation $y'' + 4y = f(x)$.

3. Let f be an odd, 2-periodic function, with $f(x) = x - x^2$ on $[0,1]$. Find a 2-periodic solution of the equation $y'' - 3y = f(x)$.

4. Let f be an odd, 4-periodic function, with $f(x) = \left\{ \begin{array}{ll} x, & 0 \le x < 1 \\ 2 - x, & 1 \le x \le 2 \end{array} \right\}$. Find a 4-periodic solution of the equation $y'' + 3y = f(x)$.

5. Let f be an even, 2-periodic function, with $f(x) = 1 - x$ on $[0,1]$. Find a 2-periodic solution of the equation $y'' + y = f(x)$.

6. Let f be an even, 4-periodic function, with $f(x) = \left\{ \begin{array}{ll} x, & 0 \le x < 1 \\ 1, & 1 \le x \le 2 \end{array} \right\}$. Find a 4-periodic solution of the equation $y'' + 4y = f(x)$.

7. Let $f(x) = 2x - x^2$ on $[0,2]$ and $f(x + 2) = f(x)$ for all x. Find a 2-periodic solution of the equation $y'' + 2y = f(x)$.

8. Let f be an even, 2-periodic function with, $f(x) = \sin(2\pi x)$ on $[0,1]$. Find a 2-periodic solution of the equation $y'' = f(x)$.

Appendix A

Formulas and Techniques

A.1   Trigonometric Identities

$\cos^2(\theta) + \sin^2(\theta) = 1$

$\cos(a + b) = \cos(a)\cos(b) - \sin(a)\sin(b)$

$\cos(a - b) = \cos(a)\cos(b) + \sin(a)\sin(b)$

$\sin(a + b) = \sin(a)\cos(b) + \cos(a)\sin(b)$

$\sin(a - b) = \sin(a)\cos(b) - \cos(a)\sin(b)$

$\sin(2\theta) = 2\sin(\theta)\cos(\theta)$

$\cos(2\theta) = \cos^2(\theta) - \sin^2(\theta) = 2\cos^2(\theta) - 1 = 1 - 2\sin^2(\theta)$

$\cos^2(\theta) = \dfrac{1}{2}[1 + \cos(2\theta)]$

$\sin^2(\theta) = \dfrac{1}{2}[1 - \cos(2\theta)]$

$\sec^2(\theta) = \tan^2(\theta) + 1$

$\csc^2(\theta) = \cot^2(\theta) + 1$

A.2   Integration Techniques

Integration by Parts

$$\int f'(x)g(x)\,dx = f(x)g(x) - \int f(x)g'(x)\,dx.$$

Proof. By the product rule of differentiation,

$$[f(x)g(x)]' = f'(x)g(x) + f(x)g'(x) \Rightarrow f(x)g(x) = \int f'(x)g(x)\,dx + \int f(x)g'(x)\,dx$$

$$\Rightarrow \int f'(x)g(x)\,dx = f(x)g(x) - \int f(x)g'(x)\,dx.$$

Integration by Substitution (Change of Variable)

$$\int f(g(x))g'(x)\,dx = \int f(u)\,du, \text{ where } u = g(x).$$

Proof. By definition of the indefinite integral as an antiderivative,

$$\frac{d}{dx}\int f(g(x))g'(x)\,dx = f(g(x))g'(x) \text{ and } \frac{d}{du}\int f(u)\,du = f(u).$$

Hence, by the chain rule,

$$\frac{d}{dx}\int f(u)\,du = \left(\frac{d}{du}\int f(u)\,du\right)\frac{du}{dx} = f(u)\frac{du}{dx} = f(g(x))g'(x).$$

Since both $\int f(g(x))g'(x)\,dx$ and $\int f(u)\,du$ have the same derivative with respect to x, they are equal (up to the addition of an arbitrary constant).

Trigonometric Integrals

1. $\int \sin^{\alpha}(x)\cos^{n}(x)\,dx$, $n \geq 1$ an odd integer and α any real number.
   Factor out $\cos(x)$ and convert $\cos^{n-1}(x)$, with $n-1$ even, into sines, employing $\cos^2(x) = 1 - \sin^2(x)$, to express the integral as

   $$\int f(\sin(x))\cos(x)\,dx.$$

   Make the substitution $u = \sin(x)$ to obtain $\int f(u)du$, which can be evaluated since $f(u)$ is a sum of constants times powers of u. Then replace u by $\sin(x)$.

2. $\int \cos^{\alpha}(x)\sin^{n}(x)\,dx$, $n \geq 1$ an odd integer and α any real number.
   Factor out $\sin(x)$ and convert $\sin^{n-1}(x)$, with $n-1$ even, into cosines, employing $\sin^2(x) = 1 - \cos^2(x)$, to express the integral as

   $$\int f(\cos(x))\sin(x)\,dx = -\int f(\cos(x))[-\sin(x)]\,dx.$$

   Make the substitution $u = \cos(x)$ to obtain $-\int f(u)du$, which can be evaluated since $f(u)$ is a sum of constants times powers of u. Then replace u by $\cos(x)$.

3. $\int \cos^{m}(x)\sin^{n}(x)\,dx$, $m \geq 0$ and $n \geq 0$ both even integers.
   Employ the identities

   $$\cos^2(x) = \frac{1}{2}[1 + \cos(2x)] \quad \text{and} \quad \sin^2(x) = \frac{1}{2}[1 - \cos(2x)]$$

in order to reduce the powers m and n by one. Repeat if necessary until only first powers of cosines and sines remain, which can then be integrated.

4. $\int \tan^{\alpha}(x) \sec^{n}(x)\, dx$, $n \geq 2$ an even integer and α any real number.

Factor out $\sec^{2}(x)$ and convert $\sec^{n-2}(x)$, $n-2$ even, into tangents, employing $\sec^{2}(x) = \tan^{2}(x) + 1$, to express the integral as

$$\int f(\tan(x)) \sec^{2}(x)\, dx.$$

Make the substitution $u = \tan(x)$ to obtain $\int f(u)\, du$, which can be evaluated since $f(u)$ is a sum of constants times powers of u. Then replace u by $\tan(x)$.

5. $\int \tan^{m}(x) \sec^{\alpha}(x)\, dx$, $m \geq 1$ an odd integer and α any real number.

Factor out $\sec(x) \tan(x)$ and convert $\tan^{m-1}(x)$, with $m-1$ even, into secants, employing $\tan^{2}(x) = \sec^{2}(x) - 1$, to express the integral as

$$\int f(\sec(x)) \sec(x) \tan(x)\, dx.$$

Make the substitution $u = \sec(x)$ to obtain $\int f(u)\, du$, which can be evaluated since $f(u)$ is a sum of constants times powers of u. Then replace u by $\sec(x)$.

6. $\int \tan^{m}(x) \sec^{n}(x)\, dx$, $m \geq 0$ an even integer and $n \geq 1$ an odd integer.

Convert $\tan^{m}(x)$ into secants employing $\tan^{2}(x) = \sec^{2}(x) - 1$, to obtain an integral containing a sum of constants times odd powers of $\sec(x)$. Then for any $k \geq 3$ an odd integer, evaluate

$$\int \sec^{k}(x)\, dx = \int \sec^{k-2}(x) \sec^{2}(x)\, dx$$

by integration by parts.

Trigonometric Substitution

1. $\int (a^{2} - x^{2})^{\frac{n}{2}}\, dx$, n an odd integer, $a > 0$ any real number.

Make the substitution $x = a\sin(t)$, $-\dfrac{\pi}{2} \leq t \leq \dfrac{\pi}{2}$, and employ the identity $a^{2} - a^{2}\sin^{2}(t) = a^{2}\cos^{2}(t)$ to obtain

$$\int (a^{2} - x^{2})^{\frac{n}{2}}\, dx = \int a^{n+1} \cos^{n+1}(t)\, dt,$$

and evaluate the trigonometric integral.

2. $\int (a^2 + x^2)^{\frac{n}{2}}\, dx$, n an odd integer, $a > 0$ any real number.

   Make the substitution $x = a\tan(t)$, $-\dfrac{\pi}{2} < t < \dfrac{\pi}{2}$, and employ the identity $a^2 + a^2\tan^2(t) = a^2\sec^2(t)$ to obtain

   $$\int (a^2 + x^2)^{\frac{n}{2}}\, dx = \int a^{n+1}\sec^{n+2}(t)\, dt,$$

   and evaluate the trigonometric integral.

3. $\int (x^2 - a^2)^{\frac{n}{2}}\, dx$, n an odd integer, $a > 0$ any real number.

   Make the substitution $x = a\sec(t)$, $0 \le t < \dfrac{\pi}{2}$ or $\pi \le t < \dfrac{3\pi}{2}$, and employ the identity $a^2\sec^2(t) - a^2 = a^2\tan^2(t)$ to obtain

   $$\int (x^2 - a^2)^{\frac{n}{2}}\, dx = \int a^{n+1}\tan^{n+1}(t)\sec(t)\, dt,$$

   and evaluate the trigonometric integral.

4. $\int (a + bx - x^2)^{\frac{n}{2}}\, dx$, n an odd integer, a and b real numbers, $b^2 + 4a > 0$. Complete the square to obtain

   $$a + bx - x^2 = \left(\frac{b^2}{4} + a\right) - \left(x - \frac{b}{2}\right)^2,$$

   and make the substitution

   $$x - \frac{b}{2} = \sqrt{\frac{b^2}{4} + a}\,\sin(t), \quad -\frac{\pi}{2} \le t \le \frac{\pi}{2},$$

   to obtain a trigonometric integral.

5. $\int (a + bx + x^2)^{\frac{n}{2}}\, dx$, n an odd integer, a and b real numbers, $b^2 - 4a < 0$. Complete the square to obtain

   $$a + bx + x^2 = \left(x + \frac{b}{2}\right)^2 + \left(a - \frac{b^2}{4}\right),$$

   and make the substitution

   $$x + \frac{b}{2} = \sqrt{a - \frac{b^2}{4}}\,\tan(t), \quad -\frac{\pi}{2} < t < \frac{\pi}{2},$$

   to obtain a trigonometric integral.

6. $\int (a + bx + x^2)^{\frac{n}{2}}\, dx$, n an odd integer, a and b real numbers, $b^2 - 4a > 0$. Complete the square to obtain

$$a + bx + x^2 = \left(x + \frac{b}{2} \right)^2 - \left(\frac{b^2}{4} - a \right),$$

and make the substitution

$$x + \frac{b}{2} = \sqrt{\frac{b^2}{4} - a}\,\sec(t), \quad 0 \le t < \frac{\pi}{2} \quad \text{or} \quad \pi \le t < \frac{3\pi}{2},$$

to obtain a trigonometric integral.

Partial Fractions

Partial fractions are required in order to evaluate integrals of rational functions, i.e., $\int \frac{P(x)}{Q(x)}\, dx$, where P and Q are polynomials. First, suppose that $\deg(P) < \deg(Q)$.

1. If Q factors into distinct linear factors, i.e.,

$$Q(x) = (a_1 x + b_1)(a_2 x + b_2) \cdots (a_n x + b_n),$$

then there exist constants $A_1, A_2, \cdots, A_n$, such that

$$\frac{P(x)}{Q(x)} = \frac{A_1}{a_1 x + b_1} + \frac{A_2}{a_2 x + b_2} + \cdots + \frac{A_n}{a_n x + b_n},$$

called the *partial fraction decomposition* of $\dfrac{P(x)}{Q(x)}$.

2. If Q contains a repeated linear factor $(ax + b)^r$, $r \ge 2$, then the partial fraction decomposition of $\dfrac{P(x)}{Q(x)}$ must include the r terms

$$\frac{B_1}{ax + b} + \frac{B_2}{(ax + b)^2} + \cdots + \frac{B_r}{(ax + b)^r},$$

where $B_1, B_2, \cdots, B_r$ are constants. These terms must be included in addition to the terms which correspond to the distinct linear factors of Q.

3. If Q contains the distinct, irreducible, quadratic factor $ax^2 + bx + c$, then the partial fraction decomposition of $\dfrac{P(x)}{Q(x)}$ must include the term

$$\frac{Ax + B}{ax^2 + bx + c},$$

where A and B are constants, in addition to the terms which correspond to the other factors of Q. A quadratic $ax^2 + bx + c$ is *irreducible* if its roots are complex, which occurs if and only if $b^2 - 4ac < 0$.

4. If Q contains the repeated, irreducible, quadratic factor $(ax^2 + bx + c)^r$, $r \geq 2$, then the partial fraction decomposition of $\dfrac{P(x)}{Q(x)}$ must include the terms

$$\frac{A_1 x + B_1}{ax^2 + bx + c} + \frac{A_2 x + B_2}{(ax^2 + bx + c)^2} + \cdots + \frac{A_r x + B_r}{(ax^2 + bx + c)^r},$$

where A_i and B_i, $1 \leq i \leq r$, are constants, in addition to the terms which correspond to the other factors of Q.

If $\deg(P) \geq \deg(Q)$, then perform long division to express $\dfrac{P(x)}{Q(x)}$ as

$$\frac{P(x)}{Q(x)} = R(x) + \frac{P_1(x)}{Q(x)},$$

where R is a polynomial and $\deg(P_1) < \deg(Q)$.

A.3   Matrix Inversion

Let A be an $n \times n$ matrix. Two methods of computing A^{-1} are given below.

1. Write down the augmented matrix $(A|I)$, where I is the $n \times n$ identity matrix, and row reduce the augmented matrix in order to transform A into I. The resulting augmented matrix is then $(I|A^{-1})$.

2. Let M_{ij} denote the determinant of the submatrix obtained from A by deleting the i-th row and j-th column, called the *ij-minor* of A. Let $A_{ij} = (-1)^{i+j} M_{ij}$, called the *ij-cofactor* of A. The *transpose* of the matrix with entries A_{ij} is called the *classical adjoint* of A, and denoted by $\mathrm{adj}(A)$. Then

$$A^{-1} = \frac{\mathrm{adj}(A)}{\det(A)},$$

i.e.,

$$A^{-1} = \frac{1}{\det(A)} \begin{pmatrix} A_{11} & A_{21} & \cdots & A_{n1} \\ A_{12} & A_{22} & \cdots & A_{n2} \\ \vdots & \vdots & \vdots & \vdots \\ A_{1n} & A_{2n} & \cdots & A_{nn} \end{pmatrix}.$$

Appendix B

Proofs of Selected Theorems

B.1   The Comparison Test

Theorem 6.11 Let $\{a_n\}$ and $\{b_n\}$ be sequences, and suppose that

$$0 \le a_n \le b_n$$

for all $n \ge k$, where k is an integer. Then:

1. If $\displaystyle\sum_{n=1}^{\infty} b_n$ converges, then $\displaystyle\sum_{n=1}^{\infty} a_n$ also converges.

2. If $\displaystyle\sum_{n=1}^{\infty} a_n$ diverges, then $\displaystyle\sum_{n=1}^{\infty} b_n$ also diverges.

Proof. Without loss of generality, assume $0 \le a_n \le b_n$ for all $n \ge 1$. Let $s_n = \displaystyle\sum_{k=1}^{n} a_k$ and $t_n = \displaystyle\sum_{k=1}^{n} b_k$. Since $a_n \ge 0$ and $b_n \ge 0$, $\{s_n\}$ and $\{t_n\}$ are increasing sequences. In addition, $0 \le s_n \le t_n$ because $0 \le a_n \le b_n$.

1. If $\displaystyle\sum_{n=1}^{\infty} b_n$ converges, then $\displaystyle\lim_{n\to\infty} t_n = t$ exists. Hence, $s_n \le t_n \le t < \infty \Rightarrow \{s_n\}$ is

   bounded above. Since it is increasing, it converges. Thus, $\displaystyle\sum_{n=1}^{\infty} a_n$ converges.

2. If $\displaystyle\sum_{n=1}^{\infty} a_n$ diverges, then $\displaystyle\lim_{n\to\infty} s_n = \infty \Rightarrow \lim_{n\to\infty} t_n = \infty$, i.e., $\displaystyle\sum_{n=1}^{\infty} b_n$ diverges.

B.2   The Limit Comparison Test

Theorem 6.12 Let $\{a_n\}$ and $\{b_n\}$ be sequences with $a_n > 0$ and $b_n > 0$ for $n \geq k$, where k is an integer, and let

$$L = \lim_{n \to \infty} \frac{a_n}{b_n}.$$

1. If $0 < L < \infty$, then either both $\sum_{n=1}^{\infty} a_n$ and $\sum_{n=1}^{\infty} b_n$ converge, or they both diverge.

2. If $L = 0$ and $\sum_{n=1}^{\infty} b_n$ converges, then $\sum_{n=1}^{\infty} a_n$ converges.

3. If $L = \infty$ and $\sum_{n=1}^{\infty} b_n$ diverges, then $\sum_{n=1}^{\infty} a_n$ diverges.

Proof. Without loss of generality, assume $k = 1$.

1. If $0 < L < \infty$, let $\varepsilon > 0$ with $\varepsilon < L$. Then there exists an integer N such that $n \geq N \Rightarrow \left| \dfrac{a_n}{b_n} - L \right| < \varepsilon$. Hence, for all $n \geq N$, $-\varepsilon < \dfrac{a_n}{b_n} - L < \varepsilon$, i.e., $L - \varepsilon < \dfrac{a_n}{b_n} < L + \varepsilon$. Let $\alpha = L - \varepsilon$ and $\beta = L + \varepsilon$. Then $0 < \alpha < \beta$, and $\alpha < \dfrac{a_n}{b_n} < \beta \Rightarrow \alpha b_n < a_n < \beta b_n$. By the comparison test, if $\sum_{n=1}^{\infty} b_n$ converges, then $\sum_{n=1}^{\infty} a_n$ converges, and if $\sum_{n=1}^{\infty} b_n$ diverges, then $\sum_{n=1}^{\infty} a_n$ diverges. In addition, if $\sum_{n=1}^{\infty} a_n$ converges, then $\sum_{n=1}^{\infty} b_n$ converges, and if $\sum_{n=1}^{\infty} a_n$ diverges, then $\sum_{n=1}^{\infty} b_n$ diverges.

2. If $L = 0$, let $\varepsilon > 0$. Then there exists an integer N such that $n \geq N \Rightarrow \left| \dfrac{a_n}{b_n} \right| < \varepsilon$, i.e., $-\varepsilon < \dfrac{a_n}{b_n} < \varepsilon$, or $-\varepsilon b_n < a_n < \varepsilon b_n$. By the comparison test, if $\sum_{n=1}^{\infty} b_n$ converges, then $\sum_{n=1}^{\infty} a_n$ converges.

3. If $L = \infty$, then $\lim_{n \to \infty} \dfrac{b_n}{a_n} = 0$. Thus, there exists an integer N such that $n \geq N \Rightarrow \left| \dfrac{b_n}{a_n} \right| < \varepsilon$, i.e., $-\varepsilon < \dfrac{b_n}{a_n} < \varepsilon$, or $-\varepsilon a_n < b_n < \varepsilon a_n$. By the comparison test, if $\sum_{n=1}^{\infty} b_n$ diverges, then $\sum_{n=1}^{\infty} a_n$ diverges.

B.3 The Alternating Series Test

Theorem 6.13 Consider the alternating series

$$\sum_{n=0}^{\infty} (-1)^n b_n.$$

If $\{b_n\}$ is decreasing for $n \geq k$, where k is an integer, and $\lim_{n \to \infty} b_n = 0$, then the series converges.

Proof. Without loss of generality, assume $\{b_n\}$ is decreasing for $n \geq 0$. Consider the sequence $\{s_n\}$ with $n = 2k$ even, i.e.,

$$
\begin{aligned}
s_{2k} &= \sum_{i=0}^{2k} (-1)^i b_i = b_1 - b_2 + b_3 - b_4 + b_5 - \cdots + b_{2k-1} - b_{2k} \\
&= (b_1 - b_2) + b_3 - b_4) + \cdots + (b_{2k-1} - b_{2k}).
\end{aligned}
$$

Since $b_i - b_{i+1} > 0$ for all $i \geq 0$, the sequence $\{s_{2k}\}$ is increasing. In addition,

$$
\begin{aligned}
s_{2k} &= \sum_{i=0}^{2k} (-1)^i b_i = b_1 - (b_2 - b_3) - (b_4 - b_5) - \cdots - (b_{2k-2} - b_{2k-1}) - b_{2k} \\
&< b_1,
\end{aligned}
$$

i.e., the sequence $\{s_{2k}\}$ is bounded above and, hence, it converges. Thus, $\lim_{k \to \infty} s_{2k} = s$ exists. Next, consider the sequence $\{s_n\}$ with $n = 2k + 1$ odd. Then

$$s_{2k+1} = s_{2k} - b_{2k+1} \quad \Rightarrow \quad \lim_{k \to \infty} s_{2k+1} = \lim_{k \to \infty} s_{2k} - \lim_{k \to \infty} b_{2k+1} = s.$$

Thus, for all $\varepsilon > 0$, there exists an integer K such that $k \geq K \Rightarrow |s_{2k} - s| < \varepsilon$ and $|s_{2k+1} - s| < \varepsilon$. It follows that $|s_n - s| < \varepsilon$ for all $n \geq N = 2K + 1$, i.e., $\lim_{n \to \infty} s_n = s$. Thus, $\sum_{n=0}^{\infty} (-1)^n b_n$ converges.

B.4 The Ratio Test

Theorem 6.16 Let $\{a_n\}$ be a sequence and suppose that

$$L = \lim_{n \to \infty} \left| \frac{a_{n+1}}{a_n} \right|$$

exists. Then:

1. If $L < 1$, then $\displaystyle\sum_{n=0}^{\infty} a_n$ converges absolutely.

2. If $L > 1$, then $\displaystyle\sum_{n=0}^{\infty} a_n$ diverges.

3. If $L = 1$, then no conclusions can be made regarding convergence.

Proof. Since $\displaystyle\lim_{n\to\infty}\left|\frac{a_{n+1}}{a_n}\right| = L \geq 0$ exists, there exists an integer k such that $a_n \neq 0$ for all $n \geq k$ because, otherwise, $\dfrac{a_{n+1}}{a_n}$ would be undefined. Assume, without loss of generality, that $k = 0$.

1. If $L < 1$, there exists $K > 0$ such that $L < K < 1$. Let $\varepsilon = K - L > 0$. Then there exists an integer N such that

$$n \geq N \;\Rightarrow\; \left|\left|\frac{a_{n+1}}{a_n}\right| - L\right| < \varepsilon \;\Rightarrow\; -\varepsilon < \left|\frac{a_{n+1}}{a_n}\right| - L < \varepsilon$$

$$\Rightarrow\; L - \varepsilon < \left|\frac{a_{n+1}}{a_n}\right| < L + \varepsilon = K$$

$$\Rightarrow\; |a_{n+1}| < K|a_n|.$$

It follows that $|a_1| < K|a_0|$, $|a_2| < K|a_1| < K^2|a_0|$, $|a_3| < K|a_2| < K^3|a_0|$, etc., and, in general, $|a_n| < K^n|a_0|$ for all $n \geq 1$. Since $\displaystyle\sum_{n=0}^{\infty} K^n|a_0| = |a_0|\sum_{n=0}^{\infty} K^n$ is a convergent geometric series, $\displaystyle\sum_{n=0}^{\infty} |a_n|$ converges by the comparison test, i.e., $\displaystyle\sum_{n=0}^{\infty} a_n$ converges absolutely.

2. If $L > 1$, there exists $K > 0$ such that $1 < K < L$. Let $\varepsilon = L - K > 0$. Then there exists an integer N such that

$$n \geq N \;\Rightarrow\; K = L - \varepsilon < \left|\frac{a_{n+1}}{a_n}\right| < L + \varepsilon \;\Rightarrow\; |a_{n+1}| > K|a_n|.$$

Hence, $|a_n| > K^n|a_0| \to \infty \Rightarrow \displaystyle\lim_{n\to\infty} |a_n| \neq 0 \Rightarrow \lim_{n\to\infty} a_n \neq 0 \Rightarrow \sum_{n=0}^{\infty} a_n$ diverges by the nth-term test.

3. If $L = 1$, the test is inconclusive, as shown by Example 6.87.

B.5 The Root Test

Theorem 6.17 Let $\{a_n\}$ be a sequence and suppose that

$$L = \lim_{n \to \infty} |a_n|^{1/n}$$

exists. Then:

1. If $L < 1$, then $\displaystyle\sum_{n=0}^{\infty} a_n$ converges absolutely.

2. If $L > 1$, then $\displaystyle\sum_{n=0}^{\infty} a_n$ diverges.

3. If $L = 1$, then no conclusions can be made regarding convergence.

Proof.

1. If $L < 1$, there exists $K > 0$ such that $L < K < 1$. Let $\varepsilon = K - L > 0$. Then there exists an integer N such that

$$n \geq N \quad \Rightarrow \quad ||a_n|^{1/n} - L| < \varepsilon \quad \Rightarrow \quad L - \varepsilon < |a_n|^{1/n} < L + \varepsilon = K$$

$\Rightarrow |a_n| < K^n \Rightarrow \displaystyle\sum_{n=0}^{\infty} |a_n|$ converges by the comparison test since $\displaystyle\sum_{n=0}^{\infty} K^n$ is a

convergent geometric series. Thus, $\displaystyle\sum_{n=0}^{\infty} a_n$ converges absolutely.

2. If $L > 1$, there exists $K > 0$ such that $1 < K < L$. Let $\varepsilon = L - K > 0$. Then there exists an integer N such that

$$n \geq N \quad \Rightarrow \quad ||a_n|^{1/n} - L| < \varepsilon \quad \Rightarrow \quad K = L - \varepsilon < |a_n|^{1/n} < L + \varepsilon$$

$\Rightarrow |a_n| > K^n \to \infty \Rightarrow \displaystyle\lim_{n \to \infty} |a_n| \neq 0 \Rightarrow \displaystyle\lim_{n \to \infty} a_n \neq 0 \Rightarrow \displaystyle\sum_{n=0}^{\infty} a_n$ diverges by the

n^{th}-term test.

3. If $L = 1$, then the test is inconclusive. For example, $\displaystyle\sum_{n=0}^{\infty} \frac{1}{n^2}$ converges and

$L = \displaystyle\lim_{n \to \infty} \left(\frac{1}{n^2} \right)^{1/n} = 1$, and $\displaystyle\sum_{n=0}^{\infty} \frac{1}{n}$ diverges and $L = \displaystyle\lim_{n \to \infty} \left(\frac{1}{n} \right)^{1/n} = 1$.

B.6   The Binomial Theorem

For any real number α, $(1 + x)^\alpha = \sum\limits_{k=0}^{\infty} \binom{\alpha}{k} x^k$ for $|x| < 1$.

Proof. Since the series converges absolutely for $|x| < 1$, let

$$f(x) = \sum_{k=0}^{\infty} \binom{\alpha}{k} x^k = 1 + \sum_{k=1}^{\infty} \binom{\alpha}{k} x^k, \quad |x| < 1.$$

If $f(x) = (1 + x)^\alpha$, then

$$f'(x) = \alpha(1 + x)^{\alpha-1} \quad \Rightarrow \quad (1 + x)f'(x) = \alpha(1 + x)^\alpha = \alpha f(x).$$

Conversely, if $(1 + x)f'(x) = \alpha f(x)$, then $\dfrac{f'(x)}{f(x)} = \dfrac{\alpha}{1 + x} \Rightarrow$

$$\ln|f(x)| = \alpha \ln(1 + x) + c = \ln[(1 + x)^\alpha] + c \quad \Rightarrow \quad f(x) = k(1 + x)^\alpha$$

and, since $(1 + x)^\alpha = 1 = f(0)$ at $x = 0$, $k = 1$ and $f(x) = (1 + x)^\alpha$. Thus, we must

show that $(1 + x)f'(x) = \alpha f(x)$. By Theorem 7.2, since $f(x) = 1 + \sum\limits_{k=1}^{\infty} \binom{\alpha}{k} x^k$,

$$
\begin{aligned}
f'(x) &= \sum_{k=1}^{\infty} k\binom{\alpha}{k} x^{k-1} = \sum_{k=0}^{\infty} (k+1)\binom{\alpha}{k+1} x^k \\
\Rightarrow (1 + x)f'(x) &= \sum_{k=0}^{\infty} (k+1)\binom{\alpha}{k+1} x^k + x\sum_{k=1}^{\infty} k\binom{\alpha}{k} x^{k-1} \\
&= \sum_{k=0}^{\infty} (k+1)\binom{\alpha}{k+1} x^k + \sum_{k=1}^{\infty} k\binom{\alpha}{k} x^k \\
&= \binom{\alpha}{1} + \sum_{k=1}^{\infty} \left[(k+1)\binom{\alpha}{k+1} + k\binom{\alpha}{k} \right] x^k \\
&= \alpha + \alpha\sum_{k=1}^{\infty} \binom{\alpha}{k} x^k = \alpha\left[1 + \sum_{k=1}^{\infty} \binom{\alpha}{k} x^k \right] = \alpha f(x),
\end{aligned}
$$

because $\binom{\alpha}{1} = \alpha$ and

$$
\begin{aligned}
&(k+1)\binom{\alpha}{k+1} + k\binom{\alpha}{k} \\
=\ & (k+1)\frac{\alpha(\alpha-1)\cdots(\alpha-k+1)(\alpha-k)}{(k+1)!} + k\frac{\alpha(\alpha-1)\cdots(\alpha-k+1)}{k!} \\
=\ & (\alpha-k)\frac{\alpha(\alpha-1)\cdots(\alpha-k+1)}{k!} + k\frac{\alpha(\alpha-1)\cdots(\alpha-k+1)}{k!} = \alpha\binom{\alpha}{k}.
\end{aligned}
$$

Appendix C

Solutions

C.1 Chapter 1 Solutions

Exercises 1.1 – page 7

1. $y' + 2x = xe^x \Rightarrow y = \int xe^x - 2x \, dx = xe^x - e^x - x^2 + c.$

2. $\frac{1}{x} y' = 4\cos(2x) \Rightarrow y = \int 4x\cos(2x) \, dx = 2x\sin(2x) - \int 2\sin(2x) \, dx$
   $= 2x\sin(2x) + \cos(2x) + c.$

3. $\frac{dy}{dx} = 2x\cos(x^2) \Rightarrow y = \int 2x\cos(x^2) \, dx = \sin(x^2) + c.$

4. $\left(\frac{dy}{dx}\right)^2 = 4x^2 e^{2x^2} \Rightarrow y' = \pm 2xe^{x^2} \Rightarrow y = \pm \int 2xe^{x^2} \, dx = \pm e^{x^2} + c.$

5. $\frac{1}{\cos(x)} y' = 2\sin(x) \Rightarrow y = \int 2\sin(x)\cos(x) \, dx = \int \sin(2x) \, dx = -\frac{1}{2}\cos(2x) + c.$

6. $\frac{dy}{dt} = \ln(t) \Rightarrow y = \int \ln(t) \, dt = t\ln(t) - t + c, \ y(1) = 2 \Rightarrow c = 3.$

7. $y' = 4\cos^2(x) \Rightarrow y = \int 4\cos^2(x) \, dx = \int 2 + 2\cos(2x) \, dx = 2x + \sin(2x) + c,$
   $y\left(\frac{\pi}{4}\right) = \frac{\pi}{2} \Rightarrow c = -1.$

8. $y' = \frac{x+3}{x^2-x-6} \Rightarrow y = \frac{1}{5} \int \frac{6}{x-3} - \frac{1}{x+2} \, dx = \frac{1}{5}[6\ln|x-3| - \ln|x+2|] + c.$

9. $\frac{dy}{dx} = 12e^{2x}\sin(3x) \Rightarrow y = \int 12e^{2x}\sin(3x) \, dx = 6e^{2x}\sin(3x) - \int 18e^{2x}\cos(3x) \, dx$
   $= 6e^{2x}\sin(3x) - 9e^{2x}\cos(3x) - \int 27e^{2x}\sin(3x) \, dx \Rightarrow \int 39e^{2x}\sin(3x) \, dx$
   $= 6e^{2x}\sin(3x) - 9e^{2x}\cos(3x) + c_1 \Rightarrow y = \frac{4}{13}[6e^{2x}\sin(3x) - 9e^{2x}\cos(3x)] + c.$

10. $\frac{dy}{dt} = 3y \Rightarrow \frac{y'}{y} = 3 \Rightarrow \ln|y| = 3t + c_1 \Rightarrow y = ce^{3t}, \ y(0) = 2 \Rightarrow c = 2.$

11. $\frac{dy}{dt} = -2y \Rightarrow \frac{y'}{y} = -2 \Rightarrow \ln|y| = -2t + c_1 \Rightarrow y = ce^{-2t}, \ y(0) = 3 \Rightarrow c = 3.$

12. $y' + \cos(x)y = 0 \Rightarrow \frac{y'}{y} = -\cos(x) \Rightarrow \ln|y| = -\sin(x) + c_1 \Rightarrow y = ce^{-\sin(x)},$
    $y(\pi) = -3 \Rightarrow c = -3.$

13. $3y^2y' = 1 \Rightarrow \int 3y^2y'\,dx = \int 1\,dx \Rightarrow \int 3y^2\,dy = \int 1\,dx \Rightarrow y^3 = x + c \Rightarrow$
$y = (x+c)^{1/3} = \sqrt[3]{x+c}$, $y(0) = 2 \Rightarrow c = 8$.

C.2   Chapter 2 Solutions

Exercises 2.1 – page 14

1. $y' = 3x^2y^2 \Rightarrow \frac{y'}{y^2} = 3x^2 \Rightarrow -\frac{1}{y} = x^3 + c \Rightarrow y = \frac{-1}{x^3+c}$, $y(0) = \frac{1}{2} \Rightarrow c = -2$.

2. $y' = \frac{\sqrt{x+1}}{y^3} \Rightarrow y^3y' = \sqrt{x+1} \Rightarrow \frac{1}{4}y^4 = \frac{2}{3}(x+1)^{3/2} + c_1 \Rightarrow y = \left[\frac{8}{3}(x+1)^{3/2} + c\right]^{1/4}$.

3. $(x^2 + 1)\frac{dy}{dx} = \frac{2x+1}{3y^2} \Rightarrow 3y^2y' = \frac{2x+1}{x^2+1} \Rightarrow y^3 = \ln(x^2 + 1) + \tan^{-1}(x) + c \Rightarrow$
$y = [\ln(x^2 + 1) + \tan^{-1}(x) + c]^{1/3}$, $y(0) = 3 \Rightarrow c = 27$.

4. $\frac{y'}{4x^2+3x-2} = \frac{x}{5y^4-4y^3+1} \Rightarrow (5y^4 - 4y^3 + 1)y' = 4x^3 + 3x^2 - 2x \Rightarrow$
$y^5 - y^4 + y = x^4 + x^3 - x^2 + c$.

5. $xy' - \frac{\ln(x)}{y} = 0 \Rightarrow yy' = \frac{\ln(x)}{x} \Rightarrow \frac{1}{2}y^2 = \frac{1}{2}[\ln(x)]^2 + c_1 \Rightarrow y = \pm\sqrt{[\ln(x)]^2 + c}$,
$y(1) = -3 \Rightarrow c = 9$ and $y = -\sqrt{[\ln(x)]^2 + 9}$.

6. $xy' = (x + 1)e^y \Rightarrow e^{-y}y' = \frac{x+1}{x} = 1 + \frac{1}{x} \Rightarrow -e^{-y} = x + \ln|x| + c \Rightarrow$
$y = -\ln(-x - \ln|x| - c)$.

7. $y' = \frac{xy+x}{xy-y} \Rightarrow \frac{y}{y+1}y' = \frac{x}{x-1} \Rightarrow (1 - \frac{1}{y+1})y' = 1 + \frac{1}{x-1} \Rightarrow$
$y - \ln|y + 1| = x + \ln|x - 1| + c$, $y(2) = -2 \Rightarrow c = -4$.

8. $\cos(x)\ln(y)\frac{dy}{dx} = y\sin(x) \Rightarrow \frac{\ln(y)}{y}y' = \tan(x) \Rightarrow \frac{1}{2}[\ln(y)]^2 = \ln|\sec(x)| + c_1 \Rightarrow$
$\ln(y) = \pm\sqrt{2\ln|\sec(x)| + c} \Rightarrow y = e^{\pm\sqrt{2\ln|\sec(x)|+c}}$, $y(0) = e^2 \Rightarrow c = 4$ and
$y = e^{\sqrt{2\ln|\sec(x)|+4}}$.

9. $y' = \frac{x^2}{y} \Rightarrow yy' = x^2 \Rightarrow \frac{1}{2}y^2 = \frac{1}{3}x^3 + c_1 \Rightarrow y = \pm\sqrt{\frac{2}{3}x^3 + c}$ is the general solution.
The orthogonal trajectories:
$y' = -\frac{y}{x^2} \Rightarrow \frac{y'}{y} = -\frac{1}{x^2} \Rightarrow \ln|y| = \frac{1}{x} + c_1 \Rightarrow y = ce^{1/x}$.

10. $y' = 2x(y^2 + 1) \Rightarrow \frac{y'}{y^2+1} = 2x \Rightarrow \tan^{-1}(y) = x^2 + c \Rightarrow y = \tan(x^2 + c)$ is the
general solution. The orthogonal trajectories: $y' = \frac{-1}{2x(y^2+1)} \Rightarrow$
$(y^2 + 1)y' = \frac{-1}{2x} \Rightarrow \frac{1}{3}y^3 + y = -\frac{1}{2}\ln|x| + c_1$, or $3\ln|x| + 6y + 2y^3 = c$.

11. $y = x^3 + c \Rightarrow y' = 3x^2$. The orthogonal trajectories: $y' = \frac{-1}{3x^2} \Rightarrow y = \frac{1}{3x} + c$.

12. $y = kx^4 \Rightarrow x^{-4}y = k \Rightarrow -4x^{-5}y + x^{-4}y' = 0 \Rightarrow y' = \frac{4y}{x}$. The orthogonal
trajectories: $y' = \frac{-x}{4y} \Rightarrow 4yy' = -x \Rightarrow 2y^2 = -\frac{1}{2}x^2 + c_1 \Rightarrow y = \pm\sqrt{c - \frac{1}{4}x^2}$.

13. $y = e^{cx} > 0 \Rightarrow x^{-1}\ln(y) = c \Rightarrow -x^{-2}\ln(y) + x^{-1}y^{-1}y' = 0 \Rightarrow y' = \frac{y\ln(y)}{x}$. The orthogonal trajectories: $y' = \frac{-x}{y\ln(y)} \Rightarrow y\ln(y)y' = -x \Rightarrow$
$\frac{1}{2}y^2\ln(y) - \frac{1}{4}y^2 = -\frac{1}{2}x^2 + c_1$, or $2x^2 - y^2 + 2y^2\ln(y) = c$.

Exercises 2.2 – page 18

1. $y' = \frac{x+y}{x} = 1 + \frac{y}{x}$, $u = \frac{y}{x} \Rightarrow u + xu' = 1 + u \Rightarrow u' = \frac{1}{x} \Rightarrow u = \ln|x| + c \Rightarrow$
   $y = x(\ln|x| + c)$, $y(1) = 2 \Rightarrow c = 2$.

2. $xyy' = y^2 - x^2 \Rightarrow y' = \frac{y}{x} - \frac{x}{y}$, $u = \frac{y}{x} \Rightarrow u + xu' = u - \frac{1}{u} \Rightarrow uu' = -\frac{1}{x} \Rightarrow$
   $\frac{1}{2}u^2 = -\ln|x| + c_1 \Rightarrow u = \pm\sqrt{c - 2\ln|x|} \Rightarrow y = \pm x\sqrt{c - 2\ln|x|}$, $y(-1) = 2$
   $\Rightarrow c = 4$ and $y = -x\sqrt{c - 2\ln|x|}$.

3. $y' = \frac{\sqrt{x}}{\sqrt{y}} + \frac{y}{x}$, $u = \frac{y}{x} \Rightarrow u + xu' = \frac{1}{\sqrt{u}} + u \Rightarrow u^{1/2}u' = \frac{1}{x} \Rightarrow \frac{2}{3}u^{3/2} = \ln|x| + c_1 \Rightarrow$
   $u = \left(\frac{3}{2}\ln|x| + c\right)^{2/3} \Rightarrow y = x\left(\frac{3}{2}\ln|x| + c\right)^{2/3}$, $y(1) = 9 \Rightarrow c = 27$.

4. $y' = \frac{y}{x} + \frac{x}{\sqrt[3]{x^2y} + \sqrt{xy} + x} = \frac{y}{x} + \frac{1}{\sqrt[3]{\frac{y}{x}} + \sqrt{\frac{y}{x}} + 1}$, $u = \frac{y}{x} \Rightarrow u + xu' = u + \frac{1}{u^{1/3} + u^{1/2} + 1} \Rightarrow$
   $\left(u^{1/3} + u^{1/2} + 1\right)u' = \frac{1}{x} \Rightarrow \frac{3}{4}u^{4/3} + \frac{2}{3}u^{3/2} + u = \ln|x| + c \Rightarrow$
   $\frac{3}{4}\left(\frac{y}{x}\right)^{4/3} + \frac{2}{3}\left(\frac{y}{x}\right)^{3/2} + \frac{y}{x} = \ln|x| + c$.

5. $y + x\sec\left(\frac{y}{x}\right) - xy' = 0 \Rightarrow y' = \frac{y}{x} + \sec(\frac{y}{x})$, $u = \frac{y}{x} \Rightarrow u + xu' = u + \sec(u)$
   $\Rightarrow \cos(u)u' = \frac{1}{x} \Rightarrow \sin(u) = \ln|x| + c \Rightarrow u = \sin^{-1}(\ln|x| + c)$
   $\Rightarrow y = x\sin^{-1}(\ln|x| + c)$, $y(1) = \frac{\pi}{3} \Rightarrow c = \frac{\sqrt{3}}{2}$.

6. $y' = \frac{2x + 3y}{3x - 2y} = \frac{2 + 3\frac{y}{x}}{3 - 2\frac{y}{x}}$, $u = \frac{y}{x} \Rightarrow u + xu' = \frac{2 + 3u}{3 - 2u} \Rightarrow xu' = \frac{2 + 2u^2}{3 - 2u} \Rightarrow \frac{3 - 2u}{1 + u^2}u' = \frac{2}{x} \Rightarrow$
   $3\tan^{-1}(u) - \ln(1 + u^2) = 2\ln|x| + c \Rightarrow 3\tan^{-1}\left(\frac{y}{x}\right) - \ln\left(1 + \frac{y^2}{x^2}\right) = 2\ln|x| + c$.

7. $y' = \frac{x^3 + x^2y + xy^2 + y^3}{x^3 + x^2y + xy^2} = \frac{1 + \frac{y}{x} + (\frac{y}{x})^2 + (\frac{y}{x})^3}{1 + \frac{y}{x} + (\frac{y}{x})^2}$, $u = \frac{y}{x} \Rightarrow u + xu' = \frac{1 + u + u^2 + u^3}{1 + u + u^2}$
   $\Rightarrow xu' = \frac{1}{1 + u + u^2} \Rightarrow (1 + u + u^2)u' = \frac{1}{x} \Rightarrow u + \frac{1}{2}u^2 + \frac{1}{3}u^3 = \ln|x| + c$
   $\Rightarrow \frac{y}{x} + \frac{1}{2}\frac{y^2}{x^2} + \frac{1}{3}\frac{y^3}{x^3} = \ln|x| + c$.

8. $yy' = 6x + y \Rightarrow y' = \frac{6x}{y} + 1$, $u = \frac{y}{x} \Rightarrow u + xu' = \frac{6}{u} + 1 \Rightarrow xu' = \frac{6 + u - u^2}{u} \Rightarrow$
   $\frac{u}{u^2 - u - 6}u' = \frac{-1}{x} \Rightarrow \left(\frac{3}{5}\frac{1}{u - 3} + \frac{2}{5}\frac{1}{u + 2}\right)u' = \frac{-1}{x} \Rightarrow \frac{3}{5}\ln|u - 3| + \frac{2}{5}\ln|u + 2| = -\ln|x| + c$
   $\Rightarrow \frac{3}{5}\ln\left|\frac{y}{x} - 3\right| + \frac{2}{5}\ln\left|\frac{y}{x} + 2\right| = -\ln|x| + c$, $y(1) = 4 \Rightarrow c = \frac{2}{5}\ln(6)$.

Exercises 2.3 – page 23

1. $y' + y = e^{-x}$, $I(x) = e^{\int 1\,dx} = e^x \Rightarrow (e^x y)' = 1 \Rightarrow e^x y = x + c \Rightarrow y = (x + c)e^{-x}$,
   $y(0) = -2 \Rightarrow c = -2$.

2. $y' - 3y = 1$, $I(x) = e^{\int -3\,dx} = e^{-3x} \Rightarrow (e^{-3x}y)' = e^{-3x} \Rightarrow e^{-3x}y = \frac{-1}{3}e^{-3x} + c \Rightarrow$
   $y = ce^{3x} - \frac{1}{3}$.

3. $e^x y' + 2e^x y - 1 = 0 \Rightarrow y' + 2y = e^{-x}$, $I(x) = e^{\int 2\,dx} = e^{2x} \Rightarrow (e^{2x}y)' = e^x \Rightarrow$
   $e^{2x}y = e^x + c \Rightarrow y = e^{-x} + ce^{-2x}$, $y(0) = -3 \Rightarrow c = -4$.

4. $y' + 2xy = 2x$, $I(x) = e^{\int 2x\,dx} = e^{x^2} \Rightarrow \left(e^{x^2}y\right)' = 2xe^{x^2} \Rightarrow e^{x^2}y = e^{x^2} + c \Rightarrow$
   $y = 1 + ce^{-x^2}$.

5. $xy' + y = \frac{1}{x} \Rightarrow y' + \frac{1}{x}y = \frac{1}{x^2}$, $I(x) = e^{\int \frac{1}{x}\,dx} = e^{\ln(x)} = x \Rightarrow (xy)' = \frac{1}{x} \Rightarrow$
   $xy = \ln(x) + c \Rightarrow y = \frac{1}{x}[\ln(x) + c]$, $y(1) = 2 \Rightarrow c = 2$.

6. $x^3 y' - 2y + 1 = 0 \Rightarrow y' - \frac{2}{x^3}y = -\frac{1}{x^3}$, $I(x) = e^{\int -\frac{2}{x^3}\,dx} = e^{\frac{1}{x^2}} \Rightarrow \left(e^{\frac{1}{x^2}}y\right)' = -\frac{1}{x^3}e^{\frac{1}{x^2}}$
   $\Rightarrow e^{\frac{1}{x^2}}y = \frac{1}{2}e^{\frac{1}{x^2}} + c \Rightarrow y = \frac{1}{2} + ce^{-\frac{1}{x^2}}$.

7. $x^2 y' + xy = \frac{1}{\ln(x)} \Rightarrow y' + \frac{1}{x}y = \frac{1}{x^2 \ln(x)}$, $I(x) = e^{\int \frac{1}{x}\,dx} = e^{\ln(x)} = x \Rightarrow (xy)' = \frac{1}{x\ln(x)}$
   $\Rightarrow xy = \ln|\ln(x)| + c \Rightarrow y = \frac{1}{x}(\ln|\ln(x)| + c)$.

8. $\cos(x)y' + \sin(x)y = \cos^4(x) \Rightarrow y' + \tan(x)y = \cos^3(x)$,
   $I(x) = e^{\int \tan(x)\,dx} = e^{\ln|\sec(x)|} = |\sec(x)| = \pm\sec(x)$, and $I(x) = \sec(x)$
   $\Rightarrow [\sec(x)y]' = \cos^2(x)$
   $\Rightarrow \sec(x)y = \int \cos^2(x)\,dx = \frac{1}{2}\int 1 + \cos(2x)\,dx = \frac{x}{2} + \frac{1}{4}\sin(2x) + c$
   $\Rightarrow y = \cos(x)\left[\frac{x}{2} + \frac{1}{4}\sin(2x) + c\right]$, $y(\pi) = \frac{\pi}{2} \Rightarrow c = -\pi$.

9. $xy' + 2y = e^{-x} \Rightarrow y' + \frac{2}{x}y = \frac{e^{-x}}{x}$, $I(x) = e^{\int \frac{2}{x}\,dx} = e^{2\ln|x|} = |x|^2 = x^2 \Rightarrow$
   $(x^2 y)' = xe^{-x} \Rightarrow x^2 y = -xe^{-x} - e^{-x} + c \Rightarrow y = \frac{1}{x^2}(c - e^{-x} - xe^{-x})$.

10. $xy' - y = \frac{x^3}{x+1} \Rightarrow y' - \frac{1}{x}y = \frac{x^2}{x+1}$, $I(x) = e^{\int -\frac{1}{x}\,dx} = e^{-\ln|x|} = \frac{1}{|x|} = \pm\frac{1}{x}$,
    and $I(x) = \frac{1}{x} \Rightarrow \left(\frac{1}{x}y\right)' = \frac{x}{x+1} = 1 - \frac{1}{x+1} \Rightarrow \frac{1}{x}y = x - \ln|x+1| + c \Rightarrow$
    $y = x(x - \ln|x+1| + c)$.

11. $y' + y = \frac{e^{-x}}{x^2+2x+2}$, $I(x) = e^{\int 1\,dx} = e^x \Rightarrow (e^x y)' = \frac{1}{x^2+2x+2}$
    $\Rightarrow e^x y = \int \frac{1}{x^2+2x+2}\,dx = \int \frac{1}{(x+1)^2+1}\,dx = \tan^{-1}(x+1) + c$
    $\Rightarrow y = e^{-x}[\tan^{-1}(x+1) + c]$.

12. $x\ln(x)y' + y = \frac{2x}{x^2-1} \Rightarrow y' + \frac{1}{x\ln(x)}y = \frac{2}{(x^2-1)\ln(x)}$,
    $I(x) = e^{\int \frac{1}{x\ln(x)}\,dx} = e^{\ln|\ln(x)|} = |\ln(x)| = \pm\ln(x)$, and $I(x) = \ln(x)$
    $\Rightarrow (\ln(x)y)' = \frac{2}{(x^2-1)} = \frac{1}{x-1} - \frac{1}{x+1} \Rightarrow \ln(x)y = \ln|x-1| - \ln(x+1) + c \Rightarrow$
    $y = \frac{1}{\ln(x)}[\ln|x-1| - \ln(x+1) + c]$.

13. $3y' - y = \frac{1}{y^2}$ is a Bernoulli equation with $\alpha = -2$. $u = y^{1-\alpha} = y^3 \Rightarrow y = u^{1/3}$
    $\Rightarrow y' = \frac{1}{3}u^{-2/3}u' \Rightarrow u^{-2/3}u' - u^{1/3} = u^{-2/3} \Rightarrow u' - u = 1$, which is linear,
    and $I(x) = e^{-x} \Rightarrow (e^{-x}u)' = e^{-x} \Rightarrow e^{-x}u = -e^{-x} + c \Rightarrow u = ce^x - 1 \Rightarrow$
    $y = u^{1/3} = (ce^x - 1)^{1/3}$, $y(0) = 2 \Rightarrow c = 9$.

14. $y' + 4y = 2e^{-x}\sqrt{y}$ is a Bernoulli equation with $\alpha = \frac{1}{2}$. $u = y^{1-\alpha} = y^{1/2}$ $\Rightarrow y = u^2 \Rightarrow y' = 2uu' \Rightarrow 2uu' + 4u^2 = 2e^{-x}u \Rightarrow u' + 2u = e^{-x}$, which is linear, and $I(x) = e^{2x} \Rightarrow (e^{2x}u)' = e^x \Rightarrow e^{2x}u = e^x + c \Rightarrow u = e^{-x} + ce^{-2x} \Rightarrow y = u^2 = (e^{-x} + ce^{-2x})^2$.

15. $2x^2y' - 2xy = -y^3\sin(x)$ is a Bernoulli equation with $\alpha = 3$. $u = y^{1-\alpha} = y^{-2}$ $\Rightarrow y = u^{-1/2} \Rightarrow y' = -\frac{1}{2}u^{-3/2}u' \Rightarrow -x^2u^{-3/2}u' - 2xu^{-1/2} = -u^{-3/2}\sin(x) \Rightarrow$ $x^2u' + 2xu = \sin(x) \Rightarrow (x^2u)' = \sin(x) \Rightarrow x^2u = -\cos(x) + c \Rightarrow u = \frac{c-\cos(x)}{x^2} \Rightarrow$ $y = u^{-1/2} = \pm\frac{x}{\sqrt{c-\cos(x)}}$, $y\left(\frac{\pi}{2}\right) = \pi \Rightarrow c = \frac{1}{4}$ and $y = \frac{x}{\sqrt{\frac{1}{4}-\cos(x)}} = \frac{2x}{\sqrt{1-4\cos(x)}}$.

16. $xyy' + y^2 - xe^x = 0 \Rightarrow xy' + y = \frac{xe^x}{y}$ is a Bernoulli equation with $\alpha = -1$. $u = y^{1-\alpha} = y^2 \Rightarrow y = u^{1/2} \Rightarrow y' = \frac{1}{2}u^{-1/2}u' \Rightarrow \frac{x}{2}u^{-1/2}u' + u^{1/2} = xe^xu^{-1/2} \Rightarrow$ $u' + \frac{2}{x}u = 2e^x$, $I(x) = e^{2\ln|x|} = x^2 \Rightarrow (x^2u)' = 2x^2e^x \Rightarrow$ $x^2u = \int 2x^2e^x\,dx = 2x^2e^x - 4xe^x + 4e^x + c \Rightarrow u = \frac{1}{x^2}(2x^2e^x - 4xe^x + 4e^x + c) \Rightarrow$ $y = u^{1/2} = \pm\frac{1}{x}\sqrt{2x^2e^x - 4xe^x + 4e^x + c}$.

17. $x\ln(x)y' + y = 2y\sqrt{y}$ is a Bernoulli equation with $\alpha = \frac{3}{2}$. $u = y^{1-\alpha} = y^{-1/2} \Rightarrow$ $y = u^{-2} \Rightarrow y' = -2u^{-3}u' \Rightarrow -2x\ln(x)u^{-3}u' + u^{-2} = 2u^{-3} \Rightarrow u' - \frac{u}{2x\ln(x)} = \frac{-1}{x\ln(x)}$, $I(x) = e^{\int -\frac{1}{2x\ln(x)}\,dx} = e^{-\frac{1}{2}\ln[\ln(x)]} = [\ln(x)]^{-1/2} \Rightarrow \{[\ln(x)]^{-1/2}u\}' = -\frac{[\ln(x)]^{-3/2}}{x} \Rightarrow$ $[\ln(x)]^{-1/2}u = 2[\ln(x)]^{-1/2} + c \Rightarrow u = 2 + c\sqrt{\ln(x)} \Rightarrow y = u^{-2} = [2 + c\sqrt{\ln(x)}]^{-2}$.

Exercises 2.4 – page 27

1. $f(x,y) = x^3 - y^2 + x^2y^2 + 1$.

   (a) $f(1,0) = 2$, $f(3,1) = 36$, $f(1,3) = 2$, $f(2,-1) = 12$.

   (b) $f_x(x,y) = 3x^2 + 2xy^2$,
       $f_x(1,0) = 3$, $f_x(3,1) = 33$, $f_x(1,3) = 21$, $f_x(2,-1) = 16$.
       $f_y(x,y) = -2y + 2x^2y$,
       $f_y(1,0) = 0$, $f_y(3,1) = 16$, $f_y(1,3) = 0$, $f_y(2,-1) = -6$.

   (c) $f_{xx}(x,y) = 6x + 2y^2$,
       $f_{xx}(1,0) = 6$, $f_{xx}(3,1) = 20$, $f_{xx}(1,3) = 24$, $f_{xx}(2,-1) = 14$,
       $f_{xy}(x,y) = f_{yx}(x,y) = 4xy$,
       $f_{xy}(1,0) = 0$, $f_{xy}(3,1) = 12$, $f_{xy}(1,3) = 12$, $f_{xy}(2,-1) = -8$.
       $f_{yy}(x,y) = 2x^2 - 2$,
       $f_{yy}(1,0) = 0$, $f_{yy}(3,1) = 16$, $f_{yy}(1,3) = 0$, $f_{yy}(2,-1) = 6$.

2. $f(x,y) = x^2\ln(y) - y^3e^x + x^3 - y^2 + 1$.
   $f_x = 2x\ln(y) - y^3e^x + 3x^2$, $f_y = \frac{x^2}{y} - 3y^2e^x - 2y$,
   $f_{xx} = 2\ln(y) - y^3e^x + 6x$, $f_{xy} = f_{yx} = \frac{2x}{y} - 3y^2e^x$, $f_{yy} = -\frac{x^2}{y^2} - 6ye^x - 2$.

3. $f(x,y) = x^4 + 3x^2y^2 + y^4$, $x(t) = t^2 + 2t$, $y(t) = t^3 - 2t$.
   $\frac{d}{dt}f(x(t),y(t)) = f_x\frac{dx}{dt} + f_y\frac{dy}{dt} = (4x^3 + 6xy^2)(2t + 2) + (6x^2y + 4y^3)(3t^2 - 2)$.

4. $f(x, y) = x^2 - \cos(y) + x\sin(y)$, $x(t) = 2t^2 + 3t - 1$, $y(t) = e^t + 2t$.
$\frac{d}{dt}f(x(t), y(t)) = [2x + \sin(y)](4t + 3) + [\sin(y) + x\cos(y)](e^t + 2)$.

5. $f(x, y) = \sin(xy) + \sqrt{xy}$, $x(t) = e^t + 1$, $y(t) = \ln(t)$.
$\frac{d}{dt}f(x(t), y(t)) = \left[y\cos(xy) + \frac{\sqrt{y}}{2\sqrt{x}}\right]e^t + \left[x\cos(xy) + \frac{\sqrt{x}}{2\sqrt{y}}\right]\frac{1}{t}$.

6. $f(x, y) = x^4 + 3x^2y^2 + y^4$, $y(x) = x^3 + 6x^2 - x$.
$\frac{d}{dx}f(x, y(x)) = f_x + f_y\frac{dy}{dx} = 4x^3 + 6xy^2 + (6x^2y + 4y^3)(3x^2 + 12x - 1)$.

7. $f(x, y) = e^y - x^2 + y^3\ln(x)$, $y(x) = \sin(x)$.
$\frac{d}{dx}f(x, y(x)) = -2x + \frac{y^3}{x} + [e^y + 3y^2\ln(x)]\cos(x)$.

8. $f(x, y) = \frac{1}{x^2+y^2} + xe^{-y}$, $y(x) = \sin(2x)$.
$\frac{d}{dx}f(x, y(x)) = \frac{-2x}{(x^2+y^2)^2} + e^{-y} + \left[\frac{-2y}{(x^2+y^2)^2} - xe^{-y}\right][2\cos(2x)]$.

9. $f(x, y) = x^4 - y^4 - 1$.
$f(x, y) = 0 \Rightarrow f_x + f_y\frac{dy}{dx} = 0 \Rightarrow \frac{dy}{dx} = -\frac{f_x}{f_y} = \frac{-4x^3}{-4y^3} = \frac{x^3}{y^3}$.

10. $f(x, y) = x^3 + y^2 - e^y$.
$f(x, y) = 0 \Rightarrow f_x + f_y\frac{dy}{dx} = 0 \Rightarrow \frac{dy}{dx} = -\frac{f_x}{f_y} = \frac{-3x^2}{2y - e^y}$.

Exercises 2.5 – page 36

1. $3x^2 + y + 1 - (3y^2 - x + 1)y' = 0$, $P_y = 1 = Q_x \Rightarrow$ the equation is exact.
$f_x = P = 3x^2 + y + 1 \Rightarrow f(x, y) = x^3 + xy + x + g(y)$,
$f_y = Q \Rightarrow x + g'(y) = x - 3y^2 - 1 \Rightarrow g'(y) = -3y^2 - 1$
$\Rightarrow g(y) = -y^3 - y + c \Rightarrow f(x, y) = x^3 + xy + x - y^3 - y + c$, and the general
solution is $f(x, y) = c_1$, or $x^3 + xy + x - y^3 - y = k$, where $k = c_1 - c$.

2. $xy + x + 1 + \left(\frac{1}{2}x^2 + y + 1\right)\frac{dy}{dx} = 0$, $P_y = x = Q_x \Rightarrow$ the equation is exact.
$f_x = P = xy + x + 1 \Rightarrow f(x, y) = \frac{1}{2}x^2y + \frac{1}{2}x^2 + x + g(y)$,
$f_y = Q \Rightarrow \frac{1}{2}x^2 + g'(y) = \frac{1}{2}x^2 + y + 1 \Rightarrow g'(y) = y + 1 \Rightarrow g(y) = \frac{1}{2}y^2 + y + c$
$\Rightarrow f(x, y) = \frac{1}{2}x^2y + \frac{1}{2}x^2 + x + \frac{1}{2}y^2 + y + c \Rightarrow \frac{1}{2}x^2y + \frac{1}{2}x^2 + x + \frac{1}{2}y^2 + y = k$.

3. $3x^2y^2 - 2x + (2x^3y + 3y^2)y' = 0$, $P_y = 6x^2y = Q_x \Rightarrow$ the equation is exact.
$f_x = P = 3x^2y^2 - 2x \Rightarrow f(x, y) = x^3y^2 - x^2 + g(y)$,
$f_y = Q \Rightarrow 2x^3y + g'(y) = 2x^3y + 3y^2 \Rightarrow g'(y) = 3y^2 \Rightarrow g(y) = y^3 + c$
$\Rightarrow f(x, y) = x^3y^2 - x^2 + y^3 + c \Rightarrow x^3y^2 - x^2 + y^3 = k$.

4. $y^3 - 3x^2y^2 + 4x^3 + (3xy^2 - 2x^3y - 4y^3)y' = 0$, $P_y = 3y^2 - 6x^2y = Q_x \Rightarrow$ the equation
is exact. $f_x = P = y^3 - 3x^2y^2 + 4x^3 \Rightarrow f(x, y) = xy^3 - x^3y^2 + x^4 + g(y)$, $f_y = Q$
$\Rightarrow 3xy^2 - 2x^3y + g'(y) = 3xy^2 - 2x^3y - 4y^3 \Rightarrow g'(y) = -4y^3 \Rightarrow g(y) = -y^4 + c$
$\Rightarrow f(x, y) = xy^3 - x^3y^2 + x^4 - y^4 + c \Rightarrow xy^3 - x^3y^2 + x^4 - y^4 = k$. $y(0) = 1 \Rightarrow$
$k = -1$.

5. $y' = \frac{3x^2y^2-y-2xy^3}{3x^2y^2-2x^3y+x} \Rightarrow 2xy^3 - 3x^2y^2 + y + (3x^2y^2 - 2x^3y + x)y' = 0$ is exact because
$P_y = 6xy^2 - 6x^2y + 1 = Q_x$. $f_x = P = 2xy^3 - 3x^2y^2 + y \Rightarrow$
$f(x,y) = x^2y^3 - x^3y^2 + xy + g(y)$, $f_y = Q \Rightarrow$
$3x^2y^2 - 2x^3y + x + g'(y) = 3x^2y^2 - 2x^3y + x \Rightarrow g'(y) = 0 \Rightarrow g(y) = c \Rightarrow$
$f(x,y) = x^2y^3 - x^3y^2 + xy + c \Rightarrow x^2y^3 - x^3y^2 + xy = k$. $y(2) = 1 \Rightarrow k = -2$.

6. $\frac{\sqrt{y}}{2\sqrt{x}} + y + \left(\frac{\sqrt{x}}{2\sqrt{y}} + x\right)\frac{dy}{dx} = 0$, $P_y = \frac{1}{4\sqrt{xy}} + 1 = Q_x \Rightarrow$ the equation is exact.
$f_x = P = \frac{\sqrt{y}}{2\sqrt{x}} + y \Rightarrow f(x,y) = \sqrt{xy} + xy + g(y)$, $f_y = Q \Rightarrow$
$\frac{\sqrt{x}}{2\sqrt{y}} + x + g'(y) = \frac{\sqrt{x}}{2\sqrt{y}} + x \Rightarrow g'(y) = 0 \Rightarrow g(y) = c \Rightarrow f(x,y) = \sqrt{xy} + xy + c$
$\Rightarrow \sqrt{xy} + xy = k$. $y(1) = 4 \Rightarrow k = 6$.

7. $(6xy + e^y)y' + xe^x + 3y^2 = 0$, $P_y = 6y = Q_x \Rightarrow$ the equation is exact.
$f_x = P = xe^x + 3y^2 \Rightarrow f(x,y) = xe^x - e^x + 3xy^2 + g(y)$, $f_y = Q \Rightarrow$
$6xy + g'(y) = 6xy + e^y \Rightarrow g'(y) = e^y \Rightarrow g(y) = e^y + c$
$\Rightarrow f(x,y) = xe^x - e^x + 3xy^2 + e^y + c \Rightarrow xe^x - e^x + 3xy^2 + e^y = k$.

8. $2xe^{x^2+y^2} + 4x^3 + \left(2ye^{x^2+y^2} - 2y\right)\frac{dy}{dx} = 0$, $P_y = 4xye^{x^2+y^2} = Q_x \Rightarrow$ the equation
is exact. $f_x = P = 2xe^{x^2+y^2} + 4x^3 \Rightarrow f(x,y) = e^{x^2+y^2} + x^4 + g(y)$, $f_y = Q$
$\Rightarrow 2ye^{x^2+y^2} + g'(y) = 2ye^{x^2+y^2} - 2y \Rightarrow g'(y) = -2y \Rightarrow g(y) = -y^2 + c \Rightarrow$
$f(x,y) = e^{x^2+y^2} + x^4 - y^2 + c \Rightarrow e^{x^2+y^2} + x^4 - y^2 = k$.

9. $e^{x+y} + x + y + \cos(x) + (e^{x+y} + x - y)y' = 0$, $P_y = e^{x+y} + 1 = Q_x \Rightarrow$ the equation is
exact. $f_x = P = e^{x+y} + x + y + \cos(x) \Rightarrow f(x,y) = e^{x+y} + \frac{1}{2}x^2 + xy + \sin(x) + g(y)$,
$f_y = Q \Rightarrow e^{x+y} + x + g'(y) = e^{x+y} + x - y \Rightarrow g'(y) = -y \Rightarrow g(y) = -\frac{1}{2}y^2 + c \Rightarrow$
$f(x,y) = e^{x+y} + \frac{1}{2}x^2 + xy + \sin(x) - \frac{1}{2}y^2 + c \Rightarrow e^{x+y} + \frac{1}{2}x^2 + xy + \sin(x) - \frac{1}{2}y^2 = k$.

10. $\frac{x}{x^2+y^2+1} - 2x + \left(\frac{y}{x^2+y^2+1} + 2y\right)\frac{dy}{dx} = 0$, $P_y = \frac{-2xy}{(x^2+y^2+1)^2} = Q_x \Rightarrow$ the equation
is exact. $f_x = P = \frac{x}{x^2+y^2+1} - 2x \Rightarrow f(x,y) = \frac{1}{2}\ln(x^2 + y^2 + 1) - x^2 + g(y)$,
$f_y = Q \Rightarrow \frac{y}{x^2+y^2+1} + g'(y) = \frac{y}{x^2+y^2+1} + 2y \Rightarrow g'(y) = 2y \Rightarrow g(y) = y^2 + c \Rightarrow$
$f(x,y) = \frac{1}{2}\ln(x^2 + y^2 + 1) - x^2 + y^2 + c \Rightarrow \frac{1}{2}\ln(x^2 + y^2 + 1) - x^2 + y^2 = k$.
$y(0) = 0 \Rightarrow k = 0$.

11. $\frac{2x+2}{x^2+y^2+2x-3y+3} + 1 + \frac{2y-3}{x^2+y^2+2x-3y+3}\frac{dy}{dx} = 0$, $P_y = \frac{-(2x+2)(2y-3)}{(x^2+y^2+2x-3y+3)^2} = Q_x \Rightarrow$ the
equation is exact. $f_x = P = \frac{2x+2}{x^2+y^2+2x-3y+3} + 1$
$\Rightarrow f(x,y) = \ln(x^2 + y^2 + 2x - 3y + 3) + x + g(y)$, $f_y = Q \Rightarrow$
$\frac{2y-3}{x^2+y^2+2x-3y+3} + g'(y) = \frac{2y-3}{x^2+y^2+2x-3y+3} \Rightarrow g'(y) = 0 \Rightarrow g(y) = c \Rightarrow$
$f(x,y) = \ln(x^2 + y^2 + 2x - 3y + 3) + x + c \Rightarrow \ln(x^2 + y^2 + 2x - 3y + 3) + x = k$.

12. $\frac{x}{\sqrt{x^2+y^2}} + 1 + \left(\frac{y}{\sqrt{x^2+y^2}} + 1\right)\frac{dy}{dx} = 0$.

   (a) $P_y = \frac{-xy}{(x^2+y^2)^{3/2}} = Q_x$ on $R = \{(x,y) : (x,y) \neq (0,0)\}$.

(b) $f_x = P = \frac{x}{\sqrt{x^2+y^2}} + 1 \Rightarrow f(x,y) = \sqrt{x^2+y^2} + x + g(y)$, $f_y = Q \Rightarrow$

$\frac{y}{\sqrt{x^2+y^2}} + g'(y) = \frac{y}{\sqrt{x^2+y^2}} + 1 \Rightarrow g'(y) = 1 \Rightarrow g(y) = y + c$

$\Rightarrow f(x,y) = \sqrt{x^2+y^2} + x + y + c \Rightarrow \sqrt{x^2+y^2} + x + y = k.$

(c) $f(x,y) = \sqrt{x^2+y^2} + x + y + c$ is a potential function, hence the equation is exact in R, even though the region R is not simply connected..

13. $\frac{y}{x^2+y^2} - \frac{x}{x^2+y^2} y' = 0$.

(a) $P_y = \frac{x^2-y^2}{(x^2+y^2)^2} = Q_x$ on $R = \{(x,y) : (x,y) \neq (0,0)\}$.

(b) $f_x = P = \frac{y}{x^2+y^2} \Rightarrow f(x,y) = \int \frac{y}{x^2+y^2} \, dx = \int \frac{1}{(\frac{x}{y})^2+1} \frac{1}{y} \, dx = \tan^{-1}(\frac{x}{y}) + g(y)$,

$f_y = Q \Rightarrow \frac{1}{(\frac{x}{y})^2+1}\left(-\frac{x}{y^2}\right) + g'(y) = \frac{-x}{x^2+y^2} + g'(y) = -\frac{x}{x^2+y^2} \Rightarrow g(y) = c \Rightarrow$

$f(x,y) = \tan^{-1}\left(\frac{x}{y}\right) + c \Rightarrow \tan^{-1}\left(\frac{x}{y}\right) = k \Rightarrow \frac{x}{y} = \tan(k) = k_1.$

(c) $f(x,y) = \tan^{-1}(\frac{x}{y}) + c$ is multi-valued in R, hence not a (well-defined) function. Hence, the equation is not exact in R. This is possible because R is not simply connected, despite the fact that $P_y = Q_x$ in R.

14. $x + 6y^2 + 4xyy' = 0$, $P_y = 12y$, $Q_x = 4y$, $P_y \neq Q_x \Rightarrow$ the equation is not exact. $\frac{P_y - Q_x}{Q} = \frac{8y}{4xy} = \frac{2}{x}$ is independent of $y \Rightarrow$ an integrating factor $I(x)$ exists, and $\frac{I'(x)}{I(x)} = \frac{2}{x} \Rightarrow \ln|I(x)| = 2\ln|x| \Rightarrow I(x) = \pm x^2$ and, with $I(x) = x^2$, the equation becomes $x^3 + 6x^2y^2 + 4x^3yy' = 0$, which is exact. Then $f_x = x^3 + 6x^2y^2$ $\Rightarrow f(x,y) = \frac{1}{4}x^4 + 2x^3y^2 + g(y)$, $f_y = 4x^3y + g'(y) = 4x^3y \Rightarrow g(y) = c \Rightarrow$ $f(x,y) = \frac{1}{4}x^4 + 2x^3y^2 + c \Rightarrow \frac{1}{4}x^4 + 2x^3y^2 = k.$ $y(2) = 0 \Rightarrow k = 4 \Rightarrow y^2 = \frac{4 - \frac{1}{4}x^4}{2x^3}$ $\Rightarrow y = \pm\sqrt{\frac{2}{x^3} - \frac{x}{8}}.$

15. $x^3 + 2y^2 + xyy' = 0$, $P_y = 4y$, $Q_x = y$, $P_y \neq Q_x \Rightarrow$ the equation is not exact. $\frac{P_y - Q_x}{Q} = \frac{3y}{xy} = \frac{3}{x}$ is independent of $y \Rightarrow$ an integrating factor $I(x)$ exists, and $\frac{I'(x)}{I(x)} = \frac{3}{x} \Rightarrow \ln|I(x)| = 3\ln|x| \Rightarrow I(x) = \pm x^3$. With $I(x) = x^3$, the equation becomes $x^6 + 2x^3y^2 + x^4yy' = 0$, which is exact. Then $f_x = x^6 + 2x^3y^2$ $\Rightarrow f(x,y) = \frac{1}{7}x^7 + \frac{1}{2}x^4y^2 + g(y)$, $f_y = x^4y + g'(y) = x^4y \Rightarrow g(y) = c \Rightarrow$ $f(x,y) = \frac{1}{7}x^7 + \frac{1}{2}x^4y^2 + c \Rightarrow \frac{1}{7}x^7 + \frac{1}{2}x^4y^2 = k.$

16. $e^{-x} - \cos(y) + \sin(y)y' = 0$, $P_y = \sin(y)$, $Q_x = 0$, $P_y \neq Q_x \Rightarrow$ the equation is not exact. $\frac{P_y - Q_x}{Q} = \frac{\sin(y)}{\sin(y)} = 1$ is independent of $y \Rightarrow$ an integrating factor $I(x)$ exists, and $\frac{I'(x)}{I(x)} = 1 \Rightarrow \ln|I(x)| = x \Rightarrow I(x) = \pm e^x$. With $I(x) = e^x$, the equation becomes $1 - e^x\cos(y) + e^x\sin(y)y' = 0$, which is exact. Then $f_x = 1 - e^x\cos(y)$ $\Rightarrow f(x,y) = x - e^x\cos(y) + g(y)$, $f_y = e^x\sin(y) + g'(y) = e^x\sin(y) \Rightarrow g(y) = c$ $\Rightarrow f(x,y) = x - e^x\cos(y) + c \Rightarrow x - e^x\cos(y) = k.$

17. $xe^{x^2} + xy^2 + yy' = 0$, $P_y = 2xy$, $Q_x = 0$, $P_y \neq Q_x \Rightarrow$ the equation is not exact. $\frac{P_y - Q_x}{Q} = \frac{2xy}{y} = 2x$ is independent of $y \Rightarrow$ an integrating factor $I(x)$ exists, and $\frac{I'(x)}{I(x)} = 2x \Rightarrow \ln|I(x)| = x^2 \Rightarrow I(x) = \pm e^{x^2}$. With $I(x) = e^{x^2}$, the equation becomes $xe^{2x^2} + xe^{x^2}y^2 + e^{x^2}yy' = 0$, which is exact. Then $f_x = xe^{2x^2} + xe^{x^2}y^2 \Rightarrow f(x,y) = \frac{1}{4}e^{2x^2} + \frac{1}{2}e^{x^2}y^2 + g(y)$, $f_y = e^{x^2}y + g'(y) = e^{x^2}y \Rightarrow g(y) = c \Rightarrow f(x,y) = \frac{1}{4}e^{2x^2} + \frac{1}{2}e^{x^2}y^2 + c \Rightarrow \frac{1}{4}e^{2x^2} + \frac{1}{2}e^{x^2}y^2 = k$.

18. $\sqrt{x} + y^2 + 4xyy' = 0$, $P_y = 2y$, $Q_x = 4y$, $P_y \neq Q_x \Rightarrow$ the equation is not exact. $\frac{P_y - Q_x}{Q} = \frac{-2y}{4xy} = \frac{-1}{2x}$ is independent of $y \Rightarrow$ an integrating factor $I(x)$ exists, and $\frac{I'(x)}{I(x)} = \frac{-1}{2x} \Rightarrow \ln|I(x)| = -\frac{1}{2}\ln(x) \Rightarrow I(x) = \pm x^{-1/2}$. With $I(x) = x^{-1/2}$, the equation becomes $1 + x^{-1/2}y^2 + 4x^{1/2}yy' = 0$, which is exact. Then $f_x = 1 + x^{-1/2}y^2 \Rightarrow f(x,y) = x + 2x^{1/2}y^2 + g(y)$, $f_y = 4x^{1/2}y + g'(y) = 4x^{1/2}y \Rightarrow g(y) = c \Rightarrow f(x,y) = x + 2x^{1/2}y^2 + c \Rightarrow x + 2\sqrt{x}\,y^2 = k$.

19. $x + y^2 + 3xyy' = 0$, $P_y = 2y$, $Q_x = 3y$, $P_y \neq Q_x \Rightarrow$ the equation is not exact. $\frac{P_y - Q_x}{Q} = \frac{-y}{3xy} = \frac{-1}{3x}$ is independent of $y \Rightarrow$ an integrating factor $I(x)$ exists, and $\frac{I'(x)}{I(x)} = \frac{-1}{3x} \Rightarrow \ln|I(x)| = -\frac{1}{3}\ln|x| \Rightarrow I(x) = \pm x^{-1/3}$. With $I(x) = x^{-1/3}$, the equation becomes $x^{2/3} + x^{-1/3}y^2 + 3x^{2/3}yy' = 0$, which is exact. Then $f_x = x^{2/3} + x^{-1/3}y^2 \Rightarrow f(x,y) = \frac{3}{5}x^{5/3} + \frac{3}{2}x^{2/3}y^2 + g(y)$, $f_y = 3x^{2/3}y + g'(y) = 3x^{2/3}y \Rightarrow g(y) = c \Rightarrow f(x,y) = \frac{3}{5}x^{5/3} + \frac{3}{2}x^{2/3}y^2 + c \Rightarrow \frac{3}{5}x^{5/3} + \frac{3}{2}x^{2/3}y^2 = k$, or $6x^{5/3} + 15x^{2/3}y^2 = k_1$, where $k_1 = 10k$.

20. $4xy + (6x^2 + y)y' = 0$, $P_y = 4x$, $Q_x = 12x$, $P_y \neq Q_x \Rightarrow$ the equation is not exact. $\frac{P_y - Q_x}{Q} = \frac{-8x}{6x^2 + y}$ is not independent of $y \Rightarrow I(x)$ does not exist. However, $\frac{Q_x - P_y}{P} = \frac{8x}{4xy} = \frac{2}{y}$ is independent of $x \Rightarrow$ an integrating factor $I(y)$ exists, and $\frac{I'(y)}{I(y)} = \frac{2}{y} \Rightarrow \ln|I(y)| = 2\ln|y| \Rightarrow I(y) = \pm y^2$. With $I(y) = y^2$, the equation becomes $4xy^3 + (6x^2y^2 + y^3)y' = 0$, which is exact. Then $f_x = 4xy^3 \Rightarrow f(x,y) = 2x^2y^3 + g(y)$, $f_y = 6x^2y^2 + g'(y) = 6x^2y^2 + y^3 \Rightarrow g'(y) = y^3 \Rightarrow g(y) = \frac{1}{4}y^4 + c \Rightarrow f(x,y) = 2x^2y^3 + \frac{1}{4}y^4 + c \Rightarrow 2x^2y^3 + \frac{1}{4}y^4 = k$, or $8x^2y^3 + y^4 = k_1$. $y(1) = 1 \Rightarrow k_1 = 9$.

21. $\sin(x) + [e^{-y} - \cos(x)]y' = 0$, $P_y = 0$, $Q_x = \sin(x)$, $P_y \neq Q_x \Rightarrow$ the equation is not exact. $\frac{Q_x - P_y}{P} = \frac{\sin(x)}{\sin(x)} = 1$ is independent of $x \Rightarrow$ an integrating factor $I(y)$ exists, and $\frac{I'(y)}{I(y)} = 1 \Rightarrow \ln|I(y)| = y \Rightarrow I(y) = \pm e^y$. With $I(y) = e^y$, the equation becomes $\sin(x)e^y + [1 - \cos(x)e^y]y' = 0$, which is exact. Then $f_x = \sin(x)e^y \Rightarrow f(x,y) = -\cos(x)e^y + g(y)$, $f_y = -\cos(x)e^y + g'(y) = 1 - \cos(x)e^y \Rightarrow g'(y) = 1 \Rightarrow g(y) = y + c \Rightarrow f(x,y) = -\cos(x)e^y + y + c \Rightarrow y - \cos(x)e^y = k$.

22. $y + (1 + 2x + xy)y' = 0$, $P_y = 1$, $Q_x = 2 + y$, $P_y \neq Q_x \Rightarrow$ the equation is not exact. $\frac{Q_x - P_y}{P} = \frac{y+1}{y} = 1 + \frac{1}{y}$ is independent of $x \Rightarrow$ an integrating factor $I(y)$ exists,

and $\frac{I'(y)}{I(y)} = 1 + \frac{1}{y} \Rightarrow \ln|I(y)| = y + \ln|y| \Rightarrow I(y) = \pm y e^y$. With $I(y) = y e^y$, the equation becomes $y^2 e^y + y e^y (1 + 2x + xy) y' = 0$, which is exact. Then $f_x = y^2 e^y \Rightarrow f(x,y) = xy^2 e^y + g(y)$, $f_y = (xy^2 + 2xy)e^y + g'(y) = y e^y (1 + 2x + xy) \Rightarrow g'(y) = y e^y \Rightarrow g(y) = y e^y - e^y + c \Rightarrow f(x,y) = xy^2 e^y + y e^y - e^y + c \Rightarrow (xy^2 + y - 1)e^y = k$.

23. $\frac{dy}{dx} = \frac{-y \ln(y)}{x \ln(y) + 2x} \Rightarrow y \ln(y) + [x \ln(y) + 2x] y' = 0$, $P_y = \ln(y) + 1$, $Q_x = \ln(y) + 2$, $P_y \neq Q_x \Rightarrow$ the equation is not exact. $\frac{Q_x - P_y}{P} = \frac{1}{y \ln(y)}$ is independent of $x \Rightarrow$ an integrating factor $I(y)$ exists, and $\frac{I'(y)}{I(y)} = \frac{1}{y \ln(y)} \Rightarrow \ln|I(y)| = \ln|\ln(y)| \Rightarrow I(y) = \pm \ln(y)$. With $I(y) = \ln(y)$, the equation becomes $y[\ln(y)]^2 + \{x[\ln(y)]^2 + 2x \ln(y)\} y' = 0$, which is exact. Then $f_x = y[\ln(y)]^2 \Rightarrow f(x,y) = xy[\ln(y)]^2 + g(y)$, $f_y = x[\ln(y)]^2 + 2x \ln(y) + g'(y) = x[\ln(y)]^2 + 2x \ln(y) \Rightarrow g(y) = c \Rightarrow f(x,y) = xy[\ln(y)]^2 + c \Rightarrow xy[\ln(y)]^2 = k$.

Chapter 2 Exercises – page 38

1. (a) $xy + y^2 - x^2 y' = 0 \Rightarrow y' = \frac{y}{x} + \left(\frac{y}{x}\right)^2$, $u = \frac{y}{x} \Rightarrow u + xu' = u + u^2 \Rightarrow u^{-2} u' = x^{-1} \Rightarrow -u^{-1} = \ln|x| + c \Rightarrow u = \frac{-1}{\ln|x|+c} \Rightarrow y = \frac{-x}{\ln|x|+c}$.

    (b) $xy + y^2 - x^2 y' = 0 \Rightarrow y' - \frac{1}{x} y = \frac{y^2}{x^2}$, $u = y^{-1} \Rightarrow y = u^{-1} \Rightarrow y' = -u^{-2} u' \Rightarrow -u^{-2} u' - \frac{1}{x} u^{-1} = \frac{u^{-2}}{x^2} \Rightarrow u' + \frac{1}{x} u = \frac{-1}{x^2}$, $I(x) = e^{\int \frac{1}{x} dx} = e^{\ln|x|} = |x|$, $I(x) = x \Rightarrow (xu)' = \frac{-1}{x} \Rightarrow xu = -\ln|x| + c \Rightarrow u = \frac{-\ln|x|+c}{x} \Rightarrow y = \frac{-x}{\ln|x|-c}$.

2. (a) $\frac{y^2}{x^2} - y' = 0 \Rightarrow \frac{1}{y^2} y' = \frac{1}{x^2} \Rightarrow -y^{-1} = -x^{-1} + c \Rightarrow y = \frac{x}{1-cx}$.

    (b) $\frac{y^2}{x^2} - y' = 0 \Rightarrow y' = \left(\frac{y}{x}\right)^2$, $u = \frac{y}{x} \Rightarrow u + xu' = u^2 \Rightarrow xu' = u^2 - u \Rightarrow \left(\frac{1}{u-1} - \frac{1}{u}\right) u' = \frac{1}{x} \Rightarrow \ln|u-1| - \ln|u| = \ln|x| + c \Rightarrow \frac{|u-1|}{|u|} = c_1 |x| \Rightarrow 1 - \frac{1}{u} = kx \Rightarrow u = \frac{1}{1-kx} \Rightarrow y = \frac{x}{1-kx}$.

    (c) $\frac{y^2}{x^2} - y' = 0 \Rightarrow y' = \frac{y^2}{x^2}$, $u = y^{-1} \Rightarrow y = u^{-1} \Rightarrow y' = -u^{-2} u' \Rightarrow -u^{-2} u' = \frac{u^{-2}}{x^2} \Rightarrow u' = \frac{-1}{x^2} \Rightarrow u = \frac{1}{x} + c \Rightarrow y = \frac{x}{1+cx}$.

    (d) $\frac{y^2}{x^2} - y' = 0$, $\frac{Q_x - P_y}{P} = \frac{-2}{y} \Rightarrow \frac{I'(y)}{I(y)} = \frac{-2}{y} \Rightarrow I(y) = \frac{1}{y^2} \Rightarrow \frac{1}{x^2} - \frac{1}{y^2} y' = 0$ is exact. $f_x = \frac{1}{x^2} \Rightarrow f(x,y) = \frac{-1}{x} + g(y)$, $f_y = g'(y) = -\frac{1}{y^2} \Rightarrow g(y) = \frac{1}{y} + c \Rightarrow \frac{1}{y} - \frac{1}{x} = k \Rightarrow y = \frac{x}{1+kx}$.

    (e) The orthogonal trajectories are given by $y' = -\frac{x^2}{y^2} \Rightarrow y^2 y' = -x^2 \Rightarrow \frac{1}{3} y^3 = -\frac{1}{3} x^3 + c \Rightarrow x^3 + y^3 = k$.

3. (a) $x + y - xy' = 0 \Rightarrow y' = 1 + \frac{y}{x}$, $u = \frac{y}{x} \Rightarrow u + xu' = 1 + u \Rightarrow u' = \frac{1}{x} \Rightarrow u = \ln|x| + c \Rightarrow y = x(\ln|x| + c)$.

    (b) $x + y - xy' = 0 \Rightarrow y' - \frac{1}{x} y = 1$, $I(x) = e^{\int \frac{-1}{x} dx} = e^{-\ln|x|} = |x|^{-1}$, $I(x) = \frac{1}{x} \Rightarrow \left(\frac{1}{x} y\right)' = \frac{1}{x} \Rightarrow \frac{1}{x} y = \ln|x| + c \Rightarrow y = x(\ln|x| + c)$.

(c) $x + y - xy' = 0$, $\frac{P_y - Q_x}{Q} = \frac{-2}{x} \Rightarrow \frac{I'(x)}{I(x)} = \frac{-2}{x} \Rightarrow I(x) = \frac{1}{x^2} \Rightarrow \frac{1}{x} + \frac{y}{x^2} - \frac{1}{x}y' = 0$
is exact. $f_x = \frac{1}{x} + \frac{y}{x^2} \Rightarrow f(x,y) = \ln|x| - \frac{y}{x} + g(y)$, $f_y = -\frac{1}{x} + g'(y) = -\frac{1}{x}$
$\Rightarrow g(y) = c \Rightarrow \ln|x| - \frac{y}{x} = k \Rightarrow y = x(\ln|x| - k)$.

(d) The orthogonal trajectories are given by $y' = \frac{-x}{x+y} = \frac{-1}{1+\frac{y}{x}}$, $u = \frac{y}{x} \Rightarrow$
$u + xu' = \frac{-1}{1+u} \Rightarrow xu' = \frac{-1-u-u^2}{1+u} \Rightarrow \int \frac{u+1}{u^2+u+1}u' \, dx = \int \frac{-1}{x} \, dx = -\ln|x| + c$.
$\frac{u+1}{u^2+u+1} = \frac{(u+\frac{1}{2})+\frac{1}{2}}{(u+\frac{1}{2})^2+\frac{3}{4}} = \frac{1}{2}\frac{2(u+\frac{1}{2})}{(u+\frac{1}{2})^2+\frac{3}{4}} + \frac{1}{\sqrt{3}}\frac{\frac{2}{\sqrt{3}}}{(\frac{2}{\sqrt{3}}u+\frac{1}{\sqrt{3}})^2+1} \Rightarrow$
$\int \frac{u+1}{u^2+u+1} \, du = \frac{1}{2}\ln\left[\left(u+\frac{1}{2}\right)^2 + \frac{3}{4}\right] + \frac{1}{\sqrt{3}}\tan^{-1}\left(\frac{2}{\sqrt{3}}u + \frac{1}{\sqrt{3}}\right) \Rightarrow$
$\frac{1}{2}\ln\left[\left(\frac{y}{x}+\frac{1}{2}\right)^2 + \frac{3}{4}\right] + \frac{1}{\sqrt{3}}\tan^{-1}\left(\frac{2}{\sqrt{3}}\frac{y}{x} + \frac{1}{\sqrt{3}}\right) = -\ln|x| + c$.

4. (a) $3xy' + 2y = 0 \Rightarrow \frac{y'}{y} = -\frac{2}{3x} \Rightarrow \ln|y| = -\frac{2}{3}\ln|x| + c \Rightarrow y = kx^{-2/3}$.

(b) $3xy' + 2y = 0 \Rightarrow y' = -\frac{2}{3}\frac{y}{x}$, $u = \frac{y}{x} \Rightarrow u + xu' = -\frac{2}{3}u \Rightarrow xu' = -\frac{5}{3}u \Rightarrow$
$\frac{u'}{u} = -\frac{5}{3}\frac{1}{x} \Rightarrow \ln|u| = -\frac{5}{3}\ln|x| + c \Rightarrow u = kx^{-5/3} \Rightarrow y = kx^{-2/3}$.

(c) $3xy' + 2y = 0 \Rightarrow y' + \frac{2}{3x}y = 0 \Rightarrow I(x) = e^{\int \frac{2}{3x} \, dx} = e^{\frac{2}{3}\ln|x|} = |x|^{2/3} = x^{2/3}$
$\Rightarrow (x^{2/3}y)' = 0 \Rightarrow x^{2/3}y = c \Rightarrow y = cx^{-2/3}$.

(d) $3xy' + 2y = 0$, $\frac{P_y - Q_x}{Q} = \frac{-1}{3x} \Rightarrow \frac{I'(x)}{I(x)} = \frac{-1}{3x} \Rightarrow I(x) = x^{-1/3} \Rightarrow$
$2x^{-1/3}y + 3x^{2/3}y' = 0$ is exact. $f_x = 2x^{-1/3}y \Rightarrow f(x,y) = 3x^{2/3}y + g(y)$,
$f_y = 3x^{2/3} + g'(y) = 3x^{2/3} \Rightarrow g(y) = c \Rightarrow 3x^{2/3}y = k \Rightarrow y = k_1 x^{-2/3}$.

(e) The orthogonal trajectories are given by $y' = \frac{3x}{2y} \Rightarrow 2yy' = 3x \Rightarrow$
$y^2 = \frac{3}{2}x^2 + c \Rightarrow 3x^2 - 2y^2 = k$.

5. $2x - 2e^{-x} - y^2 = k \Rightarrow 2 + 2e^{-x} - 2yy' = 0 \Rightarrow y' = \frac{1+e^{-x}}{y}$. The orthogonal
trajectories are given by $y' = \frac{-y}{1+e^{-x}} \Rightarrow \frac{y'}{y} = \frac{-1}{1+e^{-x}} = \frac{-e^x}{e^x+1} \Rightarrow$
$\ln|y| = -\ln(e^x + 1) + c \Rightarrow y = \frac{k}{e^x+1}$.

6. $y = 2x\ln|x| + cx \Rightarrow \frac{y}{x} - 2\ln|x| = c \Rightarrow -\frac{y}{x^2} + \frac{y'}{x} - \frac{2}{x} = 0 \Rightarrow y' = \frac{y}{x} + 2$. The
orthogonal trajectories are given by $y' = \frac{-1}{\frac{y}{x}+2}$, $u = \frac{y}{x} \Rightarrow u + xu' = \frac{-1}{u+2} \Rightarrow$
$xu' = \frac{-1-2u-u^2}{u+2} \Rightarrow \frac{u+2}{(u+1)^2}u' = \frac{-1}{x} \Rightarrow \int \frac{1}{u+1} + \frac{1}{(u+1)^2} \, du = \int \frac{-1}{x} \, dx \Rightarrow$
$\ln|u+1| - \frac{1}{u+1} = -\ln|x| + c \Rightarrow \ln\left|\frac{y}{x}+1\right| - \frac{x}{x+y} = \ln|x| + c$.

7. $f(x,y) = 0$ defines y as a function of x. Hence, $f_x + f_y\frac{dy}{dx} = 0 \Rightarrow \frac{dy}{dx} = -\frac{f_x}{f_y}$.
$f(x,y) = 0$ also defines x as a function of y. Hence, $f_x\frac{dx}{dy} + f_y = 0 \Rightarrow \frac{dx}{dy} = -\frac{f_y}{f_x}$,
and $\frac{dy}{dx} = \frac{1}{\frac{dx}{dy}}$.

8. (a) $3x - 2y + (y - 2x)y' = 0$ is exact since $P_y = -2 = Q_x$. $f_x = 3x - 2y \Rightarrow$
$f(x,y) = \frac{3}{2}x^2 - 2xy + g(y)$, $f_y = -2x + g'(y) = y - 2x \Rightarrow g'(y) = y \Rightarrow$
$g(y) = \frac{1}{2}y^2 + c \Rightarrow \frac{3}{2}x^2 - 2xy + \frac{1}{2}y^2 = k \Rightarrow y^2 - 4xy + 3x^2 - k = 0 \Rightarrow$
$y = 2x \pm \sqrt{x^2 + k}$.

(b) $3x - 2y + (y - 2x)y' = 0 \Rightarrow y' = \frac{2y-3x}{y-2x} = \frac{2\frac{y}{x}+3}{\frac{y}{x}-2}$, $u = \frac{y}{x} \Rightarrow u + xu' = \frac{2u-3}{u-2}$

$\Rightarrow xu' = \frac{-u^2+4u-3}{u-2} \Rightarrow \frac{u-2}{u^2-4u+3}u' = \frac{-1}{x} \Rightarrow \left(\frac{1}{u-1} + \frac{1}{u-3}\right)u' = \frac{-2}{x} \Rightarrow$

$\ln|u-1| + \ln|u-3| = -2\ln|x| + c \Rightarrow (u-1)(u-3) = \frac{k}{x^2} \Rightarrow u^2 - 4u + 3 - \frac{k}{x^2} = 0$

$\Rightarrow u = 2 \pm \sqrt{1 + \frac{k}{x^2}} \Rightarrow y = 2x \pm \sqrt{x^2 + k}$.

9. (a) $xe^x - x\ln(x) + y + xy' = 0$ is exact since $P_y = 1 = Q_x$. $f_y = x \Rightarrow$
$f(x,y) = xy + g(x)$, $f_x = y + g'(x) = xe^x - x\ln(x) + y \Rightarrow g'(x) = xe^x - x\ln(x)$
$\Rightarrow g(x) = xe^x - e^x - \frac{1}{2}x^2\ln(x) + \frac{1}{4}x^2 + c \Rightarrow xy + xe^x - e^x - \frac{1}{2}x^2\ln(x) + \frac{1}{4}x^2 = k$
$\Rightarrow y = \frac{e^x}{x} - e^x + \frac{1}{2}x\ln(x) - \frac{1}{4}x + \frac{k}{x}$.

(b) $xe^x - x\ln(x) + y + xy' = 0 \Rightarrow xy' + y = x\ln(x) - xe^x \Rightarrow (xy)' = x\ln(x) - xe^x$
$\Rightarrow xy = \frac{1}{2}x^2\ln(x) - \frac{1}{4}x^2 - xe^x + e^x + c \Rightarrow y = \frac{e^x}{x} - e^x + \frac{1}{2}x\ln(x) - \frac{1}{4}x + \frac{c}{x}$.

10. (a) $g(y)y' = f(x) \Rightarrow f(x) - g(y)y' = 0$ and $[f(x)]_y = 0 = [-g(y)]_x$.

(b) $y + x\ln(x)\ln(y)y' = 0 \Rightarrow \frac{\ln(y)}{y}y' = \frac{-1}{x\ln(x)} \Rightarrow \frac{1}{2}[\ln(y)]^2 = -\ln|\ln(x)| + c \Rightarrow$
$y = e^{\pm\sqrt{k-2\ln|\ln(x)|}}$.

(c) $\frac{\ln(y)}{y}y' = \frac{-1}{x\ln(x)} \Rightarrow \frac{1}{x\ln(x)} + \frac{\ln(y)}{y}y' = 0$ is exact. $f_x = \frac{1}{x\ln(x)} \Rightarrow$
$f(x,y) = \ln|\ln(x)| + g(y)$, $f_y = g'(y) = \frac{\ln(y)}{y} \Rightarrow g(y) = \frac{1}{2}[\ln(y)]^2 + c \Rightarrow$
$\ln|\ln(x)| + \frac{1}{2}[\ln(y)]^2 = k$.

11. (a) $y' = f(ax + by + c)$, $b \neq 0$, $u(x) = ax + by + c \Rightarrow u' = a + by' = a + bf(u)$
$\Rightarrow \frac{u'}{a+bf(u)} = 1$, which is separable.

(b) $y' = (x + y + 1)^2$, $u = x + y + 1 \Rightarrow u' = 1 + y' = 1 + u^2 \Rightarrow \frac{u'}{1+u^2} = 1 \Rightarrow$
$\tan^{-1}(u) = x + c \Rightarrow u = \tan(x + c) \Rightarrow y = u - x - 1 = \tan(x + c) - x - 1$.

(c) $y' = \frac{1}{\sqrt{x+y-2}}$, $u = x + y - 2 \Rightarrow u' = 1 + y' = 1 + \frac{1}{\sqrt{u}} = \frac{\sqrt{u}+1}{\sqrt{u}} \Rightarrow \frac{\sqrt{u}}{\sqrt{u}+1}u' = 1$
$\Rightarrow \int \frac{\sqrt{u}}{\sqrt{u}+1}\,du = \int 1\,dx = x + c$, and $v = \sqrt{u} \Rightarrow$
$\int \frac{\sqrt{u}}{\sqrt{u}+1}\,du = \int \frac{v}{v+1}2v\,dv = 2\int v - 1 + \frac{1}{v+1}\,dv = v^2 - 2v + 2\ln(v+1) \Rightarrow$
$x + y - 2 - 2\sqrt{x+y-2} + 2\ln(\sqrt{x+y-2} + 1) = x + c$.

(d) $y' = (x + y)\ln(x + y) - 1$, $u = x + y \Rightarrow u' = 1 + y' = u\ln(u) \Rightarrow \frac{1}{u\ln(u)}u' = 1$
$\Rightarrow \ln|\ln(u)| = x + c \Rightarrow |\ln(u)| = e^{x+c} \Rightarrow \ln(u) = ke^x \Rightarrow u = e^{ke^x} \Rightarrow$
$y = u - x = e^{ke^x} - x$.

12. (a) $a(y) + [b(y)x - c(y)]y' = 0$, $\frac{Q_x-P_y}{P} = \frac{b(y)-a'(y)}{a(y)}$ is independent of x; hence,
$I(y)$ exists.

(b) $a(y) + [b(y)x - c(y)]y' = 0 \Rightarrow a(y) + [b(y)x - c(y)]\frac{1}{x'} = 0 \Rightarrow$
$a(y)x' + b(y)x = c(y)$, which is linear for $x(y)$.

13. (a) $y + [(2y^2 + 1)x - 2y]y' = 0$, $\frac{Q_x-P_y}{P} = 2y \Rightarrow \frac{I'(y)}{I(y)} = 2y \Rightarrow I(y) = e^{y^2} \Rightarrow$
$ye^{y^2} + [(2y^2+1)x - 2y]e^{y^2}y' = 0$ is exact. $f_x = ye^{y^2} \Rightarrow f(x,y) = xye^{y^2} + g(y)$,

$f_y = (2y^2 + 1)xe^{y^2} + g'(y) = [(2y^2 + 1)x - 2y]e^{y^2} \Rightarrow g'(y) = -2ye^{y^2} \Rightarrow$
$g(y) = -e^{y^2} + c \Rightarrow (xy - 1)e^{y^2} = k.$

(b) $y + [(2y^2 + 1)x - 2y]y' = 0 \Rightarrow y + [(2y^2 + 1)x - 2y]\frac{1}{x'} = 0 \Rightarrow$
$yx' + (2y^2 + 1)x = 2y \Rightarrow x' + \left(2y + \frac{1}{y}\right)x = 2.$ The integrating factor is
$I(y) = e^{\int 2y + \frac{1}{y}\, dy} = e^{y^2 + \ln|y|} = \pm ye^{y^2}$, and $I(y) = ye^{y^2} \Rightarrow \left(ye^{y^2}x\right)' = 2ye^{y^2}$
$\Rightarrow ye^{y^2}x = e^{y^2} + c \Rightarrow (xy - 1)e^{y^2} = c.$

14. (a) $y^2 + (3xy + 2)y' = 0,\ \frac{Q_x - P_y}{P} = \frac{1}{y} = \frac{I'(y)}{I(y)} \Rightarrow I(y) = y \Rightarrow y^3 + (3xy^2 + 2y)y' = 0$
is exact. $f_x = y^3 \Rightarrow f(x, y) = xy^3 + g(y),\ f_y = 3xy^2 + g'(y) = 3xy^2 + 2y$
$\Rightarrow g(y) = y^2 + c \Rightarrow xy^3 + y^2 = k.$

(b) $y^2 + (3xy + 2)y' = 0 \Rightarrow y^2 + (3xy + 2)\frac{1}{x'} = 0 \Rightarrow y^2x' + 3yx = -2 \Rightarrow$
$x' + \frac{3}{y}x = \frac{-2}{y^2},\ I(y) = e^{\int \frac{3}{y}\, dy} = e^{3\ln|y|} = \pm y^3,\ I(x) = y^3 \Rightarrow (y^3x)' = -2y \Rightarrow$
$y^3x = -y^2 + c \Rightarrow xy^3 + y^2 = c.$

15. $1 + (xy - x^{-3}y^3)y' = 0 \Rightarrow 1 + (xy - x^{-3}y^3)\frac{1}{x'} = 0 \Rightarrow x' + yx = y^3x^{-3}$, which is a
Bernoulli equation for $x(y)$ with $\alpha = -3.\ u = x^4 \Rightarrow x = u^{1/4} \Rightarrow x' = \frac{1}{4}u^{-3/4}u'$
$\Rightarrow \frac{1}{4}u^{-3/4}u' + yu^{1/4} = y^3u^{-3/4} \Rightarrow u' + 4yu = 4y^3,\ I(y) = e^{\int 4y\, dy} = e^{2y^2} \Rightarrow$
$\left(e^{2y^2}u\right)' = 4y^3e^{2y^2} \Rightarrow e^{2y^2}u = \int y^2 \cdot 4ye^{2y^2}\, dy = y^2e^{2y^2} - \frac{1}{2}e^{2y^2} + c$ (by parts) $\Rightarrow$
$u = y^2 - \frac{1}{2} + ce^{-2y^2} \Rightarrow x = \left(y^2 - \frac{1}{2} + ce^{-2y^2}\right)^{1/4}.$

16. (a) $y' = 2\sqrt{y - 1} \Rightarrow \frac{y'}{2\sqrt{y-1}} = 1 \Rightarrow \sqrt{y - 1} = x + c \Rightarrow y = (x + c)^2 + 1.$

(b) The function $y \equiv 1$ satisfies $y' = 0 = \sqrt{y - 1}$ and is a singular solution.

(c) At every point $(x_0, 1)$ on the line $y = 1$, the line is tangent to the parabola
$y = (x - x_0)^2 + 1$ at its vertex. Hence, the line is the envelope of the
one-parameter family of parabolas.

17. (a) $(y')^2 = \frac{1 - y^2}{y^2} \Rightarrow \frac{y}{\pm\sqrt{1 - y^2}}y' = 1 \Rightarrow \mp\sqrt{1 - y^2} = x + c \Rightarrow (x + c)^2 + y^2 = 1$
$\Rightarrow f(x, y, c) = (x + c)^2 + y^2 - 1 = 0.$

(b) $y \equiv \pm 1$ are two singular solutions.

(c) $f(x, y, c) = (x + c)^2 + y^2 - 1 = 0$ and $f_c(x, y, c) = 2(x + c) = 0 \Rightarrow y^2 - 1 = 0$
$\Rightarrow y = \pm 1.$

(d) The general solution defines a one-parameter family of circles of radius 1
with centres at $(-c, 0)$ on the x-axis. At every point $(x_0, \pm 1)$ on the lines
$y = \pm 1$, the lines are tangent to the circle centred at $(x_0, 0)$. Hence, each
line is an envelope of the family of circles.

18. (a) $y = mx \pm \sqrt{m^2 + 1} \Rightarrow y' = m \Rightarrow \frac{(y')^2 + 1}{(y - xy')^2} = \frac{m^2 + 1}{(mx \pm \sqrt{m^2 + 1} - xm)^2} = 1.$

(b) $y = mx \pm \sqrt{m^2 + 1} \Rightarrow y - mx = \pm\sqrt{m^2 + 1} \Rightarrow (y - mx)^2 = m^2 + 1 \Rightarrow$
$f(x, y, m) = (y - mx)^2 - m^2 - 1 = 0.$ $f_m(x, y, m) = -2x(y - mx) - 2m = 0$
$\Rightarrow x(mx - y) = m \Rightarrow x^2 = \frac{m^2}{(mx - y)^2} = \frac{m^2}{m^2 + 1}.$

(c) $x(mx - y) = m \Rightarrow y = \frac{m(x^2 - 1)}{x} \Rightarrow$
$y^2 = \frac{m^2(x^2 - 1)^2}{x^2} = (m^2 + 1)\left(\frac{-1}{m^2 + 1}\right)^2 = \frac{1}{m^2 + 1}.$

(d) $x^2 + y^2 = \frac{m^2}{m^2 + 1} + \frac{1}{m^2 + 1} = 1 \Rightarrow g(x, y) = x^2 + y^2 - 1 = 0$ is a singular solution.

(e) The graph of the singular solution is the unit circle centred at the origin. At every point on the circle, the circle is tangent to one of the lines defined by the general solution. This can be confirmed as follows: $x^2 + y^2 = 1 \Rightarrow$ $2x + 2yy' = 0 \Rightarrow y' = -\frac{x}{y}$. Thus, the slope of the tangent to the circle at (x_0, y_0) is $m_1 = -\frac{x_0}{y_0}$. The line $y = mx \pm \sqrt{m^2 + 1}$ goes through (x_0, y_0) if and only if $y_0 = mx_0 \pm \sqrt{m^2 + 1}$. Then $(y_0 - mx_0)^2 = m^2 + 1$ and, solving for m, we obtain $m = -\frac{x_0}{y_0} = m_1$. Thus, the line is tangent to the circle at (x_0, y_0).

19. (a) $y' = \frac{y}{x} \Rightarrow \frac{y'}{y} = \frac{1}{x} \Rightarrow y = kx.$

(b) $y = kx \Rightarrow y(0) = 0$ for all values of k. Hence, $y(0) = 1$ is impossible. The reason is that $f(x, y) = \frac{y}{x}$ is not continuous at $x = 0$ and, hence, it is not continuous in a rectangular region containing $(0, 1)$.

20. (a) $y' = 3xy^{1/3} \Rightarrow y^{-1/3}y' = 3x \Rightarrow \frac{3}{2}y^{2/3} = \frac{3}{2}x^2 + c \Rightarrow y = (x^2 + k)^{3/2}.$

(b) $y = (x^2 + k)^{3/2}$ and $y(0) = 0 \Rightarrow k = 0 \Rightarrow y = x^3.$

(c) $y \equiv 0$ is a singular solution.

(d) Both $y = x^3$ and $y \equiv 0$ are solutions of the initial-value problem. Hence, the solution is not unique. The reason is that, with $f(x, y) = 3xy^{1/3}$, $f_y(x, y) = xy^{-2/3}$ is not continuous at $y = 0$ and, hence, it is not continuous in a rectangular region containing $(0, 0)$.

C.3 Chapter 3 Solutions

Exercises 3.1 – page 46

1. $y'' + 6x^2 + \sin(x) = 2 \Rightarrow y'' = 2 - 6x^2 - \sin(x) \Rightarrow y' = 2x - 2x^3 + \cos(x) + c_1$
$\Rightarrow y = x^2 - \frac{1}{2}x^4 + \sin(x) + c_1 x + c_2.$

2. $xy'' = \ln(x) \Rightarrow y'' = \frac{\ln(x)}{x} \Rightarrow y' = \frac{1}{2}[\ln(x)]^2 + c_1 \Rightarrow y = \frac{1}{2}\int[\ln(x)]^2\,dx + c_1 x + c_2.$
$\int[\ln(x)]^2\,dx = \int 1 \cdot [\ln(x)]^2\,dx = x[\ln(x)]^2 - \int 2\ln(x)\,dx$
$= x[\ln(x)]^2 - 2x\ln(x) + \int 2\,dx = x[\ln(x)]^2 - 2x\ln(x) + 2x \Rightarrow$
$y = \frac{1}{2}x[\ln(x)]^2 - x\ln(x) + x + c_1 x + c_2 = \frac{1}{2}x[\ln(x)]^2 - x\ln(x) + c_3 x + c_2.$

3. $y'' - 4\cos^2(x) = 2 \Rightarrow y'' = 4\cos^2(x) + 2 = 4 + 2\cos(2x) \Rightarrow y' = 4x + \sin(2x) + c_1$
$\Rightarrow y = 2x^2 - \frac{1}{2}\cos(2x) + c_1 x + c_2$, $y(0) = 0 \Rightarrow c_2 = \frac{1}{2}$, and $y'(0) = 1 \Rightarrow c_1 = 1$
$\Rightarrow y = 2x^2 - \frac{1}{2}\cos(2x) + x + \frac{1}{2}$.

4. $y'' = xe^x \Rightarrow y' = xe^x - e^x + c_1 \Rightarrow y = xe^x - 2e^x + c_1 x + c_2$, $y(0) = 1 \Rightarrow c_2 = 3$,
and $y'(0) = 1 \Rightarrow c_1 = 2 \Rightarrow y = xe^x - 2e^x + 2x + 3$.

5. (a) $xy'' - y' + 2y = 0$ is linear and homogeneous.

   (b) $2y'' + \ln(x)y = \sin(x)$ is linear and nonhomogeneous.

   (c) $y'' + y' + (x^2 + y^2) = 0$ is nonlinear.

   (d) $y'' + xy' = y^3$ is nonlinear.

   (e) $x^2 y'' + xy' = 2y \Rightarrow x^2 y'' + xy' - 2y = 0$ is linear and homogeneous.

   (f) $y'' + y' + y + x = 0 \Rightarrow y'' + y' + y = -x$ is linear and nonhomogeneous.

   (g) $y'' + yy' + y = 0$ is nonlinear.

6. If $y_1 = e^{r_1 x}$ and $y_2 = e^{r_2 x}$ are linearly dependent, then there exist constants c_1 and c_2, not both zero, such that $c_1 e^{r_1 x} + c_2 e^{r_2 x} = 0$ for all x. Then $x = 0 \Rightarrow c_1 + c_2 = 0 \Rightarrow c_1(e^{r_1 x} - e^{r_2 x}) = 0$ for all x, and $c_1 \neq 0$ (otherwise $c_2 = -c_1 = 0$) $\Rightarrow e^{r_1 x} = e^{r_2 x} \Rightarrow r_1 x = r_2 x$, and $x = 1 \Rightarrow r_1 = r_2$. Conversely, if $r_1 = r_2$, then $y_1 = y_2 \Rightarrow y_1$ and y_2 are linearly dependent.

7. If $y_1 = x^\alpha$ and $y_2 = x^\beta$ are linearly dependent, then there exist constants c_1 and c_2, not both zero, such that $c_1 x^\alpha + c_2 x^\beta = 0$ for all x in I. Then $x = 1 \Rightarrow c_1 + c_2 = 0 \Rightarrow c_1(x^\alpha - x^\beta) = 0$ for all x in I, and $c_1 \neq 0$ (otherwise $c_2 = -c_1 = 0$) $\Rightarrow x^\alpha = x^\beta$, and $x = 2 \Rightarrow 2^\alpha = 2^\beta \Rightarrow \alpha = \beta$. Conversely, if $\alpha = \beta$, then $y_1 = y_2 \Rightarrow y_1$ and y_2 are linearly dependent.

8. If $y_1 = x^r$ and $y_2 = e^{sx}$ are linearly dependent, then there exist constants c_1 and c_2, not both zero, such that $c_1 x^r + c_2 e^{sx} = 0$ for all x in I. Then $x = 1 \Rightarrow c_1 + c_2 e^s = 0$, $x = 2 \Rightarrow 2^r c_1 + c_2 e^{2s} = 0$, and $x = 3 \Rightarrow 3^r c_1 + c_2 e^{3s} = 0$. These three equations give $s = r\ln(2)$ and $2s = r\ln(3)$, which is impossible unless $r = s = 0$. Conversely, if $r = s = 0$, then $y_1 = y_2 = 1 \Rightarrow y_1$ and y_2 are linearly dependent.

9. If $y_1, y_2, \cdots, y_n$ are linearly dependent, then there exist constants $c_1, c_2, \cdots, c_n$, not all zero, such that $c_1 y_1 + c_2 y_2 + \cdots + c_n y_n = 0$. If $c_j \neq 0$, then $y_j = -\frac{c_1}{c_j} y_1 - \frac{c_2}{c_j} y_2 - \cdots - \frac{c_n}{c_j} y_n$, where, of course, the term $-\frac{c_j}{c_j} y_j$ is omitted from the right-hand side. Conversely, if $y_j = c_1 y_1 + c_2 y_2 + \cdots + c_n y_n$, then $c_1 y_1 + c_2 y_2 + \cdots + c_n y_n - 1 \cdot y_j = 0$, with $c_j = -1 \neq 0$.

10. The functions $y_1 = x$, $y_2 = e^x$ and $y_3 = e^{-x}$ are linearly independent. Suppose that $c_1 x + c_2 e^x + c_3 e^{-x} = 0$ for all x. Then $x = 0 \Rightarrow c_2 + c_3 = 0$, $x = 1 \Rightarrow c_1 + c_2(e - e^{-1}) = 0$, and $x = -1 \Rightarrow -c_1 + c_2(e^{-1} - e) = 0$. The unique solution of this system of three equations is $c_1 = c_2 = c_3 = 0$.

11. The functions $y_1 = x$, $y_2 = e^x$ and $y_3 = 2x$ are not linearly independent because $2 \cdot y_1 + 0 \cdot y_2 + (-1) \cdot y_3 = 0$ for all x, with $c_1 = 2 \neq 0$.

12. If $y \equiv 0$, then $1 \cdot y = 0$ for all x, with $c_1 = 1 \neq 0$. Hence, y is linearly dependent. If $y \not\equiv 0$, then there exists x_0 such that $y(x_0) \neq 0$. If $cy = 0$ for all x, then $cy(x_0) = 0 \Rightarrow c = 0$, i.e., y is linearly independent. Thus, y is linearly independent if and only if $y \not\equiv 0$.

Exercises 3.2 – page 55

1. $y'' - y' - 2y = 0$, $y = e^{rx} \Rightarrow r^2 - r - 2 = (r-2)(r+1) = 0 \Rightarrow y = c_1 e^{2x} + c_2 e^{-x}$.

2. $y'' + y' - 6y = 0$, $y = e^{rx} \Rightarrow r^2 + r - 6 = (r-2)(r+3) = 0 \Rightarrow y = c_1 e^{2x} + c_2 e^{-3x}$.
   $y(0) = 0 \Rightarrow c_2 = -c_1 \Rightarrow y = c_1(e^{2x} - e^{-3x})$, $y' = c_1(2e^{2x} + 3e^{-3x})$, and $y'(0) = 10$
   $\Rightarrow c_1 = 2 \Rightarrow y = 2(e^{2x} - e^{-3x})$. Then $y(1) = 2(e^2 - e^{-3})$ and $y'(1) = 2(2e^2 + 3e^{-3})$.

3. $y'' + 5y' + 4y = 0$, $y = e^{rx} \Rightarrow r^2 + 5r + 4 = (r+1)(r+4) = 0 \Rightarrow y = c_1 e^{-x} + c_2 e^{-4x}$.
   $y(0) = 0 \Rightarrow c_2 = -c_1 \Rightarrow y = c_1(e^{-x} - e^{-4x})$, $y' = c_1(-e^{-x} + 4e^{-4x})$, and
   $y'(0) = -6 \Rightarrow c_1 = -2 \Rightarrow y = -2(e^{-x} - e^{-4x})$.

4. $4y'' + y' - 3y = 0$, $y = e^{rx} \Rightarrow 4r^2 + r - 3 = 0 \Rightarrow r = \frac{-1 \pm 7}{8} \Rightarrow r_1 = \frac{3}{4}$, $r_2 = -1$,
   $y = c_1 e^{\frac{3}{4}x} + c_2 e^{-x}$.

5. $y'' - 3y' + y = 0$, $y = e^{rx} \Rightarrow r^2 - 3r + 1 = 0 \Rightarrow r = \frac{3 \pm \sqrt{5}}{2} \Rightarrow y_1 = e^{\frac{3+\sqrt{5}}{2}x}$ and
   $y_2 = e^{\frac{3-\sqrt{5}}{2}x}$.

6. $y'' - y = 0$, $y = e^{rx} \Rightarrow r^2 - 1 = 0 \Rightarrow r = \pm 1 \Rightarrow y = c_1 e^x + c_2 e^{-x}$, $y' = c_1 e^x - c_2 e^{-x}$,
   $y(0) = 1 \Rightarrow c_1 + c_2 = 1$, $y'(0) = 2 \Rightarrow c_1 - c_2 = 2 \Rightarrow c_1 = \frac{3}{2}$, $c_2 = -\frac{1}{2}$,
   $y = \frac{3}{2}e^x - \frac{1}{2}e^{-x}$. Then $y(1) = \frac{3e}{2} - \frac{1}{2e}$ and $y(-1) = \frac{3}{2e} - \frac{e}{2}$.

7. $9y'' - 24y' + 16y = 0$, $y = e^{rx} \Rightarrow 9r^2 - 24r + 16 = (3r-4)^2 = 0 \Rightarrow r = \frac{4}{3} \Rightarrow$
   $y_1 = e^{\frac{4}{3}x}$, $y_2 = xe^{\frac{4}{3}x}$.

8. $y'' - 10y' + 25y = 0$, $y = e^{rx} \Rightarrow r^2 - 10r + 25 = (r-5)^2 = 0 \Rightarrow r = 5 \Rightarrow$
   $y = e^{5x}(c_1 + c_2 x)$. $y(0) = 1 \Rightarrow c_1 = 1 \Rightarrow y = e^{5x}(1 + c_2 x)$,
   $y' = 5e^{5x}(1 + c_2 x) + c_2 e^{5x}$, $y'(0) = 1 \Rightarrow c_2 = -4 \Rightarrow y = e^{5x}(1 - 4x)$.

9. $4y'' - 4y' + 1 = 0$, $y = e^{rx} \Rightarrow 4r^2 - 4r + 1 = (2r-1)^2 = 0 \Rightarrow r = \frac{1}{2} \Rightarrow$
   $y = e^{\frac{1}{2}x}(c_1 + c_2 x)$.

10. $y'' = 0$, $y = e^{rx} \Rightarrow r^2 = 0 \Rightarrow r = 0 \Rightarrow y_1 = e^0 = 1$, $y_2 = xy_1 = x$, and
    $y = c_1 + c_2 x$. Alternatively, $y'' = 0 \Rightarrow y' = k_1 \Rightarrow y = k_1 x + k_2$.

11. $y'' + y' + y = 0$, $y = e^{rx} \Rightarrow r^2 + r + 1 = 0 \Rightarrow r = \frac{-1 \pm \sqrt{-3}}{2} = -\frac{1}{2} \pm i\frac{\sqrt{3}}{2} \Rightarrow$
    $y = e^{-\frac{1}{2}x}\left[c_1 \cos\left(\frac{\sqrt{3}}{2}x\right) + c_2 \sin\left(\frac{\sqrt{3}}{2}x\right)\right]$.

12. $y'' - 2y' + 2y = 0$, $y = e^{rx} \Rightarrow r^2 - 2r + 2 = 0 \Rightarrow r = \frac{2\pm\sqrt{-4}}{2} = 1 \pm i \Rightarrow$
$y = e^x[c_1 \cos(x) + c_2 \sin(x)]$. $y(0) = 0 \Rightarrow c_1 = 0 \Rightarrow y = c_2 e^x \sin(x)$,
$y' = c_2[e^x \sin(x) + e^x \cos(x)]$, and $y'(0) = 1 \Rightarrow c_2 = 1 \Rightarrow y = e^x \sin(x)$.

13. $2y'' - 4y' + 3y = 0$, $y = e^{rx} \Rightarrow 2r^2 - 4r + 3 = 0 \Rightarrow r = \frac{4\pm\sqrt{-8}}{4} = 1 \pm i\frac{\sqrt{2}}{2} \Rightarrow$
$y = e^x \left[c_1 \cos\left(\frac{\sqrt{2}}{2}x\right) + c_2 \sin\left(\frac{\sqrt{2}}{2}x\right) \right]$.

14. $y'' + 4y = 0$, $y = e^{rx} \Rightarrow r^2 + 4 = 0 \Rightarrow r = \pm 2i \Rightarrow y = c_1 \cos(2x) + c_2 \sin(2x)$.

15. (a) $y'' + y = 0$, $y = e^{rx} \Rightarrow r^2 + 1 = 0 \Rightarrow r = \pm i \Rightarrow y = c_1 \cos(x) + c_2 \sin(x)$.

   (b) $y(0) = 1$ and $y'(0) = 0 \Rightarrow y = \cos(x)$.

   (c) $y(0) = 0$ and $y'(0) = 1 \Rightarrow y = \sin(x)$.

16. $x^2 y'' + 2xy' - 6y = 0$. For $x > 0$, $y = x^r \Rightarrow r(r-1) + 2r - 6 = 0 \Rightarrow r^2 + r - 6 = 0$
$\Rightarrow (r+3)(r-2) = 0 \Rightarrow y = c_1|x|^{-3} + c_2|x|^2 = c_3 x^{-3} + c_2 x^2$ for $x \neq 0$.

17. $6x^2 y'' + 7xy' - 2y = 0$. For $x > 0$, $y = x^r \Rightarrow 6r(r-1) + 7r - 2 = 6r^2 + r - 2 = 0$
$\Rightarrow r = \frac{-1\pm 7}{12} = \frac{1}{2}, -\frac{2}{3} \Rightarrow y = c_1|x|^{1/2} + c_2 x^{-2/3}$ for $x \neq 0$.

18. $x^2 y'' - 7xy' + 16y = 0$. For $x > 0$, $y = x^r \Rightarrow r(r-1) - 7r + 16 = r^2 - 8r + 16 = 0$
$\Rightarrow (r-4)^2 = 0 \Rightarrow y = x^4[c_1 + c_2 \ln|x|]$ for $x \neq 0$. $y(1) = 0 \Rightarrow c_1 = 0 \Rightarrow$
$y = c_2 x^4 \ln|x|$, $y' = c_2[4x^3 \ln|x| + x^3]$, and $y'(1) = 2 \Rightarrow c_2 = 2 \Rightarrow y = 2x^4 \ln|x|$.
Then $y(-1) = 0$ and $y(e) = 2e^4$.

19. $9x^2 y'' - 3xy' + 4y = 0$. For $x > 0$, $y = x^r \Rightarrow 9r(r-1) - 3r + 4 = 9r^2 - 12r + 4 = 0$
$\Rightarrow (3r-2)^2 = 0 \Rightarrow y = x^{2/3}[c_1 + c_2 \ln|x|]$ for $x \neq 0$.

20. $x^2 y'' + xy' = 0$. (1) For $x > 0$, $y = x^r \Rightarrow r(r-1) + r = r^2 = 0 \Rightarrow y = c_1 + c_2 \ln|x|$
for $x \neq 0$. (2) For $x \neq 0$, $x^2 y'' + xy' = 0 \Rightarrow xy'' + y' = 0$. Integrate by parts
to obtain $xy' - \int y' \, dx + \int y' \, dx = k_1 \Rightarrow y' = \frac{k_1}{x} \Rightarrow y = k_1 \ln|x| + k_2$. (3) For
$x \neq 0$, $\frac{y''}{y'} = -\frac{1}{x} \Rightarrow \ln|y'| = -\ln|x| + c_1 \Rightarrow y' = \frac{k_1}{x} \Rightarrow y = k_1 \ln|x| + k_2$.

21. $-2x^2 y'' + 2xy' - 5y = 0 \Rightarrow 2x^2 y'' - 2xy' + 5y = 0$. For $x > 0$, $y = x^r \Rightarrow$
$2r(r-1) - 2r + 5 = 2r^2 - 4r + 5 = 0 \Rightarrow r = \frac{4\pm i\sqrt{24}}{4} = 1 \pm i\frac{\sqrt{6}}{2} \Rightarrow$
$y = x\left[c_1 \cos\left(\frac{\sqrt{6}}{2} \ln|x|\right) + c_2 \sin\left(\frac{\sqrt{6}}{2} \ln|x|\right) \right]$ for $x \neq 0$.

22. $x^2 y'' - 3xy' + 13y = 0$. For $x > 0$, $y = x^r \Rightarrow r(r-1) - 3r + 13 = r^2 - 4r + 13 = 0$
$\Rightarrow r = 2 \pm 3i \Rightarrow y = x^2[c_1 \cos(3\ln|x|) + c_2 \sin(3\ln|x|)]$ for $x \neq 0$. Then $y(1) = 0$
$\Rightarrow c_1 = 0 \Rightarrow y = c_2 x^2 \sin(3\ln|x|)$, $y' = c_2[2x \sin(3\ln|x|) + 3x \cos(3\ln|x|)]$, and
$y'(1) = 6 \Rightarrow c_2 = 2 \Rightarrow y = 2x^2 \sin(3\ln|x|)$.

23. $x^2 y'' + xy' + 4y = 0$. For $x > 0$, $y = x^r \Rightarrow r(r-1) + r + 4 = r^2 + 4 = 0 \Rightarrow$
$r = \pm 2i \Rightarrow y = c_1 \cos(2\ln|x|) + c_2 \sin(2\ln|x|)$ for $x \neq 0$.

Exercises 3.3 – page 74

1. $y'' + 4y' = -5e^x$. For $y'' + 4y' = 0$, $y = e^{rx} \Rightarrow r^2 + 4r = r(r+4) = 0 \Rightarrow y_1 = 1$ and $y_2 = e^{-4x}$. $y_p = Ae^x \Rightarrow y_p' = Ae^x$, $y_p'' = Ae^x$, and $y_p'' + 4y_p' = -5e^x \Rightarrow A = -1 \Rightarrow y_p = -e^x$. The general solution is $y = -e^x + c_1 + c_2 e^{-4x}$.

2. $y'' - y = 6e^{2x}$, $y(0) = 2$, $y'(0) = 4$. For $y'' - y = 0$, $y = e^{rx} \Rightarrow r^2 - 1 = 0 \Rightarrow$ $y_1 = e^x$ and $y_2 = e^{-x}$. $y_p = Ae^{2x} \Rightarrow y_p' = 2Ae^{2x}$, $y_p'' = 4Ae^{2x}$, and $y_p'' - y_p = 6e^{2x}$ $\Rightarrow A = 2 \Rightarrow y_p = 2e^{2x}$. The general solution is $y = 2e^{2x} + c_1 e^x + c_2 e^{-x}$. $y(0) = 2 + c_1 + c_2 = 2$ and $y'(0) = 4 + c_1 - c_2 = 4 \Rightarrow c_1 = c_2 = 0 \Rightarrow y = 2e^{2x}$.

3. $y'' - 5y' + 6y = 4e^{-2x}$. For $y'' - 5y' + 6y = 0$, $y = e^{rx} \Rightarrow$ $r^2 - 5r + 6 = (r-2)(r-3) = 0 \Rightarrow y_1 = e^{2x}$ and $y_2 = e^{3x}$. $y_p = Ae^{-2x} \Rightarrow$ $y_p' = -2Ae^{-2x}$, $y_p'' = 4Ae^{-2x}$, and $y_p'' - 5y_p' + 6y_p = 4e^{-2x} \Rightarrow A = \frac{1}{5} \Rightarrow y_p = \frac{1}{5}e^{-2x}$. The general solution is $y = \frac{1}{5}e^{-2x} + c_1 e^{2x} + c_3 e^{3x}$.

4. $y'' + 3y' - 4y = -10e^x$. For $y'' + 3y' - 4y = 0$, $y = e^{rx} \Rightarrow$ $r^2 + 3r - 4 = (r-1)(r+4) = 0 \Rightarrow y_1 = e^x$ and $y_2 = e^{-4x}$. Since e^x is a solution of the homogeneous equation, $y_p = Axe^x$. Then $y_p' = Ae^x(1+x)$, $y_p'' = Ae^x(2+x)$, and $y_p'' + 3y_p' - 4y_p = -10e^x \Rightarrow A = -2 \Rightarrow y_p = -2xe^x$. The general solution is $y = -2xe^x + c_1 e^x + c_2 e^{-4x}$.

5. $y'' + 6y' + 9y = 6e^{-3x}$. For $y'' + 6y' + 9y = 0$, $y = e^{rx}$ $\Rightarrow r^2 + 6r + 9 = (r+3)^2 = 0 \Rightarrow y_1 = e^{-3x}$ and $y_2 = xe^{-3x}$. Since e^{-3x} and xe^{-3x} are solutions of the homogeneous equation, $y_p = Ax^2 e^{-3x}$. Then $y_p' = Ae^{-3x}(2x - 3x^2)$, $y_p'' = Ae^{-3x}(2 - 12x + 9x^2)$, and $y_p'' + 6y_p' + 9y_p = 6e^{-3x} \Rightarrow$ $A = 3 \Rightarrow y_p = 3x^2 e^{-3x}$. The general solution is $y = 3x^2 e^{-3x} + c_1 e^{-3x} + c_2 xe^{-3x}$.

6. $6y'' + y' - 2y = 65\sin(x)$. For $6y'' + y' - 2y = 0$, $y = e^{rx} \Rightarrow 6r^2 + r - 2 = 0 \Rightarrow$ $y_1 = e^{\frac{1}{2}x}$ and $y_2 = e^{-\frac{2}{3}x}$. $y_p = A\cos(x) + B\sin(x) \Rightarrow y_p' = -A\sin(x) + B\cos(x)$, $y_p'' = -A\cos(x) - B\sin(x)$, and $6y_p'' + y_p' - 2y_p = 65\sin(x) \Rightarrow$
$$\left\{ \begin{array}{rcl} A + 8B & = & -65 \\ -8A + B & = & 0 \end{array} \right\} \Rightarrow A = -1 \text{ and } B = -8 \Rightarrow y_p = -\cos(x) - 8\sin(x).$$
The general solution is $y = -\cos(x) - 8\sin(x) + c_1 e^{\frac{1}{2}x} + c_2 e^{-\frac{2}{3}x}$.

7. $y'' + 2y' + y = 50\cos(3x)$, $y(0) = 0$, $y'(0) = 2$. For $y'' + 2y' + y = 0$, $y = e^{rx} \Rightarrow$ $r^2 + 2r + 1 = (r+1)^2 = 0 \Rightarrow y_1 = e^{-x}$ and $y_2 = xe^{-x}$. $y_p = A\cos(3x) + B\sin(3x)$ $\Rightarrow y_p' = -3A\sin(3x) + 3B\cos(3x)$, $y_p'' = -9A\cos(3x) - 9B\sin(3x)$, and $y_p'' + 2y_p' + y_p = (-8A + 6B)\cos(3x) + (-6A - 8B)\sin(3x) = 50\cos(3x) \Rightarrow$
$$\left\{ \begin{array}{rcl} -8A + 6B & = & 50 \\ -6A - 8B & = & 0 \end{array} \right\} \Rightarrow A = -4 \text{ and } B = 3 \Rightarrow y_p = 3\sin(3x) - 4\cos(3x).$$
The general solution is $y = 3\sin(3x) - 4\cos(3x) + c_1 e^{-x} + c_2 xe^{-x}$. $y(0) = 0 \Rightarrow$ $c_1 = 4$, $y'(0) = 2 \Rightarrow c_2 = -3 \Rightarrow y = 3\sin(3x) - 4\cos(3x) + 4e^{-x} - 3xe^{-x}$.

8. $y'' + y = 4\sin(x)$. For $y'' + y = 0$, $y = e^{rx} \Rightarrow r^2 + 1 = 0 \Rightarrow y_1 = \cos(x)$ and $y_2 = \sin(x)$. Since $\cos(x)$ and $\sin(x)$ are solutions of the homogeneous equation, $y_p = x[A\cos(x) + B\sin(x)]$. Then
$y_p' = [A\cos(x) + B\sin(x)] + x[-A\sin(x) + B\cos(x)]$,
$y_p'' = [-2A\sin(x) + 2B\cos(x)] + x[-A\cos(x) - B\sin(x)]$, and $y_p'' + y_p = 4\sin(x)$
$\Rightarrow A = -2$ and $B = 0 \Rightarrow y_p = -2x\cos(x)$. The general solution is
$y = -2x\cos(x) + c_1\cos(x) + c_2\sin(x)$.

9. $y'' + 4y = 8\cos(2x) + 12\sin(2x)$. For $y'' + 4y = 0$, $y = e^{rx} \Rightarrow r^2 + 4 = 0 \Rightarrow$ $y_1 = \cos(2x)$ and $y_2 = \sin(2x)$. Since $\cos(2x)$ and $\sin(2x)$ are solutions of the homogeneous equation, $y_p = x[A\cos(2x) + B\sin(2x)]$. Then
$y_p' = [A\cos(2x) + B\sin(2x)] + x[-2A\sin(2x) + 2B\cos(2x)]$,
$y_p'' = [-4A\sin(2x) + 4B\cos(2x)] + x[-4A\cos(2x) - 4B\sin(2x)]$, and
$y_p'' + 4y_p = 8\cos(2x) + 12\sin(2x) \Rightarrow A = -3$ and $B = 2$
$\Rightarrow y_p = x[2\sin(2x) - 3\cos(2x)]$. The general solution is
$y = x[2\sin(2x) - 3\cos(2x)] + c_1\cos(2x) + c_2\sin(2x)$.

10. $y'' + 4y' + 4y = 4\sin(x) - 3\cos(x)$. For $y'' + 4y' + 4y = 0$, $y = e^{rx} \Rightarrow$ $r^2 + 4r + 4 = (r+2)^2 = 0 \Rightarrow y_1 = e^{-2x}$ and $y_2 = xe^{-2x}$. $y_p = A\cos(x) + B\sin(x)$ $\Rightarrow y_p' = -A\sin(x) + B\cos(x)$, $y_p'' = -A\cos(x) - B\sin(x)$, and
$y_p'' + 4y_p' + 4y_p = (3A + 4B)\cos(x) + (-4A + 3B)\sin(x) = 4\sin(x) - 3\cos(x) \Rightarrow$
$\left\{ \begin{array}{rcl} 3A + 4B & = & -3 \\ -4A + 3B & = & 4 \end{array} \right\} \Rightarrow A = -1$ and $B = 0 \Rightarrow y_p = -\cos(x)$. The general
solution is $y = -\cos(x) + c_1 e^{-2x} + c_2 x e^{-2x}$.

11. $y'' - y = 4$. For $y'' - y = 0$, $y = e^{rx} \Rightarrow r^2 - 1 = (r-1)(r+1) = 0 \Rightarrow y_1 = e^x$ and $y_2 = e^{-x}$. $y_p = A \Rightarrow y_p' = y_p'' = 0$, and $y_p'' - y_p = 4 \Rightarrow A = -4 \Rightarrow y_p = -4$. The general solution is $y = -4 + c_1 e^x + c_2 e^{-x}$.

12. $y'' - y' - 12y = 3 + 12x$. For $y'' - y' - 12y = 0$, $y = e^{rx} \Rightarrow$ $r^2 - r - 12 = (r-4)(r+3) = 0 \Rightarrow y_1 = e^{4x}$ and $y_2 = e^{-3x}$. $y_p = A + Bx \Rightarrow$ $y_p' = B$, $y_p'' = 0$, and $y_p'' - y_p' - 12y_p = (-12A - B) - 12Bx = 3 + 12x \Rightarrow A = -\frac{1}{6}$ and $B = -1 \Rightarrow y_p = -\frac{1}{6} - x$. The general solution is $y = -\frac{1}{6} - x + c_1 e^{4x} + c_2 e^{-3x}$.

13. $y'' + 2y' + 3y = -9x$. For $y'' + 2y' + 3y = 0$, $y = e^{rx} \Rightarrow r^2 + 2r + 3 = 0 \Rightarrow$ $r = -1 \pm \sqrt{2}\,i \Rightarrow y_1 = e^{-x}\cos(\sqrt{2}\,x)$ and $y_2 = e^{-x}\sin(\sqrt{2}\,x)$. $y_p = A + Bx \Rightarrow$ $y_p' = B$, $y_p'' = 0$, and $y_p'' + 2y_p' + 3y_p = (2B + 3A) + 3Bx = -9x \Rightarrow A = 2$ and $B = -3 \Rightarrow y_p = 2 - 3x$. The general solution is
$y = 2 - 3x + e^{-x}[c_1\cos(\sqrt{2}\,x) + c_2\sin(\sqrt{2}\,x)]$.

14. $y'' - 9y = 2 - 3x + x^2$. For $y'' - 9y = 0$, $y = e^{rx} \Rightarrow r^2 - 9 = (r-3)(r+3) = 0$ $\Rightarrow y_1 = e^{3x}$ and $y_2 = e^{-3x}$. $y_p = A + Bx + Cx^2 \Rightarrow y_p' = B + 2Cx$, $y_p'' = 2C$, and
$y_p'' - 9y_p = (2C - 9A) - 9Bx - 9Cx^2 = 2 - 3x + x^2 \Rightarrow A = -\frac{20}{81}$, $B = \frac{1}{3}$ and
$C = -\frac{1}{9} \Rightarrow y_p = -\frac{20}{81} + \frac{1}{3}x - \frac{1}{9}x^2$. The general solution is
$y = -\frac{20}{81} + \frac{1}{3}x - \frac{1}{9}x^2 + c_1 e^{3x} + c_2 e^{-3x}$.

15. $y'' + y' = 1 + x$, $y(0) = 1$, $y'(0) = 1$. For $y'' + y' = 0$, $y = e^{rx} \Rightarrow$
$r^2 + r = r(r + 1) = 0 \Rightarrow y_1 = 1$ and $y_2 = e^{-x}$. Since 1 is a solution of the homogeneous equation, $y_p = x(A + Bx) = Ax + Bx^2$. Then $y_p' = A + 2Bx$,
$y_p'' = 2B$, and $y_p'' + y_p' = 1 + x \Rightarrow A = 0$ and $B = \frac{1}{2} \Rightarrow y_p = \frac{1}{2}x^2$. The general solution is $y = \frac{1}{2}x^2 + c_1 + c_2 e^{-x}$. $y(0) = 1 \Rightarrow c_1 + c_2 = 1$, and $y'(0) = 1 \Rightarrow$
$c_2 = -1 \Rightarrow c_1 = 2 \Rightarrow y = \frac{1}{2}x^2 + 2 - e^{-x}$.

16. $y'' - y' = 4x^3$. For $y'' - y' = 0$, $y = e^{rx} \Rightarrow r^2 - r = r(r - 1) = 0 \Rightarrow y_1 = 1$ and
$y_2 = e^x$. Since 1 is a solution of the homogeneous equation,
$y_p = x(A + Bx + Cx^2 + Dx^3) = Ax + Bx^2 + Cx^3 + Dx^4$. Then
$y_p' = A + 2Bx + 3Cx^2 + 4Dx^3$, $y_p'' = 2B + 6Cx + 12Dx^2$, and $y_p'' - y_p' = 4x^3 \Rightarrow$
$(2B - A) + (6C - 2B)x + (12D - 3C)x^2 - 4Dx^3 = 4x^3 \Rightarrow A = -24$, $B = -12$,
$C = -4$ and $D = -1 \Rightarrow y_p = -24x - 12x^2 - 4x^3 - x^4$. The general solution is
$y = -24x - 12x^2 - 4x^3 - x^4 + c_1 + c_2 e^x$.

17. $y'' - y = -2x + 4e^x + 2\sin(x)$, $y(0) = 0$, $y'(0) = 9$. For $y'' - y = 0$, $y = e^{rx}$
$\Rightarrow r^2 - 1 = (r - 1)(r + 1) = 0 \Rightarrow y_1 = e^x$ and $y_2 = e^{-x}$. For $y'' - y = -2x$,
$y_{p_1} = A + Bx \Rightarrow A = 0$ and $B = 2 \Rightarrow y_{p_1} = 2x$. For $y'' - y = 4e^x$, $y_{p_2} = Axe^x$
$\Rightarrow A = 2 \Rightarrow y_{p_2} = 2xe^x$. For $y'' - y = 2\sin(x)$, $y_{p_3} = A\cos(x) + B\sin(x)$
$\Rightarrow A = 0$ and $B = -1 \Rightarrow y_{p_3} = -\sin(x)$. Hence, $y_p = 2x + 2xe^x - \sin(x)$.
The general solution is $y = 2x + 2xe^x - \sin(x) + c_1 e^x + c_2 e^{-x}$. $y(0) = 0 \Rightarrow$
$c_1 + c_2 = 0$, and $y'(0) = 9 \Rightarrow 3 + c_1 - c_2 = 9 \Rightarrow c_1 = 3$ and $c_2 = -3 \Rightarrow$
$y = 2x + 2xe^x - \sin(x) + 3e^x - 3e^{-x}$.

18. $y'' + y' - 2y = 9e^x$. For $y'' + y' - 2y = 0$, $y = e^{rx} \Rightarrow r^2 + r - 2 = (r - 1)(r + 2) = 0 \Rightarrow$
$y_1 = e^x$ and $y_2 = e^{-2x}$, with $W(x) = \begin{vmatrix} e^x & e^{-2x} \\ e^x & -2e^{-2x} \end{vmatrix} = -3e^{-x}$ and $f(x) = 9e^x$.
Then $u_1 = \int 3\, dx = 3x$, $u_2 = \int -3e^{3x}\, dx = -e^{3x}$, and $y_p = 3xe^x - e^x$, or
$y_p = 3xe^x$. The general solution is $y = 3xe^x + c_1 e^x + c_2 e^{-2x}$.

19. $y'' - 4y' + 4y = 6xe^{2x}$. For $y'' - 4y' + 4y = 0$, $y = e^{rx} \Rightarrow r^2 - 4r + 4 = (r - 2)^2 = 0$
$\Rightarrow y_1 = e^{2x}$ and $y_2 = xe^{2x}$, with $W(x) = \begin{vmatrix} e^{2x} & xe^{2x} \\ 2e^{2x} & e^{2x} + 2xe^{2x} \end{vmatrix} = e^{4x}$ and
$f(x) = 6xe^{2x}$. Then $u_1 = \int -6x^2\, dx = -2x^3$, $u_2 = \int 6x\, dx = 3x^2$, and
$y_p = -2x^3 e^{2x} + 3x^3 e^{2x} = x^3 e^{2x}$. The general solution is $y = x^3 e^{2x} + c_1 e^{2x} + c_2 xe^{2x}$.

20. $y'' + y' = 1$, $y(0) = 2$, $y'(0) = 4$. For $y'' + y' = 0$, $y = e^{rx} \Rightarrow r^2 + r = r(r + 1) = 0$
$\Rightarrow y_1 = 1$ and $y_2 = e^{-x}$, with $W(x) = \begin{vmatrix} 1 & e^{-x} \\ 0 & -e^{-x} \end{vmatrix} = -e^{-x}$ and $f(x) = 1$. Then
$u_1 = \int 1\, dx = x$, $u_2 = \int -e^x\, dx = -e^x$, and $y_p = x - 1$, or $y_p = x$. The general
solution is $y = x + c_1 + c_2 e^{-x}$. $y(0) = 2 \Rightarrow c_1 + c_2 = 2$, $y'(0) = 4 \Rightarrow 1 - c_2 = 4$
$\Rightarrow c_2 = -3$, $c_1 = 5$, and $y = x + 5 - 3e^{-x}$.

21. $y'' + 9y = 6\sin(3x)$. For $y'' + 9y = 0$, $y = e^{rx} \Rightarrow r^2 + 9 = 0 \Rightarrow y_1 = \cos(3x)$ and $y_2 = \sin(3x)$, with $W(x) = \begin{vmatrix} \cos(3x) & \sin(3x) \\ -3\sin(3x) & 3\cos(3x) \end{vmatrix} = 3$ and $f(x) = 6\sin(3x)$.
Then
$u_1 = -\int 2\sin^2(3x)\, dx = -\int 1 - \cos(6x)\, dx = -x + \frac{1}{6}\sin(6x)$,
$u_2 = \int 2\sin(3x)\cos(3x)\, dx = \int \sin(6x)\, dx = -\frac{1}{6}\cos(6x)$, and
$y_p = [-x + \frac{1}{6}\sin(6x)]\cos(3x) - \frac{1}{6}\cos(6x)\sin(3x) = -x\cos(3x) + \frac{1}{6}\sin(3x)$, or
$y_p = -x\cos(3x)$. The general solution is $y = -x\cos(3x) + c_1\cos(3x) + c_2\sin(3x)$.

22. $y'' + y = \sec(x)$. For $y'' + y = 0$, $y = e^{rx} \Rightarrow r^2 + 1 = 0 \Rightarrow y_1 = \cos(x)$ and $y_2 = \sin(x)$, with $W(x) = \begin{vmatrix} \cos(x) & \sin(x) \\ -\sin(x) & \cos(x) \end{vmatrix} = 1$ and $f(x) = \sec(x)$. Then
$u_1 = -\int \tan(x)\, dx = -\ln|\sec(x)|$, $u_2 = \int 1\, dx = x$, and
$y_p = -\cos(x)\ln|\sec(x)| + x\sin(x)$. The general solution is
$y = x\sin(x) - \cos(x)\ln|\sec(x)| + c_1\cos(x) + c_2\sin(x)$.

23. $y'' + 6y' + 13y = 16e^{-3x}\cos(2x)$. For $y'' + 6y' + 13y = 0$, $y = e^{rx} \Rightarrow r^2 + 6r + 13 = 0 \Rightarrow r = -3 \pm 2i \Rightarrow y_1 = e^{-3x}\cos(2x)$ and $y_2 = e^{-3x}\sin(2x)$, with $W(x) = \begin{vmatrix} e^{-3x}\cos(2x) & e^{-3x}\sin(2x) \\ -3e^{-3x}\cos(2x) - 2e^{-3x}\sin(2x) & -3e^{-3x}\sin(2x) + 2e^{-3x}\cos(2x) \end{vmatrix} = 2e^{-6x}$ and
$f(x) = 16e^{-3x}\cos(2x)$. Then
$u_1 = -8\int \sin(2x)\cos(2x)\, dx = -4\int \sin(4x)\, dx = \cos(4x)$,
$u_2 = 8\int \cos^2(2x)\, dx = 4\int 1 + \cos(4x)\, dx = 4x + \sin(4x)$, and
$y_p = \cos(4x)e^{-3x}\cos(2x) + [4x + \sin(4x)]e^{-3x}\sin(2x)$
$= 4xe^{-3x}\sin(2x) + e^{-3x}\cos(2x)$, or $y_p = 4xe^{-3x}\sin(2x)$.
The general solution is $y = 4xe^{-3x}\sin(2x) + c_1e^{-3x}\cos(2x) + c_2e^{-3x}\sin(2x)$.

24. $y'' - 4y' + 13y = \frac{9e^{2x}}{\cos(3x)}$. For $y'' - 4y' + 13y = 0$, $y = e^{rx} \Rightarrow r^2 - 4r + 13 = 0 \Rightarrow r = 2 \pm 3i \Rightarrow y_1 = e^{2x}\cos(3x)$ and $y_2 = e^{2x}\sin(3x)$, with
$W(x) = \begin{vmatrix} e^{2x}\cos(3x) & e^{2x}\sin(3x) \\ 2e^{2x}\cos(3x) - 3e^{2x}\sin(3x) & 2e^{2x}\sin(3x) + 3e^{2x}\cos(3x) \end{vmatrix} = 3e^{4x}$ and
$f(x) = \frac{9e^{2x}}{\cos(3x)}$. Then $u_1 = -3\int \tan(3x)\, dx = -\ln|\sec(3x)|$, $u_2 = 3\int 1\, dx = 3x$,
and $y_p = -e^{2x}\cos(3x)\ln|\sec(3x)| + 3xe^{2x}\sin(3x)$. The general solution is
$y = 3xe^{2x}\sin(3x) - e^{2x}\cos(3x)\ln|\sec(3x)| + c_1e^{2x}\cos(3x) + c_2e^{2x}\sin(3x)$.

25. $y'' - 2y' + y = e^x\ln(x)$, $x > 0$. For $y'' - 2y' + y = 0$, $y = e^{rx} \Rightarrow r^2 - 2r + 1 = (r-1)^2 = 0 \Rightarrow y_1 = e^x$ and $y_2 = xe^x$, with
$W(x) = \begin{vmatrix} e^x & xe^x \\ e^x & e^x + xe^x \end{vmatrix} = e^{2x}$ and $f(x) = e^x\ln(x)$. Then
$u_1 = -\int x\ln(x)\, dx = -\frac{x^2}{2}\ln(x) + \frac{x^2}{4}$, $u_2 = \int \ln(x)\, dx = x\ln(x) - x$, and
$y_p = \left[\frac{x^2}{4} - \frac{x^2}{2}\ln(x)\right]e^x + [x\ln(x) - x]xe^x = e^x\left[\frac{1}{2}x^2\ln(x) - \frac{3}{4}x^2\right]$. The general
solution is $y = e^x\left[\frac{1}{2}x^2\ln(x) - \frac{3}{4}x^2\right] + c_1e^x + c_2xe^x$.

26. $y'' + 3y' + 2y = \sin(e^x)$. For $y'' + 3y' + 2y = 0$, $y = e^{rx} \Rightarrow$
$r^2 + 3r + 2 = (r+1)(r+2) = 0 \Rightarrow y_1 = e^{-x}$ and $y_2 = e^{-2x}$, with
$$W(x) = \begin{vmatrix} e^{-x} & e^{-2x} \\ -e^{-x} & -2e^{-2x} \end{vmatrix} = -e^{-3x} \text{ and } f(x) = \sin(e^x). \text{ Then}$$
$u_1 = \int e^x \sin(e^x)\, dx$ and $u_2 = -\int e^{2x} \sin(e^x)\, dx$. The substitution $u = e^x$,
$\frac{du}{dx} = e^x$, then gives $u_1 = \int \sin(u)\, du = -\cos(u) = -\cos(e^x)$ and, by integration
by parts, $u_2 = -\int u \sin(u)\, du = u\cos(u) - \sin(u) = e^x \cos(e^x) - \sin(e^x)$. Then
$y_p = -e^{-x}\cos(e^x) + e^{-2x}[e^x \cos(e^x) - \sin(e^x)] = -e^{-2x}\sin(e^x)$, and the general
solution is $y = -e^{-2x}\sin(e^x) + c_1 e^{-x} + c_2 e^{-2x}$.

27. $x^2 y'' - 6y = 10x^5$.
For $x^2 y'' - 6y = 0$ and $x > 0$, $y = x^r \Rightarrow r^2 - r - 6 = (r-3)(r+2) = 0 \Rightarrow$
$y_1 = x^3$ and $y_2 = x^{-2}$. These solutions are defined for all $x \neq 0$, with
$$W(x) = \begin{vmatrix} x^3 & x^{-2} \\ 3x^2 & -2x^{-3} \end{vmatrix} = -5 \text{ and } f(x) = 10x^3. \text{ Then } u_1 = 2\int x\, dx = x^2,$$
$u_2 = -2\int x^6\, dx = -\frac{2}{7}x^7$, and $y_p = x^2 x^3 - \frac{2}{7}x^7 x^{-2} = \frac{5}{7}x^5$. The general solution
is $y = \frac{5}{7}x^5 + c_1 x^3 + c_2 x^{-2}$ for $x \neq 0$.

28. $x^2 y'' - 4xy' + 6y = x^4 e^x$.
For $x^2 y'' - 4xy' + 6y = 0$ and $x > 0$, $y = x^r \Rightarrow r^2 - 5r + 6 = (r-2)(r-3) = 0$
$\Rightarrow y_1 = x^2$ and $y_2 = x^3$, defined for all real x, with $W(x) = \begin{vmatrix} x^2 & x^3 \\ 2x & 3x^2 \end{vmatrix} = x^4$
and $f(x) = x^2 e^x$. Then $u_1 = -\int xe^x\, dx = e^x - xe^x$, $u_2 = \int e^x\, dx = e^x$, and
$y_p = (e^x - xe^x)x^2 + x^3 e^x = x^2 e^x$. The general solution is $y = x^2 e^x + c_1 x^2 + c_2 x^3$
for all real x.

29. $x^2 y'' + 5xy' + 3y = 4xe^{x^2}$, $y(1) = e$, $y'(1) = e$.
For $x^2 y'' + 5xy' + 3y = 0$ and $x > 0$, $y = x^r \Rightarrow r^2 + 4r + 3 = (r+1)(r+3) = 0 \Rightarrow$
$y_1 = x^{-1}$ and $y_2 = x^{-3}$, defined for all $x \neq 0$, with $W(x) = \begin{vmatrix} x^{-1} & x^{-3} \\ -x^{-2} & -3x^{-4} \end{vmatrix} =$
$-2x^{-5}$ and $f(x) = \frac{4e^{x^2}}{x}$. Then $u_1 = 2\int xe^{x^2}\, dx = e^{x^2}$ and $u_2 = -2\int x^3 e^{x^2}\, dx$.
Integration by parts gives
$u_2 = -\int x^2 \cdot 2xe^{x^2}\, dx = -x^2 e^{x^2} + \int 2xe^{x^2}\, dx = -x^2 e^{x^2} + e^{x^2}$. Hence,
$y_p = e^{x^2} x^{-1} + e^{x^2}(1 - x^2)x^{-3} = x^{-3} e^{x^2}$. The general solution for $x \neq 0$ is
$y = x^{-3} e^{x^2} + c_1 x^{-1} + c_2 x^{-3}$. $y(1) = e \Rightarrow c_1 + c_2 = 0 \Rightarrow y = x^{-3} e^{x^2} + c_1(x^{-1} - x^{-3})$
$\Rightarrow y' = -3x^{-4} e^{x^2} + 2x^{-2} e^{x^2} + c_1(-x^{-2} + 3x^{-4})$, and $y'(1) = e \Rightarrow c_1 = e \Rightarrow c_2 = -e$
$\Rightarrow y = x^{-3} e^{x^2} + e(x^{-1} - x^{-3})$.

30. $x^2 y'' - 2xy' + 2y = x^3 \cos(x)$.
For $x^2 y'' - 2xy' + 2y = 0$ and $x > 0$, $y = x^r \Rightarrow r^2 - 3r + 2 = (r-1)(r-2) = 0$
$\Rightarrow y_1 = x$ and $y_2 = x^2$, defined for all real x, with $W(x) = \begin{vmatrix} x & x^2 \\ 1 & 2x \end{vmatrix} = x^2$
and $f(x) = x\cos(x)$. Then $u_1 = -\int x\cos(x)\, dx = -x\sin(x) - \cos(x)$, $u_2 =$

$\int \cos(x)\,dx = \sin(x)$, and $y_p = -[x\sin(x)+\cos(x)]x + [\sin(x)]x^2 = -x\cos(x)$. The general solution is $y = c_1 x + c_2 x^2 - x\cos(x)$ for all real x.

31. $x^2 y'' + xy' - y = x^2 \sin(x)$.

For $x^2 y'' + xy' - y = 0$ and $x > 0$, $y = x^r \Rightarrow r^2 - 1 = 0 \Rightarrow r = \pm 1 \Rightarrow y_1 = x$ and $y_2 = x^{-1}$, defined for all $x \neq 0$, with $W(x) = \begin{vmatrix} x & x^{-1} \\ 1 & -x^{-2} \end{vmatrix} = -2x^{-1}$ and $f(x) = \sin(x)$. Then $u_1 = \frac{1}{2}\int \sin(x)\,dx = -\frac{1}{2}\cos(x)$, $u_2 = -\frac{1}{2}\int x^2 \sin(x)\,dx = \frac{1}{2}x^2\cos(x) - \int x\cos(x)\,dx = \frac{1}{2}x^2\cos(x) - x\sin(x) - \cos(x)$, and $y_p = -\frac{1}{2}x\cos(x) + x^{-1}\left[\frac{1}{2}x^2\cos(x) - x\sin(x) - \cos(x)\right] = -\sin(x) - \frac{\cos(x)}{x}$. The general solution is $y = -\sin(x) - \frac{\cos(x)}{x} + c_1 x + c_2 x^{-1}$ for $x \neq 0$.

32. $x^2 y'' + 3xy' + y = \frac{\ln(x)}{x}$, $x > 0$.

For $x^2 y'' + 3xy' + y = 0$, $y = x^r \Rightarrow r^2 + 2r + 1 = (r+1)^2 = 0 \Rightarrow y_1 = x^{-1}$ and $y_2 = x^{-1}\ln(x)$, with $W(x) = \begin{vmatrix} x^{-1} & x^{-1}\ln(x) \\ -x^{-2} & -x^{-2}\ln(x) + x^{-2} \end{vmatrix} = x^{-3}$ and $f(x) = \frac{\ln(x)}{x^3}$. Then $u_1 = -\int \frac{[\ln(x)]^2}{x}\,dx = -\frac{1}{3}[\ln(x)]^3$, $u_2 = \int \frac{\ln(x)}{x}\,dx = \frac{1}{2}[\ln(x)]^2$, and $y_p = -\frac{1}{3}x^{-1}[\ln(x)]^3 + \frac{1}{2}x^{-1}[\ln(x)]^3 = \frac{1}{6}x^{-1}[\ln(x)]^3$. The general solution for $x > 0$ is $y = \frac{1}{6}x^{-1}[\ln(x)]^3 + c_1 x^{-1} + c_2 x^{-1}\ln(x)$.

33. $x^2 y'' - 3xy' + 4y = x^2 \ln(x)$, $x > 0$.

For $x^2 y'' - 3xy' + 4y = 0$, $y = x^r \Rightarrow r^2 - 4r + 4 = (r-2)^2 = 0 \Rightarrow y_1 = x^2$ and $y_2 = x^2 \ln(x)$, with $W(x) = \begin{vmatrix} x^2 & x^2\ln(x) \\ 2x & 2x\ln(x) + x \end{vmatrix} = x^3$ and $f(x) = \ln(x)$. Then $u_1 = -\int \frac{[\ln(x)]^2}{x}\,dx = -\frac{1}{3}[\ln(x)]^3$, $u_2 = \int \frac{\ln(x)}{x}\,dx = \frac{1}{2}[\ln(x)]^2$, and $y_p = -\frac{1}{3}x^2[\ln(x)]^3 + \frac{1}{2}x^2[\ln(x)]^3 = \frac{1}{6}x^2[\ln(x)]^3$. The general solution for $x > 0$ is $y = \frac{1}{6}x^2[\ln(x)]^3 + c_1 x^2 + c_2 x^2 \ln(x)$.

34. $x^2 y'' - 3xy' + 13y = 9x^2$.

For $x^2 y'' - 3xy' + 13y = 0$ and $x > 0$, $y = x^r \Rightarrow r^2 - 4r + 13 = 0 \Rightarrow r = 2 \pm 3i \Rightarrow y_1 = x^2 \cos[3\ln(x)]$ and $y_2 = x^2 \sin[3\ln(x)]$, with $W(x) = \begin{vmatrix} x^2\cos[3\ln(x)] & x^2\sin[3\ln(x)] \\ 2x\cos[3\ln(x)] - 3x\sin[3\ln(x)] & 2x\sin[3\ln(x)] + 3x\cos[3\ln(x)] \end{vmatrix} = 3x^3$, and $f(x) = 9$. Then $u_1 = -3\int \frac{\sin[3\ln(x)]}{x}\,dx = \cos[3\ln(x)]$, $u_2 = 3\int \frac{\cos[3\ln(x)]}{x}\,dx = \sin[3\ln(x)]$, and $y_p = x^2\cos^2[3\ln(x)] + x^2\sin^2[3\ln(x)] = x^2$. Since y_p is a particular solution of the nonhomogeneous equation for any real x, the general solution for $x \neq 0$ is $y = x^2[1 + c_1\cos(3\ln|x|) + c_2\sin(3\ln|x|)]$.

35. $x^2 y'' + 7xy' + 13y = \frac{4}{x^3 \cos^2[2\ln(x)]}$, $x > 0$.

For $x^2 y'' + 7xy' + 13y = 0$, $y = x^r \Rightarrow r^2 + 6r + 13 = 0 \Rightarrow r = -3 \pm 2i \Rightarrow y_1 = x^{-3}\cos[2\ln(x)]$ and $y_2 = x^{-3}\sin[2\ln(x)]$, with $W(x) = \begin{vmatrix} x^{-3}\cos[2\ln(x)] & x^{-3}\sin[2\ln(x)] \\ -3x^{-4}\cos[2\ln(x)] - 2x^{-4}\sin[2\ln(x)] & -3x^{-4}\sin[2\ln(x)] + 2x^{-4}\cos[2\ln(x)] \end{vmatrix}$

$= 2x^{-7}$ and $f(x) = \frac{4}{x^5 \cos^2[2\ln(x)]}$. The substitution $u = 2\ln(x)$, $\frac{du}{dx} = \frac{2}{x}$, then gives

$u_1 = -2\int \frac{\sin[2\ln(x)]}{x\cos^2[2\ln(x)]}\,dx = -\int \frac{\sin(u)}{\cos^2(u)}\,du = -\frac{1}{\cos(u)} = -\frac{1}{\cos[2\ln(x)]}$,

$u_2 = 2\int \frac{1}{x\cos[2\ln(x)]}\,dx = \int \sec(u)\,du = \ln|\sec(u) + \tan(u)| = $

$\ln|\sec[2\ln(x)] + \tan[2\ln(x)]|$, and

$y_p = -x^{-3} + x^{-3}\sin[2\ln(x)]\ln|\sec[2\ln(x)] + \tan[2\ln(x)]|$. The general solution for $x > 0$ is $y = $

$x^{-3}\{\sin[2\ln(x)]\ln|\sec[2\ln(x)] + \tan[2\ln(x)]| - 1 + c_1\cos[2\ln(x)] + c_2\sin[2\ln(x)]\}$.

36. $x^2 y'' - 5xy' + 13y = 8x^3\sin[2\ln(x)]$, $x > 0$.

For $x^2 y'' - 5xy' + 13y = 0$, $y = x^r \Rightarrow r^2 - 6r + 13 = 0 \Rightarrow r = 3 \pm 2i \Rightarrow$ $y_1 = x^3\cos[2\ln(x)]$ and $y_2 = x^3\sin[2\ln(x)]$, with

$W(x) = \begin{vmatrix} x^3\cos[2\ln(x)] & x^3\sin[2\ln(x)] \\ 3x^2\cos[2\ln(x)] - 2x^2\sin[2\ln(x)] & 3x^2\sin[2\ln(x)] + 2x^2\cos[2\ln(x)] \end{vmatrix}$

$= 2x^5$ and $f(x) = 8x\sin[2\ln(x)]$. The substitution $u = 2\ln(x)$, $\frac{du}{dx} = \frac{2}{x}$, then gives

$u_1 = -4\int \frac{\sin^2[2\ln(x)]}{x}\,dx = -2\int \sin^2(u)\,du = \int \cos(2u) - 1\,du = \frac{1}{2}\sin(2u) - u$

$= \frac{1}{2}\sin[4\ln(x)] - 2\ln(x)$,

$u_2 = 4\int \frac{\sin[2\ln(x)]\cos[2\ln(x)]}{x}\,dx = 2\int \sin(u)\cos(u)\,du = \int \sin(2u)\,du = -\frac{1}{2}\cos(2u)$

$= -\frac{1}{2}\cos[4\ln(x)]$, and

$y_p = \{\frac{1}{2}\sin[4\ln(x)] - 2\ln(x)\}x^3\cos[2\ln(x)] - \frac{1}{2}\cos[4\ln(x)]x^3\sin[2\ln(x)]$

$= \frac{1}{2}x^3\{\sin[4\ln(x)]\cos[2\ln(x)] - \cos[4\ln(x)]\sin[2\ln(x)]\} - 2x^3\ln(x)\cos[2\ln(x)]$

$= \frac{1}{2}x^3\sin[2\ln(x)] - 2x^3\ln(x)\cos[2\ln(x)]$, or $y_p = -2x^3\ln(x)\cos[2\ln(x)]$. The general solution is $y = x^3\{c_1\cos[2\ln(x)] + c_2\sin[2\ln(x)] - 2\ln(x)\cos[2\ln(x)]\}$.

37. $4x^2 y'' + 4xy' - y = x^2$.

For $4x^2 y'' + 4xy' - y = 0$ and $x > 0$, $y = x^r \Rightarrow 4r(r-1) + 4r - 1 = 4r^2 - 1 = 0$ $\Rightarrow y_1 = x^{1/2}$ and $y_2 = x^{-1/2}$, with $W(x) = \begin{vmatrix} x^{1/2} & x^{-1/2} \\ \frac{1}{2}x^{-1/2} & -\frac{1}{2}x^{-3/2} \end{vmatrix} = -x^{-1}$ and

$f(x) = \frac{1}{4}$. Then $u_1 = \frac{1}{4}\int x^{1/2}\,dx = \frac{1}{6}x^{3/2}$, $u_2 = -\frac{1}{4}\int x^{3/2}\,dx = -\frac{1}{10}x^{5/2}$, and $y_p = \frac{1}{15}x^2$. Since y_p is a particular solution of the nonhomogeneous equation for all real x, the general solution for $x \neq 0$ is $y = \frac{1}{15}x^2 + c_1|x|^{1/2} + c_2|x|^{-1/2}$.

Exercises 3.4 – page 83

1. $\frac{y''}{y'-2} = \frac{2}{x} + 3x^2$ and $z(x) = y'(x) \Rightarrow \frac{z'}{z-2} = \frac{2}{x} + 3x^2 \Rightarrow \ln|z-2| = 2\ln|x| + x^3 + c_1$ $\Rightarrow z - 2 = k_1 x^2 e^{x^3} \Rightarrow y = \int k_1 x^2 e^{x^3} + 2\,dx = \frac{1}{3}k_1 e^{x^3} + 2x + k_2$.

2. $x^2 y'' = (y')^2$ and $z(x) = y'(x) \Rightarrow x^2 z' = z^2 \Rightarrow \frac{z'}{z^2} = \frac{1}{x^2} \Rightarrow -\frac{1}{z} = -\frac{1}{x} + c \Rightarrow$ $z = \frac{x}{1-cx} \Rightarrow y = \int \frac{x}{1-cx}\,dx = -\frac{1}{c}\int 1 - \frac{1}{1-cx}\,dx = -\frac{x}{c} - \frac{1}{c^2}\ln|1 - cx| + k$, if $c \neq 0$. If $c = 0$, then $z = x \Rightarrow y = \frac{x^2}{2} + k_1$.

3. $y'' - x(y')^3 = 0$ and $z(x) = y'(x) \Rightarrow z' - xz^3 = 0 \Rightarrow z^{-3}z' = x \Rightarrow -\frac{1}{2}z^{-2} = \frac{1}{2}x^2 + c$
$\Rightarrow z^2 = \frac{1}{k - x^2} \Rightarrow z = \frac{\pm 1}{\sqrt{k - x^2}}$ and is real if and only if $k = \mu^2 > 0$. Then
$x = \mu \sin(t) \Rightarrow y = \pm \int \frac{1}{\sqrt{\mu^2 - x^2}} \, dx = \pm \int 1 \, dt = \pm t + c_1 = \pm \sin^{-1}\left(\frac{x}{\mu}\right) + c_1$.

4. $y'y'' + x = 0$ and $z(x) = y'(x) \Rightarrow zz' + x = 0 \Rightarrow \frac{1}{2}z^2 = -\frac{1}{2}x^2 + c \Rightarrow$
$z = \pm\sqrt{k - x^2}$ and is real if and only if $k = \mu^2 > 0$. Then $x = \mu \sin(t) \Rightarrow$
$y = \pm \int \sqrt{\mu^2 - x^2} \, dx = \pm \mu^2 \int \cos^2(t) \, dt = \pm\frac{\mu^2}{2} \int 1 + \cos(2t) \, dt$
$= \pm\frac{\mu^2}{2} \left[t + \frac{1}{2}\sin(2t) \right] + c_1 = \pm\frac{\mu^2}{2}[t + \sin(t)\cos(t)] + c_1 =$
$\pm\frac{\mu^2}{2} \left[\sin^{-1}\left(\frac{x}{\mu}\right) + \frac{x\sqrt{\mu^2 - x^2}}{\mu^2} \right] + c_1$.

5. $xy'' = y' \ln(y') - y' \ln(x)$ and $z(x) = y'(x) \Rightarrow xz' = z\ln(z) - z\ln(x) \Rightarrow$
$z' = \frac{z}{x} \ln(\frac{z}{x})$, which is homogeneous, and $u = \frac{z}{x} \Rightarrow u + xu' = u\ln(u) \Rightarrow$
$xu' = u[\ln(u) - 1] \Rightarrow \frac{u'}{u[\ln(u) - 1]} = \frac{1}{x} \Rightarrow \ln|\ln(u) - 1| = \ln(x) + c \Rightarrow$
$\ln(u) - 1 = kx \Rightarrow u = e^{kx+1} \Rightarrow z = xe^{kx+1}$, and $k = \pm e^c \neq 0$. Hence,
$y = \int xe^{kx+1} \, dx = \frac{1}{k}xe^{kx+1} - \frac{1}{k^2}e^{kx+1} + k_1$.

6. $y'' + 2y' = 2e^{-x}\sqrt{y'}$ and $z(x) = y'(x) \Rightarrow z' + 2z = 2e^{-x}\sqrt{z}$, which is a Bernoulli
equation with $\alpha = \frac{1}{2}$. Then $u = z^{1/2} \Rightarrow z = u^2 \Rightarrow z' = 2uu' \Rightarrow$
$2uu' + 2u^2 = 2e^{-x}u \Rightarrow u' + u = e^{-x}$, which is linear, with the integrating factor
$I(x) = e^x$. Then $(e^x u)' = 1 \Rightarrow e^x u = x + c \Rightarrow u = (x+c)e^{-x} \Rightarrow z = (x+c)^2 e^{-2x}$
$\Rightarrow y = \int (x+c)^2 e^{-2x} \, dx = -\frac{1}{2}(x+c)^2 e^{-2x} + \int (x+c)e^{-2x} \, dx$
$= -\frac{1}{2}(x+c)^2 e^{-2x} - \frac{1}{2}(x+c)e^{-2x} + \frac{1}{2}\int e^{-2x} \, dx$
$= -\frac{1}{2}(x+c)^2 e^{-2x} - \frac{1}{2}(x+c)e^{-2x} - \frac{1}{4}e^{-2x} + k$.

7. $x^4 + (y')^2 - xy'y'' = 0$ and $z(x) = y'(x) \Rightarrow x^4 + z^2 - xzz' = 0$, with
$P(x, z) = x^4 + z^2$, $Q(x, z) = -xz$, $\frac{P_z - Q_x}{Q} = -\frac{3}{x} = \frac{I'(x)}{I(x)} \Rightarrow I(x) = x^{-3}$ is an
integrating factor. Then $x + x^{-3}z^2 - x^{-2}zz' = 0$ is exact. $f_x = x + x^{-3}z^2 \Rightarrow$
$f(x, z) = \frac{1}{2}x^2 - \frac{1}{2}x^{-2}z^2 + g(z)$, and $f_z = -x^{-2}z \Rightarrow f(x, z) = \frac{1}{2}x^2 - \frac{1}{2}x^{-2}z^2 + c$
and $\frac{1}{2}x^2 - \frac{1}{2}x^{-2}z^2 = c_1$, or $x^2 - x^{-2}z^2 = k$, and $z = \pm x\sqrt{x^2 - k}$. Then
$y = \pm \int x\sqrt{x^2 - k} \, dx = \pm\frac{1}{3}(x^2 - k)^{3/2} + k_1$.

8. $y'' = (2x - y' + 3)^2 + 2$ and $z(x) = y'(x) \Rightarrow z' = (2x - z + 3)^2 + 2$. Let
$u = 2x - z + 3$. Then $u' = 2 - z' = 2 - (u^2 + 2) = -u^2$, which is separable.
Then $-\frac{u'}{u^2} = 1 \Rightarrow \frac{1}{u} = x + c \Rightarrow u = \frac{1}{x+c} \Rightarrow 2x - z + 3 = \frac{1}{x+c} \Rightarrow z = 2x + 3 - \frac{1}{x+c}$
$\Rightarrow y = \int 2x + 3 - \frac{1}{x+c} \, dx = x^2 + 3x - \ln|x+c| + k$.

9. $y'' + (2 - 6y + 12y^2)(y')^3 = 0$ and $v(y) = y'(x) \Rightarrow vv' + (2 - 6y + 12y^2)v^3 = 0$. If
$v = 0$, then $y = c$. If $v \neq 0$, then $-\frac{v'}{v^2} = 2 - 6y + 12y^2 \Rightarrow \frac{1}{v} = 2y - 3y^2 + 4y^3 + c_1$
$\Rightarrow (2y - 3y^2 + 4y^3 + c_1)y' = 1 \Rightarrow y^2 - y^3 + y^4 + c_1 y = x + c_2$.

10. $y'' = (y')^2 \tan(y)$ and $v(y) = y'(x) \Rightarrow vv' = v^2 \tan(y)$. If $v = 0$, then $y = c$. If
$v \neq 0$, then $\frac{v'}{v} = \tan(y) \Rightarrow \ln|v| = \ln|\sec(y)| + c_1 \Rightarrow v = k\sec(y) \Rightarrow \cos(y)y' = k$

$\Rightarrow \sin(y) = kx + k_1 \Rightarrow y = \sin^{-1}(kx + k_1)$.

11. $yy'' = y'(y'-1)\ln(y'-1)$ and $v(y) = y'(x) \Rightarrow yvv' = v(v-1)\ln(v-1)$, with $v \neq 0$ since $\ln(-1)$ is undefined. Then $\frac{v'}{(v-1)\ln(v-1)} = \frac{1}{y} \Rightarrow \ln|\ln(v-1)| = \ln|y| + c \Rightarrow$ $\ln(v-1) = ky \Rightarrow v = e^{ky} + 1 \Rightarrow \frac{y'}{e^{ky}+1} = 1 \Rightarrow \frac{e^{-ky}y'}{1+e^{-ky}} = 1$ and $k = \pm e^c \neq 0$. Then $-\frac{1}{k}\ln(1+e^{-ky}) = x + k_1 \Rightarrow 1 + e^{-ky} = e^{-k(x+k_1)} \Rightarrow -ky = \ln[e^{-k(x+k_1)} - 1]$ $\Rightarrow y = -\frac{1}{k}\ln[e^{-k(x+k_1)} - 1]$.

12. $\sin(y)y'' + \cos(y)(y')^2 = (y')^3$ and $v(y) = y'(x) \Rightarrow \sin(y)vv' + \cos(y)v^2 = v^3$. If $v = 0$, then $y = c$. If $v \neq 0$, then $\sin(y)v' + \cos(y)v = v^2$, which is a Bernoulli equation with $\alpha = 2$. Then $u = v^{-1} \Rightarrow v = u^{-1} \Rightarrow v' = -u^{-2}u'$ $\Rightarrow -\sin(y)u^{-2}u' + \cos(y)u^{-1} = u^{-2}$, or $-\sin(y)u' + \cos(y)u = 1$, which is linear. The standard form is $u' - \cot(y)u = -\csc(y)$, with the integrating factor $I(y) = e^{-\int \cot(y)\,dy} = e^{\ln|\csc(y)|} = |\csc(y)|$, and with $I(y) = \csc(y)$, the equation becomes $\csc(y)u' - \csc(y)\cot(y)u = -\csc^2(y)$, i.e., $[\csc(y)u]' = -\csc^2(y)$. Then $\csc(y)u = \cot(y) + k \Rightarrow u = \cos(y) + k\sin(y) \Rightarrow v = \frac{1}{\cos(y)+k\sin(y)} \Rightarrow$ $[\cos(y) + k\sin(y)]y' = 1 \Rightarrow \sin(y) - k\cos(y) = x + k_1$.

13. $y'' = 2yy'$ and $v(y) = y'(x) \Rightarrow vv' = 2yv$. If $v = 0$, then $y = c$. If $v \neq 0$, then $v' = 2y \Rightarrow v = y^2 + k \Rightarrow \frac{y'}{y^2+k} = 1 \Rightarrow \int \frac{1}{y^2+k}\,dy = x + c_1$. If $k = 0$, then $-\frac{1}{y} = x + c_1 \Rightarrow y = \frac{-1}{x+c_1}$. If $k = \mu^2 > 0$, then $y = \mu\tan(t) \Rightarrow$ $\int \frac{1}{y^2+\mu^2}\,dy = \int \frac{1}{\mu}\,dt = \frac{t}{\mu} = \frac{1}{\mu}\tan^{-1}\left(\frac{y}{\mu}\right) \Rightarrow y = \mu\tan[\mu(x+c_1)]$. If $k = -\mu^2 < 0$, then $\int \frac{1}{y^2-\mu^2}\,dy = \frac{1}{2\mu}\int \frac{1}{y-\mu} - \frac{1}{y+\mu}\,dy = \frac{1}{2\mu}(\ln|y-\mu| - \ln|y+\mu|) = \frac{1}{2\mu}\ln\left|\frac{y-\mu}{y+\mu}\right| = x + c_1 \Rightarrow \frac{y-\mu}{y+\mu} = k_1 e^{2\mu x} \Rightarrow y(1 - k_1 e^{2\mu x}) = \mu(k_1 e^{2\mu x} + 1) \Rightarrow y = \mu\frac{k_1 e^{2\mu x}+1}{1-k_1 e^{2\mu x}}$.

14. $y'' - (y')^2 = 1$ and $z(x) = y'(x) \Rightarrow z' - z^2 = 1 \Rightarrow \frac{z'}{z^2+1} = 1 \Rightarrow \tan^{-1}(z) = x + c$ $\Rightarrow z = \tan(x+c) \Rightarrow y = \int \tan(x+c)\,dx = \ln|\sec(x+c)| + k$.

15. $\sqrt{1+y'}\,y'' = 1$ and $z(x) = y'(x) \Rightarrow \sqrt{1+z}\,z' = 1 \Rightarrow \frac{2}{3}(1+z)^{3/2} = x + c \Rightarrow$ $(1+z)^{3/2} = \frac{3}{2}x + c_1 \Rightarrow z = \left(\frac{3}{2}x + c_1\right)^{2/3} - 1$ $\Rightarrow y = \int \left(\frac{3}{2}x + c_1\right)^{2/3} - 1\,dx = \frac{2}{5}\left(\frac{3}{2}x + c_1\right)^{5/3} - x + c_2$.

16. $e^{y'}y'' = 1$ and $z(x) = y'(x) \Rightarrow e^z z' = 1 \Rightarrow e^z = x + c \Rightarrow z = \ln(x+c) \Rightarrow$ $y = \int \ln(x+c)\,dx$. Let $u = x + c$ and integrate by parts to obtain $\int 1 \cdot \ln(u)\,du = u\ln(u) - u + c_1$. Hence, $y = (x+c)\ln(x+c) - \ln(x+c) + c_1$.

17. $\cos(y')y'' = 1$ and $z(x) = y'(x) \Rightarrow \cos(z)z' = 1 \Rightarrow \sin(z) = x + c \Rightarrow$ $z = \sin^{-1}(x+c) \Rightarrow y = \int \sin^{-1}(x+c)\,dx$. Let $u = x + c$ and integrate by parts to obtain $\int 1 \cdot \sin^{-1}(u)\,du = u\sin^{-1}(u) - \int \frac{u}{\sqrt{1-u^2}}\,du = u\sin^{-1}(u) + \sqrt{1-u^2} + c_1$. Hence, $y = (x+c)\sin^{-1}(x+c) + \sqrt{1-(x+c)^2} + c_1$.

18. $y'' = y'\sqrt{1 - (y')^2}$ and $v(y) = y'(x) \Rightarrow vv' = v\sqrt{1 - v^2}$. If $v = 0$, then $y = c$. If
$v \neq 0$, then $\frac{v'}{\sqrt{1-v^2}} = 1 \Rightarrow \sin^{-1}(v) = y + c_1 \Rightarrow v = \sin(y + c_1) \Rightarrow \csc(y + c_1)y' = 1$
$\Rightarrow -\ln|\csc(y + c_1) + \cot(y + c_1)| = x + k \Rightarrow \csc(y + c_1) + \cot(y + c_1) = k_1 e^{-x}$.

Chapter 3 Exercises – page 84

1. The standard form of the equation is $y'' + \frac{1}{x}y' + (1 - \frac{1}{4x^2})y = 0$, with $p(x) = \frac{1}{x}$
and $y_1 = \frac{\cos(x)}{\sqrt{x}} \Rightarrow u'(x) = \frac{1}{y_1^2}e^{-\int \frac{1}{x}dx} = \frac{x}{\cos^2(x)}\frac{1}{x} = \sec^2(x)$
$\Rightarrow u = \int \sec^2(x)\,dx = \tan(x) \Rightarrow y_2 = uy_1 = \tan(x)\frac{\cos(x)}{\sqrt{x}} = \frac{\sin(x)}{\sqrt{x}}$.

2. $y'' + xy' + y = 0$, $p(x) = x$, $y_1 = e^{-x^2/2} \Rightarrow u'(x) = \frac{1}{y_1^2}e^{-\int x\,dx} = e^{x^2}e^{-x^2/2} = e^{x^2/2}$
$\Rightarrow u = \int e^{x^2/2}\,dx \Rightarrow y_2 = uy_1 = e^{-x^2/2}\int e^{x^2/2}\,dx$.

3. The standard form of the equation is $y'' + (1 + \frac{1}{2x})y' - \frac{1}{2x^2}y = 0$, with $p(x) = $
$1 + \frac{1}{2x}$ and $y_1 = x^{-1/2}e^{-x} \Rightarrow u'(x) = \frac{1}{y_1^2}e^{-\int 1 + \frac{1}{2x}dx} = xe^{2x}e^{-x-\frac{1}{2}\ln(x)} = x^{1/2}e^x \Rightarrow$
$u = \int x^{1/2}e^x\,dx \Rightarrow y_2 = uy_1 = x^{-1/2}e^{-x}\int x^{1/2}e^x\,dx$.

4. $y'' + y = \cos(x)$. For $y'' + y = 0$, $y_1 = \cos(x)$ and $y_2 = \sin(x)$.

   (a) $y_p = x[A\cos(x) + B\sin(x)] \Rightarrow$
   $y_p' = [A\cos(x) + B\sin(x)] + x[-A\sin(x) + B\cos(x)]$,
   $y_p'' = [-2A\sin(x) + 2B\cos(x)] + x[-A\cos(x) - B\sin(x)]$,
   $y_p'' + y_p = -2A\sin(x) + 2B\cos(x) = \cos(x) \Rightarrow A = 0$ and $B = \frac{1}{2} \Rightarrow$
   $y_p = \frac{1}{2}x\sin(x) \Rightarrow y = \frac{1}{2}x\sin(x) + c_1\cos(x) + c_2\sin(x)$.

   (b) $W(x) = 1$, $f(x) = \cos(x)$,
   $u_1 = -\int \sin(x)\cos(x)\,dx = -\frac{1}{2}\int \sin(2x)\,dx = \frac{1}{4}\cos(2x)$,
   $u_2 = \int \cos^2(x)\,dx = \frac{1}{2}\int 1 + \cos(2x)\,dx = \frac{1}{2}x + \frac{1}{4}\sin(2x)$,
   $y_p = \frac{1}{4}\cos(2x)\cos(x) + [\frac{1}{2}x + \frac{1}{4}\sin(2x)]\sin(x) = \frac{1}{2}x\sin(x) + \frac{1}{4}\cos(x)$, or
   $y_p = \frac{1}{2}x\sin(x) \Rightarrow y = \frac{1}{2}x\sin(x) + c_1\cos(x) + c_2\sin(x)$.

5. $y'' - y' - 2y = 8x^2$. For $y'' - y' - 2y = 0$, $y_1 = e^{-x}$ and $y_2 = e^{2x}$.

   (a) $y_p = A + Bx + Cx^2$, $y_p' = B + 2Cx$, $y_p'' = 2C$,
   $y_p'' - y_p' - 2y_p = 2C - (B + 2Cx) - 2(A + Bx + Cx^2) = $
   $(2C - B - 2A) - (2C + 2B)x - 2Cx^2 = 8x^2 \Rightarrow A = -6$, $B = 4$, $C = -4$
   $\Rightarrow y_p = -6 + 4x - 4x^2 \Rightarrow y = -6 + 4x - 4x^2 + c_1e^{-x} + c_2e^{2x}$.

   (b) $W(x) = 3e^x$, $f(x) = 8x^2$,
   $u_1 = -\frac{8}{3}\int x^2e^x\,dx = -\frac{8}{3}x^2e^x + \frac{16}{3}\int xe^x\,dx = -\frac{8}{3}x^2e^x + \frac{16}{3}xe^x - \frac{16}{3}e^x$,
   $u_2 = \frac{8}{3}\int x^2e^{-2x}\,dx$
   $= -\frac{4}{3}x^2e^{-2x} + \frac{8}{3}\int xe^{-2x}\,dx = -\frac{4}{3}x^2e^{-2x} - \frac{4}{3}xe^{-2x} - \frac{2}{3}e^{-2x}$,
   $y_p = \left(-\frac{8}{3}x^2e^x + \frac{16}{3}xe^x - \frac{16}{3}e^x\right)e^{-x} + \left(-\frac{4}{3}x^2e^{-2x} - \frac{4}{3}xe^{-2x} - \frac{2}{3}e^{-2x}\right)e^{2x}$
   $= -4x^2 + 4x - 6 \Rightarrow y = -6 + 4x - 4x^2 + c_1e^{-x} + c_2e^{2x}$.

6. $y'' - y = \cos(x) - 5\sin(2x)$. For $y'' - y = 0$, $y_1 = e^x$ and $y_2 = e^{-x}$.

(a) For $y'' - y = \cos(x)$, $y_{p_1} = A\cos(x) + B\sin(x)$, $y_{p_1}'' = -A\cos(x) - B\sin(x)$,
$y_{p_1}'' - y_{p_1} = -2A\cos(x) - 2B\sin(x) = \cos(x) \Rightarrow A = -\frac{1}{2}$, $B = 0 \Rightarrow$
$y_{p_1} = -\frac{1}{2}\cos(x)$. For $y'' - y = -5\sin(2x)$, $y_{p_2} = A\cos(2x) + B\sin(2x)$,
$y_{p_2}'' = -4A\cos(2x) - 4B\sin(2x)$,
$y_{p_2}'' - y_{p_2} = -5A\cos(2x) - 5B\sin(2x) = -5\sin(2x) \Rightarrow A = 0$, $B = 1 \Rightarrow$
$y_{p_2} = \sin(2x) \Rightarrow y_p = -\frac{1}{2}\cos(x) + \sin(2x) \Rightarrow$
$y = -\frac{1}{2}\cos(x) + \sin(2x) + c_1 e^x + c_2 e^{-2x}$.

(b) $W(x) = -2$, $f(x) = \cos(x) - 5\sin(2x)$,
$u_1 = \frac{1}{2}\int e^{-x}[\cos(x) - 5\sin(2x)]\,dx = \frac{1}{2}\int e^{-x}\cos(x)\,dx - \frac{5}{2}\int e^{-x}\sin(2x)\,dx$,
$u_2 = -\frac{1}{2}\int e^x[\cos(x) - 5\sin(2x)]\,dx = -\frac{1}{2}\int e^x\cos(x)\,dx + \frac{5}{2}\int e^x\sin(2x)\,dx$.
$\int e^{-x}\cos(x)\,dx$
$= -e^{-x}\cos(x) - \int e^{-x}\sin(x)\,dx = -e^{-x}\cos(x) + e^{-x}\sin(x) - \int e^{-x}\cos(x)$
$\Rightarrow \int e^{-x}\cos(x)\,dx = \frac{1}{2}e^{-x}[\sin(x) - \cos(x)]$,
$\int e^x\cos(x)\,dx$
$= e^x\cos(x) + \int e^x\sin(x)\,dx = e^x\cos(x) + e^x\sin(x) - \int e^x\cos(x)$
$\Rightarrow \int e^x\cos(x)\,dx = \frac{1}{2}e^x[\cos(x) + \sin(x)]$,
$\int e^{-x}\sin(2x)\,dx = -e^{-x}\sin(2x) + 2\int e^{-x}\cos(2x)\,dx$
$= -e^{-x}\sin(2x) - 2e^{-x}\cos(2x) - 4\int e^{-x}\sin(2x)$
$\Rightarrow \int e^{-x}\sin(2x)\,dx = -\frac{1}{5}e^{-x}[\sin(2x) + 2\cos(2x)]$,
$\int e^x\sin(2x)\,dx$
$= e^x\sin(2x) - 2\int e^x\cos(2x)\,dx = e^x\sin(2x) - 2e^x\cos(2x) - 4\int e^x\sin(2x)$
$\Rightarrow \int e^x\sin(2x)\,dx = \frac{1}{5}e^x[\sin(2x) - 2\cos(2x)]$,
$u_1 = \frac{1}{4}e^{-x}[\sin(x) - \cos(x)] + \frac{1}{2}e^{-x}[\sin(2x) + 2\cos(2x)]$,
$u_2 = -\frac{1}{4}e^x[\cos(x) + \sin(x)] + \frac{1}{2}e^x[\sin(2x) - 2\cos(2x)]$,
$y_p = -\frac{1}{2}\cos(x) + \sin(2x)$, and $y = -\frac{1}{2}\cos(x) + \sin(2x) + c_1 e^x + c_2 e^{-x}$.

7. $y'' - 2y' - 8y = 24(x^2 + 1)e^{4x}$.
   For $y'' - 2y' - 8y = 0$, $y_1 = e^{-2x}$ and $y_2 = e^{4x}$.

(a) $y_p = x(A + Bx + Cx^2)e^{4x} = (Ax + Bx^2 + Cx^3)e^{4x}$,
$y_p' = [A + (4A + 2B)x + (4B + 3C)x^2 + 4Cx^3]e^{4x}$,
$y_p'' = [(8A + 2B) + (16A + 16B + 6C)x + (16B + 24C)x^2 + 16Cx^3]e^{4x}$,
$y_p'' - 2y_p' - 8y_p = [(6A + 2B) + (12B + 6C)x + 18Cx^2]e^{4x} = 24(x^2 + 1)e^{4x}$
$\Rightarrow C = \frac{4}{3}$, $B = -\frac{2}{3}$, $A = \frac{38}{9} \Rightarrow y_p = \left(\frac{38}{9}x - \frac{2}{3}x^2 + \frac{4}{3}x^3\right)e^{4x}$
$\Rightarrow y = \left(\frac{38}{9}x - \frac{2}{3}x^2 + \frac{4}{3}x^3\right)e^{4x} + c_1 e^{-2x} + c_2 e^{4x}$.

(b) $W(x) = \begin{vmatrix} e^{-2x} & e^{4x} \\ -2e^{-2x} & 4e^{4x} \end{vmatrix} = 6e^{2x}$, $u_1 = -4\int(x^2 + 1)e^{6x}\,dx$
$= -\frac{2}{3}(x^2 + 1)e^{6x} + \frac{4}{3}\int xe^{6x}\,dx = -\frac{2}{3}(x^2 + 1)e^{6x} + \frac{2}{9}xe^{6x} - \frac{2}{9}\int e^{6x}\,dx$
$= -\frac{2}{3}(x^2 + 1)e^{6x} + \frac{2}{9}xe^{6x} - \frac{1}{27}e^{6x} = \left(-\frac{2}{3}x^2 + \frac{2}{9}x - \frac{19}{27}\right)e^{6x}$,
$u_2 = 4\int x^2 + 1\,dx = \frac{4}{3}x^3 + 4x$, $y_p = \left[\left(-\frac{2}{3}x^2 + \frac{2}{9}x - \frac{19}{27}\right) + \left(\frac{4}{3}x^3 + 4x\right)\right]e^{4x}$,

or $y_p = \left(\frac{4}{3}x^3 - \frac{2}{3}x^2 + \frac{38}{9}x\right)e^{4x}$, and
$y = \left(\frac{4}{3}x^3 - \frac{2}{3}x^2 + \frac{38}{9}x\right)e^{4x} + c_1 e^{-2x} + c_2 e^{4x}$.

8. (a) $a(x - x_0)^2 y'' + b(x - x_0)y' + cy = 0$, $t = x - x_0$ and $y(x) = z(t) \Rightarrow$
$\frac{dy}{dx} = \frac{dz}{dt}\frac{dt}{dx} = \frac{dz}{dt}$ and $\frac{d^2y}{dx^2} = \frac{d^2z}{dt^2}\frac{dt}{dx} = \frac{d^2z}{dt^2}$. Hence, the equation for $y(x)$
transforms into the Euler equation $at^2 z'' + btz' + cz = 0$ for $z(t)$.

(b) $t = x - 3$ and $y(x) = z(t)$ transforms $2(x - 3)^2 y'' + 3(x - 3)y' + y = 0$ into
$2t^2 z'' + 3tz' + z = 0$. For $t > 0$, $z = t^r \Rightarrow 2r(r-1) + 3r + 1 = 2r^2 + r + 1 = 0 \Rightarrow$
$r = \frac{-1 \pm i\sqrt{7}}{4} = -\frac{1}{4} \pm i\frac{\sqrt{7}}{4} \Rightarrow z = |t|^{-1/4}\left[c_1 \cos\left(\frac{\sqrt{7}}{4}\ln|t|\right) + c_2 \sin\left(\frac{\sqrt{7}}{4}\ln|t|\right)\right]$
for $t \neq 0 \Rightarrow y = |x - 3|^{-1/4}\left[c_1 \cos\left(\frac{\sqrt{7}}{4}\ln|x - 3|\right) + c_2 \sin\left(\frac{\sqrt{7}}{4}\ln|x - 3|\right)\right]$
for $x \neq 3$.

9. (a) $ax^2 y'' + bxy' + cy = 0$, $x > 0$, $t = \ln(x)$ and $y(x) = z(t) \Rightarrow \frac{dy}{dx} = \frac{dz}{dt}\frac{dt}{dx} = \frac{dz}{dt}\frac{1}{x}$,
$\frac{d^2y}{dx^2} = \frac{d^2z}{dt^2}\left(\frac{1}{x}\right)^2 + \frac{dz}{dt}\left(\frac{-1}{x^2}\right)$. Hence, the Euler equation for $y(x)$ transforms into
$az'' + (b - a)z' + cz = 0$, which has constant coefficients.

(b) $z = e^{rt} \Rightarrow ar^2 + (b - a)r + c = 0$, and $y = x^r \Rightarrow ar(r - 1) + br + c = 0 \Rightarrow$
$ar^2 + (b - a)r + c = 0$.

(c) $e^{rt} = e^{r\ln(x)} = e^{\ln(x^r)} = x^r \Rightarrow z = c_1 e^{r_1 t} + c_2 e^{r_2 t} = c_1 x^{r_1} + c_2 x^{r_2} = y$,
$z = e^{rt}(c_1 + c_2 t) = x^r[c_1 + c_2 \ln(x)] = y$, and
$z = e^{\alpha t}[c_1 \cos(\beta t) + c_2 \sin(\beta t)] = x^\alpha\{c_1 \cos[\beta \ln(x)] + c_2 \sin[\beta \ln(x)]\} = y$.

10. $x^2 y'' - xy' + y = \frac{x}{\ln(x)}$, $x > 0$.

(a) For $x^2 y'' - xy' + y = 0$, $y_1 = x$ and $y_2 = x \ln(x)$.
$W(x) = \begin{vmatrix} x & x\ln(x) \\ 1 & \ln(x) + 1 \end{vmatrix} = x$, $f(x) = \frac{1}{x\ln(x)}$, $u_1 = -\int \frac{1}{x} dx = -\ln(x)$,
$u_2 = \int \frac{1}{x\ln(x)} dx = \ln|\ln(x)|$, $y_p = -x\ln(x) + x\ln(x)\ln|\ln(x)|$, or
$y_p = x\ln(x)\ln|\ln(x)| \Rightarrow y = x\ln(x)\ln|\ln(x)| + c_1 x + c_2 x\ln(x)$.

(b) $t = \ln(x)$ and $y(x) = z(t) \Rightarrow z'' - 2z' + z = \frac{e^t}{t}$.

(c) For $z'' - 2z' + z = 0$, $z = e^{rt} \Rightarrow r^2 - 2r + 1 = (r - 1)^2 = 0 \Rightarrow z_1 = e^t$
and $z_2 = te^t$. $W(t) = \begin{vmatrix} e^t & te^t \\ e^t & e^t + te^t \end{vmatrix} = e^{2t}$, $f(t) = \frac{e^t}{t}$, $u_1 = -\int 1\,dt = -t$,
$u_2 = \int \frac{1}{t} dt = \ln|t|$, $z_p = -te^t + te^t\ln|t|$, or $z_p = te^t\ln|t|$
$\Rightarrow z = te^t\ln|t| + c_1 e^t + c_2 te^t$.

(d) $y(x) = z(t) = z(\ln(x)) = x\ln(x)\ln|\ln(x)| + c_1 x + c_2 x\ln(x)$, as in part (a).

11. $4x^2 y'' + 4xy' - y = x^2|x|^{1/2}$.

(a) For $4x^2 y'' + 4xy' - y = 0$, $x > 0$, $y = x^r \Rightarrow 4r(r - 1) + 4r - 1 = 0 \Rightarrow$
$4r^2 - 1 = 0 \Rightarrow y_1 = x^{1/2}$ and $y_2 = x^{-1/2}$.
$W(x) = \begin{vmatrix} x^{1/2} & x^{-1/2} \\ \frac{1}{2}x^{-1/2} & -\frac{1}{2}x^{-3/2} \end{vmatrix} = -x^{-1}$, $f(x) = \frac{x^{1/2}}{4}$,

$u_1 = \frac{1}{4} \int x \, dx = \frac{x^2}{8}, \; u_2 = -\frac{1}{4} \int x^2 \, dx = -\frac{x^3}{12},$

$y_p = \frac{x^2}{8} x^{1/2} - \frac{x^3}{12} x^{-1/2} = \frac{x^{5/2}}{24}, \; y = \frac{x^{5/2}}{24} + c_1 x^{1/2} + c_2 x^{-1/2}.$

(b) For $x < 0$, $y_1 = (-x)^{1/2}$, $y_2 = (-x)^{-1/2}$, $f(x) = \frac{(-x)^{1/2}}{4}$,

$W(x) = \begin{vmatrix} (-x)^{1/2} & (-x)^{-1/2} \\ -\frac{1}{2}(-x)^{-1/2} & \frac{1}{2}(-x)^{-3/2} \end{vmatrix} = (-x)^{-1},$

$u_1 = \frac{1}{4} \int x \, dx = \frac{x^2}{8}, \; u_2 = \frac{1}{4} \int x^2 \, dx = \frac{x^3}{12},$

$y_p = \frac{x^2}{8}(-x)^{1/2} + \frac{x^3}{12}(-x)^{-1/2} = \frac{(-x)^{5/2}}{8} - \frac{(-x)^{5/2}}{12} = \frac{(-x)^{5/2}}{24},$

$y = \frac{(-x)^{5/2}}{24} + c_1(-x)^{1/2} + c_2(-x)^{-1/2}.$

(c) $y = \frac{|x|^{5/2}}{24} + c_1 |x|^{1/2} + c_2 |x|^{-1/2}$ for any $x \neq 0$.

12. $y'' + y' = 2x$.

(a) For $y'' + y' = 0$, $y_1 = 1$ and $y_2 = e^{-x}$. $y_p = x(A + Bx) = Ax + Bx^2$,
$y'_p = A + 2Bx$, $y''_p = 2B$, $y''_p + y'_p = (A + 2B) + 2Bx = 2x \Rightarrow B = 1$, $A = -2$
$\Rightarrow y_p = -2x + x^2 \Rightarrow y = x^2 - 2x + c_1 + c_2 e^{-x}.$

(b) $W(x) = \begin{vmatrix} 1 & e^{-x} \\ 0 & -e^{-x} \end{vmatrix} = -e^{-x}$, $f(x) = 2x$, $u_1 = 2 \int x \, dx = x^2$,
$u_2 = -2 \int x e^x \, dx = -2x e^x + 2 e^x$, $y_p = x^2 + (-2x e^x + 2 e^x) e^{-x} = x^2 - 2x + 2$,
or $y_p = x^2 - 2x$, and $y = x^2 - 2x + c_1 + c_2 e^{-x}.$

(c) $z(x) = y'(x) \Rightarrow z' + z = 2x$, $I(x) = e^{\int 1 \, dx} = e^x \Rightarrow (e^x z)' = 2x e^x$
$\Rightarrow e^x z = 2 \int x e^x \, dx = 2x e^x - 2 e^x + c \Rightarrow z = 2x - 2 + c e^{-x}$
$\Rightarrow y = x^2 - 2x - c e^{-x} + k.$

13. $x^2 y'' + xy' = 1$, $x > 0$.

(a) For $x^2 y'' + xy' = 0$, $y_1 = 1$ and $y_2 = \ln(x)$. $W(x) = \begin{vmatrix} 1 & \ln(x) \\ 0 & \frac{1}{x} \end{vmatrix} = \frac{1}{x}$,
$f(x) = \frac{1}{x^2}$, $u_1 = -\int \frac{\ln(x)}{x} \, dx = -\frac{1}{2}[\ln(x)]^2$, $u_2 = \int \frac{1}{x} \, dx = \ln(x)$,
$y_p = -\frac{1}{2}[\ln(x)]^2 + [\ln(x)]^2 = \frac{1}{2}[\ln(x)]^2 \Rightarrow y = \frac{1}{2}[\ln(x)]^2 + c_1 + c_2 \ln(x).$

(b) $z(x) = y'(x) \Rightarrow x^2 z' + xz = 1 \Rightarrow z' + \frac{1}{x} z = \frac{1}{x^2}$, $I(x) = e^{\int \frac{1}{x} \, dx} = e^{\ln(x)} = x \Rightarrow$
$(xz)' = \frac{1}{x} \Rightarrow xz = \ln(x) + c \Rightarrow z = \frac{\ln(x)}{x} + \frac{c}{x} \Rightarrow y = \frac{1}{2}[\ln(x)]^2 + c \ln(x) + k.$

14. $3y'y'' = 1$.

(a) $z(x) = y'(x) \Rightarrow 3zz' = 1 \Rightarrow \frac{3}{2} z^2 = x + c_1 \Rightarrow z^2 = \frac{2}{3} x + c_2 \Rightarrow z = \left(\frac{2}{3} x + c_2\right)^{1/2}$
$\Rightarrow y = \int \left(\frac{2}{3} x + c_2\right)^{1/2} \, dx = \left(\frac{2}{3} x + c_2\right)^{3/2} + c.$

(b) $v(y) = y'(x) \Rightarrow 3v^2 v' = 1 \Rightarrow v^3 = y + k_1 \Rightarrow v = (y + k_1)^{1/3} \Rightarrow \frac{y'}{(y+k_1)^{1/3}} = 1$
$\Rightarrow \frac{3}{2}(y + k_1)^{2/3} = x + k_2 \Rightarrow y = \left(\frac{2}{3} x + k_3\right)^{3/2} - k_1.$

15. (a) $y_2'' + p(x)y_2' + q(x)y_2 = 0$ and $y_1'' + p(x)y_1' + q(x)y_1 = 0$
    $\Rightarrow y_1[y_2'' + p(x)y_2' + q(x)y_2] = 0$ and $y_2[y_1'' + p(x)y_1' + q(x)y_1] = 0$
    $\Rightarrow (y_1y_2'' - y_1''y_2) + p(x)(y_1y_2' - y_1'y_2) = 0 \Rightarrow W'(x) + p(x)W(x) = 0$.

    (b) $I(x) = e^{\int p(x)\,dx} \Rightarrow [e^{\int p(x)\,dx}W(x)]' = 0 \Rightarrow e^{\int p(x)\,dx}W(x) = c$
    $\Rightarrow W(x) = ce^{-\int p(x)\,dx}$.

    (c) If $c = 0$, then $W(x) \equiv 0$ on I, and if $c \neq 0$, then $W(x) \neq 0$ for any x in I
    since $e^{-\int p(x)\,dx} > 0$ for any continuous function $p(x)$.

    (d) Suppose that y_1 and y_2 are linearly dependent on I. Then there exist
    constants c_1 and c_2, not both 0, such that $c_1y_1 + c_2y_2 = 0$ on I. If $c_1 \neq 0$,
    then $y_1 = -\frac{c_2}{c_1}y_2 \Rightarrow y_1' = -\frac{c_2}{c_1}y_2' \Rightarrow W(x) = y_1y_2' - y_1'y_2 = 0$. Similarly
    if $c_2 \neq 0$. Conversely, if $W(x) = y_1y_2' - y_1'y_2 \equiv 0$ on I, then $\frac{y_2'}{y_2} = \frac{y_1'}{y_1} \Rightarrow$
    $\ln|y_2| = \ln|y_1| + c \Rightarrow y_2 = ky_1$, i.e., y_1 and y_2 are linearly dependent on I.

    (e) Suppose that y_1 and y_2 are linearly independent on I. If $W(x) \equiv 0$ on
    I, then, by part (d), y_1 and y_2 are linearly dependent on I, which is a
    contradiction. Hence, $W(x) \neq 0$ on I. Conversely, suppose that $W(x) \neq 0$
    on I. If y_1 and y_2 are linearly dependent on I, then, by part (d), $W(x) \equiv 0$
    on I, which is a contradiction. Hence, y_1 and y_2 are linearly independent
    on I.

16. $x^2y'' - xy' = 0$ on the interval $I = (-1, 1)$.

    (a) For $x > 0$, $y = x^r \Rightarrow r^2 - 2r = 0 \Rightarrow y_1 = 1$ and $y_2 = x^2$, valid for all x.

    (b) $W(x) = \begin{vmatrix} 1 & x^2 \\ 0 & 2x \end{vmatrix} = 2x$.

    (c) At $x_0 = 0$, $W(0) = 0$.

    (d) The result of part (c) does not contradict the result of part (e) in Exercise
    15 because the standard form of the equation is $y'' - \frac{1}{x}y' = 0$, and $p(x) = -\frac{1}{x}$
    is discontinuous at $x = 0$, hence not continuous on I.

C.4   Chapter 4 Solutions

Section 4.1 Exercises – page 101

1. $y''' - 6y'' + 11y' - 6y = 0$, $y = e^{rx} \Rightarrow P(r) = r^3 - 6r^2 + 11r - 6 = 0 \Rightarrow$
   $(r-1)(r^2 - 5r + 6) = (r-1)(r-2)(r-3) = 0 \Rightarrow y = c_1e^x + c_2e^{2x} + c_3e^{3x}$.

2. $y''' - 2y'' - y' + 2y = 0$, $y = e^{rx} \Rightarrow P(r) = r^3 - 2r^2 - r + 2 = 0 \Rightarrow$
   $(r-1)(r^2 - r - 2) = (r-1)(r+1)(r-2) = 0 \Rightarrow y = c_1e^x + c_2e^{-x} + c_3e^{2x}$
   $\Rightarrow y' = c_1e^x - c_2e^{-x} + 2c_3e^{2x}$, $y'' = c_1e^x + c_2e^{-x} + 4c_3e^{2x}$, $y(0) = 6$, $y'(0) = 0$,

$$y''(0) = 0 \Rightarrow \begin{Bmatrix} c_1 + c_2 + c_3 &=& 6 \\ c_1 - c_2 + 2c_3 &=& 0 \\ c_1 + c_2 + 4c_3 &=& 0 \end{Bmatrix} \Rightarrow c_1 = 6, \ c_2 = 2, \ c_3 = -2, \text{ and}$$

$y = 6e^x + 2e^{-x} - 2e^{2x}$.

3. $9y''' + 9y'' - y' - y = 0$, $y = e^{rx} \Rightarrow P(r) = 9r^3 + 9r^2 - r - 1 = 0 \Rightarrow$
$(r+1)(9r^2 - 1) = (r+1)(3r-1)(3r+1) = 0 \Rightarrow y = c_1 e^{-x} + c_2 e^{\frac{1}{3}x} + c_3 e^{-\frac{1}{3}x}$.

4. $y''' - 5y'' + 8y' - 4y = 0$, $y = e^{rx} \Rightarrow P(r) = r^3 - 5r^2 + 8r - 4 = 0 \Rightarrow$
$(r-1)(r^2 - 4r + 4) = (r-1)(r-2)^2 = 0 \Rightarrow y = c_1 e^x + c_2 e^{2x} + c_3 x e^{2x}$.

5. $y''' - 6y'' + 12y' - 8y = 0$, $y = e^{rx} \Rightarrow P(r) = r^3 - 6r^2 + 12r - 8 = 0 \Rightarrow$
$(r-2)(r^2 - 4r + 4) = (r-2)^3 = 0 \Rightarrow y = c_1 e^{2x} + c_2 x e^{2x} + c_3 x^2 e^{2x}$.

6. $y''' + y'' - y' - y = 0$, $y = e^{rx} \Rightarrow P(r) = r^3 + r^2 - r - 1 = 0 \Rightarrow$
$(r-1)(r^2 + 2r + 1) = (r-1)(r+1)^2 = 0 \Rightarrow y = c_1 e^x + c_2 e^{-x} + c_3 x e^{-x} \Rightarrow$
$y' = c_1 e^x - c_2 e^{-x} + c_3(e^{-x} - xe^{-x})$, $y'' = c_1 e^x + c_2 e^{-x} + c_3(-2e^{-x} + xe^{-x})$,
$$y(0) = 0, \ y'(0) = 3, \ y''(0) = 2 \Rightarrow \begin{Bmatrix} c_1 + c_2 &=& 0 \\ c_1 - c_2 + c_3 &=& 3 \\ c_1 + c_2 - 2c_3 &=& 2 \end{Bmatrix} \Rightarrow c_1 = 2, \ c_2 = -2,$$
$c_3 = -1$, and $y = 2e^x - 2e^{-x} - xe^{-x}$.

7. $y''' - 5y'' + 17y' - 13y = 0$, $y = e^{rx} \Rightarrow P(r) = r^3 - 5r^2 + 17r - 13 = 0 \Rightarrow$
$(r-1)(r^2 - 4r + 13) = 0 \Rightarrow r_1 = 1$ and $r_2, \overline{r_2} = \frac{4 \pm \sqrt{-36}}{2} = 2 \pm 3i \Rightarrow$
$y = c_1 e^x + e^{2x}[c_2 \cos(3x) + c_3 \sin(3x)]$.

8. $y^{(4)} - 5y'' + 4y = 0$, $y = e^{rx} \Rightarrow P(r) = r^4 - 5r^2 + 4 = (r^2 - 1)(r^2 - 4) = 0 \Rightarrow$
$(r-1)(r+1)(r-2)(r+2) = 0 \Rightarrow y = c_1 e^x + c_2 e^{-x} + c_3 e^{2x} + c_4 e^{-2x}$.

9. $y^{(4)} - 2y''' - y'' + 2y' = 0$, $y = e^{rx} \Rightarrow P(r) = r^4 - 2r^3 - r^2 + 2r = 0 \Rightarrow$
$r(r-1)(r^2 - r - 2) = r(r-1)(r+1)(r-2) = 0 \Rightarrow y = c_1 + c_2 e^x + c_3 e^{-x} + c_4 e^{2x} \Rightarrow$
$y' = c_2 e^x - c_3 e^{-x} + 2c_4 e^{2x}$, $y'' = c_2 e^x + c_3 e^{-x} + 4c_4 e^{2x}$, $y''' = c_2 e^x - c_3 e^{-x} + 8c_4 e^{2x}$,
$$y(0) = 0, \ y'(0) = 2, \ y''(0) = 0, \ y'''(0) = 8 \Rightarrow \begin{Bmatrix} c_1 + c_2 + c_3 + c_4 &=& 0 \\ c_2 - c_3 + 2c_4 &=& 2 \\ c_2 + c_3 + 4c_4 &=& 0 \\ c_2 - c_3 + 8c_4 &=& 8 \end{Bmatrix} \Rightarrow$$
$c_1 = 3, \ c_2 = -2, \ c_3 = -2, \ c_4 = 1$, and $y = 3 - 2e^x - 2e^{-x} + e^{2x}$.

10. $y^{(4)} - 7y''' + 17y'' - 17y' + 6y = 0$, $y = e^{rx} \Rightarrow P(r) = r^4 - 7r^3 + 17r^2 - 17r + 6 = 0$
$\Rightarrow (r-1)(r-2)(r^2 - 4r + 3) = (r-1)^2(r-2)(r-3) = 0$
$\Rightarrow y = c_1 e^x + c_2 x e^x + c_3 e^{2x} + c_4 e^{3x}$.

11. $y^{(4)} - y''' - 3y'' + 5y' - 2y = 0$, $y = e^{rx} \Rightarrow P(r) = r^4 - r^3 - 3r^2 + 5r - 2 = 0 \Rightarrow$
$(r-1)(r+2)(r^2 - 2r + 1) = (r-1)^3(r+2) = 0 \Rightarrow y = c_1 e^x + c_2 x e^x + c_3 x^2 e^x + c_4 e^{-2x}$.

12. $y^{(4)} - 4y''' + 6y'' - 4y' + y = 0$, $y = e^{rx} \Rightarrow P(r) = r^4 - 4r^3 + 6r^2 - 4r + 1 = 0$. Since $r_1 = 1$ is a root of both $P(r)$ and $P'(r) = 4r^3 - 12r^2 + 12r - 4$, $(r-1)^2$ is a factor of $P(r)$. Hence, $P(r) = (r-1)^2(r^2 - 2r + 1) = (r-1)^4 = 0$
$\Rightarrow y = c_1 e^x + c_2 x e^x + c_3 x^2 e^x + c_4 x^3 e^x$.

13. $y^{(4)} - 6y''' + 13y'' - 12y' + 4y = 0$, $y = e^{rx} \Rightarrow P(r) = r^4 - 6r^3 + 13r^2 - 12r + 4 = 0$
$\Rightarrow (r-1)(r-2)(r^2 - 3r + 2) = (r-1)^2(r-2)^2 = 0$
$\Rightarrow y = c_1 e^x + c_2 x e^x + c_3 e^{2x} + c_4 x e^{2x}$.

14. $y^{(4)} + 2y''' + 4y'' - 2y' - 5y = 0$, $y = e^{rx} \Rightarrow P(r) = r^4 + 2r^3 + 4r^2 - 2r - 5 = 0 \Rightarrow$
$(r-1)(r+1)(r^2 + 2r + 5) = 0 \Rightarrow r_1 = 1$, $r_2 = -1$, $r_3, \overline{r_3} = \frac{-2 \pm \sqrt{-16}}{2} = -1 \pm 2i$
$\Rightarrow y = c_1 e^x + c_2 e^{-x} + c_3 e^{-x} \cos(2x) + c_4 e^{-x} \sin(2x)$.

15. $y^{(4)} + 10y''' + 41y'' + 76y' + 52y = 0$, $y = e^{rx} \Rightarrow$
$P(r) = r^4 + 10r^3 + 41r^2 + 76r + 52 = 0$. Since $r_1 = -2$ is a root of both $P(r)$ and $P'(r) = 4r^3 + 30r^2 + 82r + 76$, $(r+2)^2$ is a factor of $P(r)$. Hence, $P(r) = (r+2)^2(r^2 + 6r + 13) = 0 \Rightarrow r_1 = -2$, $r_2, \overline{r_2} = \frac{-6 \pm \sqrt{-16}}{2} = -3 \pm 2i \Rightarrow$
$y = c_1 e^{-2x} + c_2 x e^{-2x} + c_3 e^{-3x} \cos(2x) + c_4 e^{-3x} \sin(2x)$.

16. $y^{(4)} + 5y'' + 4y = 0$, $y = e^{rx} \Rightarrow P(r) = r^4 + 5r^2 + 4 = (r^2 + 1)(r^2 + 4) = 0 \Rightarrow$
$r_1, \overline{r_1} = \pm i$, $r_2, \overline{r_2} = \pm 2i \Rightarrow y = c_1 \cos(x) + c_2 \sin(x) + c_3 \cos(2x) + c_4 \sin(2x)$.

17. $y^{(4)} + 4y = 0$, $y = e^{rx} \Rightarrow P(r) = r^4 + 4 = 0$. $P(r) = (r^2 + ar + 2)(r^2 + br + 2)$
$\Rightarrow a = \pm 2$, $b = \mp 2 \Rightarrow P(r) = (r^2 + 2r + 2)(r^2 - 2r + 2) = 0 \Rightarrow r_1, \overline{r_1} = -1 \pm i$,
$r_2, \overline{r_2} = 1 \pm i \Rightarrow y = c_1 e^{-x} \cos(x) + c_2 e^{-x} \sin(x) + c_3 e^x \cos(x) + c_4 e^x \sin(x)$.

18. $y^{(4)} - 8y''' + 26y'' - 40y' + 25y = 0$, $y = e^{rx} \Rightarrow P(r) = r^4 - 8r^3 + 26r^2 - 40r + 25 = 0$.
$P(r) = (r^2 + ar + 5)(r^2 + br + 5) \Rightarrow a = b = -4 \Rightarrow P(r) = (r^2 - 4r + 5)^2 = 0 \Rightarrow$
$r_1, \overline{r_1} = 2 \pm i \Rightarrow y = c_1 e^{2x} \cos(x) + c_2 e^{2x} \sin(x) + c_3 x e^{2x} \cos(x) + c_4 x e^{2x} \sin(x)$.

19. $x^3 y''' + x^2 y'' - 2xy' + 2y = 0$. For $x > 0$, $y = x^r \Rightarrow$
$P(r) = r(r-1)(r-2) + r(r-1) - 2r + 2 = (r-1)[r(r-2) + r - 2] = (r-1)[r^2 - r - 2] = (r-1)(r-2)(r+1) = 0 \Rightarrow y = c_1 x + c_2 x^2 + c_3 x^{-1}$, $x \neq 0$.

20. $x^3 y''' - 2x^2 y'' + 3xy' - 3y = 0$. For $x > 0$, $y = x^r \Rightarrow$
$P(r) = r(r-1)(r-2) - 2r(r-1) + 3r - 3 = (r-1)[r(r-2) - 2r + 3] = (r-1)^2(r-3) = 0 \Rightarrow y = c_1 x + c_2 x \ln|x| + c_3 x^3$, $x \neq 0$.

21. $x^3 y''' + xy' - y = 0$. For $x > 0$, $y = x^r \Rightarrow P(r) = r(r-1)(r-2) + r - 1 = 0 \Rightarrow$
$(r-1)[r(r-2) + 1] = (r-1)^3 = 0 \Rightarrow y = c_1 x + c_2 x \ln|x| + c_3 x(\ln|x|)^2$, $x \neq 0$.

22. $x^3 y''' + 8x^2 y'' + 13xy' - 13y = 0$. For $x > 0$, $y = x^r \Rightarrow$
$P(r) = r(r-1)(r-2) + 8r(r-1) + 13r - 13 = (r-1)[r(r-2) + 8r + 13]$
$= (r-1)(r^2 + 6r + 13) = 0 \Rightarrow r_1 = 1$ and $r_2, \overline{r_2} = \frac{-6 \pm \sqrt{-16}}{2} = -3 \pm 2i \Rightarrow$
$y = c_1 x + c_2 x^{-3} \cos[2\ln(x)] + c_3 x^{-3} \sin[2\ln(x)]$,
$y' = c_1 + (2c_3 - 3c_2)x^{-4} \cos[2\ln(x)] - (2c_2 + 3c_3)x^{-4} \sin[2\ln(x)]$,

$y'' = [-4(2c_3 - 3c_2) - 2(2c_2 + 3c_3)]x^{-5}\cos[2\ln(x)]$
$+ [4(2c_2 + 3c_3) - 2(2c_3 - 3c_2)]x^{-5}\sin[2\ln(x)]$, or
$y'' = (8c_2 - 14c_3)x^{-5}\cos[2\ln(x)] + (14c_2 + 8c_3)x^{-5}\sin[2\ln(x)]$. Then $y(1) = 0$,
$y'(1) = 6$ and $y''(1) = -2 \Rightarrow c_1 + c_2 = 0$, $c_1 - 3c_2 + 2c_3 = 6$ and $8c_2 - 14c_3 = -2 \Rightarrow$
$c_1 = 2$, $c_2 = -2$ and $c_3 = -1$. Hence, $y = 2x - 2x^{-3}\cos[2\ln(x)] - x^{-3}\sin[2\ln(x)]$.

23. $x^4 y^{(4)} + x^3 y''' + x^2 y'' - 2xy' + 2y = 0$. For $x > 0$, $y = x^r \Rightarrow$
$P(r) = r(r-1)(r-2)(r-3) + r(r-1)(r-2) + r(r-1) - 2r + 2 = 0 \Rightarrow$
$(r-1)[r(r-2)(r-3) + r(r-2) + r - 2] = (r-1)(r-2)[r(r-3) + r + 1] =$
$(r-1)^3(r-2) = 0 \Rightarrow y = c_1 x + c_2 x \ln|x| + c_3 x(\ln|x|)^2 + c_4 x^2$, $x \neq 0$.

24. $x^4 y^{(4)} - x^3 y''' + 5x^2 y'' - 10xy' + 10y = 0$. For $x > 0$, $y = x^r \Rightarrow$
$P(r) = r(r-1)(r-2)(r-3) - r(r-1)(r-2) + 5r(r-1) - 10r + 10 = 0 \Rightarrow$
$(r-1)[r(r-2)(r-3) - r(r-2) + 5r - 10] = (r-1)(r-2)[r(r-3) - r + 5] =$
$(r-1)(r-2)(r^2 - 4r + 5) = 0 \Rightarrow r_1 = 1$, $r_2 = 2$ and $r_3, \overline{r_3} = \frac{4 \pm \sqrt{-4}}{2} = 2 \pm i$
$\Rightarrow y = c_1 x + c_2 x^2 + c_3 x^2 \cos(\ln|x|) + c_4 x^2 \sin(\ln|x|)$, $x \neq 0$.

25. $x^4 y^{(4)} + 6x^3 y''' + 6x^2 y'' - 2xy' + 2y = 0$. For $x > 0$, $y = x^r \Rightarrow$
$P(r) = r(r-1)(r-2)(r-3) + 6r(r-1)(r-2) + 6r(r-1) - 2r + 2 = 0 \Rightarrow$
$(r-1)[r(r-2)(r-3) + 6r(r-2) + 6r - 2] = (r-1)(r^3 + r^2 - 2)$
$= (r-1)^2(r^2 + 2r + 2) = 0 \Rightarrow r_1 = 1$ and $r_2, \overline{r_2} = \frac{-2 \pm \sqrt{-4}}{2} = -1 \pm i$
$\Rightarrow y = c_1 x + c_2 x \ln|x| + c_3 x^{-1}\cos(\ln|x|) + c_4 x^{-1}\sin(\ln|x|)$, $x \neq 0$.

26. $x^4 y^{(4)} + 2x^3 y''' + 3x^2 y'' - 3xy' + 4y = 0$. For $x > 0$, $y = x^r \Rightarrow$
$P(r) = r(r-1)(r-2)(r-3) + 2r(r-1)(r-2) + 3r(r-1) - 3r + 4 = 0$.
$P(r) = r^4 - 4r^3 + 8r^2 - 8r + 4 = (r^2 + ar + 2)(r^2 + br + 2) \Rightarrow a = b = -2$
$\Rightarrow r^4 - 4r^3 + 8r^2 - 8r + 4 = (r^2 - 2r + 2)^2 = 0 \Rightarrow r_1, \overline{r_1} = \frac{2 \pm \sqrt{-4}}{2} = 1 \pm i$
$\Rightarrow y = c_1 x \cos(\ln|x|) + c_2 x \sin(\ln|x|) + c_3 x \ln|x|\cos(\ln|x|) + c_4 x \ln|x|\sin(\ln|x|)$.

Section 4.2 Exercises – page 118

1. $y''' - 3y'' - y' + 3y = 8e^{2x}$. For $y''' - 3y'' - y' + 3y = 0$, $y = e^{rx} \Rightarrow$
$P(r) = (r^2 - 1)(r - 3) = 0 \Rightarrow y_1 = e^x$, $y_2 = e^{-x}$ and $y_3 = e^{3x}$. With $f(x) = 8e^{2x}$,

$W(x) = \begin{vmatrix} e^x & e^{-x} & e^{3x} \\ e^x & -e^{-x} & 3e^{3x} \\ e^x & e^{-x} & 9e^{3x} \end{vmatrix} = e^x[-9e^{2x} - 3e^{2x}] - e^{-x}[9e^{4x} - 3e^{4x}] + e^{3x}[2] =$

$-16e^{3x}$,

$\Delta_1(x) = \begin{vmatrix} 0 & e^{-x} & e^{3x} \\ 0 & -e^{-x} & 3e^{3x} \\ f(x) & e^{-x} & 9e^{3x} \end{vmatrix} = f(x)[3e^{2x} + e^{2x}] = 4e^{2x}f(x) = 32e^{4x}$,

$\Delta_2(x) = \begin{vmatrix} e^x & 0 & e^{3x} \\ e^x & 0 & 3e^{3x} \\ e^x & f(x) & 9e^{3x} \end{vmatrix} = -f(x)[3e^{4x} - e^{4x}] = -2e^{4x}f(x) = -16e^{6x}$,

$$\Delta_3(x) = \begin{vmatrix} e^x & e^{-x} & 0 \\ e^x & -e^{-x} & 0 \\ e^x & e^{-x} & f(x) \end{vmatrix} = f(x)[-1-1] = -2f(x) = -16e^{2x},$$

$u_1 = -2 \int e^x \, dx = -2e^x$, $u_2 = \int e^{3x} \, dx = \frac{1}{3}e^{3x}$, $u_3 = \int e^{-x} \, dx = -e^{-x} \Rightarrow$
$y_p = -\frac{8}{3}e^{2x} \Rightarrow y = -\frac{8}{3}e^{2x} + c_1 e^x + c_2 e^{-x} + c_3 e^{3x}$.

2. $y''' - 3y'' + 2y' = 8xe^{2x}$. For $y''' - 3y'' + 2y' = 0$, $y = e^{rx} \Rightarrow$
$P(r) = r(r-1)(r-2) = 0 \Rightarrow y_1 = 1$, $y_2 = e^x$ and $y_3 = e^{2x}$. With $f(x) = 8xe^{2x}$,

$$W(x) = \begin{vmatrix} 1 & e^x & e^{2x} \\ 0 & e^x & 2e^{2x} \\ 0 & e^x & 4e^{2x} \end{vmatrix} = 2e^{3x}, \; \Delta_1(x) = e^{3x}f(x) = 8xe^{5x},$$

$\Delta_2(x) = -2e^{2x}f(x) = -16xe^{4x}$, $\Delta_3(x) = e^x f(x) = 8xe^{3x}$,
$u_1 = 4 \int xe^{2x} \, dx = 2xe^{2x} - e^{2x}$, $u_2 = -8 \int xe^x \, dx = -8xe^x + 8e^x$,
$u_3 = 4 \int x \, dx = 2x^2 \Rightarrow$
$y_p = (2xe^{2x} - e^{2x}) + (8e^x - 8xe^x)e^x + 2x^2e^{2x} = 7e^{2x} - 6xe^{2x} + 2x^2e^{2x}$, or
$y_p = (2x^2 - 6x)e^{2x} \Rightarrow y = (2x^2 - 6x)e^{2x} + c_1 + c_2 e^x + c_3 e^{2x}$.

3. $y''' - 2y'' + y' = -2e^x \cos(x)$. For $y''' - 2y'' + y' = 0$, $y = e^{rx} \Rightarrow$
$P(r) = r(r-1)^2 = 0 \Rightarrow y_1 = 1$, $y_2 = e^x$ and $y_3 = xe^x$. With $f(x) = -2e^x \cos(x)$,

$$W(x) = \begin{vmatrix} 1 & e^x & xe^x \\ 0 & e^x & e^x + xe^x \\ 0 & e^x & 2e^x + xe^x \end{vmatrix} = e^{2x}, \; \Delta_1(x) = e^{2x}f(x) = -2e^{3x}\cos(x),$$

$\Delta_2(x) = -(1+x)e^x f(x) = 2(1+x)e^{2x}\cos(x)$, $\Delta_3(x) = e^x f(x) = -2e^{2x}\cos(x)$,
$u_1 = -2 \int e^x \cos(x) \, dx = -2e^x \cos(x) - 2 \int e^x \sin(x) \, dx$
$= -2e^x \cos(x) - 2e^x \sin(x) + 2 \int e^x \cos(x) \, dx$
$\Rightarrow -4 \int e^x \cos(x) \, dx = -2e^x[\cos(x) + \sin(x)] \Rightarrow u_1 = -e^x[\cos(x) + \sin(x)]$,
$u_2 = 2 \int (1+x)\cos(x) \, dx = 2(1+x)\sin(x) + 2\cos(x)$,
$u_3 = -2 \int \cos(x) \, dx = -2\sin(x)$
$\Rightarrow y_p = -e^x[\cos(x) + \sin(x)] + [2(1+x)\sin(x) + 2\cos(x)]e^x - 2xe^x \sin(x)$
$= e^x[\cos(x) + \sin(x)] \Rightarrow y = e^x[\cos(x) + \sin(x)] + c_1 + c_2 e^x + c_3 xe^x$.

4. $y''' - y'' + 2y = 10e^x$. For $y''' - y'' + 2y = 0$, $y = e^{rx} \Rightarrow$
$P(r) = (r+1)(r^2 - 2r + 2) = 0 \Rightarrow r_1 = -1$ and $r = 1 \pm i \Rightarrow y_1 = e^{-x}$,
$y_2 = e^x \cos(x)$ and $y_2 = e^x \sin(x)$. With $f(x) = 10e^x$,

$$W(x) = \begin{vmatrix} e^{-x} & e^x \cos(x) & e^x \sin(x) \\ -e^{-x} & e^x \cos(x) - e^x \sin(x) & e^x \sin(x) + e^x \cos(x) \\ e^{-x} & -2e^x \sin(x) & 2e^x \cos(x) \end{vmatrix}$$

$= e^{-x}[2e^{2x}] + e^{-x}[2e^{2x}] + e^{-x}[e^{2x}] = 5e^x$, $\Delta_1(x) = e^{2x}f(x) = 10e^{3x}$,
$\Delta_2(x) = -[2\sin(x) + \cos(x)]f(x) = -10e^x[2\sin(x) + \cos(x)]$,
$\Delta_3(x) = [2\cos(x) - \sin(x)]f(x) = 10e^x[2\cos(x) - \sin(x)]$,
$u_1 = 2 \int e^{2x} \, dx = e^{2x}$, $u_2 = -2 \int 2\sin(x) + \cos(x) \, dx = 4\cos(x) - 2\sin(x)$,
$u_3 = 2 \int 2\cos(x) - \sin(x) \, dx = 4\sin(x) + 2\cos(x) \Rightarrow$
$y_p = e^{2x}[e^{-x}] + [4\cos(x) - 2\sin(x)][e^x \cos(x)] + [4\sin(x) + 2\cos(x)][e^x \sin(x)] = 5e^x$
$\Rightarrow y = 5e^x + c_1 e^{-x} + c_2 e^x \cos(x) + c_3 e^x \sin(x)$.

5. $y''' - y'' + y' - y = 4\sin(x) + 4\cos(x)$. For $y''' - y'' + y' - y = 0$, $y = e^{rx} \Rightarrow$
$P(r) = (r-1)(r^2+1) \Rightarrow y_1 = e^x$, $y_2 = \cos(x)$ and $y_3 = \sin(x)$. With

$$f(x) = 4[\sin(x) + \cos(x)], \; W(x) = \begin{vmatrix} e^x & \cos(x) & \sin(x) \\ e^x & -\sin(x) & \cos(x) \\ e^x & -\cos(x) & -\sin(x) \end{vmatrix} = 2e^x,$$

$\Delta_1(x) = f(x) = 4[\sin(x) + \cos(x)]$,
$\Delta_2(x) = -e^x[\cos(x) - \sin(x)]f(x) = -4e^x[\cos(x) - \sin(x)][\sin(x) + \cos(x)]$
$= -4e^x[\cos^2(x) - \sin^2(x)] = -4e^x\cos(2x)$,
$\Delta_3(x) = -e^x[\sin(x) + \cos(x)]f(x) = -4e^x[\sin(x) + \cos(x)]^2 = -4e^x[1 + \sin(2x)]$,
$u_1 = 2\int e^{-x}[\sin(x) + \cos(x)]\,dx = -2e^{-x}\cos(x)$,
$u_2 = -2\int \cos(2x)\,dx = -\sin(2x)$,
$u_3 = -2\int 1 + \sin(2x)\,dx = -2x + \cos(2x) \Rightarrow$
$y_p = -2\cos(x) - \sin(2x)\cos(x) + [-2x + \cos(2x)]\sin(x)$
$= -2\cos(x) - 2x\sin(x) + [\sin(x)\cos(2x) - \cos(x)\sin(2x)]$
$= -2\cos(x) - 2x\sin(x) - \sin(x)$, or $y_p = -2x\sin(x)$
$\Rightarrow y = -2x\sin(x) + c_1e^x + c_2\cos(x) + c_3\sin(x)$.

6. $y''' - y'' = 20x^3$. For $y''' - y'' = 0$, $y = e^{rx} \Rightarrow P(r) = r^2(r-1) = 0 \Rightarrow$

$y_1 = 1$, $y_2 = x$ and $y_3 = e^x$. With $f(x) = 20x^3$, $W(x) = \begin{vmatrix} 1 & x & e^x \\ 0 & 1 & e^x \\ 0 & 0 & e^x \end{vmatrix} = e^x$,

$\Delta_1(x) = (xe^x - e^x)f(x) = 20(x^4 - x^3)e^x$, $\Delta_2(x) = -e^x f(x) = -20x^3 e^x$,
$\Delta_3(x) = f(x) = 20x^3$, $u_1 = 20\int x^4 - x^3\,dx = 4x^5 - 5x^4$,
$u_2 = -20\int x^3\,dx = -5x^4$, $u_3 = 20\int x^3 e^{-x}\,dx = -20x^3 e^{-x} + 60\int x^2 e^{-x}\,dx =$
$-20x^3 e^{-x} - 60x^2 e^{-x} + 120\int xe^{-x}\,dx = -20x^3 e^{-x} - 60x^2 e^{-x} - 120xe^{-x} - 120e^{-x}$
$\Rightarrow y_p = (4x^5 - 5x^4) - 5x^5 - [20x^3 + 60x^2 + 120x + 120]$
$= -x^5 - 5x^4 - 20x^3 - 60x^2 - 120x - 120$, or $y_p = -(x^5 + 5x^4 + 20x^3 + 60x^2) \Rightarrow$
$y = -(x^5 + 5x^4 + 20x^3 + 60x^2) + c_1 + c_2 x + c_3 e^x$ is the general solution. Then
$y' = -(5x^4 + 20x^3 + 60x^2 + 120x) + c_2 + c_3 e^x$,
$y'' = -(20x^3 + 60x^2 + 120x + 120) + c_3 e^x$, and $y(0) = 20$, $y'(0) = 0$ and
$y''(0) = -20 \Rightarrow c_1 + c_3 = 20$, $c_2 + c_3 = 0$ and $-120 + c_3 = -20 \Rightarrow c_1 = -80$,
$c_2 = -100$ and $c_3 = 100 \Rightarrow y = -(x^5 + 5x^4 + 20x^3 + 60x^2) - 80 - 100x + 100e^x$.

7. $y''' - 2y'' = 5\sin(x)$. For $y''' - 2y'' = 0$, $y = e^{rx} \Rightarrow P(r) = r^2(r-2) = 0 \Rightarrow y_1 = 1$,

$y_2 = x$ and $y_3 = e^{2x}$. With $f(x) = 5\sin(x)$, $W(x) = \begin{vmatrix} 1 & x & e^{2x} \\ 0 & 1 & 2e^{2x} \\ 0 & 0 & 4e^{2x} \end{vmatrix} = 4e^{2x}$,

$\Delta_1(x) = [2xe^{2x} - e^{2x}]f(x) = 5(2x-1)e^{2x}\sin(x)$,
$\Delta_2(x) = -2e^{2x}f(x) = -10e^{2x}\sin(x)$, $\Delta_3(x) = f(x) = 5\sin(x)$,
$u_1 = \frac{5}{4}\int(2x-1)\sin(x)\,dx = -\frac{5}{4}(2x-1)\cos(x) + \frac{5}{2}\sin(x)$,
$u_2 = -\frac{5}{2}\int \sin(x) = \frac{5}{2}\cos(x)$,
$u_3 = \frac{5}{4}\int e^{-2x}\sin(x)\,dx = -\frac{5}{4}e^{-2x}\cos(x) - \frac{5}{2}\int e^{-2x}\cos(x)\,dx$
$= -\frac{5}{4}e^{-2x}\cos(x) - \frac{5}{2}e^{-2x}\sin(x) - 5\int e^{-2x}\sin(x)\,dx \Rightarrow \frac{25}{4}\int e^{-2x}\sin(x)\,dx =$

$-e^{-2x}\left[\frac{5}{2}\sin(x)+\frac{5}{4}\cos(x)\right]\Rightarrow u_3=-e^{-2x}\left[\frac{1}{2}\sin(x)+\frac{1}{4}\cos(x)\right]\Rightarrow$
$y_p=-\frac{5}{4}(2x-1)\cos(x)+\frac{5}{2}\sin(x)+\frac{5}{2}x\cos(x)-\left[\frac{1}{2}\sin(x)+\frac{1}{4}\cos(x)\right]$
$=2\sin(x)+\cos(x)\Rightarrow y=2\sin(x)+\cos(x)+c_1+c_2x+c_3e^{2x}.$

8. $y^{(4)}-y''=2.$ For $y^{(4)}-y''=0,$ $y=e^{rx}\Rightarrow P(r)=r^2(r^2-1)=0\Rightarrow y_1=1,$

$y_2=x,$ $y_3=e^x$ and $y_4=e^{-x}\Rightarrow W(x)=\begin{vmatrix}1 & x & e^x & e^{-x}\\ 0 & 1 & e^x & -e^{-x}\\ 0 & 0 & e^x & e^{-x}\\ 0 & 0 & e^x & -e^{-x}\end{vmatrix}=-2,$ and with

$f(x)=2,$ $\Delta_1(x)=-2xf(x)=-4x,$ $\Delta_2(x)=2f(x)=4,$
$\Delta_3(x)=-e^{-x}f(x)=-2e^{-x},$ $\Delta_4(x)=e^xf(x)=2e^x,$ $u_1=2\int x\,dx=x^2,$
$u_2=-\int 2\,dx=-2x,$ $u_3=\int e^{-x}\,dx=-e^{-x},$ $u_4=-\int e^x\,dx=-e^x\Rightarrow$
$y_p=-x^2-2,$ or $y_p=-x^2\Rightarrow y=-x^2+c_1+c_2x+c_3e^x+c_4e^{-x}.$

9. $y^{(4)}+y''=6x.$ For $y^{(4)}+y''=0,$ $y=e^{rx}\Rightarrow P(r)=r^2(r^2+1)=0\Rightarrow y_1=1,$
$y_2=x,$ $y_3=\cos(x)$ and $y_4=\sin(x)\Rightarrow W(x)=$
$\begin{vmatrix}1 & x & \cos(x) & \sin(x)\\ 0 & 1 & -\sin(x) & \cos(x)\\ 0 & 0 & -\cos(x) & -\sin(x)\\ 0 & 0 & \sin(x) & -\cos(x)\end{vmatrix}=-\sin(x)[-\sin(x)]-\cos(x)[-\cos(x)]=1$
(along the fourth row) and, with $f(x)=6x,$ $\Delta_1(x)=-f(x)[x-0]=-6x^2,$
$\Delta_2(x)=f(x)[1]=6x,$ $\Delta_3(x)=-f(x)[-\sin(x)]=6x\sin(x),$
$\Delta_4(x)=f(x)[-\cos(x)]=-6x\cos(x),$ $u_1=-6\int x^2\,dx=-2x^3,$
$u_2=6\int x\,dx=3x^2,$ $u_3=6\int x\sin(x)\,dx=-6x\cos(x)+6\sin(x),$
$u_4=-6\int x\cos(x)\,dx=-6x\sin(x)-6\cos(x)\Rightarrow$
$y_p=x^3+[6\sin(x)-6x\cos(x)]\cos(x)-[6\cos(x)+6x\sin(x)]\sin(x)=x^3-6x,$
or $y_p=x^3\Rightarrow y=x^3+c_1+c_2x+c_3\cos(x)+c_4\sin(x).$

10. $x^3y'''-x^2y''+2xy'-2y=x.$ For $x^3y'''-x^2y''+2xy'-2y=0,$ $x>0,$ $y=x^r\Rightarrow$
$P(r)=(r-1)^2(r-2)=0\Rightarrow y_1=x,$ $y_2=x\ln(x)$ and $y_3=x^2.$ With $f(x)=\frac{1}{x^2},$
$W(x)=\begin{vmatrix}x & x\ln(x) & x^2\\ 1 & \ln(x)+1 & 2x\\ 0 & \frac{1}{x} & 2\end{vmatrix}=x[2\ln(x)]-[2x\ln(x)-x]=x,$
$\Delta_1(x)=f(x)[x^2\ln(x)-x^2]=\ln(x)-1,$ $\Delta_2(x)=-f(x)[x^2]=-1,$
$\Delta_3(x)=f(x)[x]=\frac{1}{x},$ $u_1=\int\frac{\ln(x)-1}{x}\,dx=\frac{1}{2}[\ln(x)]^2-\ln(x),$
$u_2=-\int\frac{1}{x}\,dx=-\ln(x),$ $u_3=\int\frac{1}{x^2}\,dx=-\frac{1}{x}\Rightarrow$
$y_p=\{\frac{1}{2}[\ln(x)]^2-\ln(x)\}x-\ln(x)[x\ln(x)]-\frac{1}{x}[x^2]=-\frac{1}{2}x[\ln(x)]^2-x\ln(x)-x,$
or $y_p=-\frac{1}{2}x[\ln(x)]^2\Rightarrow y=-\frac{1}{2}x[\ln(x)]^2+c_1x+c_2x\ln(x)+c_3x^2.$

11. $x^3y'''+5x^2y''+2xy'-2y=\frac{1}{x}.$ For $x^3y'''+5x^2y''+2xy'-2y=0,$ $x>0,$ $y=x^r$
$\Rightarrow P(r)=(r-1)(r+1)(r+2)=0\Rightarrow y_1=x,$ $y_2=x^{-1}$ and $y_3=x^{-2}.$ With

$f(x)=\frac{1}{x^4},$ $W(x)=\begin{vmatrix}x & x^{-1} & x^{-2}\\ 1 & -x^{-2} & -2x^{-3}\\ 0 & 2x^{-3} & 6x^{-4}\end{vmatrix}=x[-2x^{-6}]-[4x^{-5}]=-6x^{-5},$

$\Delta_1(x) = f(x)[-x^{-4}] = -x^{-8}$, $\Delta_2(x) = -f(x)[-3x^{-2}] = 3x^{-6}$,
$\Delta_3(x) = f(x)[-2x^{-1}] = -2x^{-5}$, $u_1 = \frac{1}{6}\int x^{-3}\,dx = -\frac{1}{12}x^{-2}$,
$u_2 = -\frac{1}{2}\int x^{-1}\,dx = -\frac{1}{2}\ln(x)$, $u_3 = \int \frac{1}{3}\,dx = \frac{1}{3}x$
$\Rightarrow y_p = -\frac{1}{12}x^{-1} - \frac{1}{2}\ln(x)[x^{-1}] + \frac{1}{3}x^{-1}$, or $y_p = -\frac{1}{2}x^{-1}\ln(x)$
$\Rightarrow y = -\frac{1}{2}x^{-1}\ln(x) + c_1 x + c_2 x^{-1} + c_3 x^{-2}$.

12. $x^3 y''' + 2x^2 y'' = 1$. For $x^3 y''' + 2x^2 y'' = 0$, $x > 0$, $y = x^r \Rightarrow P(r) = r^2(r-1) = 0 \Rightarrow$
$y_1 = 1$, $y_2 = \ln(x)$ and $y_3 = x$. With $f(x) = \frac{1}{x^3}$, $W(x) = \begin{vmatrix} 1 & \ln(x) & x \\ 0 & \frac{1}{x} & 1 \\ 0 & -\frac{1}{x^2} & 0 \end{vmatrix} = \frac{1}{x^2}$,

$\Delta_1(x) = f(x)[\ln(x) - 1] = \frac{\ln(x)-1}{x^3}$, $\Delta_2(x) = -f(x)[1] = -\frac{1}{x^3}$,
$\Delta_3(x) = f(x)[\frac{1}{x}] = \frac{1}{x^4}$, $u_1 = \int \frac{\ln(x)-1}{x}\,dx = \frac{1}{2}[\ln(x)]^2 - \ln(x)$,
$u_2 = -\int \frac{1}{x}\,dx = -\ln(x)$, $u_3 = \int \frac{1}{x^2}\,dx = -\frac{1}{x}$
$\Rightarrow y_p = \frac{1}{2}[\ln(x)]^2 - \ln(x) - [\ln(x)]^2 - 1$, or $y_p = -\frac{1}{2}[\ln(x)]^2$
$\Rightarrow y = -\frac{1}{2}[\ln(x)]^2 + c_1 + c_2\ln(x) + c_3 x$ is the general solution. Then
$y' = -\frac{1}{x}\ln(x) + c_2\frac{1}{x} + c_3$, $y'' = \frac{1}{x^2}\ln(x) - \frac{1}{x^2} - c_2\frac{1}{x^2}$, and $y(1) = 5$, $y'(1) = 1$ and
$y''(1) = 0 \Rightarrow c_1 + c_3 = 5$, $c_2 + c_3 = 1$, $-1 - c_2 = 0 \Rightarrow c_1 = 3$, $c_2 = -1$ and $c_3 = 2$
$\Rightarrow y = -\frac{1}{2}[\ln(x)]^2 + 3 - \ln(x) + 2x$.

13. $x^3 y''' + x^2 y'' - xy' = 4x^2$. For $x^3 y''' + x^2 y'' - xy' = 0$, $x > 0$, $y = x^r \Rightarrow$
$P(r) = r^2(r-2) \Rightarrow y_1 = 1$, $y_2 = \ln(x)$ and $y_3 = x^2$. With $f(x) = \frac{4}{x}$,
$W(x) = \begin{vmatrix} 1 & \ln(x) & x^2 \\ 0 & \frac{1}{x} & 2x \\ 0 & -\frac{1}{x^2} & 2 \end{vmatrix} = \frac{4}{x}$, $\Delta_1(x) = f(x)[2x\ln(x) - x] = 8\ln(x) - 4$,
$\Delta_2(x) = -f(x)[2x] = -8$, $\Delta_3(x) = f(x)[\frac{1}{x}] = \frac{4}{x^2}$,
$u_1 = \int 2x\ln(x) - x\,dx = x^2\ln(x) - x^2$, $u_2 = -\int 2x\,dx = -x^2$,
$u_3 = \int \frac{1}{x}\,dx = \ln(x) \Rightarrow y_p = x^2\ln(x) - x^2$, or $y_p = x^2\ln(x) \Rightarrow$
$y = x^2\ln(x) + c_1 + c_2\ln(x) + c_3 x^2$.

14. $x^3 y''' + 2x^2 y'' - 2xy' = x^3\cos(x)$. For $x^3 y''' + 2x^2 y'' - 2xy' = 0$, $x > 0$, $y = x^r$
$\Rightarrow P(r) = r(r+1)(r-2) = 0 \Rightarrow y_1 = 1$, $y_2 = x^{-1}$ and $y_3 = x^2$. With
$f(x) = \cos(x)$, $W(x) = \begin{vmatrix} 1 & x^{-1} & x^2 \\ 0 & -x^{-2} & 2x \\ 0 & 2x^{-3} & 2 \end{vmatrix} = -6x^{-2}$, $\Delta_1(x) = f(x)[3] = 3\cos(x)$,
$\Delta_2(x) = -f(x)[2x] = -2x\cos(x)$, $\Delta_3(x) = f(x)[-x^{-2}] = -x^{-2}\cos(x)$,
$u_1 = -\frac{1}{2}\int x^2\cos(x)\,dx = -\frac{1}{2}x^2\sin(x) + \int x\sin(x)\,dx$
$= -\frac{1}{2}x^2\sin(x) - x\cos(x) + \sin(x)$,
$u_2 = \frac{1}{3}\int x^3\cos(x)\,dx = \frac{1}{3}x^3\sin(x) - \int x^2\sin(x)\,dx$
$= \frac{1}{3}x^3\sin(x) + x^2\cos(x) - 2\int x\cos(x)\,dx$
$= \frac{1}{3}x^3\sin(x) + x^2\cos(x) - 2x\sin(x) - 2\cos(x)$, $u_3 = \frac{1}{6}\int \cos(x)\,dx = \frac{1}{6}\sin(x) \Rightarrow$
$y_p = \left[-\frac{1}{2}x^2\sin(x) - x\cos(x) + \sin(x)\right] +$
$\left[\frac{1}{3}x^3\sin(x) + x^2\cos(x) - 2x\sin(x) - 2\cos(x)\right]x^{-1} + \left[\frac{1}{6}\sin(x)\right]x^2$
$= -\sin(x) - 2x^{-1}\cos(x) \Rightarrow y = -\sin(x) - 2x^{-1}\cos(x) + c_1 + c_2 x^{-1} + c_3 x^2$.

15. $x^3 y''' + 3x^2 y'' + 2xy' = 1$. For $x^3 y''' + 3x^2 y'' + 2xy' = 0$, $x > 0$, $y = x^r \Rightarrow P(r) = r(r^2 + 1) = 0 \Rightarrow y_1 = 1$, $y_2 = \cos[\ln(x)]$ and $y_3 = \sin[\ln(x)]$. With $f(x) = \frac{1}{x^3}$,

$$W(x) = \begin{vmatrix} 1 & \cos[\ln(x)] & \sin[\ln(x)] \\ 0 & -\frac{1}{x}\sin[\ln(x)] & \frac{1}{x}\cos[\ln(x)] \\ 0 & \frac{1}{x^2}\sin[\ln(x)] - \frac{1}{x^2}\cos[\ln(x)] & -\frac{1}{x^2}\cos[\ln(x)] - \frac{1}{x^2}\sin[\ln(x)] \end{vmatrix} = \frac{1}{x^3},$$

$\Delta_1(x) = f(x)\left[\frac{1}{x}\right] = \frac{1}{x^4}$, $\Delta_2(x) = -f(x)\left\{\frac{1}{x}\cos[\ln(x)]\right\} = -\frac{1}{x^4}\cos[\ln(x)]$,
$\Delta_3(x) = f(x)\left\{-\frac{1}{x}\sin[\ln(x)]\right\} = -\frac{1}{x^4}\sin[\ln(x)]$, $u_1 = \int \frac{1}{x}\,dx = \ln(x)$,
$u_2 = -\int \frac{\cos[\ln(x)]}{x}\,dx = -\sin[\ln(x)]$, $u_3 = -\int \frac{\sin[\ln(x)]}{x}\,dx = \cos[\ln(x)]$
$\Rightarrow y_p = \ln(x) \Rightarrow y = \ln(x) + c_1 + c_2\cos[\ln(x)] + c_3\sin[\ln(x)]$.

16. $x^3 y''' + 3x^2 y'' = x^2 \sin(x)$. For $x^3 y''' + 3x^2 y'' = 0$, $x > 0$, $y = x^r \Rightarrow$
$P(r) = r(r^2 - 1) = 0 \Rightarrow y_1 = 1$, $y_2 = x$ and $y_3 = x^{-1}$. With $f(x) = \frac{\sin(x)}{x}$,

$$W(x) = \begin{vmatrix} 1 & x & x^{-1} \\ 0 & 1 & -x^{-2} \\ 0 & 0 & 2x^{-3} \end{vmatrix} = 2x^{-3}, \quad \Delta_1(x) = f(x)[-2x^{-1}] = -2x^{-2}\sin(x),$$

$\Delta_2(x) = -f(x)[-x^{-2}] = x^{-3}\sin(x)$, $\Delta_3(x) = f(x) = x^{-1}\sin(x)$,
$u_1 = -\int x\sin(x)\,dx = x\cos(x) - \sin(x)$, $u_2 = \frac{1}{2}\int \sin(x)\,dx = -\frac{1}{2}\cos(x)$,
$u_3 = \frac{1}{2}\int x^2 \sin(x)\,dx = -\frac{1}{2}x^2\cos(x) + \int x\cos(x)\,dx$
$= -\frac{1}{2}x^2\cos(x) + x\sin(x) + \cos(x) \Rightarrow$
$y_p = [x\cos(x) - \sin(x)] - \frac{1}{2}x\cos(x) + \left[-\frac{1}{2}x^2\cos(x) + x\sin(x) + \cos(x)\right]x^{-1}$
$= x^{-1}\cos(x) \Rightarrow y = x^{-1}\cos(x) + c_1 + c_2 x + c_3 x^{-1}$.

17. $y''' - 3y'' - y' + 3y = 8e^{2x}$. By Exercise 1, $P(r) = (r-1)(r+1)(r-3)$
$\Rightarrow (D-1)(D+1)(D-3)y = 8e^{2x} \Rightarrow (D-2)(D-1)(D+1)(D-3)y = (D-2)[8e^{2x}] = 0 \Rightarrow y = c_1 e^{2x} + c_2 e^x + c_3 e^{-x} + c_4 e^{3x} \Rightarrow y_p = ae^{2x}$, $y_p' = 2ae^{2x}$,
$y_p'' = 4ae^{2x}$, $y_p''' = 8ae^{2x}$, and $y_p''' - 3y_p'' - y_p' + 3y = 8e^{2x} \Rightarrow -3a = 8 \Rightarrow a = -\frac{8}{3}$
$\Rightarrow y_p = -\frac{8}{3}e^{2x}$.

18. $y''' - y'' + 2y = 10e^x$. By Exercise 4, $P(r) = (r+1)(r^2 - 2r + 2) \Rightarrow$
$(D+1)(D^2 - 2D + 2)y = 10e^x \Rightarrow (D-1)(D+1)(D^2 - 2D + 2)y = (D-1)[10e^x] = 0$
$\Rightarrow y = c_1 e^x + c_2 e^{-x} + c_3 e^x\cos(x) + c_4 e^x\sin(x) \Rightarrow y_p = ae^x$, $y_p' = y_p'' = y_p''' = ae^x$,
and $y_p''' - y_p'' + 2y_p = 10e^x \Rightarrow 2a = 10 \Rightarrow a = 5 \Rightarrow y_p = 5e^x$.

19. $y''' - y'' = 20x^3$. By Exercise 6, $P(r) = r^2(r-1) \Rightarrow D^2(D-1)y = 20x^3 \Rightarrow$
$D^4 D^2 (D-1)y = D^4[20x^3] = 0 \Rightarrow D^6(D-1)y = 0 \Rightarrow$
$y = c_1 + c_2 x + c_3 x^2 + c_4 x^3 + c_5 x^4 + c_6 x^5 + c_7 e^x \Rightarrow y_p = ax^2 + bx^3 + cx^4 + dx^5$,
$y_p' = 2ax + 3bx^2 + 4cx^3 + 5dx^4$, $y_p'' = 2a + 6bx + 12cx^2 + 20dx^3$,
$y_p''' = 6b + 24cx + 60dx^2$, and $y_p''' - y_p'' = 20x^3 \Rightarrow$
$[6b + 24cx + 60dx^2] - [2a + 6bx + 12cx^2 + 20dx^3] = 20x^3 \Rightarrow d = -1$, $60d - 12c = 0$
$\Rightarrow c = -5$, $24c - 6b = 0 \Rightarrow b = -20$, $6b - 2a = 0 \Rightarrow a = -60 \Rightarrow$
$y_p = -60x^2 - 20x^3 - 5x^4 - x^5$.

20. $y''' - 2y'' = 5\sin(x)$. By Exercise 7, $P(r) = r^2(r-2) \Rightarrow D^2(D-2)y = 5\sin(x)$
$\Rightarrow (D^2 + 1)D^2(D-2)y = (D^2 + 1)[5\sin(x)] = 0 \Rightarrow$

$y = c_1 + c_2 x + c_3 e^{2x} + c_4 \cos(x) + c_5 \sin(x) \Rightarrow y_p = a\cos(x) + b\sin(x)$,
$y_p' = -a\sin(x) + b\cos(x)$, $y_p'' = -a\cos(x) - b\sin(x)$, $y_p''' = a\sin(x) - b\cos(x)$, and
$y_p''' - 2y_p'' = 5\sin(x) \Rightarrow [a\sin(x) - b\cos(x)] - 2[-a\cos(x) - b\sin(x)] = 5\sin(x)$
$\Rightarrow 2a - b = 0$ and $a + 2b = 5 \Rightarrow a = 1$ and $b = 2 \Rightarrow y_p = \cos(x) + 2\sin(x)$.

21. $y''' - 3y'' + 2y' = 8xe^{2x}$. By Exercise 2, $P(r) = r(r-1)(r-2) \Rightarrow$
   $D(D-1)(D-2)y = 8xe^{2x} \Rightarrow (D-2)^2 D(D-1)(D-2)y = (D-2)^2[8xe^{2x}] = 0$
   $\Rightarrow D(D-1)(D-2)^3 y = 0 \Rightarrow y = c_1 + c_2 e^x + c_3 e^{2x} + c_4 x e^{2x} + c_5 x^2 e^{2x} \Rightarrow$
   $y_p = (ax + bx^2)e^{2x}$, $y_p' = (a + 2bx)e^{2x} + 2(ax + bx^2)e^{2x} = [a + (2a+2b)x + 2bx^2]e^{2x}$,
   $y_p'' = [(2a+2b) + 4bx]e^{2x} + 2[a + (2a+2b)x + 2bx^2]e^{2x}$
   $= [(4a+2b) + (4a+8b)x + 4bx^2]e^{2x}$,
   $y_p''' = [(4a+8b) + 8bx]e^{2x} + 2[(4a+2b) + (4a+8b)x + 4bx^2]e^{2x}$
   $= [(12a+12b) + (8a+24b)x + 8bx^2]e^{2x}$, and $y_p''' - 3y_p'' + 2y_p' = 8xe^{2x} \Rightarrow$
   $[(12a+12b) + (8a+24b)x + 8bx^2]e^{2x} - 3[(4a+2b) + (4a+8b)x + 4bx^2]e^{2x} +$
   $2[a + (2a+2b)x + 2bx^2]e^{2x} = 8xe^{2x} \Rightarrow 2a + 6b + 4bx = 8x \Rightarrow b = 2$ and $2a + 6b = 0$
   $\Rightarrow a = -6 \Rightarrow y_p = (2x^2 - 6x)e^{2x}$.

22. $y''' - y'' + y' - y = 4\sin(x) + 4\cos(x)$. By Exercise 5, $P(r) = (r-1)(r^2 + 1)$
   $\Rightarrow (D-1)(D^2+1)y = 4\sin(x) + 4\cos(x) \Rightarrow (D^2+1)(D-1)(D^2+1)y =$
   $(D^2+1)[4\sin(x) + 4\cos(x)] = 0 \Rightarrow (D-1)(D^2+1)^2 y = 0 \Rightarrow$
   $y = c_1 e^x + c_2 \cos(x) + c_3 \sin(x) + c_4 x\cos(x) + c_5 x\sin(x) \Rightarrow$
   $y_p = ax\cos(x) + bx\sin(x) = x[a\cos(x) + b\sin(x)]$,
   $y_p' = [a\cos(x) + b\sin(x)] + x[-a\sin(x) + b\cos(x)]$,
   $y_p'' = [-2a\sin(x) + 2b\cos(x)] + x[-a\cos(x) - b\sin(x)]$,
   $y_p''' = [-3a\cos(x) - 3b\sin(x)] + x[a\sin(x) - b\cos(x)]$, and
   $y_p''' - y_p'' + y_p' - y_p = 4\sin(x) + 4\cos(x) \Rightarrow$
   $(-2b - 2a)\cos(x) + (2a - 2b)\sin(x) = 4\sin(x) + 4\cos(x) \Rightarrow 2a - 2b = 4$ and
   $-2a - 2b = 4 \Rightarrow a = 0$ and $b = -2 \Rightarrow y_p = -2x\sin(x)$.

23. $y''' - 2y'' + y' = -2e^x \cos(x)$. By Exercise 3, $P(r) = r(r-1)^2 \Rightarrow$
   $D(D-1)^2 y = -2e^x \cos(x) \Rightarrow$
   $(D^2 - 2D + 2)D(D-1)^2 y = (D^2 - 2D + 2)[-2e^x \cos(x)] = 0 \Rightarrow$
   $y = c_1 + c_2 e^x + c_3 x e^x + c_4 e^x \cos(x) + c_5 e^x \sin(x) \Rightarrow y_p = e^x[a\cos(x) + b\sin(x)]$,
   $y_p' = e^x[(a+b)\cos(x) + (b-a)\sin(x)]$,
   $y_p'' = e^x[(a+b)\cos(x) + (b-a)\sin(x)] + e^x[-(a+b)\sin(x) + (b-a)\cos(x)]$
   $= e^x[2b\cos(x) - 2a\sin(x)]$, $y_p''' = e^x[(2b-2a)\cos(x) - (2a+2b)\sin(x)]$, and
   $y_p''' - 2y_p'' + y_p' = -2e^x \cos(x) \Rightarrow e^x[(-a-b)\cos(x) + (a-b)\sin(x)] = -2e^x\cos(x)$
   $\Rightarrow a - b = 0$ and $-a - b = -2 \Rightarrow a = b = 1 \Rightarrow y_p = e^x[\cos(x) + \sin(x)]$.

24. $y^{(4)} - y'' = 2$. By Exercise 8, $P(r) = r^2(r^2 - 1) \Rightarrow D^2(D^2 - 1)y = 2 \Rightarrow$
   $D^3(D-1)(D+1)y = D[2] = 0 \Rightarrow y = c_1 + c_2 x + c_3 x^2 + c_4 e^x + c_5 e^{-x} \Rightarrow y_p = ax^2$,
   $y_p' = 2ax$, $y_p'' = 2a$, $y_p''' = y_p^{(4)} = 0$, and $y_p^{(4)} - y_p'' = 2 \Rightarrow -2a = 2 \Rightarrow a = -1 \Rightarrow$
   $y_p = -x^2$.

25. $y^{(4)} + y'' = 6x$. By Exercise 9, $P(r) = r^2(r^2 + 1) \Rightarrow D^2(D^2 + 1)y = 6x \Rightarrow$ $D^4(D^2 + 1)y = D^2[6x] = 0 \Rightarrow y = c_1 + c_2x + c_3x^2 + c_4x^3 + c_5\cos(x) + c_6\sin(x)$ $\Rightarrow y_p = ax^2 + bx^3$, $y'_p = 2ax + 3bx^2$, $y''_p = 2a + 6bx$, $y'''_p = 6b$, $y^{(4)}_p = 0$, and $y^{(4)}_p + y''_p = 6x \Rightarrow 2a + 6bx = 6x \Rightarrow a = 0$ and $b = 1 \Rightarrow y_p = x^3$.

Chapter 4 Exercises – page 119

1. $y''' - y'' - 2y' = 12$.

   (a) For $y''' - y'' - 2y' = 0$, $y = e^{rx} \Rightarrow P(r) = r(r + 1)(r - 2) = 0 \Rightarrow y_1 = 1$,
   $y_2 = e^{-x}$ and $y_3 = e^{2x}$, and $W(x) = \begin{vmatrix} 1 & e^{-x} & e^{2x} \\ 0 & -e^{-x} & 2e^{2x} \\ 0 & e^{-x} & 4e^{2x} \end{vmatrix} = -6e^x$. With
   $f(x) = 12$, $\Delta_1(x) = f(x)[3e^x] = 36e^x$, $\Delta_2(x) = -f(x)[2e^{2x}] = -24e^{2x}$,
   $\Delta_3(x) = f(x)[-e^{-x}] = -12e^{-x}$, $u_1 = -\int 6\,dx = -6x$,
   $u_2 = 4\int e^x\,dx = 4e^x$, $u_3 = 2\int e^{-2x}\,dx = -e^{-2x} \Rightarrow y_p = 3 - 6x$, or $y_p = -6x$
   $\Rightarrow y = -6x + c_1 + c_2e^{-x} + c_3e^{2x}$.

   (b) $P(r) = r(r + 1)(r - 2) \Rightarrow D(D + 1)(D - 2)y = 12 \Rightarrow D^2(D + 1)(D - 2)y = D[12] = 0 \Rightarrow y = c_1 + c_2x + c_3e^{-x} + c_4e^{2x} \Rightarrow y_p = ax$, $y'_p = a$, $y''_p = y'''_p = 0$,
   and $y'''_p - y''_p - 2y'_p = 12 \Rightarrow -2a = 12 \Rightarrow a = -6 \Rightarrow y_p = -6x \Rightarrow$
   $y = -6x + c_1 + c_3e^{-x} + c_4e^{2x}$.

   (c) $y''' - y'' - 2y' = 12 \Rightarrow y'' - y' - 2y = 12x + c_1$. For $y'' - y' - 2y = 0$,
   $y = e^{rx} \Rightarrow P(r) = r^2 - r - 2 = (r - 2)(r + 1) = 0 \Rightarrow y_1 = e^{2x}$ and
   $y_2 = e^{-x}$. $y_p = ax + b \Rightarrow y'_p = a$, $y''_p = 0$ and $y''_p - y'_p - 2y_p = 12x + c_1 \Rightarrow$
   $-a - 2[a + bx] = 12x + c_1 \Rightarrow a = -\frac{c_1}{3}$ and $b = -6 \Rightarrow y_p = -\frac{c_1}{3} - 6x \Rightarrow$
   $y = -\frac{c_1}{3} - 6x + c_2e^{2x} + c_3e^{-x} = -6x + c_4 + c_2e^{2x} + c_3e^{-x}$.

2. $x^3y''' + x^2y'' = x$. For $x^3y''' + x^2y'' = 0$, $x > 0$, $y = x^r \Rightarrow P(r) = r(r - 1)^2 = 0$
   $\Rightarrow y_1 = 1$, $y_2 = x$ and $y_3 = x\ln(x)$, and $W(x) = \begin{vmatrix} 1 & x & x\ln(x) \\ 0 & 1 & \ln(x) + 1 \\ 0 & 0 & \frac{1}{x} \end{vmatrix} = \frac{1}{x}$.
   With $f(x) = \frac{1}{x^2}$, $\Delta_1(x) = f(x)[x] = \frac{1}{x}$, $\Delta_2(x) = -f(x)[\ln(x) + 1] = -\frac{\ln(x) + 1}{x^2}$,
   $\Delta_3(x) = f(x)[1] = \frac{1}{x^2}$, $u_1 = \int 1\,dx = x$, $u_2 = -\int \frac{\ln(x) + 1}{x}\,dx = -\frac{1}{2}[\ln(x)]^2 - \ln(x)$,
   $u_3 = \int \frac{1}{x}\,dx = \ln(x) \Rightarrow y_p = x - \left\{\frac{1}{2}[\ln(x)]^2 + \ln(x)\right\}x + \ln(x)[x\ln(x)]$, or
   $y_p = \frac{1}{2}x[\ln(x)]^2 \Rightarrow y = \frac{1}{2}x[\ln(x)]^2 + c_1 + c_2x + c_3x\ln(x)$.

3. $x^3y''' + x^2y'' = \frac{4}{x}$. By Exercise 2, $W(x) = \frac{1}{x}$. $f(x) = \frac{4}{x^4} \Rightarrow \Delta_1(x) = f(x)[x] = \frac{4}{x^3}$,
   $\Delta_2(x) = -f(x)[\ln(x) + 1] = -4\frac{\ln(x) + 1}{x^4}$, $\Delta_3(x) = f(x)[1] = \frac{4}{x^4}$,
   $u_1 = \int \frac{4}{x^2}\,dx = -\frac{4}{x}$, $u_2 = -4\int \frac{\ln(x) + 1}{x^3}\,dx = 2x^{-2}\ln(x) + x^{-2} + 2x^{-2} = 2\frac{\ln(x)}{x^2} + \frac{3}{x^2}$,
   $u_3 = \int \frac{4}{x^3}\,dx = -\frac{2}{x^2} \Rightarrow y_p = -\frac{4}{x} + \left[2\frac{\ln(x)}{x^2} + \frac{3}{x^2}\right]x - \frac{2}{x^2}[x\ln(x)] = -\frac{1}{x} \Rightarrow$
   $y = -\frac{1}{x} + c_1 + c_2x + c_3x\ln(x)$.

4. $y''' - y'' = 20x^3 \Rightarrow y'' - y' = 5x^4 + c_1 \Rightarrow y' - y = x^5 + c_1 x + c_2$. $I(x) = e^{-x} \Rightarrow$
$(e^{-x}y)' = (x^5 + c_1 x + c_2)e^{-x} \Rightarrow e^{-x}y = \int(x^5 + c_1 x + c_2)e^{-x}\,dx$
$= -(x^5 + c_1 x + c_2)e^{-x} + \int(5x^4 + c_1)e^{-x}\,dx$
$= -(x^5 + c_1 x + c_2)e^{-x} - (5x^4 + c_1)e^{-x} + \int 20x^3 e^{-x}\,dx$
$= -(x^5 + c_1 x + c_2)e^{-x} - (5x^4 + c_1)e^{-x} - 20x^3 e^{-x} + \int 60x^2 e^{-x}\,dx$
$= -(x^5 + c_1 x + c_2)e^{-x} - (5x^4 + c_1)e^{-x} - 20x^3 e^{-x} - 60x^2 e^{-x} + \int 120x e^{-x}\,dx =$
$-(x^5 + c_1 x + c_2)e^{-x} - (5x^4 + c_1)e^{-x} - 20x^3 e^{-x} - 60x^2 e^{-x} - 120x e^{-x} - 120e^{-x} + c_3$
$\Rightarrow y = -(x^5 + c_1 x + c_2) - (5x^4 + c_1) - 20x^3 - 60x^2 - 120x - 120 + c_3 e^x$
$= -x^5 - 5x^4 - 20x^3 - 60x^2 + c_5 + c_4 x + c_3 e^x.$

5. $x^4 y^{(4)} - 4x^3 y''' + 12x^2 y'' - 24xy' + 24y = x^4$.
For $x^4 y^{(4)} - 4x^3 y''' + 12x^2 y'' - 24xy' + 24y = 0$, $x > 0$, $y = x^r \Rightarrow$
$P(r) = (r-1)(r-2)(r-3)(r-4) = 0 \Rightarrow y_1 = x$, $y_2 = x^2$, $y_3 = x^3$ and $y_4 = x^4$,

and $W(x) = \begin{vmatrix} x & x^2 & x^3 & x^4 \\ 1 & 2x & 3x^2 & 4x^3 \\ 0 & 2 & 6x & 12x^2 \\ 0 & 0 & 6 & 24x \end{vmatrix} = -6 \begin{vmatrix} x & x^2 & x^4 \\ 1 & 2x & 4x^3 \\ 0 & 2 & 12x^2 \end{vmatrix} + 24x \begin{vmatrix} x & x^2 & x^3 \\ 1 & 2x & 3x^2 \\ 0 & 2 & 6x \end{vmatrix}$

$= -6[x(16x^3) - 10x^4] + 24x[x(6x^2) - 4x^3] = 12x^4$. With $f(x) = 1$,

$\Delta_1(x) = -\begin{vmatrix} x^2 & x^3 & x^4 \\ 2x & 3x^2 & 4x^3 \\ 2 & 6x & 12x^2 \end{vmatrix} = -[x^2(12x^4) - x^3(16x^3) + x^4(6x^2)] = -2x^6$,

$\Delta_2(x) = \begin{vmatrix} x & x^3 & x^4 \\ 1 & 3x^2 & 4x^3 \\ 0 & 6x & 12x^2 \end{vmatrix} = x(12x^4) - 6x^5 = 6x^5$, $\Delta_3(x) = -6x^4$, $\Delta_4(x) = 2x^3$,

$u_1 = -\frac{1}{6}\int x^2\,dx = -\frac{1}{18}x^3$, $u_2 = \frac{1}{2}\int x\,dx = \frac{1}{4}x^2$, $u_3 = -\frac{1}{2}\int 1\,dx = -\frac{1}{2}x$,
$u_4 = \frac{1}{6}\int \frac{1}{x}\,dx = \frac{1}{6}\ln(x) \Rightarrow y_p = -\frac{11}{36}x^4 + \frac{1}{6}x^4 \ln(x)$, or $y_p = \frac{1}{6}x^4 \ln(x) \Rightarrow$
$y = \frac{1}{6}x^4 \ln(x) + c_1 x + c_2 x^2 + c_3 x^3 + c_4 x^4$.

6. $x^3 y''' - x^2 y'' + 10xy' = 156x^2 \sin[3\ln(x)]$. For $x^3 y''' - x^2 y'' + 10xy' = 0$, $x > 0$,
$y = x^r \Rightarrow P(r) = r(r^2 - 4r + 13) = 0 \Rightarrow r_1 = 0$ and $r = 2 \pm 3i \Rightarrow y_1 = 1$,
$y_2 = x^2 \cos[3\ln(x)]$ and $y_3 = x^2 \sin[3\ln(x)]$. With $f(x) = 156\frac{\sin[3\ln(x)]}{x}$, $W(x) =$
$\begin{vmatrix} 1 & x^2\cos[3\ln(x)] & x^2\sin[3\ln(x)] \\ 0 & 2x\cos[3\ln(x)] - 3x\sin[3\ln(x)] & 2x\sin[3\ln(x)] + 3x\cos[3\ln(x)] \\ 0 & -7\cos[3\ln(x)] - 9\sin 3\ln(x) & 9\cos[3\ln(x)] - 7\sin[3\ln(x)] \end{vmatrix} = 39x,$
$\Delta_1(x) = f(x)[3x^3] = 468x^2 \sin[3\ln(x)]$,
$\Delta_2(x) = -f(x)\{2x\sin[3\ln(x)] + 3x\cos[3\ln(x)]\}$
$= -312\sin^2[3\ln(x)] - 468\sin[3\ln(x)]\cos[3\ln(x)]$,
$= -156 + 156\cos[6\ln(x)] - 234\sin[6\ln(x)]$,
$\Delta_3(x) = f(x)\{2x\cos[3\ln(x)] - 3x\sin[3\ln(x)]\}$
$= 312\sin[3\ln(x)]\cos[3\ln(x)] - 468\sin^2[3\ln(x)]$
$= 156\sin[6\ln(x)] - 234 + 234\cos[6\ln(x)]$,
$u_1 = 12\int x\sin[3\ln(x)]\,dx$. $x = e^t \Rightarrow u_1 = 12\int e^{2t}\sin(3t)\,dt$, and integration by
parts gives $u_1 = \frac{24}{13}e^{2t}\sin(3t) - \frac{36}{13}e^{2t}\cos(3t) = \frac{24}{13}x^2\sin[3\ln(x)] - \frac{36}{13}x^2\cos[3\ln(x)]$,

$u_2 = \int -\frac{4}{x} + 4\frac{\cos[6\ln(x)]}{x} - 6\frac{\sin[6\ln(x)]}{x}\,dx = -4\ln(x) + \frac{2}{3}\sin[6\ln(x)] + \cos[6\ln(x)]$,

$u_3 = \int 4\frac{\sin[6\ln(x)]}{x} - \frac{6}{x} + 6\frac{\cos[6\ln(x)]}{x}\,dx = -\frac{2}{3}\cos[6\ln(x)] - 6\ln(x) + \sin[6\ln(x)] \Rightarrow$

$y_p = \frac{24}{13}x^2\sin[3\ln(x)] - \frac{36}{13}x^2\cos[3\ln(x)] +$

$x^2\cos[3\ln(x)]\left\{-4\ln(x) + \frac{2}{3}\sin[6\ln(x)] + \cos[6\ln(x)]\right\} +$

$x^2\sin[3\ln(x)]\left\{-\frac{2}{3}\cos[6\ln(x)] - 6\ln(x) + \sin[6\ln(x)]\right\}$. Ignoring the first two terms because they are homogeneous solutions,

$y_p = \frac{2}{3}x^2\{\sin[6\ln(x)]\cos[3\ln(x)] - \cos[6\ln(x)]\sin[3\ln(x)]\}$

$+x^2\{\cos[6\ln(x)]\cos[3\ln(x)] + \sin[6\ln(x)]\sin[3\ln(x)]\}$

$-4x^2\ln(x)\cos[3\ln(x)] - 6x^2\ln(x)\sin[3\ln(x)]$

$= \frac{2}{3}x^2\sin[3\ln(x)] + x^2\cos[3\ln(x)] - 4x^2\ln(x)\cos[3\ln(x)] - 6x^2\ln(x)\sin[3\ln(x)]$,

or $y_p = -4x^2\ln(x)\cos[3\ln(x)] - 6x^2\ln(x)\sin[3\ln(x)] \Rightarrow y = c_1 + c_2x^2\cos[3\ln(x)] + c_3x^2\sin[3\ln(x)] - 4x^2\ln(x)\cos[3\ln(x)] - 6x^2\ln(x)\sin[3\ln(x)]$.

7. Let $P(r) = a_0 + a_1r + a_2r^2 + \cdots + a_nr^n$, with a_i, $0 \le i \le n$, real. Then $P(z) = 0$
   $\Rightarrow a_0 + a_1z + a_2z^2 + \cdots + a_nz^n = 0 \Rightarrow \overline{a_0 + a_1z + a_2z^2 + \cdots + a_nz^n} = 0 \Rightarrow$
   $a_0 + a_1\overline{z} + a_2\overline{z}^2 + \cdots + a_n\overline{z}^n = 0$ since $\overline{a_i} = a_i$, $0 \le i \le n$. Thus, $P(\overline{z}) = 0$.

8. No, because $W(x) = \begin{vmatrix} 1 & x & x^3 \\ 0 & 1 & 3x^2 \\ 0 & 0 & 6x \end{vmatrix} = 6x = 0$ at $x = 0$ and $W(x) \ne 0$ for $x \ne 0$,

   in contradiction of Theorem 4.8.

9. $y''' + 3y'' + 3y' + y = 2xe^{-x}\cos(x)$. For $y''' + 3y'' + 3y' + y = 0$, $y = e^{rx} \Rightarrow$
   $P(r) = (r+1)^3 = 0 \Rightarrow y_1 = e^{-x}$, $y_2 = xe^{-x}$ and $y_3 = x^2e^{-x}$, and

   $W(x) = \begin{vmatrix} e^{-x} & xe^{-x} & x^2e^{-x} \\ -e^{-x} & e^{-x} - xe^{-x} & 2xe^{-x} - x^2e^{-x} \\ e^{-x} & -2e^{-x} + xe^{-x} & 2e^{-x} - 4xe^{-x} + x^2e^{-x} \end{vmatrix}$

   $= e^{-3x}\begin{vmatrix} 1 & x & x^2 \\ -1 & 1-x & 2x-x^2 \\ 1 & x-2 & 2-4x+x^2 \end{vmatrix}$

   $= e^{-3x}[(1-x)(2-4x+x^2) - (x-2)(2x-x^2) + x(2-4x+x^2) - x^2(x-2) + x(2x-x^2) - x^2(1-x)] = 2e^{-3x}$. With $f(x) = 2xe^{-x}\cos(x)$,

   $\Delta_1(x) = f(x)[x(2x-x^2) - x^2(1-x)]e^{-2x} = x^2e^{-2x}f(x) = 2x^3e^{-3x}\cos(x)$,

   $\Delta_2(x) = -f(x)[(2x-x^2) + x^2]e^{-2x} = -2xe^{-2x}f(x) = -4x^2e^{-3x}\cos(x)$,

   $\Delta_3(x) = f(x)[(1-x) + x]e^{-2x} = e^{-2x}f(x) = 2xe^{-3x}\cos(x)$,

   $u_1 = \int x^3\cos(x)\,dx = x^3\sin(x) - 3\int x^2\sin(x)\,dx$

   $= x^3\sin(x) + 3x^2\cos(x) - 6\int x\cos(x)\,dx$

   $= x^3\sin(x) + 3x^2\cos(x) - 6x\sin(x) - 6\cos(x)$,

   $u_2 = -2\int x^2\cos(x)\,dx = -2x^2\sin(x) + 4\int x\sin(x)\,dx$

   $= -2x^2\sin(x) - 4x\cos(x) + 4\sin(x)$,

   $u_3 = \int x\cos(x)\,dx = x\sin(x) + \cos(x) \Rightarrow$

   $y_p = [x^3\sin(x) + 3x^2\cos(x) - 6x\sin(x) - 6\cos(x)]e^{-x} +$

   $[-2x^2\sin(x) - 4x\cos(x) + 4\sin(x)]xe^{-x} + [x\sin(x) + \cos(x)]x^2e^{-x}$

$$= -2xe^{-x}\sin(x) - 6e^{-x}\cos(x) \Rightarrow$$
$$y = -2xe^{-x}\sin(x) - 6e^{-x}\cos(x) + c_1 e^{-x} + c_2 xe^{-x} + c_3 x^2 e^{-x}.$$

10. By Exercise 9 , $P(r) = (r+1)^3$. $xe^{-x}\cos(x)$ and $xe^{-x}\sin(x)$ are solutions of a fourth-order equation for which the indicial equation has the roots $r = -1 \pm i$ of multiplicity 2 $\Rightarrow (r+1)^2 = -1 \Rightarrow r^2 + 2r + 2 = 0$ and $(r^2 + 2r + 2)^2 = 0$ is the indicial equation $\Rightarrow (D^2 + 2D + 2)^2$ is the annihilator of $xe^{-x}\cos(x)$ of minimal degree. Hence, $(D+1)^3 y = xe^{-x}\cos(x) \Rightarrow$
$(D^2 + 2D + 2)^2 (D+1)^3 y = (D^2 + 2D + 2)^2 [2xe^{-x}\cos(x)] = 0 \Rightarrow y = c_1 e^{-x}\cos(x) + c_2 e^{-x}\sin(x) + c_3 xe^{-x}\cos(x) + c_4 xe^{-x}\sin(x) + c_5 e^{-x} + c_6 xe^{-x} + c_7 x^2 e^{-x} \Rightarrow$
$y_p = (a+bx)e^{-x}\cos(x) + (c+dx)e^{-x}\sin(x),$
$y_p' = be^{-x}\cos(x) - (a+bx)e^{-x}\cos(x) - (a+bx)e^{-x}\sin(x) + de^{-x}\sin(x) - (c+dx)e^{-x}\sin(x) + (c+dx)e^{-x}\cos(x)$
$= [(b-a+c) + (d-b)x]e^{-x}\cos(x) + [(d-a-c) - (b+d)x]e^{-x}\sin(x),$
$y_p'' = (d-b)e^{-x}\cos(x) - [(b-a+c) + (d-b)x]e^{-x}\cos(x) - [(b-a+c) + (d-b)x]e^{-x}\sin(x) - (b+d)e^{-x}\sin(x) - [(d-a-c) - (b+d)x]e^{-x}\sin(x) + [(d-a-c) - (b+d)x]e^{-x}\cos(x)$
$= [(2d-2b-2c) - 2dx]e^{-x}\cos(x) + [(2a-2b-2d) + 2bx]e^{-x}\sin(x).$
$y_p''' = -2de^{-x}\cos(x) - [(2d-2b-2c) - 2dx]e^{-x}\cos(x) - [(2d-2b-2c) - 2dx]e^{-x}\sin(x) + 2be^{-x}\sin(x) - [(2a-2b-2d) + 2bx]e^{-x}\sin(x) + [(2a-2b-2d) + 2bx]e^{-x}\cos(x)$
$= [(2a+2c-6d) + (2b+2d)x]e^{-x}\cos(x) + [(6b+2c-2a) + (2d-2b)x]e^{-x}\sin(x),$
and $y_p''' + 3y_p'' + 3y_p' + y_p = 2xe^{-x}\cos(x) \Rightarrow$
$[(2a+2c-6d) + (2b+2d)x]e^{-x}\cos(x) + [(6b+2c-2a) + (2d-2b)x]e^{-x}\sin(x) + 3[(2d-2b-2c) - 2dx]e^{-x}\cos(x) + 3[(2a-2b-2d) + 2bx]e^{-x}\sin(x) + 3[(b-a+c) + (d-b)x]e^{-x}\cos(x) + 3[(d-a-c) - (b+d)x]e^{-x}\sin(x) + (a+bx)e^{-x}\cos(x) + (c+dx)e^{-x}\sin(x) = 2xe^{-x}\cos(x) \Rightarrow$
$[-(3b+c) - dx]e^{-x}\cos(x) + [(a-3d) + bx]e^{-x}\sin(x) = 2xe^{-x}\cos(x) \Rightarrow c = 0,$
$d = -2,\ 3b+c = 0,\ a-3d = 0 \Rightarrow b = 0,\ a = -6 \Rightarrow$
$y_p = -6e^{-x}\cos(x) - 2xe^{-x}\sin(x) \Rightarrow$
$y = -6e^{-x}\cos(x) - 2xe^{-x}\sin(x) + c_5 e^{-x} + c_6 xe^{-x} + c_7 x^2 e^{-x}.$

C.5   Chapter 5 Solutions

Exercises 5.1 – page 168

1. $\left\{ \begin{array}{l} x' = -5x + 6y \\ y' = -3x + 4y \end{array} \right\} \Rightarrow A = \begin{pmatrix} -5 & 6 \\ -3 & 4 \end{pmatrix}, \begin{vmatrix} \lambda + 5 & -6 \\ 3 & \lambda - 4 \end{vmatrix} = (\lambda - 1)(\lambda + 2) = 0$
   $\Rightarrow \lambda_1 = 1,\ \lambda_2 = -2.$
   For $\lambda_1 = 1$, $\begin{pmatrix} 6 & -6 \\ 3 & -3 \end{pmatrix} \begin{pmatrix} a \\ b \end{pmatrix} = \begin{pmatrix} 0 \\ 0 \end{pmatrix} \Rightarrow a = b \Rightarrow \mathbf{v}_1 = \begin{pmatrix} 1 \\ 1 \end{pmatrix}.$
   For $\lambda_2 = -2$, $\begin{pmatrix} 3 & -6 \\ 3 & -6 \end{pmatrix} \begin{pmatrix} a \\ b \end{pmatrix} = \begin{pmatrix} 0 \\ 0 \end{pmatrix} \Rightarrow a = 2b \Rightarrow \mathbf{v}_2 = \begin{pmatrix} 2 \\ 1 \end{pmatrix}.$

$\mathbf{x}_1(t) = e^t \begin{pmatrix} 1 \\ 1 \end{pmatrix}$, $\mathbf{x}_2(t) = e^{-2t} \begin{pmatrix} 2 \\ 1 \end{pmatrix}$, $\mathbf{x}(t) = c_1 \mathbf{x}_1(t) + c_2 \mathbf{x}_2(t) \Rightarrow$
$x(t) = c_1 e^t + 2c_2 e^{-2t}$, $y(t) = c_1 e^t + c_2 e^{-2t}$.

2. $\left\{ \begin{array}{l} x' = 3x + y \\ y' = -2x \end{array} \right\} \Rightarrow A = \begin{pmatrix} 3 & 1 \\ -2 & 0 \end{pmatrix}$, $\begin{vmatrix} \lambda - 3 & -1 \\ 2 & \lambda \end{vmatrix} = (\lambda - 1)(\lambda - 2) = 0 \Rightarrow$
$\lambda_1 = 1, \lambda_2 = 2$.
For $\lambda_1 = 1$, $\begin{pmatrix} -2 & -1 \\ 2 & 1 \end{pmatrix} \begin{pmatrix} a \\ b \end{pmatrix} = \begin{pmatrix} 0 \\ 0 \end{pmatrix} \Rightarrow b = -2a \Rightarrow \mathbf{v}_1 = \begin{pmatrix} 1 \\ -2 \end{pmatrix}$.
For $\lambda_2 = 2$, $\begin{pmatrix} -1 & -1 \\ 2 & 2 \end{pmatrix} \begin{pmatrix} a \\ b \end{pmatrix} = \begin{pmatrix} 0 \\ 0 \end{pmatrix} \Rightarrow b = -a \Rightarrow \mathbf{v}_2 = \begin{pmatrix} 1 \\ -1 \end{pmatrix}$.
$\mathbf{x}_1(t) = e^t \begin{pmatrix} 1 \\ -2 \end{pmatrix}$, $\mathbf{x}_2(t) = e^{2t} \begin{pmatrix} 1 \\ -1 \end{pmatrix}$, $\mathbf{x}(t) = c_1 \mathbf{x}_1(t) + c_2 \mathbf{x}_2(t) \Rightarrow$
$x(t) = c_1 e^t + c_2 e^{2t}$, $y(t) = -2c_1 e^t - c_2 e^{2t}$.

3. $A = \begin{pmatrix} 1 & 1 \\ 0 & 2 \end{pmatrix}$, $\begin{vmatrix} \lambda - 1 & -1 \\ 0 & \lambda - 2 \end{vmatrix} = (\lambda - 1)(\lambda - 2) = 0 \Rightarrow \lambda_1 = 1, \lambda_2 = 2$.
For $\lambda_1 = 1$, $\begin{pmatrix} 0 & -1 \\ 0 & -1 \end{pmatrix} \begin{pmatrix} a \\ b \end{pmatrix} = \begin{pmatrix} 0 \\ 0 \end{pmatrix} \Rightarrow b = 0 \Rightarrow \mathbf{v}_1 = \begin{pmatrix} 1 \\ 0 \end{pmatrix}$.
For $\lambda_2 = 2$, $\begin{pmatrix} 1 & -1 \\ 0 & 0 \end{pmatrix} \begin{pmatrix} a \\ b \end{pmatrix} = \begin{pmatrix} 0 \\ 0 \end{pmatrix} \Rightarrow b = a \Rightarrow \mathbf{v}_2 = \begin{pmatrix} 1 \\ 1 \end{pmatrix}$.
$\mathbf{x}_1(t) = e^t \begin{pmatrix} 1 \\ 0 \end{pmatrix}$, $\mathbf{x}_2(t) = e^{2t} \begin{pmatrix} 1 \\ 1 \end{pmatrix}$, $\mathbf{x}(t) = c_1 \mathbf{x}_1(t) + c_2 \mathbf{x}_2(t)$.

4. $A = \begin{pmatrix} 1 & 0 \\ 1 & 2 \end{pmatrix}$, $\begin{vmatrix} \lambda - 1 & 0 \\ -1 & \lambda - 2 \end{vmatrix} = (\lambda - 1)(\lambda - 2) = 0 \Rightarrow \lambda_1 = 1, \lambda_2 = 2$.
For $\lambda_1 = 1$, $\begin{pmatrix} 0 & 0 \\ -1 & -1 \end{pmatrix} \begin{pmatrix} a \\ b \end{pmatrix} = \begin{pmatrix} 0 \\ 0 \end{pmatrix} \Rightarrow b = -a \Rightarrow \mathbf{v}_1 = \begin{pmatrix} 1 \\ -1 \end{pmatrix}$.
For $\lambda_2 = 2$, $\begin{pmatrix} 1 & 0 \\ -1 & 0 \end{pmatrix} \begin{pmatrix} a \\ b \end{pmatrix} = \begin{pmatrix} 0 \\ 0 \end{pmatrix} \Rightarrow a = 0 \Rightarrow \mathbf{v}_2 = \begin{pmatrix} 0 \\ 1 \end{pmatrix}$.
$\mathbf{x}_1(t) = e^t \begin{pmatrix} 1 \\ -1 \end{pmatrix}$, $\mathbf{x}_2(t) = e^{2t} \begin{pmatrix} 0 \\ 1 \end{pmatrix}$, $X(t) = \begin{pmatrix} e^t & 0 \\ -e^t & e^{2t} \end{pmatrix}$.

5. $A = \begin{pmatrix} 2 & 0 \\ 0 & 2 \end{pmatrix}$, $\begin{vmatrix} \lambda - 2 & 0 \\ 0 & \lambda - 2 \end{vmatrix} = (\lambda - 2)^2 = 0 \Rightarrow \lambda_1 = 2$.
For $\lambda_1 = 2$, $\begin{pmatrix} 0 & 0 \\ 0 & 0 \end{pmatrix} \begin{pmatrix} a \\ b \end{pmatrix} = \begin{pmatrix} 0 \\ 0 \end{pmatrix} \Rightarrow a$ and b are free $\Rightarrow \mathbf{v}_1 = \begin{pmatrix} 1 \\ 0 \end{pmatrix}$,
$\mathbf{v}_2 = \begin{pmatrix} 0 \\ 1 \end{pmatrix}$, $\mathbf{x}_1(t) = e^{2t} \begin{pmatrix} 1 \\ 0 \end{pmatrix}$, $\mathbf{x}_2(t) = e^{2t} \begin{pmatrix} 0 \\ 1 \end{pmatrix}$, $X(t) = \begin{pmatrix} e^{2t} & 0 \\ 0 & e^{2t} \end{pmatrix}$.

6. $\left\{ \begin{array}{l} x' = x - y \\ y' = 2x + 4y \end{array} \right\}$, $x(0) = 2, y(0) = 1 \Rightarrow A = \begin{pmatrix} 1 & -1 \\ 2 & 4 \end{pmatrix}$, $\mathbf{x}(0) = \begin{pmatrix} 2 \\ 1 \end{pmatrix}$.
$\begin{vmatrix} \lambda - 1 & 1 \\ -2 & \lambda - 4 \end{vmatrix} = (\lambda - 2)(\lambda - 3) = 0 \Rightarrow \lambda_1 = 2, \lambda_2 = 3$.

For $\lambda_1 = 2$, $\begin{pmatrix} 1 & 1 \\ -2 & -2 \end{pmatrix} \begin{pmatrix} a \\ b \end{pmatrix} = \begin{pmatrix} 0 \\ 0 \end{pmatrix} \Rightarrow b = -a \Rightarrow \mathbf{v}_1 = \begin{pmatrix} 1 \\ -1 \end{pmatrix}$.

For $\lambda_2 = 3$, $\begin{pmatrix} 2 & 1 \\ -2 & -1 \end{pmatrix} \begin{pmatrix} a \\ b \end{pmatrix} = \begin{pmatrix} 0 \\ 0 \end{pmatrix} \Rightarrow b = -2a \Rightarrow \mathbf{v}_2 = \begin{pmatrix} 1 \\ -2 \end{pmatrix}$.

$\mathbf{x}_1(t) = e^{2t} \begin{pmatrix} 1 \\ -1 \end{pmatrix}$, $\mathbf{x}_2(t) = e^{3t} \begin{pmatrix} 1 \\ -2 \end{pmatrix}$, $X(t) = \begin{pmatrix} e^{2t} & e^{3t} \\ -e^{2t} & -2e^{3t} \end{pmatrix}$,

$X(0) = \begin{pmatrix} 1 & 1 \\ -1 & -2 \end{pmatrix}$, $X(0)^{-1} = \begin{pmatrix} 2 & 1 \\ -1 & -1 \end{pmatrix}$, $\mathbf{x}(t) = X(t)X(0)^{-1}\mathbf{x}(0)$

$= \begin{pmatrix} e^{2t} & e^{3t} \\ -e^{2t} & -2e^{3t} \end{pmatrix} \begin{pmatrix} 2 & 1 \\ -1 & -1 \end{pmatrix} \begin{pmatrix} 2 \\ 1 \end{pmatrix} = \begin{pmatrix} 5e^{2t} - 3e^{3t} \\ -5e^{2t} + 6e^{3t} \end{pmatrix}$.

7. $A = \begin{pmatrix} 1 & 3 \\ -1 & -3 \end{pmatrix}$, $\begin{vmatrix} \lambda - 1 & -3 \\ 1 & \lambda + 3 \end{vmatrix} = \lambda(\lambda + 2) = 0 \Rightarrow \lambda_1 = 0$, $\lambda_2 = -2$.

For $\lambda_1 = 0$, $\begin{pmatrix} -1 & -3 \\ 1 & 3 \end{pmatrix} \begin{pmatrix} a \\ b \end{pmatrix} = \begin{pmatrix} 0 \\ 0 \end{pmatrix} \Rightarrow a = -3b \Rightarrow \mathbf{v}_1 = \begin{pmatrix} -3 \\ 1 \end{pmatrix}$.

For $\lambda_2 = -2$, $\begin{pmatrix} -3 & -3 \\ 1 & 1 \end{pmatrix} \begin{pmatrix} a \\ b \end{pmatrix} = \begin{pmatrix} 0 \\ 0 \end{pmatrix} \Rightarrow b = -a \Rightarrow \mathbf{v}_2 = \begin{pmatrix} 1 \\ -1 \end{pmatrix}$.

$\mathbf{x}_1(t) = \begin{pmatrix} -3 \\ 1 \end{pmatrix}$, $\mathbf{x}_2(t) = e^{-2t} \begin{pmatrix} 1 \\ -1 \end{pmatrix}$, $X(t) = \begin{pmatrix} -3 & e^{-2t} \\ 1 & -e^{-2t} \end{pmatrix}$.

8. $\left\{ \begin{array}{l} x' = 2y \\ y' = 2x \end{array} \right\} \Rightarrow A = \begin{pmatrix} 0 & 2 \\ 2 & 0 \end{pmatrix}$, $\begin{vmatrix} \lambda & -2 \\ -2 & \lambda \end{vmatrix} = (\lambda - 2)(\lambda + 2) = 0 \Rightarrow \lambda_1 = 2$, $\lambda_2 = -2$.

For $\lambda_1 = 2$, $\begin{pmatrix} 2 & -2 \\ -2 & 2 \end{pmatrix} \begin{pmatrix} a \\ b \end{pmatrix} = \begin{pmatrix} 0 \\ 0 \end{pmatrix} \Rightarrow a = b \Rightarrow \mathbf{v}_1 = \begin{pmatrix} 1 \\ 1 \end{pmatrix}$.

For $\lambda_2 = -2$, $\begin{pmatrix} -2 & -2 \\ -2 & -2 \end{pmatrix} \begin{pmatrix} a \\ b \end{pmatrix} = \begin{pmatrix} 0 \\ 0 \end{pmatrix} \Rightarrow b = -a \Rightarrow \mathbf{v}_2 = \begin{pmatrix} 1 \\ -1 \end{pmatrix}$.

$\mathbf{x}_1(t) = e^{2t} \begin{pmatrix} 1 \\ 1 \end{pmatrix}$, $\mathbf{x}_2(t) = e^{-2t} \begin{pmatrix} 1 \\ -1 \end{pmatrix}$, $\mathbf{x}(t) = c_1\mathbf{x}_1(t) + c_2\mathbf{x}_2(t) \Rightarrow$

$x(t) = c_1e^{2t} + c_2e^{-2t}$, $y(t) = c_1e^{2t} - c_2e^{-2t}$.

9. $\left\{ \begin{array}{l} x' = x \\ y' = -2x + 3y \\ z' = -x + y + 2z \end{array} \right\} \Rightarrow A = \begin{pmatrix} 1 & 0 & 0 \\ -2 & 3 & 0 \\ -1 & 1 & 2 \end{pmatrix}$,

$\begin{vmatrix} \lambda - 1 & 0 & 0 \\ 2 & \lambda - 3 & 0 \\ 1 & -1 & \lambda - 2 \end{vmatrix} = (\lambda - 1)(\lambda - 2)(\lambda - 3) = 0 \Rightarrow \lambda_1 = 1$, $\lambda_2 = 2$, $\lambda_3 = 3$.

For $\lambda_1 = 1$, $\begin{pmatrix} 0 & 0 & 0 \\ 2 & -2 & 0 \\ 1 & -1 & -1 \end{pmatrix} \begin{pmatrix} a \\ b \\ c \end{pmatrix} = \begin{pmatrix} 0 \\ 0 \\ 0 \end{pmatrix} \Rightarrow a = b$ and $a - b - c = 0 \Rightarrow$

$\mathbf{v}_1 = \begin{pmatrix} 1 \\ 1 \\ 0 \end{pmatrix} \Rightarrow \mathbf{x}_1(t) = e^t \begin{pmatrix} 1 \\ 1 \\ 0 \end{pmatrix}$.

For $\lambda_2 = 2$, $\begin{pmatrix} 1 & 0 & 0 \\ 2 & -1 & 0 \\ 1 & -1 & 0 \end{pmatrix} \begin{pmatrix} a \\ b \\ c \end{pmatrix} = \begin{pmatrix} 0 \\ 0 \\ 0 \end{pmatrix} \Rightarrow a = 0,\ a - b = 0$ and $2a - b = 0$

$\Rightarrow \mathbf{v}_2 = \begin{pmatrix} 0 \\ 0 \\ 1 \end{pmatrix} \Rightarrow \mathbf{x}_2(t) = e^{2t} \begin{pmatrix} 0 \\ 0 \\ 1 \end{pmatrix}$.

For $\lambda_3 = 3$, $\begin{pmatrix} 2 & 0 & 0 \\ 2 & 0 & 0 \\ 1 & -1 & 1 \end{pmatrix} \begin{pmatrix} a \\ b \\ c \end{pmatrix} = \begin{pmatrix} 0 \\ 0 \\ 0 \end{pmatrix} \Rightarrow a = 0$ and $a - b + c = 0 \Rightarrow$

$\mathbf{v}_3 = \begin{pmatrix} 0 \\ 1 \\ 1 \end{pmatrix} \Rightarrow \mathbf{x}_3(t) = e^{3t} \begin{pmatrix} 0 \\ 1 \\ 1 \end{pmatrix}$. $\mathbf{x}(t) = c_1 \mathbf{x}_1(t) + c_2 \mathbf{x}_2(t) + c_3 \mathbf{x}_3(t) \Rightarrow$

$x(t) = c_1 e^t,\ y(t) = c_1 e^t + c_3 e^{3t},\ z(t) = c_2 e^{2t} + c_3 e^{3t}$.

10. $A = \begin{pmatrix} 1 & -3 & 3 \\ -4 & -2 & 4 \\ -1 & -3 & 5 \end{pmatrix}$, $\begin{vmatrix} \lambda - 1 & 3 & -3 \\ 4 & \lambda + 2 & -4 \\ 1 & 3 & \lambda - 5 \end{vmatrix} = (\lambda - 2)(\lambda + 2)(\lambda - 4) = 0 \Rightarrow$

$\lambda_1 = 2,\ \lambda_2 = -2,\ \lambda_3 = 4$.

For $\lambda_1 = 2$, $\begin{pmatrix} 1 & 3 & -3 \\ 4 & 4 & -4 \\ 1 & 3 & -3 \end{pmatrix} \begin{pmatrix} a \\ b \\ c \end{pmatrix} = \begin{pmatrix} 0 \\ 0 \\ 0 \end{pmatrix} \Rightarrow \begin{pmatrix} 1 & 3 & -3 \\ 0 & -8 & 8 \\ 0 & 0 & 0 \end{pmatrix} \begin{pmatrix} a \\ b \\ c \end{pmatrix} =$

$\begin{pmatrix} 0 \\ 0 \\ 0 \end{pmatrix} \Rightarrow b = c \Rightarrow a = 0 \Rightarrow \mathbf{v}_1 = \begin{pmatrix} 0 \\ 1 \\ 1 \end{pmatrix} \Rightarrow \mathbf{x}_1(t) = e^{2t} \begin{pmatrix} 0 \\ 1 \\ 1 \end{pmatrix}$.

For $\lambda_2 = -2$, $\begin{pmatrix} -3 & 3 & -3 \\ 4 & 0 & -4 \\ 1 & 3 & -7 \end{pmatrix} \begin{pmatrix} a \\ b \\ c \end{pmatrix} = \begin{pmatrix} 0 \\ 0 \\ 0 \end{pmatrix} \Rightarrow a = c \Rightarrow b = 2c \Rightarrow$

$\mathbf{v}_2 = \begin{pmatrix} 1 \\ 2 \\ 1 \end{pmatrix} \Rightarrow \mathbf{x}_2(t) = e^{-2t} \begin{pmatrix} 1 \\ 2 \\ 1 \end{pmatrix}$.

For $\lambda_3 = 4$, $\begin{pmatrix} 3 & 3 & -3 \\ 4 & 6 & -4 \\ 1 & 3 & -1 \end{pmatrix} \begin{pmatrix} a \\ b \\ c \end{pmatrix} = \begin{pmatrix} 0 \\ 0 \\ 0 \end{pmatrix} \Rightarrow \begin{pmatrix} 0 & -6 & 0 \\ 0 & -6 & 0 \\ 1 & 3 & -1 \end{pmatrix} \begin{pmatrix} a \\ b \\ c \end{pmatrix} =$

$\begin{pmatrix} 0 \\ 0 \\ 0 \end{pmatrix} \Rightarrow b = 0 \Rightarrow a = c \Rightarrow \mathbf{v}_3 = \begin{pmatrix} 1 \\ 0 \\ 1 \end{pmatrix} \Rightarrow \mathbf{x}_3(t) = e^{4t} \begin{pmatrix} 1 \\ 0 \\ 1 \end{pmatrix}$.

$X(t) = \begin{pmatrix} 0 & e^{-2t} & e^{4t} \\ e^{2t} & 2e^{-2t} & 0 \\ e^{2t} & e^{-2t} & e^{4t} \end{pmatrix}$.

11. $A = \begin{pmatrix} -1 & 0 & 2 \\ -2 & 1 & 2 \\ 0 & 0 & 1 \end{pmatrix}$, $\begin{vmatrix} \lambda + 1 & 0 & -2 \\ 2 & \lambda - 1 & -2 \\ 0 & 0 & \lambda - 1 \end{vmatrix} = (\lambda - 1)^2 (\lambda + 1) = 0 \Rightarrow \lambda_1 = 1,$

$m_1 = 2$, $\lambda_2 = -1$.

For $\lambda_1 = 1$, $\begin{pmatrix} 2 & 0 & -2 \\ 2 & 0 & -2 \\ 0 & 0 & 0 \end{pmatrix} \begin{pmatrix} a \\ b \\ c \end{pmatrix} = \begin{pmatrix} 0 \\ 0 \\ 0 \end{pmatrix} \Rightarrow a = c \Rightarrow \mathbf{v}_1 = \begin{pmatrix} 1 \\ 0 \\ 1 \end{pmatrix}$,

$\mathbf{v}_2 = \begin{pmatrix} 0 \\ 1 \\ 0 \end{pmatrix} \Rightarrow \mathbf{x}_1(t) = e^t \begin{pmatrix} 1 \\ 0 \\ 1 \end{pmatrix}$, $\mathbf{x}_2(t) = e^t \begin{pmatrix} 0 \\ 1 \\ 0 \end{pmatrix}$.

For $\lambda_2 = -1$, $\begin{pmatrix} 0 & 0 & -2 \\ 2 & -2 & -2 \\ 0 & 0 & -2 \end{pmatrix} \begin{pmatrix} a \\ b \\ c \end{pmatrix} = \begin{pmatrix} 0 \\ 0 \\ 0 \end{pmatrix} \Rightarrow c = 0 \Rightarrow a = b \Rightarrow$

$\mathbf{v}_3 = \begin{pmatrix} 1 \\ 1 \\ 0 \end{pmatrix} \Rightarrow \mathbf{x}_3(t) = e^{-t} \begin{pmatrix} 1 \\ 1 \\ 0 \end{pmatrix}$. $X(t) = \begin{pmatrix} e^t & 0 & e^{-t} \\ 0 & e^t & e^{-t} \\ e^t & 0 & 0 \end{pmatrix}$.

12. $\left\{ \begin{array}{l} x' = -3x + y \\ y' = -4x - 3y \end{array} \right\} \Rightarrow A = \begin{pmatrix} -3 & 1 \\ -4 & -3 \end{pmatrix}$, $\begin{vmatrix} \lambda + 3 & -1 \\ 4 & \lambda + 3 \end{vmatrix} = \lambda^2 + 6\lambda + 13 = 0$

$\Rightarrow \lambda, \overline{\lambda} = -3 \pm 2i$.

For $\lambda = -3 + 2i$, $\begin{pmatrix} 2i & -1 \\ 4 & 2i \end{pmatrix} \begin{pmatrix} a \\ b \end{pmatrix} = \begin{pmatrix} 0 \\ 0 \end{pmatrix} \Rightarrow b = 2ia \Rightarrow \mathbf{v} = \begin{pmatrix} 1 \\ 2i \end{pmatrix} \Rightarrow$

$z(t) = e^{-3t}[\cos(2t) + i\sin(2t)] \left[\begin{pmatrix} 1 \\ 0 \end{pmatrix} + i \begin{pmatrix} 0 \\ 2 \end{pmatrix} \right] \Rightarrow$

$\mathbf{x}_1(t) = e^{-3t} \begin{pmatrix} \cos(2t) \\ -2\sin(2t) \end{pmatrix}$, $\mathbf{x}_2(t) = e^{-3t} \begin{pmatrix} \sin(2t) \\ 2\cos(2t) \end{pmatrix}$, $\mathbf{x}(t) = c_1\mathbf{x}_1(t) + c_2\mathbf{x}_2(t)$

$\Rightarrow x(t) = e^{-3t}[c_1\cos(2t) + c_2\sin(2t)]$, $y(t) = e^{-3t}[-2c_1\sin(2t) + 2c_2\cos(2t)]$.

13. $A = \begin{pmatrix} 0 & -1 \\ 13 & -6 \end{pmatrix}$, $\begin{vmatrix} \lambda & 1 \\ -13 & \lambda + 6 \end{vmatrix} = \lambda^2 + 6\lambda + 13 = 0 \Rightarrow \lambda, \overline{\lambda} = -3 \pm 2i$.

For $\lambda = -3 + 2i$, $\begin{pmatrix} -3 + 2i & 1 \\ -13 & 3 + 2i \end{pmatrix} \begin{pmatrix} a \\ b \end{pmatrix} = \begin{pmatrix} 0 \\ 0 \end{pmatrix} \Rightarrow b = 3 - 2ia \Rightarrow$

$\mathbf{v} = \begin{pmatrix} 1 \\ 3 - 2i \end{pmatrix} \Rightarrow z(t) = e^{-3t}[\cos(2t) + i\sin(2t)] \left[\begin{pmatrix} 1 \\ 3 \end{pmatrix} + i \begin{pmatrix} 0 \\ -2 \end{pmatrix} \right] \Rightarrow$

$\mathbf{x}_1(t) = e^{-3t} \begin{pmatrix} \cos(2t) \\ 3\cos(2t) + 2\sin(2t) \end{pmatrix}$, $\mathbf{x}_2(t) = e^{-3t} \begin{pmatrix} \sin(2t) \\ 3\sin(2t) - 2\cos(2t) \end{pmatrix}$,

$\mathbf{x}(t) = c_1\mathbf{x}_1(t) + c_2\mathbf{x}_2(t)$.

14. $A = \begin{pmatrix} 2 & -2 \\ 1 & 0 \end{pmatrix}$, $\begin{vmatrix} \lambda - 2 & 2 \\ -1 & \lambda \end{vmatrix} = \lambda^2 - 2\lambda + 2 = 0 \Rightarrow \lambda, \overline{\lambda} = 1 \pm i$.

For $\lambda = 1 + i$, $\begin{pmatrix} -1 + i & 2 \\ -1 & 1 + i \end{pmatrix} \begin{pmatrix} a \\ b \end{pmatrix} = \begin{pmatrix} 0 \\ 0 \end{pmatrix} \Rightarrow a = (1 + i)b \Rightarrow$

$\mathbf{v} = \begin{pmatrix} 1 + i \\ 1 \end{pmatrix} \Rightarrow z(t) = e^t[\cos(t) + i\sin(t)] \left[\begin{pmatrix} 1 \\ 1 \end{pmatrix} + i \begin{pmatrix} 1 \\ 0 \end{pmatrix} \right] \Rightarrow$

$\mathbf{x}_1(t) = e^t \begin{pmatrix} \cos(t) - \sin(t) \\ \cos(t) \end{pmatrix}$, $\mathbf{x}_2(t) = e^t \begin{pmatrix} \sin(t) + \cos(t) \\ \sin(t) \end{pmatrix}$,

$$X(t) = e^t \begin{pmatrix} \cos(t) - \sin(t) & \sin(t) + \cos(t) \\ \cos(t) & \sin(t) \end{pmatrix}.$$

15. $A = \begin{pmatrix} 1 & -1 \\ 1 & 1 \end{pmatrix}$, $\begin{vmatrix} \lambda - 1 & 1 \\ -1 & \lambda - 1 \end{vmatrix} = \lambda^2 - 2\lambda + 2 = 0 \Rightarrow \lambda, \overline{\lambda} = 1 \pm i.$

For $\lambda = 1 + i$, $\begin{pmatrix} i & 1 \\ -1 & i \end{pmatrix} \begin{pmatrix} a \\ b \end{pmatrix} = \begin{pmatrix} 0 \\ 0 \end{pmatrix} \Rightarrow b = -ia \Rightarrow \mathbf{v} = \begin{pmatrix} 1 \\ -i \end{pmatrix} \Rightarrow$

$z(t) = e^t[\cos(t) + i\sin(t)] \left[\begin{pmatrix} 1 \\ 0 \end{pmatrix} + i \begin{pmatrix} 0 \\ -1 \end{pmatrix} \right] \Rightarrow$

$\mathbf{x}_1(t) = e^t \begin{pmatrix} \cos(t) \\ \sin(t) \end{pmatrix}$, $\mathbf{x}_2(t) = e^t \begin{pmatrix} \sin(t) \\ -\cos(t) \end{pmatrix}$, $X(t) = e^t \begin{pmatrix} \cos(t) & \sin(t) \\ \sin(t) & -\cos(t) \end{pmatrix}$,

$X(0) = \begin{pmatrix} 1 & 0 \\ 0 & -1 \end{pmatrix}$, $X(0)^{-1} = \begin{pmatrix} 1 & 0 \\ 0 & -1 \end{pmatrix}$, $\mathbf{x}(t) = X(t)X(0)^{-1}\mathbf{x}_0 = $

$e^t \begin{pmatrix} \cos(t) & \sin(t) \\ \sin(t) & -\cos(t) \end{pmatrix} \begin{pmatrix} 1 & 0 \\ 0 & -1 \end{pmatrix} \begin{pmatrix} 2 \\ -1 \end{pmatrix} = e^t \begin{pmatrix} 2\cos(t) + \sin(t) \\ 2\sin(t) - \cos(t) \end{pmatrix}.$

16. $\begin{cases} x' = x \\ y' = 2x + 2y - 2z \\ z' = x + y \end{cases} \Rightarrow A = \begin{pmatrix} 1 & 0 & 0 \\ 2 & 2 & -2 \\ 1 & 1 & 0 \end{pmatrix},$

$\begin{vmatrix} \lambda - 1 & 0 & 0 \\ -2 & \lambda - 2 & 2 \\ -1 & -1 & \lambda \end{vmatrix} = (\lambda - 1)(\lambda^2 - 2\lambda + 2) = 0 \Rightarrow \lambda_1 = 1, \lambda_2, \overline{\lambda}_2 = 1 \pm i.$

For $\lambda_1 = 1$, $\begin{pmatrix} 0 & 0 & 0 \\ -2 & -1 & 2 \\ -1 & -1 & 1 \end{pmatrix} \begin{pmatrix} a \\ b \\ c \end{pmatrix} = \begin{pmatrix} 0 \\ 0 \\ 0 \end{pmatrix} \Rightarrow b = 0 \Rightarrow c = a \Rightarrow$

$\mathbf{v}_1 = \begin{pmatrix} 1 \\ 0 \\ 1 \end{pmatrix} \Rightarrow \mathbf{x}_1(t) = e^t \begin{pmatrix} 1 \\ 0 \\ 1 \end{pmatrix}.$

For $\lambda_2 = 1 + i$, $\begin{pmatrix} i & 0 & 0 \\ -2 & i - 1 & 2 \\ -1 & -1 & i + 1 \end{pmatrix} \begin{pmatrix} a \\ b \\ c \end{pmatrix} = \begin{pmatrix} 0 \\ 0 \\ 0 \end{pmatrix} \Rightarrow a = 0 \Rightarrow b = (i+1)c$

$\Rightarrow \mathbf{v}_2 = \begin{pmatrix} 0 \\ 1 + i \\ 1 \end{pmatrix} \Rightarrow z(t) = e^t[\cos(t) + i\sin(t)] \left[\begin{pmatrix} 0 \\ 1 \\ 1 \end{pmatrix} + i \begin{pmatrix} 0 \\ 1 \\ 0 \end{pmatrix} \right] \Rightarrow$

$\mathbf{x}_2(t) = e^t \begin{pmatrix} 0 \\ \cos(t) - \sin(t) \\ \cos(t) \end{pmatrix}$, $\mathbf{x}_3(t) = e^t \begin{pmatrix} 0 \\ \sin(t) + \cos(t) \\ \sin(t) \end{pmatrix},$

$\mathbf{x}(t) = c_1\mathbf{x}_1(t) + c_2\mathbf{x}_2(t) + c_3\mathbf{x}_3(t) \Rightarrow x(t) = c_1 e^t,$

$y(t) = c_2 e^t[\cos(t) - \sin(t)] + c_3 e^t[\sin(t) + \cos(t)], z(t) = e^t[c_1 + c_2\cos(t) + c_3\sin(t)].$

17. $A = \begin{pmatrix} 0 & 0 & 1 \\ 0 & 1 & 0 \\ -1 & 2 & 0 \end{pmatrix}$, $\begin{vmatrix} \lambda & 0 & -1 \\ 0 & \lambda - 1 & 0 \\ 1 & -2 & \lambda \end{vmatrix} = (\lambda - 1)(\lambda^2 + 1) = 0 \Rightarrow \lambda_1 = 1,$

$\lambda_2, \overline{\lambda}_2 = \pm i.$

For $\lambda_1 = 1$, $\begin{pmatrix} 1 & 0 & -1 \\ 0 & 0 & 0 \\ 1 & -2 & 1 \end{pmatrix} \begin{pmatrix} a \\ b \\ c \end{pmatrix} = \begin{pmatrix} 0 \\ 0 \\ 0 \end{pmatrix} \Rightarrow c = a \Rightarrow b = a \Rightarrow$

$\mathbf{v}_1 = \begin{pmatrix} 1 \\ 1 \\ 1 \end{pmatrix} \Rightarrow \mathbf{x}_1(t) = e^t \begin{pmatrix} 1 \\ 1 \\ 1 \end{pmatrix}.$

For $\lambda_2 = i$, $\begin{pmatrix} i & 0 & -1 \\ 0 & i-1 & 0 \\ 1 & -2 & i \end{pmatrix} \begin{pmatrix} a \\ b \\ c \end{pmatrix} = \begin{pmatrix} 0 \\ 0 \\ 0 \end{pmatrix} \Rightarrow b = 0 \Rightarrow c = ia \Rightarrow$

$\mathbf{v}_2 = \begin{pmatrix} 1 \\ 0 \\ i \end{pmatrix} \Rightarrow z(t) = [\cos(t) + i\sin(t)] \left[\begin{pmatrix} 1 \\ 0 \\ 0 \end{pmatrix} + i \begin{pmatrix} 0 \\ 0 \\ 1 \end{pmatrix} \right] \Rightarrow$

$\mathbf{x}_2(t) = \begin{pmatrix} \cos(t) \\ 0 \\ -\sin(t) \end{pmatrix}$, $\mathbf{x}_3(t) = \begin{pmatrix} \sin(t) \\ 0 \\ \cos(t) \end{pmatrix}$, $\mathbf{x}(t) = c_1\mathbf{x}_1(t) + c_2\mathbf{x}_2(t) + c_3\mathbf{x}_3(t).$

18. $A = \begin{pmatrix} 0 & 0 & 0 & 1 \\ 0 & 1 & -1 & 0 \\ 0 & 1 & 1 & 0 \\ -1 & 0 & 0 & 0 \end{pmatrix}$, $\begin{vmatrix} \lambda & 0 & 0 & -1 \\ 0 & \lambda-1 & 1 & 0 \\ 0 & -1 & \lambda-1 & 0 \\ 1 & 0 & 0 & \lambda \end{vmatrix} = (\lambda^2+1)(\lambda^2-2\lambda+2) = 0$

$\Rightarrow \lambda_1, \overline{\lambda}_1 = \pm i, \lambda_2, \overline{\lambda}_2 = 1 \pm i.$

For $\lambda_1 = i$, $\begin{pmatrix} i & 0 & 0 & -1 \\ 0 & i-1 & 1 & 0 \\ 0 & -1 & i-1 & 0 \\ 1 & 0 & 0 & i \end{pmatrix} \begin{pmatrix} a \\ b \\ c \\ d \end{pmatrix} = \begin{pmatrix} 0 \\ 0 \\ 0 \\ 0 \end{pmatrix} \Rightarrow b = c = 0, d = ia \Rightarrow$

$\mathbf{v}_1 = \begin{pmatrix} 1 \\ 0 \\ 0 \\ i \end{pmatrix} \Rightarrow z_1(t) = [\cos(t) + i\sin(t)] \left[\begin{pmatrix} 1 \\ 0 \\ 0 \\ 0 \end{pmatrix} + i \begin{pmatrix} 0 \\ 0 \\ 0 \\ 1 \end{pmatrix} \right] \Rightarrow$

$\mathbf{x}_1(t) = \begin{pmatrix} \cos(t) \\ 0 \\ 0 \\ -\sin(t) \end{pmatrix}$, $\mathbf{x}_2(t) = \begin{pmatrix} \sin(t) \\ 0 \\ 0 \\ \cos(t) \end{pmatrix}.$

For $\lambda_2 = 1+i$, $\begin{pmatrix} 1+i & 0 & 0 & -1 \\ 0 & i & 1 & 0 \\ 0 & -1 & i & 0 \\ 1 & 0 & 0 & 1+i \end{pmatrix} \begin{pmatrix} a \\ b \\ c \\ d \end{pmatrix} = \begin{pmatrix} 0 \\ 0 \\ 0 \\ 0 \end{pmatrix} \Rightarrow a = d = 0, b = ic$

$\Rightarrow \mathbf{v}_2 = \begin{pmatrix} 0 \\ i \\ 1 \\ 0 \end{pmatrix} \Rightarrow z_2(t) = e^t[\cos(t) + i\sin(t)] \left[\begin{pmatrix} 0 \\ 0 \\ 1 \\ 0 \end{pmatrix} + i \begin{pmatrix} 0 \\ 1 \\ 0 \\ 0 \end{pmatrix} \right] \Rightarrow$

$$\mathbf{x}_3(t) = e^t \begin{pmatrix} 0 \\ -\sin(t) \\ \cos(t) \\ 0 \end{pmatrix}, \ \mathbf{x}_4(t) = e^t \begin{pmatrix} 0 \\ \cos(t) \\ \sin(t) \\ 0 \end{pmatrix},$$

$$X(t) = \begin{pmatrix} \cos(t) & \sin(t) & 0 & 0 \\ 0 & 0 & -e^t\sin(t) & e^t\cos(t) \\ 0 & 0 & e^t\cos(t) & e^t\sin(t) \\ -\sin(t) & \cos(t) & 0 & 0 \end{pmatrix}.$$

19. $\left\{\begin{array}{l} x' = x + 3y \\ y' = y \end{array}\right\} \Rightarrow A = \begin{pmatrix} 1 & 3 \\ 0 & 1 \end{pmatrix}, \ \begin{vmatrix} \lambda - 1 & -3 \\ 0 & \lambda - 1 \end{vmatrix} = (\lambda - 1)^2 = 0 \Rightarrow \lambda_1 = 1,$
$m_1 = 2.$
For $\lambda_1 = 1, \begin{pmatrix} 0 & -3 \\ 0 & 0 \end{pmatrix} \begin{pmatrix} a \\ b \end{pmatrix} = \begin{pmatrix} 0 \\ 0 \end{pmatrix} \Rightarrow b = 0 \Rightarrow \mathbf{v}_1 = \begin{pmatrix} 1 \\ 0 \end{pmatrix} \Rightarrow$
$\mathbf{x}_1(t) = e^t \begin{pmatrix} 1 \\ 0 \end{pmatrix}, \ \mathbf{x}_2(t) = e^t(t\mathbf{u}_0 + \mathbf{u}_1), \ \mathbf{u}_0 = \mathbf{v}_1, \ (A - \lambda_1 I)\mathbf{u}_1 = \mathbf{u}_0 \Rightarrow$
$\begin{pmatrix} 0 & 3 \\ 0 & 0 \end{pmatrix} \begin{pmatrix} a \\ b \end{pmatrix} = \begin{pmatrix} 1 \\ 0 \end{pmatrix} \Rightarrow 3b = 1 \Rightarrow \mathbf{u}_1 = \begin{pmatrix} 0 \\ 1/3 \end{pmatrix} \Rightarrow \mathbf{x}_2(t) = e^t \begin{pmatrix} t \\ 1/3 \end{pmatrix},$
$\mathbf{x}(t) = c_1\mathbf{x}_1(t) + c_2\mathbf{x}_2(t) \Rightarrow x(t) = e^t(c_1 + c_2 t), \ y(t) = \frac{1}{3}c_2 e^t.$

20. $A = \begin{pmatrix} -4 & 9 \\ -1 & 2 \end{pmatrix}, \ \begin{vmatrix} \lambda + 4 & -9 \\ 1 & \lambda - 2 \end{vmatrix} = (\lambda + 1)^2 = 0 \Rightarrow \lambda_1 = -1, \ m_1 = 2.$
For $\lambda_1 = -1, \begin{pmatrix} 3 & -9 \\ 1 & -3 \end{pmatrix} \begin{pmatrix} a \\ b \end{pmatrix} = \begin{pmatrix} 0 \\ 0 \end{pmatrix} \Rightarrow a = 3b \Rightarrow \mathbf{v}_1 = \begin{pmatrix} 3 \\ 1 \end{pmatrix} \Rightarrow$
$\mathbf{x}_1(t) = e^{-t} \begin{pmatrix} 3 \\ 1 \end{pmatrix}, \ \mathbf{x}_2(t) = e^{-t}(t\mathbf{u}_0 + \mathbf{u}_1), \ \mathbf{u}_0 = \mathbf{v}_1, \ (A - \lambda_1 I)\mathbf{u}_1 = \mathbf{u}_0 \Rightarrow$
$\begin{pmatrix} -3 & 9 \\ -1 & 3 \end{pmatrix} \begin{pmatrix} a \\ b \end{pmatrix} = \begin{pmatrix} 3 \\ 1 \end{pmatrix} \Rightarrow 3b - a = 1 \Rightarrow \mathbf{u}_1 = \begin{pmatrix} -1 \\ 0 \end{pmatrix} \Rightarrow$
$\mathbf{x}_2(t) = e^{-t} \begin{pmatrix} 3t - 1 \\ t \end{pmatrix}, \ \mathbf{x}(t) = c_1\mathbf{x}_1(t) + c_2\mathbf{x}_2(t).$

21. $A = \begin{pmatrix} 2 & 0 \\ 2 & 2 \end{pmatrix}, \ \begin{vmatrix} \lambda - 2 & 0 \\ -2 & \lambda - 2 \end{vmatrix} = (\lambda - 2)^2 = 0 \Rightarrow \lambda_1 = 2, \ m_1 = 2.$
For $\lambda_1 = 2, \begin{pmatrix} 0 & 0 \\ -2 & 0 \end{pmatrix} \begin{pmatrix} a \\ b \end{pmatrix} = \begin{pmatrix} 0 \\ 0 \end{pmatrix} \Rightarrow a = 0 \Rightarrow \mathbf{v}_1 = \begin{pmatrix} 0 \\ 1 \end{pmatrix} \Rightarrow$
$\mathbf{x}_1(t) = e^{2t} \begin{pmatrix} 0 \\ 1 \end{pmatrix}, \ \mathbf{x}_2(t) = e^{2t}(t\mathbf{u}_0 + \mathbf{u}_1), \ \mathbf{u}_0 = \mathbf{v}_1, \ (A - \lambda_1 I)\mathbf{u}_1 = \mathbf{u}_0 \Rightarrow$
$\begin{pmatrix} 0 & 0 \\ 2 & 0 \end{pmatrix} \begin{pmatrix} a \\ b \end{pmatrix} = \begin{pmatrix} 0 \\ 1 \end{pmatrix} \Rightarrow 2a = 1 \Rightarrow \mathbf{u}_1 = \begin{pmatrix} 1/2 \\ 0 \end{pmatrix} \Rightarrow$
$\mathbf{x}_2(t) = e^{2t} \begin{pmatrix} 1/2 \\ t \end{pmatrix}, \ X(t) = e^{2t} \begin{pmatrix} 0 & 1/2 \\ 1 & t \end{pmatrix}.$

22. $\begin{cases} x' = 3x - y \\ y' = x + 2y - z \\ z' = 3y - z \end{cases} \Rightarrow A = \begin{pmatrix} 3 & -1 & 0 \\ 1 & 2 & -1 \\ 0 & 3 & -1 \end{pmatrix},$

$\begin{vmatrix} \lambda - 3 & 1 & 0 \\ -1 & \lambda - 2 & 1 \\ 0 & -3 & \lambda + 1 \end{vmatrix} = (\lambda - 1)^2(\lambda - 2) = 0 \Rightarrow \lambda_1 = 2, \lambda_2 = 1, m_2 = 2.$

For $\lambda_1 = 2$, $\begin{pmatrix} -1 & 1 & 0 \\ -1 & 0 & 1 \\ 0 & -3 & 3 \end{pmatrix} \begin{pmatrix} a \\ b \\ c \end{pmatrix} = \begin{pmatrix} 0 \\ 0 \\ 0 \end{pmatrix} \Rightarrow a = b = c \Rightarrow \mathbf{v}_1 = \begin{pmatrix} 1 \\ 1 \\ 1 \end{pmatrix}$

$\Rightarrow \mathbf{x}_1(t) = e^{2t} \begin{pmatrix} 1 \\ 1 \\ 1 \end{pmatrix}.$

For $\lambda_2 = 1$, $\begin{pmatrix} -2 & 1 & 0 \\ -1 & -1 & 1 \\ 0 & -3 & 2 \end{pmatrix} \begin{pmatrix} a \\ b \\ c \end{pmatrix} = \begin{pmatrix} 0 \\ 0 \\ 0 \end{pmatrix} \Rightarrow b = 2a, c = 3a \Rightarrow$

$\mathbf{v}_2 = \begin{pmatrix} 1 \\ 2 \\ 3 \end{pmatrix} \Rightarrow \mathbf{x}_2(t) = e^t \begin{pmatrix} 1 \\ 2 \\ 3 \end{pmatrix}, \mathbf{x}_3(t) = e^t(t\mathbf{u}_0 + \mathbf{u}_1), \mathbf{u}_0 = \mathbf{v}_2,$

$(A - \lambda_2 I)\mathbf{u}_1 = \mathbf{u}_0 \Rightarrow \begin{pmatrix} 2 & -1 & 0 \\ 1 & 1 & -1 \\ 0 & 3 & -2 \end{pmatrix} \begin{pmatrix} a \\ b \\ c \end{pmatrix} = \begin{pmatrix} 1 \\ 2 \\ 3 \end{pmatrix} \Rightarrow \mathbf{u}_1 = \begin{pmatrix} 1 \\ 1 \\ 0 \end{pmatrix} \Rightarrow$

$\mathbf{x}_3(t) = e^t \begin{pmatrix} t + 1 \\ 2t + 1 \\ 3t \end{pmatrix}, \mathbf{x}(t) = c_1\mathbf{x}_1(t) + c_2\mathbf{x}_2(t) + c_3\mathbf{x}_3(t) \Rightarrow$

$x(t) = c_1 e^{2t} + e^t[c_2 + c_3(t + 1)], y(t) = c_1 e^{2t} + e^t[2c_2 + c_3(2t + 1)],$
$z(t) = c_1 e^{2t} + e^t(3c_2 + 3c_3 t).$

23. $A = \begin{pmatrix} 4 & 2 & 1 \\ 0 & 4 & 0 \\ 0 & 0 & 6 \end{pmatrix}, \begin{vmatrix} \lambda - 4 & -2 & -1 \\ 0 & \lambda - 4 & 0 \\ 0 & 0 & \lambda - 6 \end{vmatrix} = (\lambda - 4)^2(\lambda - 6) = 0 \Rightarrow \lambda_1 = 6,$

$\lambda_2 = 4, m_2 = 2.$

For $\lambda_1 = 6$, $\begin{pmatrix} 2 & -2 & -1 \\ 0 & 2 & 0 \\ 0 & 0 & 0 \end{pmatrix} \begin{pmatrix} a \\ b \\ c \end{pmatrix} = \begin{pmatrix} 0 \\ 0 \\ 0 \end{pmatrix} \Rightarrow b = 0, c = 2a \Rightarrow$

$\mathbf{v}_1 = \begin{pmatrix} 1 \\ 0 \\ 2 \end{pmatrix} \Rightarrow \mathbf{x}_1(t) = e^{6t} \begin{pmatrix} 1 \\ 0 \\ 2 \end{pmatrix}.$

For $\lambda_2 = 4$, $\begin{pmatrix} 0 & -2 & -1 \\ 0 & 0 & 0 \\ 0 & 0 & -2 \end{pmatrix} \begin{pmatrix} a \\ b \\ c \end{pmatrix} = \begin{pmatrix} 0 \\ 0 \\ 0 \end{pmatrix} \Rightarrow b = c = 0 \Rightarrow \mathbf{v}_2 = \begin{pmatrix} 1 \\ 0 \\ 0 \end{pmatrix}$

$\Rightarrow \mathbf{x}_2(t) = e^{4t} \begin{pmatrix} 1 \\ 0 \\ 0 \end{pmatrix}, \mathbf{x}_3(t) = e^{4t}(t\mathbf{u}_0 + \mathbf{u}_1), \mathbf{u}_0 = \mathbf{v}_2, (A - \lambda_2 I)\mathbf{u}_1 = \mathbf{u}_0$

$$\Rightarrow \begin{pmatrix} 0 & 2 & 1 \\ 0 & 0 & 0 \\ 0 & 0 & 2 \end{pmatrix} \begin{pmatrix} a \\ b \\ c \end{pmatrix} = \begin{pmatrix} 1 \\ 0 \\ 0 \end{pmatrix} \Rightarrow c = 0,\ 2b = 1 \Rightarrow \mathbf{u}_1 = \begin{pmatrix} 0 \\ 1/2 \\ 0 \end{pmatrix} \Rightarrow$$

$$\mathbf{x}_3(t) = e^{4t} \begin{pmatrix} t \\ 1/2 \\ 0 \end{pmatrix},\ \mathbf{x}(t) = c_1 \mathbf{x}_1(t) + c_2 \mathbf{x}_2(t) + c_3 \mathbf{x}_3(t).$$

24. $A = \begin{pmatrix} -3 & 1 & -2 \\ -3 & 1 & -6 \\ -1 & 1 & -4 \end{pmatrix}$, $\begin{vmatrix} \lambda+3 & -1 & 2 \\ 3 & \lambda-1 & 6 \\ 1 & -1 & \lambda+4 \end{vmatrix} = (\lambda+2)^3 = 0 \Rightarrow \lambda_1 = -2$,

$m_1 = 3$.

For $\lambda_1 = -2$, $\begin{pmatrix} 1 & -1 & 2 \\ 3 & -3 & 6 \\ 1 & -1 & 2 \end{pmatrix} \begin{pmatrix} a \\ b \\ c \end{pmatrix} = \begin{pmatrix} 0 \\ 0 \\ 0 \end{pmatrix} \Rightarrow a - b + 2c = 0 \Rightarrow$

$\mathbf{v}_1 = \begin{pmatrix} 1 \\ 1 \\ 0 \end{pmatrix}$, $\mathbf{v}_2 = \begin{pmatrix} 0 \\ 2 \\ 1 \end{pmatrix} \Rightarrow \mathbf{x}_1(t) = e^{-2t} \begin{pmatrix} 1 \\ 1 \\ 0 \end{pmatrix}$, $\mathbf{x}_2(t) = e^{-2t} \begin{pmatrix} 0 \\ 2 \\ 1 \end{pmatrix}$,

$\mathbf{x}_3(t) = e^{-2t}(t\mathbf{u}_0 + \mathbf{u}_1)$, $\mathbf{u}_0 = \alpha\mathbf{v}_1 + \beta\mathbf{v}_2$, $(A - \lambda_1 I)\mathbf{u}_1 = \mathbf{u}_0 \Rightarrow$

$\begin{pmatrix} -1 & 1 & -2 \\ -3 & 3 & -6 \\ -1 & 1 & -2 \end{pmatrix} \begin{pmatrix} a \\ b \\ c \end{pmatrix} = \begin{pmatrix} \alpha \\ \alpha+2\beta \\ \beta \end{pmatrix} \Rightarrow \alpha = \beta,\ -a + b + 2c = \alpha,\ \alpha = 1$,

$a = c = 0,\ b = 1 \Rightarrow \mathbf{u}_1 = \begin{pmatrix} 0 \\ 1 \\ 0 \end{pmatrix}$, $\mathbf{u}_0 = \begin{pmatrix} 1 \\ 3 \\ 1 \end{pmatrix} \Rightarrow \mathbf{x}_3(t) = e^{-2t} \begin{pmatrix} t \\ 3t+1 \\ t \end{pmatrix}$,

$X(t) = e^{-2t} \begin{pmatrix} 1 & 0 & t \\ 1 & 2 & 3t+1 \\ 0 & 1 & t \end{pmatrix}$.

25. $A = \begin{pmatrix} 7 & -3 & -15 \\ 2 & 0 & -5 \\ 2 & -1 & -4 \end{pmatrix}$, $\begin{vmatrix} \lambda-7 & 3 & 15 \\ -2 & \lambda & 5 \\ -2 & 1 & \lambda+4 \end{vmatrix} = (\lambda-1)^3 = 0 \Rightarrow \lambda_1 = 1,\ m_1 = 3$.

For $\lambda_1 = 1$, $\begin{pmatrix} -6 & 3 & 15 \\ -2 & 1 & 5 \\ -2 & 1 & 5 \end{pmatrix} \begin{pmatrix} a \\ b \\ c \end{pmatrix} = \begin{pmatrix} 0 \\ 0 \\ 0 \end{pmatrix} \Rightarrow -2a + b + 5c = 0 \Rightarrow$

$\mathbf{v}_1 = \begin{pmatrix} 1 \\ 2 \\ 0 \end{pmatrix}$, $\mathbf{v}_2 = \begin{pmatrix} 0 \\ -5 \\ 1 \end{pmatrix} \Rightarrow \mathbf{x}_1(t) = e^t \begin{pmatrix} 1 \\ 2 \\ 0 \end{pmatrix}$, $\mathbf{x}_2(t) = e^t \begin{pmatrix} 0 \\ -5 \\ 1 \end{pmatrix}$,

$\mathbf{x}_3(t) = e^t(t\mathbf{u}_0 + \mathbf{u}_1)$, $\mathbf{u}_0 = \alpha\mathbf{v}_1 + \beta\mathbf{v}_2$, $(A - \lambda_1 I)\mathbf{u}_1 = \mathbf{u}_0 \Rightarrow$

$\begin{pmatrix} 6 & -3 & -15 \\ 2 & -1 & -5 \\ 2 & -1 & -5 \end{pmatrix} \begin{pmatrix} a \\ b \\ c \end{pmatrix} = \begin{pmatrix} \alpha \\ 2\alpha-5\beta \\ \beta \end{pmatrix} \Rightarrow \alpha = 3\beta,\ 2a - b - 5c = \beta,\ \beta = 1$,

$$a = c = 0,\ b = -1 \Rightarrow \mathbf{u}_1 = \begin{pmatrix} 0 \\ -1 \\ 0 \end{pmatrix},\ \mathbf{u}_0 = \begin{pmatrix} 3 \\ 1 \\ 1 \end{pmatrix} \Rightarrow \mathbf{x}_3(t) = e^t \begin{pmatrix} 3t \\ t-1 \\ t \end{pmatrix},$$

$$X(t) = e^t \begin{pmatrix} 1 & 0 & 3t \\ 2 & -5 & t-1 \\ 0 & 1 & t \end{pmatrix}.$$

26. $A = \begin{pmatrix} -2 & 1 & 0 \\ -1 & 0 & 0 \\ 0 & 0 & -1 \end{pmatrix},\ \begin{vmatrix} \lambda+2 & -1 & 0 \\ 1 & \lambda & 0 \\ 0 & 0 & \lambda+1 \end{vmatrix} = (\lambda+1)^3 = 0 \Rightarrow \lambda_1 = -1,$

$m_1 = 3.$

For $\lambda_1 = -1,\ \begin{pmatrix} 1 & -1 & 0 \\ 1 & -1 & 0 \\ 0 & 0 & 0 \end{pmatrix} \begin{pmatrix} a \\ b \\ c \end{pmatrix} = \begin{pmatrix} 0 \\ 0 \\ 0 \end{pmatrix} \Rightarrow a = b \Rightarrow$

$\mathbf{v}_1 = \begin{pmatrix} 1 \\ 1 \\ 0 \end{pmatrix},\ \mathbf{v}_2 = \begin{pmatrix} 0 \\ 0 \\ 1 \end{pmatrix} \Rightarrow \mathbf{x}_1(t) = e^{-t} \begin{pmatrix} 1 \\ 1 \\ 0 \end{pmatrix},\ \mathbf{x}_2(t) = e^{-t} \begin{pmatrix} 0 \\ 0 \\ 1 \end{pmatrix},$

$\mathbf{x}_3(t) = e^{-t}(t\mathbf{u}_0 + \mathbf{u}_1),\ \mathbf{u}_0 = \alpha\mathbf{v}_1 + \beta\mathbf{v}_2,\ (A - \lambda_1 I)\mathbf{u}_1 = \mathbf{u}_0 \Rightarrow$

$\begin{pmatrix} -1 & 1 & 0 \\ -1 & 1 & 0 \\ 0 & 0 & 0 \end{pmatrix} \begin{pmatrix} a \\ b \\ c \end{pmatrix} = \begin{pmatrix} \alpha \\ \alpha \\ \beta \end{pmatrix} \Rightarrow \beta = 0,\ b - a = \alpha,\ \alpha = 1,\ a = c = 0,\ b = 1$

$\Rightarrow \mathbf{u}_1 = \begin{pmatrix} 0 \\ 1 \\ 0 \end{pmatrix},\ \mathbf{u}_0 = \begin{pmatrix} 1 \\ 1 \\ 0 \end{pmatrix} \Rightarrow \mathbf{x}_3(t) = e^{-t} \begin{pmatrix} t \\ t+1 \\ 0 \end{pmatrix},$

$\mathbf{x}(t) = c_1\mathbf{x}_1(t) + c_2\mathbf{x}_2(t) + c_3\mathbf{x}_3(t) \Rightarrow x(t) = e^{-t}(c_1 + c_3 t),\ y(t) = e^{-t}[c_1 + c_3(t+1)],$
$z(t) = c_2 e^{-t}.$

27. $A = \begin{pmatrix} -2 & 0 & 1 \\ 1 & -1 & 0 \\ -1 & 0 & 0 \end{pmatrix},\ \begin{vmatrix} \lambda+2 & 0 & -1 \\ -1 & \lambda+1 & 0 \\ 1 & 0 & \lambda \end{vmatrix} = (\lambda+1)^3 = 0 \Rightarrow \lambda_1 = -1,$

$m_1 = 3.$

For $\lambda_1 = -1,\ \begin{pmatrix} 1 & 0 & -1 \\ -1 & 0 & 0 \\ 1 & 0 & -1 \end{pmatrix} \begin{pmatrix} a \\ b \\ c \end{pmatrix} = \begin{pmatrix} 0 \\ 0 \\ 0 \end{pmatrix} \Rightarrow a = c = 0 \Rightarrow \mathbf{v}_1 = \begin{pmatrix} 0 \\ 1 \\ 0 \end{pmatrix}$

$\Rightarrow \mathbf{x}_1(t) = e^{-t} \begin{pmatrix} 0 \\ 1 \\ 0 \end{pmatrix},\ \mathbf{x}_2(t) = e^{-t}(t\mathbf{u}_0 + \mathbf{u}_1),\ \mathbf{u}_0 = \mathbf{v}_1,\ (A - \lambda_1 I)\mathbf{u}_1 = \mathbf{u}_0 \Rightarrow$

$\begin{pmatrix} -1 & 0 & 1 \\ 1 & 0 & 0 \\ -1 & 0 & 1 \end{pmatrix} \begin{pmatrix} a \\ b \\ c \end{pmatrix} = \begin{pmatrix} 0 \\ 1 \\ 0 \end{pmatrix} \Rightarrow a = c = 1 \Rightarrow \mathbf{u}_1 = \begin{pmatrix} 1 \\ 0 \\ 1 \end{pmatrix} \Rightarrow$

$\mathbf{x}_2(t) = e^{-t} \begin{pmatrix} 1 \\ t \\ 1 \end{pmatrix},\ \mathbf{x}_3(t) = e^{-t} \left(\tfrac{1}{2}t^2 \mathbf{u}_0 + t\mathbf{u}_1 + \mathbf{u}_2\right),\ (A - \lambda_1 I)\mathbf{u}_2 = \mathbf{u}_1 \Rightarrow$

$$\begin{pmatrix} -1 & 0 & 1 \\ 1 & 0 & 0 \\ -1 & 0 & 1 \end{pmatrix} \begin{pmatrix} a \\ b \\ c \end{pmatrix} = \begin{pmatrix} 1 \\ 0 \\ 1 \end{pmatrix} \Rightarrow a = 0,\ c = 1 \Rightarrow \mathbf{u}_2 = \begin{pmatrix} 0 \\ 0 \\ 1 \end{pmatrix} \Rightarrow$$

$$\mathbf{x}_3(t) = e^{-t} \begin{pmatrix} t \\ \frac{1}{2}t^2 \\ t+1 \end{pmatrix},\ \mathbf{x}(t) = c_1\mathbf{x}_1(t) + c_2\mathbf{x}_2(t) + c_3\mathbf{x}_3(t).$$

28. $A = \begin{pmatrix} 2 & -1 & 1 \\ 1 & 0 & 1 \\ -1 & 1 & 1 \end{pmatrix}$, $\begin{vmatrix} \lambda-2 & 1 & -1 \\ -1 & \lambda & -1 \\ 1 & -1 & \lambda-1 \end{vmatrix} = (\lambda-1)^3 = 0 \Rightarrow \lambda_1 = 1,\ m_1 = 3.$

For $\lambda_1 = 1$, $\begin{pmatrix} -1 & 1 & -1 \\ -1 & 1 & -1 \\ 1 & -1 & 0 \end{pmatrix} \begin{pmatrix} a \\ b \\ c \end{pmatrix} = \begin{pmatrix} 0 \\ 0 \\ 0 \end{pmatrix} \Rightarrow a = b,\ c = 0 \Rightarrow$

$$\mathbf{v}_1 = \begin{pmatrix} 1 \\ 1 \\ 0 \end{pmatrix} \Rightarrow \mathbf{x}_1(t) = e^t \begin{pmatrix} 1 \\ 1 \\ 0 \end{pmatrix},\ \mathbf{x}_2(t) = e^t(t\mathbf{u}_0 + \mathbf{u}_1),\ \mathbf{u}_0 = \mathbf{v}_1,$$

$$(A-\lambda_1 I)\mathbf{u}_1 = \mathbf{u}_0 \Rightarrow \begin{pmatrix} 1 & -1 & 1 \\ 1 & -1 & 1 \\ -1 & 1 & 0 \end{pmatrix} \begin{pmatrix} a \\ b \\ c \end{pmatrix} = \begin{pmatrix} 1 \\ 1 \\ 0 \end{pmatrix} \Rightarrow a = b,\ c = 1 \Rightarrow \mathbf{u}_1 =$$

$$\begin{pmatrix} 0 \\ 0 \\ 1 \end{pmatrix} \Rightarrow \mathbf{x}_2(t) = e^t \begin{pmatrix} t \\ t \\ 1 \end{pmatrix},\ \mathbf{x}_3(t) = e^t \left(\tfrac{1}{2}t^2\mathbf{u}_0 + t\mathbf{u}_1 + \mathbf{u}_2\right),\ (A-\lambda_1 I)\mathbf{u}_2 = \mathbf{u}_1$$

$$\Rightarrow \begin{pmatrix} 1 & -1 & 1 \\ 1 & -1 & 1 \\ -1 & 1 & 0 \end{pmatrix} \begin{pmatrix} a \\ b \\ c \end{pmatrix} = \begin{pmatrix} 0 \\ 0 \\ 1 \end{pmatrix} \Rightarrow b - a = 1,\ c = 1 \Rightarrow \mathbf{u}_2 = \begin{pmatrix} 0 \\ 1 \\ 1 \end{pmatrix} \Rightarrow$$

$$\mathbf{x}_3(t) = e^t \begin{pmatrix} \frac{1}{2}t^2 \\ \frac{1}{2}t^2+1 \\ t+1 \end{pmatrix},\ \mathbf{x}(t) = c_1\mathbf{x}_1(t) + c_2\mathbf{x}_2(t) + c_3\mathbf{x}_3(t).$$

29. $A = \begin{pmatrix} 1 & 1 & 0 & 1 \\ -1 & 1 & -1 & 0 \\ 0 & 0 & 1 & 1 \\ 0 & 0 & -1 & 1 \end{pmatrix}$, $\begin{vmatrix} \lambda-1 & -1 & 0 & -1 \\ 1 & \lambda-1 & 1 & 0 \\ 0 & 0 & \lambda-1 & -1 \\ 0 & 0 & 1 & \lambda-1 \end{vmatrix} = (\lambda^2 - 2\lambda + 2)^2 = 0$

$\Rightarrow \lambda_1, \overline{\lambda}_1 = 1 \pm i,\ m_1 = 2.$

For $\lambda_1 = 1+i$, $\begin{pmatrix} i & -1 & 0 & -1 \\ 1 & i & 1 & 0 \\ 0 & 0 & i & -1 \\ 0 & 0 & 1 & i \end{pmatrix} \begin{pmatrix} a \\ b \\ c \\ d \end{pmatrix} = \begin{pmatrix} 0 \\ 0 \\ 0 \\ 0 \end{pmatrix} \Rightarrow c = d = 0,\ b = ia \Rightarrow$

$$\mathbf{v}_1 = \begin{pmatrix} 1 \\ i \\ 0 \\ 0 \end{pmatrix} \Rightarrow \mathbf{z}_1(t) = e^t[\cos(t) + i\sin(t)] \left[\begin{pmatrix} 1 \\ 0 \\ 0 \\ 0 \end{pmatrix} + i \begin{pmatrix} 0 \\ 1 \\ 0 \\ 0 \end{pmatrix} \right] \Rightarrow$$

$$\mathbf{x}_1(t) = e^t \begin{pmatrix} \cos(t) \\ -\sin(t) \\ 0 \\ 0 \end{pmatrix}, \ \mathbf{x}_2(t) = e^t \begin{pmatrix} \sin(t) \\ \cos(t) \\ 0 \\ 0 \end{pmatrix}, \ \mathbf{z}_2(t) = e^{(1+i)t}(t\mathbf{u}_0 + \mathbf{u}_1),$$

$$\mathbf{u}_0 = \mathbf{v}_1, \ (A - \lambda_1 I)\mathbf{u}_1 = \mathbf{u}_0 \Rightarrow \begin{pmatrix} -i & 1 & 0 & 1 \\ -1 & -i & -1 & 0 \\ 0 & 0 & -i & 1 \\ 0 & 0 & -1 & -i \end{pmatrix} \begin{pmatrix} a \\ b \\ c \\ d \end{pmatrix} = \begin{pmatrix} 1 \\ i \\ 0 \\ 0 \end{pmatrix} \Rightarrow$$

$$d = 1, \ c = -i, \ b = ia \Rightarrow \mathbf{u}_1 = \begin{pmatrix} 0 \\ 0 \\ -i \\ 1 \end{pmatrix} \Rightarrow$$

$$\mathbf{z}_2(t) = e^t[\cos(t) + i\sin(t)] \left[\begin{pmatrix} t \\ 0 \\ 0 \\ 1 \end{pmatrix} + i \begin{pmatrix} 0 \\ t \\ -1 \\ 0 \end{pmatrix} \right] \Rightarrow \mathbf{x}_3(t) = e^t \begin{pmatrix} t\cos(t) \\ -t\sin(t) \\ \sin(t) \\ \cos(t) \end{pmatrix},$$

$$\mathbf{x}_4(t) = e^t \begin{pmatrix} t\sin(t) \\ t\cos(t) \\ -\cos(t) \\ \sin(t) \end{pmatrix}, \ \mathbf{x}(t) = c_1\mathbf{x}_1(t) + c_2\mathbf{x}_2(t) + c_3\mathbf{x}_3(t) + c_4\mathbf{x}_4(t).$$

Exercises 5.2 – page 186

1. $A = \begin{pmatrix} 2 & 0 \\ 1 & -1 \end{pmatrix}, \ \mathbf{f}(t) = \begin{pmatrix} 3e^{2t} \\ e^t \end{pmatrix}, \ \begin{vmatrix} \lambda - 2 & 0 \\ -1 & \lambda + 1 \end{vmatrix} = (\lambda - 2)(\lambda + 1) = 0 \Rightarrow$

$\lambda_1 = 2, \ \lambda_2 = -1, \ \mathbf{v}_1 = \begin{pmatrix} 3 \\ 1 \end{pmatrix}, \ \mathbf{v}_2 = \begin{pmatrix} 0 \\ 1 \end{pmatrix}, \ X(t) = \begin{pmatrix} 3e^{2t} & 0 \\ e^{2t} & e^{-t} \end{pmatrix},$

$X(t)^{-1}\mathbf{f}(t) = \frac{1}{3} \begin{pmatrix} e^{-2t} & 0 \\ -e^t & 3e^t \end{pmatrix} \begin{pmatrix} 3e^{2t} \\ e^t \end{pmatrix} = \begin{pmatrix} 1 \\ e^{2t} - e^{3t} \end{pmatrix}, \ \int X(t)^{-1}\mathbf{f}(t)\, dt =$

$\begin{pmatrix} t \\ \frac{1}{2}e^{2t} - \frac{1}{3}e^{3t} \end{pmatrix}, \ \mathbf{x}(t) = \begin{pmatrix} 3e^{2t} & 0 \\ e^{2t} & e^{-t} \end{pmatrix} \left[\begin{pmatrix} c_1 \\ c_2 \end{pmatrix} + \begin{pmatrix} t \\ \frac{1}{2}e^{2t} - \frac{1}{3}e^{3t} \end{pmatrix} \right]$

$= \begin{pmatrix} 3c_1e^{2t} + 3te^{2t} \\ c_1e^{2t} + c_2e^{-t} + te^{2t} + \frac{1}{2}e^t - \frac{1}{3}e^{2t} \end{pmatrix}.$

2. $A = \begin{pmatrix} 0 & 4 \\ -1 & 0 \end{pmatrix}, \ \mathbf{f}(t) = \begin{pmatrix} 4\cos(2t) \\ -2\sin(2t) \end{pmatrix}, \ \begin{vmatrix} \lambda & -4 \\ 1 & \lambda \end{vmatrix} = \lambda^2 + 4 = 0 \Rightarrow \lambda, \overline{\lambda} = \pm 2i,$

$\mathbf{v} = \begin{pmatrix} 2i \\ -1 \end{pmatrix}, \ \mathbf{z}(t) = [\cos(2t) + i\sin(2t)] \left[\begin{pmatrix} 0 \\ -1 \end{pmatrix} + i \begin{pmatrix} 2 \\ 0 \end{pmatrix} \right],$

$X(t) = \begin{pmatrix} -2\sin(2t) & 2\cos(2t) \\ -\cos(2t) & -\sin(2t) \end{pmatrix}, \ X(t)^{-1} = \frac{1}{2} \begin{pmatrix} -\sin(2t) & -2\cos(2t) \\ \cos(2t) & -2\sin(2t) \end{pmatrix},$

$X(t)^{-1}\mathbf{f}(t) = \frac{1}{2} \begin{pmatrix} -\sin(2t) & -2\cos(2t) \\ \cos(2t) & -2\sin(2t) \end{pmatrix} \begin{pmatrix} 4\cos(2t) \\ -2\sin(2t) \end{pmatrix} = \begin{pmatrix} 0 \\ 2 \end{pmatrix},$

$$\int X(t)^{-1}\mathbf{f}(t)\,dt = \begin{pmatrix} 0 \\ 2t \end{pmatrix},$$

$$\mathbf{x}(t) = \begin{pmatrix} -2\sin(2t) & 2\cos(2t) \\ -\cos(2t) & -\sin(2t) \end{pmatrix}\left[\begin{pmatrix} c_1 \\ c_2 \end{pmatrix} + \begin{pmatrix} 0 \\ 2t \end{pmatrix} \right]$$

$$= \begin{pmatrix} -2c_1\sin(2t) + 2c_2\cos(2t) + 4t\cos(2t) \\ -c_1\cos(2t) - c_2\sin(2t) - 2t\sin(2t) \end{pmatrix}.$$

3. $A = \begin{pmatrix} -1 & 4 \\ -1 & 3 \end{pmatrix}$, $\mathbf{f}(t) = e^t\begin{pmatrix} t^2 \\ t \end{pmatrix}$, $\begin{vmatrix} \lambda+1 & -4 \\ 1 & \lambda-3 \end{vmatrix} = (\lambda-1)^2 = 0 \Rightarrow \lambda_1 = 1,$

$\mathbf{v}_1 = \begin{pmatrix} 2 \\ 1 \end{pmatrix}$, $(A-\lambda_1 I)\mathbf{u}_1 = \mathbf{u}_0 = \mathbf{v}_1 \Rightarrow \mathbf{u}_1 = \begin{pmatrix} -1 \\ 0 \end{pmatrix}$, $X(t) = e^t\begin{pmatrix} 2 & 2t-1 \\ 1 & t \end{pmatrix}$,

$X(t)^{-1} = e^{-t}\begin{pmatrix} t & 1-2t \\ -1 & 2 \end{pmatrix}$, $X(t)^{-1}\mathbf{f}(t) = \begin{pmatrix} t & 1-2t \\ -1 & 2 \end{pmatrix}\begin{pmatrix} t^2 \\ t \end{pmatrix} =$

$\begin{pmatrix} t^3 - 2t^2 + t \\ -t^2 + 2t \end{pmatrix}$, $\int X(t)^{-1}\mathbf{f}(t)\,dt = \begin{pmatrix} \frac{1}{4}t^4 - \frac{2}{3}t^3 + \frac{1}{2}t^2 \\ -\frac{1}{3}t^3 + t^2 \end{pmatrix}$,

$\mathbf{x}(t) = e^t\begin{pmatrix} 2 & 2t-1 \\ 1 & t \end{pmatrix}\left[\begin{pmatrix} c_1 \\ c_2 \end{pmatrix} + \begin{pmatrix} \frac{1}{4}t^4 - \frac{2}{3}t^3 + \frac{1}{2}t^2 \\ -\frac{1}{3}t^3 + t^2 \end{pmatrix} \right]$

$= e^t\begin{pmatrix} 2c_1 + c_2(2t-1) - \frac{1}{6}t^4 + t^3 \\ c_1 + c_2 t - \frac{1}{12}t^4 + \frac{1}{3}t^3 + \frac{1}{2}t^2 \end{pmatrix}.$

4. $A = \begin{pmatrix} 2 & -2 \\ 1 & 4 \end{pmatrix}$, $\mathbf{f}(t) = \begin{pmatrix} 0 \\ 2 \end{pmatrix}$, $\begin{vmatrix} \lambda-2 & 2 \\ -1 & \lambda-4 \end{vmatrix} = \lambda^2 - 6\lambda + 10 = 0 \Rightarrow$

$\lambda, \overline{\lambda} = 3 \pm i$, $\mathbf{v} = \begin{pmatrix} -2 \\ 1+i \end{pmatrix}$, $\mathbf{z}(t) = e^{3t}[\cos(t) + i\sin(t)]\left[\begin{pmatrix} -2 \\ 1 \end{pmatrix} + i\begin{pmatrix} 0 \\ 1 \end{pmatrix} \right]$,

$X(t) = e^{3t}\begin{pmatrix} -2\cos(t) & -2\sin(t) \\ \cos(t) - \sin(t) & \sin(t) + \cos(t) \end{pmatrix}$,

$X(t)^{-1}\mathbf{f}(t) = -\frac{1}{2}e^{-3t}\begin{pmatrix} \sin(t) + \cos(t) & 2\sin(t) \\ \sin(t) - \cos(t) & -2\cos(t) \end{pmatrix}\begin{pmatrix} 0 \\ 2 \end{pmatrix}$

$= 2e^{-3t}\begin{pmatrix} -\sin(t) \\ \cos(t) \end{pmatrix}$, $\int X(t)^{-1}\mathbf{f}(t)\,dt = \frac{1}{5}e^{-3t}\begin{pmatrix} 3\sin(t) + \cos(t) \\ \sin(t) - 3\cos(t) \end{pmatrix}$, $\mathbf{x}(t) =$

$e^{3t}\begin{pmatrix} -2\cos(t) & -2\sin(t) \\ \cos(t) - \sin(t) & \sin(t) + \cos(t) \end{pmatrix}\left[\begin{pmatrix} c_1 \\ c_2 \end{pmatrix} + \frac{1}{5}e^{-3t}\begin{pmatrix} 3\sin(t) + \cos(t) \\ \sin(t) - 3\cos(t) \end{pmatrix} \right]$

$= \begin{pmatrix} -2e^{3t}[c_1\cos(t) + c_2\sin(t)] - \frac{2}{5} \\ c_1 e^{3t}[\cos(t) - \sin(t)] + c_2 e^{3t}[\sin(t) + \cos(t)] - \frac{2}{5} \end{pmatrix}.$

5. $A = \begin{pmatrix} 1 & 0 \\ 0 & 2 \end{pmatrix}$, $\mathbf{f}(t) = \begin{pmatrix} e^t \\ 2e^{2t} \end{pmatrix}$, $\mathbf{x}_0 = \begin{pmatrix} 3 \\ 2 \end{pmatrix}$, $\lambda_1 = 1$, $\lambda_2 = 2$, $\mathbf{v}_1 = \begin{pmatrix} 1 \\ 0 \end{pmatrix}$,

$\mathbf{v}_2 = \begin{pmatrix} 0 \\ 2 \end{pmatrix}$, $X(t) = \begin{pmatrix} e^t & 0 \\ 0 & 2e^{2t} \end{pmatrix}$, $X(t)^{-1}\mathbf{f}(t) = \begin{pmatrix} e^{-t} & 0 \\ 0 & \frac{1}{2}e^{-2t} \end{pmatrix}\begin{pmatrix} e^t \\ 2e^{2t} \end{pmatrix} =$

$\begin{pmatrix} 1 \\ 1 \end{pmatrix}$, $\int_0^t X(s)^{-1}\mathbf{f}(s)\,ds = \int_0^t \begin{pmatrix} 1 \\ 1 \end{pmatrix}\,ds = \begin{pmatrix} t \\ t \end{pmatrix}$,

$X(0)^{-1}\mathbf{x}_0 = \begin{pmatrix} 1 & 0 \\ 0 & \frac{1}{2} \end{pmatrix}\begin{pmatrix} 3 \\ 2 \end{pmatrix} = \begin{pmatrix} 3 \\ 1 \end{pmatrix}$, $\mathbf{x}(t) = \begin{pmatrix} e^t & 0 \\ 0 & 2e^{2t} \end{pmatrix}\left[\begin{pmatrix} 3 \\ 1 \end{pmatrix} + \begin{pmatrix} t \\ t \end{pmatrix} \right]$

$$= \begin{pmatrix} (t+3)e^t \\ 2(t+1)e^{2t} \end{pmatrix}.$$

6. $A = \begin{pmatrix} 0 & -1 \\ 1 & 0 \end{pmatrix}$, $\mathbf{f}(t) = \begin{pmatrix} 1 \\ 1 \end{pmatrix}$, $\mathbf{x}_0 = \begin{pmatrix} 2 \\ 1 \end{pmatrix}$, $\begin{vmatrix} \lambda & 1 \\ -1 & \lambda \end{vmatrix} = \lambda^2 + 1 = 0 \Rightarrow$

$\lambda, \overline{\lambda} = \pm i$, $\mathbf{v} = \begin{pmatrix} i \\ 1 \end{pmatrix}$, $\mathbf{z}(t) = [\cos(t) + i\sin(t)]\left[\begin{pmatrix} 0 \\ 1 \end{pmatrix} + i\begin{pmatrix} 1 \\ 0 \end{pmatrix}\right]$,

$X(t) = \begin{pmatrix} -\sin(t) & \cos(t) \\ \cos(t) & \sin(t) \end{pmatrix}$, $X(t)^{-1}\mathbf{f}(t) = \begin{pmatrix} -\sin(t) & \cos(t) \\ \cos(t) & \sin(t) \end{pmatrix}\begin{pmatrix} 1 \\ 1 \end{pmatrix} =$

$\begin{pmatrix} \cos(t) - \sin(t) \\ \cos(t) + \sin(t) \end{pmatrix}$, $\int_0^t X(s)^{-1}\mathbf{f}(s)\,ds = \begin{pmatrix} \sin(s) + \cos(s) \\ \sin(s) - \cos(s) \end{pmatrix}\Big|_0^t =$

$\begin{pmatrix} \sin(t) + \cos(t) - 1 \\ \sin(t) - \cos(t) + 1 \end{pmatrix}$, $X(0)^{-1}\mathbf{x}_0 = \begin{pmatrix} 0 & 1 \\ 1 & 0 \end{pmatrix}\begin{pmatrix} 2 \\ 1 \end{pmatrix} = \begin{pmatrix} 1 \\ 2 \end{pmatrix}$,

$\mathbf{x}(t) = \begin{pmatrix} -\sin(t) & \cos(t) \\ \cos(t) & \sin(t) \end{pmatrix}\left[\begin{pmatrix} 1 \\ 2 \end{pmatrix} + \begin{pmatrix} \sin(t) + \cos(t) - 1 \\ \sin(t) - \cos(t) + 1 \end{pmatrix}\right]$

$= \begin{pmatrix} -\sin(t) & \cos(t) \\ \cos(t) & \sin(t) \end{pmatrix}\begin{pmatrix} \sin(t) + \cos(t) \\ \sin(t) - \cos(t) + 3 \end{pmatrix} = \begin{pmatrix} 3\cos(t) - 1 \\ 3\sin(t) + 1 \end{pmatrix}.$

7. $A = \begin{pmatrix} -2 & -1 \\ 4 & -6 \end{pmatrix}$, $\mathbf{f}(t) = e^{-4t}\begin{pmatrix} 1 \\ 2 \end{pmatrix}$, $\mathbf{x}_0 = \begin{pmatrix} 0 \\ 1 \end{pmatrix}$, $\begin{vmatrix} \lambda + 2 & 1 \\ -4 & \lambda + 6 \end{vmatrix} = (\lambda + 4)^2$

$= 0 \Rightarrow \lambda_1 = -4$, $\mathbf{v}_1 = \begin{pmatrix} 1 \\ 2 \end{pmatrix}$, $(A - \lambda_1 I)\mathbf{u}_1 = \mathbf{u}_0 = \mathbf{v}_1 \Rightarrow \mathbf{u}_1 = \begin{pmatrix} 0 \\ -1 \end{pmatrix}$,

$X(t) = e^{-4t}\begin{pmatrix} 1 & t \\ 2 & 2t - 1 \end{pmatrix}$, $X(t)^{-1}\mathbf{f}(t) = e^{4t}\begin{pmatrix} 1 - 2t & t \\ 2 & -1 \end{pmatrix}e^{-4t}\begin{pmatrix} 1 \\ 2 \end{pmatrix} =$

$\begin{pmatrix} 1 \\ 0 \end{pmatrix}$, $\int_0^t X(s)^{-1}\mathbf{f}(s)\,ds = \begin{pmatrix} s \\ 0 \end{pmatrix}\Big|_0^t = \begin{pmatrix} t \\ 0 \end{pmatrix}$, $X(0)^{-1}\mathbf{x}_0 = \begin{pmatrix} 1 & 0 \\ 2 & -1 \end{pmatrix}\begin{pmatrix} 0 \\ 1 \end{pmatrix}$

$= \begin{pmatrix} 0 \\ -1 \end{pmatrix}$, $\mathbf{x}(t) = e^{-4t}\begin{pmatrix} 1 & t \\ 2 & 2t - 1 \end{pmatrix}\left[\begin{pmatrix} 0 \\ -1 \end{pmatrix} + \begin{pmatrix} t \\ 0 \end{pmatrix}\right] = e^{-4t}\begin{pmatrix} 0 \\ 1 \end{pmatrix}.$

8. $A = \begin{pmatrix} 1 & 0 & 0 \\ 4 & -1 & 0 \\ -1 & 0 & 2 \end{pmatrix}$, $\mathbf{f}(t) = e^t\begin{pmatrix} 1 \\ 2 \\ -1 \end{pmatrix}$ and $\mathbf{x}_0 = \begin{pmatrix} 1 \\ 3 \\ 1 \end{pmatrix}$,

$\begin{vmatrix} \lambda - 1 & 0 & 0 \\ -4 & \lambda + 1 & 0 \\ 1 & 0 & \lambda - 2 \end{vmatrix} = (\lambda - 1)(\lambda + 1)(\lambda - 2) = 0 \Rightarrow \lambda_1 = 1, \lambda_2 = -1, \lambda_3 = 2,$

$\mathbf{v}_1 = \begin{pmatrix} 1 \\ 2 \\ 1 \end{pmatrix}$, $\mathbf{v}_2 = \begin{pmatrix} 0 \\ 1 \\ 0 \end{pmatrix}$, $\mathbf{v}_3 = \begin{pmatrix} 0 \\ 0 \\ 1 \end{pmatrix}$, $X(t) = \begin{pmatrix} e^t & 0 & 0 \\ 2e^t & e^{-t} & 0 \\ e^t & 0 & e^{2t} \end{pmatrix}$,

$X(t)^{-1} = \begin{pmatrix} e^{-t} & 0 & 0 \\ -2e^t & e^t & 0 \\ -e^{-2t} & 0 & e^{-2t} \end{pmatrix}$, $X(t)^{-1}\mathbf{f}(t) = \begin{pmatrix} e^{-t} & 0 & 0 \\ -2e^t & e^t & 0 \\ -e^{-2t} & 0 & e^{-2t} \end{pmatrix}\begin{pmatrix} e^t \\ 2e^t \\ -e^t \end{pmatrix}$

$$= \begin{pmatrix} 1 \\ 0 \\ -2e^{-t} \end{pmatrix}, \; \int_0^t X(s)^{-1}\mathbf{f}(s)\,ds = \begin{pmatrix} s \\ 0 \\ 2e^{-s} \end{pmatrix}\Big|_0^t = \begin{pmatrix} t \\ 0 \\ 2e^{-t} - 2 \end{pmatrix},$$

$$X(0)^{-1}\mathbf{x}_0 = \begin{pmatrix} 1 & 0 & 0 \\ -2 & 1 & 0 \\ -1 & 0 & 1 \end{pmatrix}\begin{pmatrix} 1 \\ 3 \\ 1 \end{pmatrix} = \begin{pmatrix} 1 \\ 1 \\ 0 \end{pmatrix},$$

$$\mathbf{x}(t) = \begin{pmatrix} e^t & 0 & 0 \\ 2e^t & e^{-t} & 0 \\ e^t & 0 & e^{2t} \end{pmatrix}\left[\begin{pmatrix} 1 \\ 1 \\ 0 \end{pmatrix} + \begin{pmatrix} t \\ 0 \\ 2e^{-t} - 2 \end{pmatrix} \right] = \begin{pmatrix} (t+1)e^t \\ 2(t+1)e^t + e^{-t} \\ (t+3)e^t - 2e^{2t} \end{pmatrix}.$$

Chapter 5 Exercises – page 186

1. $y'' - 2y' + y = 0$.

   (a) $y = e^{rt} \Rightarrow r^2 - 2r + 1 = (r-1)^2 = 0 \Rightarrow r = 1 \Rightarrow y_1(t) = e^t$, $y_2(t) = te^t$,
   $y(t) = c_1 e^t + c_2 t e^t$.

   (b) $x_1 = y$ and $x_2 = y' \Rightarrow x_1' = y' = x_2$ and $x_2' = y'' = 2y' - y = 2x_2 - x_1$.

   (c) $A = \begin{pmatrix} 0 & 1 \\ -1 & 2 \end{pmatrix}$, $\begin{vmatrix} \lambda & -1 \\ 1 & \lambda - 2 \end{vmatrix} = (\lambda - 1)^2 = 0 \Rightarrow \lambda_1 = 1, \; \mathbf{v}_1 = \begin{pmatrix} 1 \\ 1 \end{pmatrix}$

   $\Rightarrow \mathbf{x}_1(t) = e^t \begin{pmatrix} 1 \\ 1 \end{pmatrix}$, $\mathbf{x}_2(t) = e^t(t\mathbf{u}_0 + \mathbf{u}_1)$, $\mathbf{u}_0 = \mathbf{v}_1$, $(A - \lambda_1 I)\mathbf{u}_1 = \mathbf{u}_0$

   $\Rightarrow \mathbf{u}_1 = \begin{pmatrix} 0 \\ 1 \end{pmatrix} \Rightarrow \mathbf{x}_2(t) = e^t \begin{pmatrix} t \\ t+1 \end{pmatrix} \Rightarrow \mathbf{x}(t) = c_1\mathbf{x}_1(t) + c_2\mathbf{x}_2(t) \Rightarrow$
   $x_1(t) = (c_1 + c_2 t)e^t$, $x_2(t) = [c_1 + c_2(t+1)]e^t$, and $x_1(t) = y(t)$.

   (d) $W[y_1(t)\, y_2(t)] = \begin{vmatrix} y_1(t) & y_2(t) \\ y_1'(t) & y_2'(t) \end{vmatrix} = \begin{vmatrix} e^t & te^t \\ e^t & (t+1)e^t \end{vmatrix} = e^{2t}$ and

   $W[\mathbf{x}_1(t)\, \mathbf{x}_2(t)] = |\, \mathbf{x}_1(t) \;\; \mathbf{x}_2(t)\, | = \begin{vmatrix} e^t & te^t \\ e^t & (t+1)e^t \end{vmatrix} = e^{2t} = W[y_1(t)\, y_2(t)]$.

2. Let $X(t)$ be a fundamental matrix for the system $\mathbf{x}' = A\mathbf{x}$.

   (a) Since $X(0)^{-1}$ is nonsingular, $Y(t) = X(t)X(0)^{-1}$ is a fundamental matrix
   by Theorem 5.4, and $Y(0) = X(0)X(0)^{-1} = I$. The solution of $\mathbf{x}' = A\mathbf{x}$,
   $\mathbf{x}(0) = \mathbf{x}_0$, is $\mathbf{x}(t) = Y(t)\mathbf{x}_0$.

   (b) Since $X(t_0)^{-1}$ is nonsingular, $Z(t) = X(t)X(t_0)^{-1}$ is a fundamental matrix
   by Theorem 5.4, and $Z(t_0) = X(t_0)X(t_0)^{-1} = I$. The solution of $\mathbf{x}' = A\mathbf{x}$,
   $\mathbf{x}(t_0) = \mathbf{x}_0$, is $\mathbf{x}(t) = Z(t)\mathbf{x}_0$. Part (a) is the special case where $t_0 = 0$.

3. $\left\{ \begin{array}{l} x' = 2x \\ y' = x - 2y \end{array} \right\}$.

(a) $A = \begin{pmatrix} 2 & 0 \\ 1 & -2 \end{pmatrix}$, $\begin{vmatrix} \lambda - 2 & 0 \\ -1 & \lambda + 2 \end{vmatrix} = (\lambda - 2)(\lambda + 2) = 0 \Rightarrow \lambda_1 = 2$,

$\lambda_2 = -2$, $\mathbf{v}_1 = \begin{pmatrix} 4 \\ 1 \end{pmatrix}$, $\mathbf{v}_2 = \begin{pmatrix} 0 \\ 1 \end{pmatrix}$, $\mathbf{x}_1(t) = e^{2t} \begin{pmatrix} 4 \\ 1 \end{pmatrix}$, $\mathbf{x}_2(t) = e^{-2t} \begin{pmatrix} 0 \\ 1 \end{pmatrix}$,

$\mathbf{x}(t) = c_1 \mathbf{x}_1(t) + c_2 \mathbf{x}_2(t) \Rightarrow x(t) = 4c_1 e^{2t}$, $y(t) = c_1 e^{2t} + c_2 e^{-2t}$.

(b) $x' = 2x \Rightarrow x(t) = c_1 e^{2t} \Rightarrow y' = c_1 e^{2t} - 2y \Rightarrow y' + 2y = c_1 e^{2t} \Rightarrow (e^{2t} y)' = c_1 e^{4t}$
$\Rightarrow e^{2t} y = \frac{1}{4} c_1 e^{4t} + c_2 \Rightarrow y(t) = \frac{1}{4} c_1 e^{2t} + c_2 e^{-2t}$ and, replacing the arbitrary
constant c_1 by $4c_1$, the solution coincides with the one in part (a).

(c) $y' = x - 2y \Rightarrow y'' = x' - 2y' = 2x - 2(x - 2y) = 4y \Rightarrow y'' - 4y = 0$.

(d) $y = e^{rt} \Rightarrow r^2 - 4 = (r - 2)(r + 2) = 0 \Rightarrow y(t) = c_1 e^{2t} + c_2 e^{-2t} \Rightarrow$
$x(t) = 2y(t) + y'(t) = 2[c_1 e^{2t} + c_2 e^{-2t}] + [2c_1 e^{2t} - 2c_2 e^{-2t}] = 4c_1 e^{2t}$, as in
part (a).

4. $\mathbf{x}' = A\mathbf{x}$, $A = \begin{pmatrix} -7 & 12 \\ -4 & 7 \end{pmatrix}$.

(a) $\begin{vmatrix} \lambda + 7 & -12 \\ 4 & \lambda - 7 \end{vmatrix} = \lambda^2 - 1 = (\lambda - 1)(\lambda + 1) = 0 \Rightarrow \lambda_1 = 1$, $\lambda_2 = -1$,

$\mathbf{v}_1 = \begin{pmatrix} 3 \\ 2 \end{pmatrix}$, $\mathbf{v}_2 = \begin{pmatrix} 2 \\ 1 \end{pmatrix} \Rightarrow \mathbf{x}_1(t) = e^t \begin{pmatrix} 3 \\ 2 \end{pmatrix}$, $\mathbf{x}_2(t) = e^{-t} \begin{pmatrix} 2 \\ 1 \end{pmatrix}$,

$\mathbf{x}(t) = c_1 \mathbf{x}_1(t) + c_2 \mathbf{x}_2(t) = \begin{pmatrix} 3c_1 e^t + 2c_2 e^{-t} \\ 2c_1 e^t + c_2 e^{-t} \end{pmatrix}$.

(b) $P = (\mathbf{v}_1 \ \mathbf{v}_2) = \begin{pmatrix} 3 & 2 \\ 2 & 1 \end{pmatrix} \Rightarrow P^{-1} A P = D = \begin{pmatrix} 1 & 0 \\ 0 & -1 \end{pmatrix} \Rightarrow A = PDP^{-1}$.

Thus, $\mathbf{x}' = A\mathbf{x} \Rightarrow \mathbf{x}' = PDP^{-1} \mathbf{x} \Rightarrow (P^{-1} \mathbf{x})' = P^{-1} \mathbf{x}' = D(P^{-1} \mathbf{x}) \Rightarrow$
$\mathbf{y}' = D\mathbf{y}$, where $\mathbf{y} = P^{-1} \mathbf{x}$.

(c) $\mathbf{y}' = D\mathbf{y}$ with $\mathbf{y} = \begin{pmatrix} y_1 \\ y_2 \end{pmatrix}$ and $D = \begin{pmatrix} 1 & 0 \\ 0 & -1 \end{pmatrix} \Rightarrow y_1' = y_1$ and $y_2' = -y_2$

$\Rightarrow y_1(t) = c_1 e^t$, $y_2(t) = c_2 e^{-t} \Rightarrow \mathbf{y}(t) = \begin{pmatrix} c_1 e^t \\ c_2 e^{-t} \end{pmatrix}$.

(d) $\mathbf{x}(t) = P\mathbf{y}(t) = \begin{pmatrix} 3 & 2 \\ 2 & 1 \end{pmatrix} \begin{pmatrix} c_1 e^t \\ c_2 e^{-t} \end{pmatrix} = \begin{pmatrix} 3c_1 e^t + 2c_2 e^{-t} \\ 2c_1 e^t + c_2 e^{-t} \end{pmatrix}$, as in part (a).

5. $A = \begin{pmatrix} 1 & 0 & 0 & 0 \\ 0 & 1 & 0 & 0 \\ 0 & 0 & 1 & 1 \\ 0 & 0 & 0 & 1 \end{pmatrix}$, $|\lambda I - A| = (\lambda - 1)^4 = 0 \Rightarrow \lambda_1 = 1$, $m_1 = 4$. For $\lambda_1 = 1$,

$(\lambda_1 I - A)\mathbf{v} = \mathbf{0} \Rightarrow \begin{pmatrix} 0 & 0 & 0 & 0 \\ 0 & 0 & 0 & 0 \\ 0 & 0 & 0 & -1 \\ 0 & 0 & 0 & 0 \end{pmatrix} \begin{pmatrix} a \\ b \\ c \\ d \end{pmatrix} = \begin{pmatrix} 0 \\ 0 \\ 0 \\ 0 \end{pmatrix} \Rightarrow d = 0 \Rightarrow$

$$\mathbf{v}_1 = \begin{pmatrix} 1 \\ 0 \\ 0 \\ 0 \end{pmatrix}, \ \mathbf{v}_2 = \begin{pmatrix} 0 \\ 1 \\ 0 \\ 0 \end{pmatrix}, \ \mathbf{v}_3 = \begin{pmatrix} 0 \\ 0 \\ 1 \\ 0 \end{pmatrix} \Rightarrow \mathbf{x}_1(t) = e^t \begin{pmatrix} 1 \\ 0 \\ 0 \\ 0 \end{pmatrix},$$

$$\mathbf{x}_2(t) = e^t \begin{pmatrix} 0 \\ 1 \\ 0 \\ 0 \end{pmatrix}, \ \mathbf{x}_3(t) = e^t \begin{pmatrix} 0 \\ 0 \\ 1 \\ 0 \end{pmatrix}, \ \mathbf{x}_4(t) = e^t(t\mathbf{u}_0 + \mathbf{u}_1),$$

$$\mathbf{u}_0 = \alpha \mathbf{v}_1 + \beta \mathbf{v}_2 + \gamma \mathbf{v}_3 = \begin{pmatrix} \alpha \\ \beta \\ \gamma \\ 0 \end{pmatrix}, \ (A - \lambda_1 I)\mathbf{u}_1 = \mathbf{u}_0 \Rightarrow$$

$$\begin{pmatrix} 0 & 0 & 0 & 0 \\ 0 & 0 & 0 & 0 \\ 0 & 0 & 0 & 1 \\ 0 & 0 & 0 & 0 \end{pmatrix} \begin{pmatrix} a \\ b \\ c \\ d \end{pmatrix} = \begin{pmatrix} \alpha \\ \beta \\ \gamma \\ 0 \end{pmatrix} \Rightarrow \alpha = \beta = 0 \text{ and } d = \gamma, \text{ and } \gamma = 1 \Rightarrow$$

$$\mathbf{u}_1 = \begin{pmatrix} 0 \\ 0 \\ 0 \\ 1 \end{pmatrix}, \ \mathbf{u}_0 = \begin{pmatrix} 0 \\ 0 \\ 1 \\ 0 \end{pmatrix} \Rightarrow \mathbf{x}_4(t) = e^t \begin{pmatrix} 0 \\ 0 \\ t \\ 1 \end{pmatrix}, \ X(t) = e^t \begin{pmatrix} 1 & 0 & 0 & 0 \\ 0 & 1 & 0 & 0 \\ 0 & 0 & 1 & t \\ 0 & 0 & 0 & 1 \end{pmatrix}.$$

6. $A = \begin{pmatrix} 1 & 1 & 0 & 0 \\ 0 & 1 & 1 & 0 \\ 0 & 0 & 1 & 1 \\ 0 & 0 & 0 & 1 \end{pmatrix}$, $|\lambda I - A| = (\lambda - 1)^4 = 0 \Rightarrow \lambda_1 = 1$, $m_1 = 4$. For $\lambda_1 = 1$,

$$(\lambda_1 I - A)\mathbf{v} = \mathbf{0} \Rightarrow \begin{pmatrix} 0 & -1 & 0 & 0 \\ 0 & 0 & -1 & 0 \\ 0 & 0 & 0 & -1 \\ 0 & 0 & 0 & 0 \end{pmatrix} \begin{pmatrix} a \\ b \\ c \\ d \end{pmatrix} = \begin{pmatrix} 0 \\ 0 \\ 0 \\ 0 \end{pmatrix} \Rightarrow b = c = d = 0$$

$$\Rightarrow \mathbf{v}_1 = \begin{pmatrix} 1 \\ 0 \\ 0 \\ 0 \end{pmatrix} \Rightarrow \mathbf{x}_1(t) = e^t \begin{pmatrix} 1 \\ 0 \\ 0 \\ 0 \end{pmatrix}, \ \mathbf{x}_2(t) = e^t(t\mathbf{u}_0 + \mathbf{u}_1), \ \mathbf{u}_0 = \mathbf{v}_1,$$

$$(A - \lambda_1 I)\mathbf{u}_1 = \mathbf{u}_0 \Rightarrow \begin{pmatrix} 0 & 1 & 0 & 0 \\ 0 & 0 & 1 & 0 \\ 0 & 0 & 0 & 1 \\ 0 & 0 & 0 & 0 \end{pmatrix} \begin{pmatrix} a \\ b \\ c \\ d \end{pmatrix} = \begin{pmatrix} 1 \\ 0 \\ 0 \\ 0 \end{pmatrix} \Rightarrow c = d = 0, \ b = 1 \Rightarrow$$

$$\mathbf{u}_1 = \begin{pmatrix} 0 \\ 1 \\ 0 \\ 0 \end{pmatrix} \Rightarrow \mathbf{x}_2(t) = e^t \begin{pmatrix} t \\ 1 \\ 0 \\ 0 \end{pmatrix}, \ \mathbf{x}_3(t) = e^t \left(\tfrac{1}{2}t^2 \mathbf{u}_0 + t\mathbf{u}_1 + \mathbf{u}_2 \right),$$

$$(A - \lambda_1 I)\mathbf{u}_2 = \mathbf{u}_1 \Rightarrow \begin{pmatrix} 0 & 1 & 0 & 0 \\ 0 & 0 & 1 & 0 \\ 0 & 0 & 0 & 1 \\ 0 & 0 & 0 & 0 \end{pmatrix} \begin{pmatrix} a \\ b \\ c \\ d \end{pmatrix} = \begin{pmatrix} 0 \\ 1 \\ 0 \\ 0 \end{pmatrix} \Rightarrow b = d = 0, \; c = 1$$

$$\Rightarrow \mathbf{u}_2 = \begin{pmatrix} 0 \\ 0 \\ 1 \\ 0 \end{pmatrix} \Rightarrow \mathbf{x}_3(t) = e^t \begin{pmatrix} \frac{1}{2}t^2 \\ t \\ 1 \\ 0 \end{pmatrix}, \; \mathbf{x}_4(t) = e^t \left(\tfrac{1}{6}t^3 \mathbf{u}_0 + \tfrac{1}{2}t^2 \mathbf{u}_1 + t\mathbf{u}_2 + \mathbf{u}_3 \right),$$

$$(A - \lambda_1 I)\mathbf{u}_3 = \mathbf{u}_2 \Rightarrow \begin{pmatrix} 0 & 1 & 0 & 0 \\ 0 & 0 & 1 & 0 \\ 0 & 0 & 0 & 1 \\ 0 & 0 & 0 & 0 \end{pmatrix} \begin{pmatrix} a \\ b \\ c \\ d \end{pmatrix} = \begin{pmatrix} 0 \\ 0 \\ 1 \\ 0 \end{pmatrix} \Rightarrow b = c = 0, \; d = 1 \Rightarrow$$

$$\mathbf{u}_3 = \begin{pmatrix} 0 \\ 0 \\ 0 \\ 1 \end{pmatrix} \Rightarrow \mathbf{x}_4(t) = e^t \begin{pmatrix} \frac{1}{6}t^3 \\ \frac{1}{2}t^2 \\ t \\ 1 \end{pmatrix}, \; X(t) = e^t \begin{pmatrix} 1 & t & \frac{1}{2}t^2 & \frac{1}{6}t^3 \\ 0 & 1 & t & \frac{1}{2}t^2 \\ 0 & 0 & 1 & t \\ 0 & 0 & 0 & 1 \end{pmatrix}.$$

7. If $c_1\mathbf{x}_1(t) + c_2\mathbf{x}_2(t) \equiv 0$, then $t = 0 \Rightarrow c_1\mathbf{a} + c_2\mathbf{b} = 0$, and $t = \frac{\pi}{2} \Rightarrow c_2\mathbf{a} - c_1\mathbf{b} = 0$ $\Rightarrow (c_1^2 + c_2^2)\mathbf{b} = 0 \Rightarrow c_1 = c_2 = 0$ since $\mathbf{b} \neq 0$.

C.6   Chapter 6 Solutions

Exercises 6.1 – page 205

1. $\{5, \; 7, \; 9, \; 11, \; \cdots\} = \{2n + 3\}_{n=1}^{\infty}$

2. $\{-6, \; -3, \; 0, \; 3, \; \cdots\} = \{3n\}_{n=-2}^{\infty}$

3. $\left\{1, \; -\frac{1}{2}, \; \frac{1}{3}, \; -\frac{1}{4}, \; \cdots\right\} = \left\{\frac{(-1)^{n-1}}{n}\right\}_{n=1}^{\infty}$

4. $\left\{1, \; \frac{1}{4}, \; \frac{1}{9}, \; \frac{1}{16}, \; \cdots\right\} = \left\{\frac{1}{n^2}\right\}_{n=1}^{\infty}$

5. $\left\{1, \; \frac{1}{3}, \; \frac{1}{9}, \; \frac{1}{27}, \; \cdots\right\} = \left\{\frac{1}{3^n}\right\}_{n=0}^{\infty}$

6. $\left\{0, \; 1 - \frac{1}{2}, \; 1 - \frac{1}{3}, \; 1 - \frac{1}{4}, \; \cdots\right\} = \left\{1 - \frac{1}{n}\right\}_{n=1}^{\infty}$

7. $\left\{\frac{1}{2}, \; \frac{2}{3}, \; \frac{3}{4}, \; \frac{4}{5}, \; \cdots\right\} = \left\{\frac{n}{n+1}\right\}_{n=1}^{\infty}$

8. $\left\{ 1 - \frac{1}{2}, \; \frac{1}{2} - \frac{2}{4}, \; \frac{1}{3} - \frac{3}{8}, \; \frac{1}{4} - \frac{4}{16}, \; \cdots \right\} = \left\{\frac{1}{n} - \frac{n}{2^n}\right\}_{n=1}^{\infty}$

9. $\left\{\frac{\sqrt{n^2+1}}{2n+1}\right\}_{n=0}^{\infty} = \left\{1, \; \frac{\sqrt{2}}{3}, \; \frac{\sqrt{5}}{5}, \; \frac{\sqrt{10}}{7}, \; \frac{\sqrt{17}}{9}, \; \cdots\right\}.$

10. $a_1 = 2$, $a_2 = 3$, $a_n = a_{n-1} - a_{n-2}$ for $n \geq 3 \Rightarrow a_3 = 1$, $a_4 = -2$, $a_5 = -3$.

11. $b_n = a_{n+1} + \frac{n}{2^n}$ for all $n \geq 1 \Rightarrow b_{n+1} = a_{n+2} + \frac{n+1}{2^{n+1}}$ for $n \geq 0$ and $b_{n-1} = a_n + \frac{n-1}{2^{n-1}}$ for $n \geq 2$.

12. $\left\{ \frac{1}{3}, \frac{1}{5}, \frac{1}{7}, \frac{1}{9}, \cdots \right\} = \left\{ \frac{1}{2n+1} \right\}_{n=1}^{\infty} = \left\{ \frac{1}{2n+3} \right\}_{n=0}^{\infty} = \left\{ \frac{1}{2n-1} \right\}_{n=2}^{\infty}$.

13. $a_n = \frac{1}{n^{\pi}} \to 0 \Rightarrow \{a_n\}$ converges.

14. $a_n = \frac{-1}{n^{-3}} = -n^3 \to -\infty \Rightarrow \{a_n\}$ diverges.

15. $a_n = \frac{1}{3^n} \to 0 \Rightarrow \{a_n\}$ converges.

16. $a_n = 2^{-n} = \frac{1}{2^n} \to 0 \Rightarrow \{a_n\}$ converges.

17. $a_n = \left(\frac{9}{10} \right)^n \to 0 \Rightarrow \{a_n\}$ converges.

18. $a_n = \frac{(-2)^n}{3^n} = \left(-\frac{2}{3} \right)^n \to 0 \Rightarrow \{a_n\}$ converges.

19. $a_n = \frac{3^n}{(-2)^n} = \left(-\frac{3}{2} \right)^n$, and $\lim\limits_{n \to \infty} a_n$ does not exist $\Rightarrow \{a_n\}$ diverges.

20. $a_n = \frac{3}{\sqrt{n}} \to 0 \Rightarrow \{a_n\}$ converges.

21. $a_n = \frac{10^{1,000,000,000,000}}{n^{0.0000000001}} \to 0 \Rightarrow \{a_n\}$ converges.

22. $a_n = 3 - \frac{2}{n^2} + \frac{5}{4^n} \to 3 \Rightarrow \{a_n\}$ converges.

23. $a_n = n + \frac{1}{3^n} \to \infty \Rightarrow \{a_n\}$ diverges.

24. $a_n = \frac{3n^2 - 2n - 3}{2n^2 + 3n + 1} = \frac{3 - \frac{2}{n} - \frac{3}{n^2}}{2 + \frac{3}{n} + \frac{1}{n^2}} \to \frac{3}{2} \Rightarrow \{a_n\}$ converges.

25. $a_n = \frac{3n^3 - 2n - 3}{4n^2 + n + 1} = \frac{3n - \frac{2}{n} - \frac{3}{n^2}}{4 + \frac{1}{n} + \frac{1}{n^2}} \to \infty \Rightarrow \{a_n\}$ diverges.

26. $a_n = \frac{3n^2 - 2n - 3}{2n^3 + 2n - 1} = \frac{\frac{3}{n} - \frac{2}{n^2} - \frac{3}{n^3}}{2 + \frac{2}{n^2} - \frac{1}{n^3}} \to 0 \Rightarrow \{a_n\}$ converges.

27. $a_n = \frac{3n^2 - 2n - 3}{\sqrt{2n^4 + 3n + 1}} = \frac{3 - \frac{2}{n} - \frac{3}{n^2}}{\sqrt{2 + \frac{3}{n^3} + \frac{1}{n^4}}} \to \frac{3}{\sqrt{2}} \Rightarrow \{a_n\}$ converges.

28. $a_n = \frac{3n^2 - 2n - 3}{\sqrt{2n^5 - 2n + 1}} = \frac{\frac{3}{n^{1/2}} - \frac{2}{n^{3/2}} - \frac{3}{n^{5/2}}}{\sqrt{2 - \frac{2}{n^4} + \frac{1}{n^5}}} \to 0 \Rightarrow \{a_n\}$ converges.

29. $a_n = \frac{3n^2 - 2n - 3}{\sqrt{2n^3 - n + 1}} = \frac{3n^{1/2} - \frac{2}{n^{1/2}} - \frac{3}{n^{3/2}}}{\sqrt{2 - \frac{1}{n^2} + \frac{1}{n^3}}} \to \infty \Rightarrow \{a_n\}$ diverges.

30. $a_n = n^2 - 2\sqrt{n} = (n^2 - 2\sqrt{n}) \frac{n^2 + 2\sqrt{n}}{n^2 + 2\sqrt{n}} = \frac{n^4 - 4n}{n^2 + 2\sqrt{n}} = \frac{n^2 - \frac{4}{n}}{1 + 2\sqrt{\frac{1}{n^3}}} \to \infty \Rightarrow \{a_n\}$ diverges.

31. $a_n = \sqrt{n^2+n} - \sqrt{n^2-n} = (\sqrt{n^2+n} - \sqrt{n^2-n})\frac{\sqrt{n^2+n}+\sqrt{n^2-n}}{\sqrt{n^2+n}+\sqrt{n^2-n}} = \frac{2n}{\sqrt{n^2+n}+\sqrt{n^2-n}}$
    $\frac{2}{\sqrt{1+\frac{1}{n}}+\sqrt{1-\frac{1}{n}}} \to 1 \Rightarrow \{a_n\}$ converges.

32. $a_n = n - \sqrt{n^2+n} = (n - \sqrt{n^2+n})\frac{n+\sqrt{n^2+n}}{n+\sqrt{n^2+n}} = \frac{-n}{n+\sqrt{n^2+n}} = \frac{-1}{1+\sqrt{1+\frac{1}{n}}} \to -\frac{1}{2} \Rightarrow$
    $\{a_n\}$ converges.

33. $a_n = \sqrt{n^3+1} - n = (\sqrt{n^3+1} - n)\frac{\sqrt{n^3+1}+n}{\sqrt{n^3+1}+n} = \frac{n^3+1-n^2}{\sqrt{n^3+1}+n} = \frac{n^{3/2}+\frac{1}{n^{3/2}}-n^{1/2}}{\sqrt{1+\frac{1}{n^3}}+\frac{1}{n^{1/2}}}$
    $= \frac{n^{1/2}(n-1)+\frac{1}{n^{3/2}}}{\sqrt{1+\frac{1}{n^3}}+\frac{1}{n^{1/2}}} \to \infty \Rightarrow \{a_n\}$ diverges.

34. $a_n = \frac{(-2)^n}{3^n n^2} = \left(-\frac{2}{3}\right)^n \frac{1}{n^2} \to 0$ by Theorem 6.1 since $\left(-\frac{2}{3}\right)^n \to 0$ and $\frac{1}{n^2} \to 0$.
    Hence, $\{a_n\}$ converges.

35. $a_n = \frac{(-1)^{n-1}}{n} \to 0$ by Theorem 6.2 since $\left|\frac{(-1)^{n-1}}{n}\right| = \frac{1}{n} \to 0$. Hence, $\{a_n\}$
    converges.

36. $a_n = \frac{1-(-1)^n}{n} = \frac{1}{n} - \frac{(-1)^n}{n} \to 0$ by Theorem 6.1 since $\frac{1}{n} \to 0$ and $\frac{(-1)^n}{n} \to 0$ by
    Theorem 6.2. Hence, $\{a_n\}$ converges.

37. $a_n = \frac{[\ln(n)]^2}{n}$. Let $f(x) = \frac{[\ln(x)]^2}{x}$. By L'Hôpital's rule, $\lim_{x\to\infty} \frac{[\ln(x)]^2}{x} = \lim_{x\to\infty} \frac{[2\ln(x)]\frac{1}{x}}{1}$
    $= \lim_{x\to\infty} \frac{2\ln(x)}{x} = \lim_{x\to\infty} \frac{2\frac{1}{x}}{1} = \lim_{x\to\infty} \frac{2}{x} = 0 \Rightarrow \lim_{n\to\infty} \frac{[\ln(n)]^2}{n} = 0$ by Theorem 6.3. Hence,
    $\{a_n\}$ converges.

38. $a_n = \frac{n}{e^n}$. Let $f(x) = \frac{x}{e^x}$. By L'Hôpital's rule, $\lim_{x\to\infty} \frac{x}{e^x} = \lim_{x\to\infty} \frac{1}{e^x} = 0 \Rightarrow$
    $\lim_{n\to\infty} \frac{n}{e^n} = 0$ by Theorem 6.3. Hence, $\{a_n\}$ converges.

39. $a_n = \frac{n^3}{e^n}$. Let $f(x) = \frac{x^3}{e^x}$. By L'Hôpital's rule, $\lim_{x\to\infty} \frac{x^3}{e^x} = \lim_{x\to\infty} \frac{3x^2}{e^x} = \lim_{x\to\infty} \frac{6x}{e^x} =$
    $\lim_{x\to\infty} \frac{6}{e^x} = 0 \Rightarrow \lim_{n\to\infty} \frac{n^3}{e^n} = 0$ by Theorem 6.3. Hence, $\{a_n\}$ converges.

40. $a_n = \frac{[\ln(n)]^p}{n^q}$, $p > 0$, $q > 0$. $a_n \to 0$ if and only if $\{a_n^{1/p}\} = \frac{\ln(n)}{n^{q/p}} \to 0$. Let
    $f(x) = \frac{\ln(x)}{x^{q/p}}$. By L'Hôpital's rule, $\lim_{x\to\infty} \frac{\ln(x)}{x^{q/p}} = \lim_{x\to\infty} \frac{1/x}{\frac{q}{p}x^{\frac{q}{p}-1}} = \lim_{x\to\infty} \frac{p}{qx^{q/p}} = 0 \Rightarrow$
    $\lim_{n\to\infty} \frac{[\ln(n)]^p}{n^q} = 0$ by Theorem 6.3. Hence, $\{a_n\}$ converges.

41. $a_n = n^{1/n}$. Let $f(x) = x^{1/x} = e^{\frac{\ln(x)}{x}}$. By L'Hôpital's rule, $\lim_{x\to\infty} \frac{\ln(x)}{x} = \lim_{x\to\infty} \frac{1}{x} = 0$
    $\Rightarrow \lim_{x\to\infty} e^{\frac{\ln(x)}{x}} = e^0 = 1 \Rightarrow \lim_{n\to\infty} n^{1/n} = 1$ by Theorem 6.3. Hence, $\{a_n\}$ converges.

42. $a_n = [\ln(n)]^{1/\ln(n)}$. Let $f(x) = [\ln(x)]^{1/\ln(x)} = e^{\frac{1}{\ln(x)}\ln[\ln(x)]}$. By L'Hôpital's
    rule, $\lim_{x\to\infty} \frac{\ln[\ln(x)]}{\ln(x)} = \lim_{x\to\infty} \frac{\frac{1}{\ln(x)}\frac{1}{x}}{\frac{1}{x}} = \lim_{x\to\infty} \frac{1}{\ln(x)} = 0 \Rightarrow \lim_{x\to\infty} e^{\frac{1}{\ln(x)}\ln[\ln(x)]} = 1 \Rightarrow$
    $\lim_{n\to\infty} [\ln(n)]^{1/\ln(n)} = 1$ by Theorem 6.3. Hence, $\{a_n\}$ converges.

43. $a_n = [\ln(n)]^{1/n}$. Let $f(x) = [\ln(x)]^{1/x} = e^{\frac{1}{x}\ln[\ln(x)]}$. By L'Hôpital's rule, $\lim\limits_{x\to\infty} \frac{\ln[\ln(x)]}{x} = \lim\limits_{x\to\infty} \frac{1}{x\ln(x)} = 0 \Rightarrow \lim\limits_{x\to\infty}[\ln(x)]^{1/x} = 1 \Rightarrow \lim\limits_{n\to\infty}[\ln(n)]^{1/n} = 1$ by Theorem 6.3. Hence, $\{a_n\}$ converges.

44. $a_n = n^{1/\ln(n)} = e^{\ln(n^{1/\ln(n)})} = e^{\frac{1}{\ln(n)}\ln(n)} = e$ for all $n \geq 2 \Rightarrow \lim\limits_{n\to\infty} a_n = \lim\limits_{n\to\infty} e = e$. Hence, $\{a_n\}$ converges.

45. $a_n = \frac{\cos(n)}{n}$. $-1 \leq \cos(n) \leq 1 \Rightarrow -\frac{1}{n} \leq \frac{\cos(n)}{n} \leq \frac{1}{n}$, and $\lim\limits_{n\to\infty}\left(-\frac{1}{n}\right) = \lim\limits_{n\to\infty}\frac{1}{n} = 0$ $\Rightarrow \lim\limits_{n\to\infty}\frac{\cos(n)}{n} = 0$ by Theorem 6.4. Hence, $\{a_n\}$ converges. Alternatively, $0 \leq \left|\frac{\cos(n)}{n}\right| \leq \frac{1}{n}$ and $\lim\limits_{n\to\infty} 0 = \lim\limits_{n\to\infty}\frac{1}{n} = 0 \Rightarrow \lim\limits_{n\to\infty}\left|\frac{\cos(n)}{n}\right| = 0$ by Theorem 6.4 and, hence, $\lim\limits_{n\to\infty}\frac{\cos(n)}{n} = 0$ by Theorem 6.2.

46. $a_n = \frac{\sin(n^2)}{\sqrt{n}}$. $0 \leq \left|\frac{\sin(n^2)}{\sqrt{n}}\right| \leq \frac{1}{\sqrt{n}}$ and $\lim\limits_{n\to\infty} 0 = \lim\limits_{n\to\infty}\frac{1}{\sqrt{n}} = 0 \Rightarrow \lim\limits_{n\to\infty}\left|\frac{\sin(n^2)}{\sqrt{n}}\right| = 0$ by Theorem 6.4 and, hence, $\lim\limits_{n\to\infty}\frac{\sin(n^2)}{\sqrt{n}} = 0$ by Theorem 6.2. Hence, $\{a_n\}$ converges.

47. $a_n = \frac{e^n}{n!} = \frac{e\cdot e\cdot e\cdots e\cdot e}{1\cdot 2\cdot 3\cdots(n-1)\cdot n} = \frac{e\cdot e}{1\cdot 2}\cdot\frac{e}{3}\cdot\frac{e}{4}\cdots\frac{e}{n-1}\cdot\frac{e}{n} \leq \frac{e^2}{2}\cdot\frac{e}{n} = \frac{e^3}{2n}$ for $n \geq 4 \Rightarrow$ $0 \leq a_n \leq \frac{e^3}{2n}$ and $\lim\limits_{n\to\infty} 0 = \lim\limits_{n\to\infty}\frac{e^3}{2n} = 0 \Rightarrow \lim\limits_{n\to\infty} a_n = 0$ by Theorem 6.4. Hence, $\{a_n\}$ converges.

48. $a_n = \frac{(2n)!}{2^n n^{2n}} = \frac{1}{2^n}\cdot\frac{1\cdot 2\cdot 3\cdots(n-1)\cdot n}{n\cdot n\cdot n\cdots n\cdot n}\cdot\frac{(n+1)\cdot(n+2)\cdots 2n}{n\cdot n\cdot n\cdots n\cdot n} \leq \frac{1}{2^n}\cdot\frac{1}{n}\cdot 2^n = \frac{1}{n} \Rightarrow 0 \leq a_n \leq \frac{1}{n}$ and $\lim\limits_{n\to\infty} 0 = \lim\limits_{n\to\infty}\frac{1}{n} = 0 \Rightarrow \lim\limits_{n\to\infty} a_n = 0$ by Theorem 6.4. Hence, $\{a_n\}$ converges.

49. $a_n = \frac{3}{2^n} > \frac{3}{2^{n+1}} = a_{n+1} \Rightarrow \{a_n\}$ is decreasing for $n \geq 1$.

50. $a_n = 2 - \frac{1}{n} < 2 - \frac{1}{n+1} = a_{n+1} \Rightarrow \{a_n\}$ is increasing for $n \geq 1$.

51. $n+1 > n \Rightarrow \frac{1}{n+1} < \frac{1}{n} \Rightarrow -\frac{1}{n+1} > -\frac{1}{n} \Rightarrow 1 - \frac{1}{n+1} > 1 - \frac{1}{n} \Rightarrow \frac{1}{1-\frac{1}{n+1}} < \frac{1}{1-\frac{1}{n}} \Rightarrow$ $\frac{-1}{1-\frac{1}{n+1}} > \frac{-1}{1-\frac{1}{n}} \Rightarrow \{a_n\} = \left\{\frac{-1}{1-\frac{1}{n}}\right\}$ is increasing for $n \geq 2$.

52. $a_n = \frac{n}{\ln(n)}$. Let $f(x) = \frac{x}{\ln(x)}$. Then $f'(x) = \frac{\ln(x)-1}{[\ln(x)]^2} > 0$ for $x > e \Rightarrow f$ is increasing on $(e, \infty) \Rightarrow \{a_n\}$ is increasing for $n \geq 3 > e$.

53. $a_n = \frac{n\ln(n)}{e^n}$. Let $f(x) = \frac{x\ln(x)}{e^x} = xe^{-x}\ln(x)$. Then $f'(x) = e^{-x}[\ln(x)-x\ln(x)+1]$ $= e^{-x}[(1-x)\ln(x)+1]$, $f'(1) > 0$, $f'(2) > 0$, and $f'(x) < 0$ for $x \geq e \Rightarrow \{a_n\}$ is decreasing for $n \geq 3 > e$ (but not for $n \geq 2$).

54. $a_n = \frac{\sin(n)}{n^2} \Rightarrow \{a_n\}$ is not monotone.

55. $a_n = \frac{n}{\sqrt{n+1}} \geq 0 \Rightarrow \{a_n\}$ is bounded below by 0. $\lim\limits_{n\to\infty}\frac{n}{\sqrt{n+1}} = \lim\limits_{n\to\infty}\frac{\sqrt{n}}{\sqrt{1+\frac{1}{n}}} = \infty$ $\Rightarrow \{a_n\}$ is not bounded above $\Rightarrow \{a_n\}$ is unbounded.

56. $a_n = \frac{1}{2^n} - \ln(n)$ is decreasing since both $\left\{\frac{1}{2^n}\right\}$ and $\{-\ln(n)\}$ are decreasing. Since $a_1 = \frac{1}{2}$, $a_n \leq \frac{1}{2}$ for all $n \geq 1 \Rightarrow \{a_n\}$ is bounded above by $\frac{1}{2}$. Since $\lim_{n\to\infty} a_n = -\infty$, $\{a_n\}$ is not bounded below $\Rightarrow \{a_n\}$ is unbounded.

57. $a_n = \frac{-1}{1-\frac{1}{n+1}} \Rightarrow \{a_n\}$ is increasing for $n \geq 1$ by Exercise 51 with n replaced by $n+1$. $a_1 = -2$ and $\lim_{n\to\infty} a_n = -1 \Rightarrow -2 \leq a_n \leq -1 \Rightarrow \{a_n\}$ is bounded.

58. $a_n = n^2 e^{-n}$. Let $f(x) = x^2 e^{-x}$. Then $f'(x) = e^{-x}[2x - x^2] = xe^{-x}(2-x) \Rightarrow$ $f'(x) > 0$ on $(0, 2)$ and $f'(x) < 0$ on $(2, \infty) \Rightarrow f(x) \leq f(2) = 4e^{-2}$ on $(0, \infty) \Rightarrow$ $0 \leq a_n \leq 4e^{-2}$ for $n \geq 1 \Rightarrow \{a_n\}$ is bounded.

59. If $n = 1$, then $1 = \sum_{i=1}^{1} i^2 = \frac{1(1+1)(2+1)}{6}$. Assume $\sum_{i=1}^{n} i^2 = \frac{n(n+1)(2n+1)}{6}$. Then
$$\sum_{i=1}^{n+1} i^2 = \sum_{i=1}^{n} i^2 + (n+1)^2 = \frac{n(n+1)(2n+1)}{6} + (n+1)^2 = \frac{n(n+1)(2n+1)+6(n+1)^2}{6} =$$
$$\frac{(n+1)[n(2n+1)+6(n+1)]}{6} = \frac{(n+1)[2n^2+7n+6]}{6} = \frac{(n+1)(n+2)(2n+3)}{6} = \frac{(n+1)[(n+1)+1][2(n+1)+1]}{6}.$$

60. $a_1 = 1 < 3$, and if $a_n < 3$, then $a_{n+1} = 1 + \sqrt{a_n} < 1 + \sqrt{3} < 3 \Rightarrow a_n < 3$ for all $n \geq 1$, by induction. Hence, $\{a_n\}_{n=1}^{\infty}$ is bounded above. $a_1 = 1 < 1 + \sqrt{1} = a_2$, and if $a_n < a_{n+1}$, then $\sqrt{a_n} < \sqrt{a_{n+1}} \Rightarrow 1 + \sqrt{a_n} < 1 + \sqrt{a_{n+1}} \Rightarrow a_{n+1} < a_{n+2}$ $\Rightarrow \{a_n\}_{n=1}^{\infty}$ is increasing for $n \geq 1$, by induction. Since $\{a_n\}_{n=1}^{\infty}$ is increasing and bounded above, it converges by Theorem 6.6. Let $L = \lim_{n\to\infty} a_n$. Then $a_{n+1} = 1 + \sqrt{a_n} \Rightarrow L = 1 + \sqrt{L} \Rightarrow (L-1)^2 = L \Rightarrow L^2 - 3L + 1 = 0 \Rightarrow$ $L = \frac{3\pm\sqrt{5}}{2}$. Since $a_n \geq 1$ for all $n \geq 1$, $L \geq 1$ and, hence, $L = \frac{3+\sqrt{5}}{2}$.

61. If $\lim_{n\to\infty} a_n = L$, then $a_{n+1} = 1 - \frac{2}{a_n} \Rightarrow L = 1 - \frac{2}{L} \Rightarrow L^2 - L + 2 = 0 \Rightarrow L = \frac{1\pm\sqrt{-7}}{2}$ is complex, which is impossible since every a_n is real. Hence, L does not exist, i.e., $\{a_n\}$ diverges.

62. $a_1 = 2 \Rightarrow 1 \leq a_1 \leq 2$, and if $1 \leq a_n \leq 2$, then $\frac{1}{2} \leq \frac{1}{a_n} \leq 1 \Rightarrow -1 \leq -\frac{1}{a_n} \leq -\frac{1}{2}$ $\Rightarrow 1 \leq 2 - \frac{1}{a_n} \leq \frac{3}{2} \Rightarrow 1 \leq a_{n+1} \leq 2 \Rightarrow 1 \leq a_n \leq 2$ for all $n \geq 1$, by induction. $a_1 = 2 > \frac{3}{2} = a_2$, and $a_n > a_{n+1} \Rightarrow \frac{1}{a_n} < \frac{1}{a_{n+1}} \Rightarrow -\frac{1}{a_n} > -\frac{1}{a_{n+1}} \Rightarrow$ $2 - \frac{1}{a_n} > 2 - \frac{1}{a_{n+1}} \Rightarrow a_{n+1} > a_{n+2} \Rightarrow a_n > a_{n+1}$ for all $n \geq 1$, by induction. Hence, $\{a_n\}$ coverges by Theorem 6.6. Then $L = \lim_{n\to\infty} a_n \Rightarrow L = 2 - \frac{1}{L} \Rightarrow$ $L^2 - 2L + 1 = 0 \Rightarrow (L-1)^2 = 0 \Rightarrow L = 1$.

Exercises 6.2 – page 240

1. $\sum_{n=0}^{\infty} \frac{1}{2^n}$, $s_0 = 1$, $s_1 = 1 + \frac{1}{2}$, $s_2 = 1 + \frac{1}{2} + \frac{1}{4}$, $s_3 = 1 + \frac{1}{2} + \frac{1}{4} + \frac{1}{8}$, $s_4 = 1 + \frac{1}{2} + \frac{1}{4} + \frac{1}{8} + \frac{1}{16}$.

2. $\sum_{n=1}^{\infty} \frac{1}{n}$, $s_1 = 1$, $s_2 = 1 + \frac{1}{2}$, $s_3 = 1 + \frac{1}{2} + \frac{1}{3}$, $s_4 = 1 + \frac{1}{2} + \frac{1}{3} + \frac{1}{4}$, $s_5 = 1 + \frac{1}{2} + \frac{1}{3} + \frac{1}{4} + \frac{1}{5}$.

3. $s = \lim_{n \to \infty} s_n = \lim_{n \to \infty} \frac{3n-1}{2n+1} = \frac{3}{2}$.

4. $\sum_{n=0}^{\infty} \frac{1}{5^n} = \sum_{n=0}^{\infty} \left(\frac{1}{5}\right)^n = \frac{1}{1-\frac{1}{5}} = \frac{5}{4}$.

5. $\sum_{n=0}^{\infty} \frac{2^n}{(-5)^n} = \sum_{n=0}^{\infty} \left(-\frac{2}{5}\right)^n = \frac{1}{1+\frac{2}{5}} = \frac{5}{7}$.

6. $\sum_{n=1}^{\infty} \frac{2 \cdot 3^n}{5^n} = 2 \sum_{n=1}^{\infty} \left(\frac{3}{5}\right)^n = 2 \frac{\frac{3}{5}}{1-\frac{3}{5}} = 3$.

7. $\sum_{n=2}^{\infty} \frac{1}{3^n} = \sum_{n=2}^{\infty} \left(\frac{1}{3}\right)^n = \frac{(\frac{1}{3})^2}{1-\frac{1}{3}} = \frac{1}{6}$.

8. $\sum_{n=0}^{\infty} 5 \cdot 2^{3n} 3^{-2n} = 5 \sum_{n=0}^{\infty} \left(\frac{8}{9}\right)^n = \frac{5}{1-\frac{8}{9}} = 45$.

9. $\sum_{n=1}^{\infty} 5 \cdot 3^{2n} 2^{-4n} = 5 \sum_{n=1}^{\infty} \left(\frac{9}{16}\right)^n = 5 \frac{\frac{9}{16}}{1-\frac{9}{16}} = \frac{45}{7}$.

10. $\sum_{n=2}^{\infty} 5^n (-2)^{-3n} = \sum_{n=2}^{\infty} \left(-\frac{5}{8}\right)^n = \frac{(-\frac{5}{8})^2}{1+\frac{5}{8}} = \frac{25}{104}$.

11. $\sum_{n=0}^{\infty} \frac{2}{4n^2+8n+3} = \sum_{n=0}^{\infty} \left(\frac{1}{2n+1} - \frac{1}{2n+3}\right)$, $s_n = \left(1 - \frac{1}{3}\right) + \left(\frac{1}{3} - \frac{1}{5}\right) + \cdots + \left(\frac{1}{2n+1} - \frac{1}{2n+3}\right) =$

    $1 - \frac{1}{2n+3} \Rightarrow \sum_{n=0}^{\infty} \frac{2}{4n^2+8n+3} = \lim_{n \to \infty} s_n = 1$.

12. $\sum_{n=1}^{\infty} \frac{2\sqrt{n^2+3}}{n}$ diverges by the nth-term test because $\lim_{n \to \infty} \frac{2\sqrt{n^2+3}}{n} = 2 \neq 0$.

13. $\sum_{n=0}^{\infty} \frac{\cos(n)}{2+\sin^2(n)}$ diverges by the nth-term test because $\lim_{n \to \infty} \frac{\cos(n)}{2+\sin^2(n)} \neq 0$.

14. $\sum_{n=0}^{\infty} [1 - (-1)^n]$ diverges by the nth-term test because $\lim_{n \to \infty} [1 - (-1)^n] \neq 0$.

15. $\sum_{n=0}^{\infty} \frac{n^3+2n^2-1}{n^2+n+1}$ diverges by the nth-term test because $\lim_{n \to \infty} \frac{n^3+2n^2-1}{n^2+n+1} = \infty \neq 0$.

16. $\sum_{n=1}^{\infty} \frac{1}{n^2\sqrt{n}} = \sum_{n=1}^{\infty} \frac{1}{n^{5/2}}$ converges because it is a p-series with $p = \frac{5}{2} > 1$.

17. $\sum_{n=1}^{\infty} \frac{\sqrt{n}}{n^2} = \sum_{n=1}^{\infty} \frac{1}{n^{3/2}}$ converges because it is a p-series with $p = \frac{3}{2} > 1$.

18. $\sum_{n=1}^{\infty} \frac{1}{n^{r+1}}$, $r > 0$, converges because it is a p-series with $p = r + 1 > 1$.

19. $\displaystyle\sum_{n=1}^{\infty} n^{r-1} = \sum_{n=1}^{\infty} \frac{1}{n^{1-r}}$, $r \geq 0$, diverges because it is a p-series with $p = 1 - r \leq 1$.

20. $\displaystyle\sum_{n=1}^{\infty} \frac{1}{2n-1}$ diverges by the integral test because $\int_1^{\infty} \frac{1}{2x-1}\, dx = \frac{1}{2}\ln(2x-1)\big|_1^{\infty} = \infty$.

21. $\displaystyle\sum_{n=1}^{\infty} 2ne^{-n^2}$ converges by the integral test because $\int_1^{\infty} 2xe^{-x^2}\, dx =$
    $-e^{-x^2}\big|_1^{\infty} = e^{-1} < \infty$.

22. $\displaystyle\sum_{n=2}^{\infty} \frac{1}{n[\ln(n)]^p}$, $p < 1$, diverges by the integral test because $\int_2^{\infty} \frac{1}{x[\ln(x)]^p}\, dx =$
    $\frac{1}{1-p}[\ln(x)]^{1-p}\big|_2^{\infty} = \infty$.

23. $\displaystyle\sum_{n=2}^{\infty} \frac{1}{n[\ln(n)]^p}$, $p > 1$, converges by the integral test because $\int_2^{\infty} \frac{1}{x[\ln(x)]^p}\, dx =$
    $\frac{1}{1-p}[\ln(x)]^{1-p}\big|_2^{\infty} = \frac{1}{p-1}[\ln(2)]^{1-p} < \infty$.

24. (a) $s = \displaystyle\sum_{n=1}^{\infty} \frac{3}{n^4} \approx s_2 = 3 + \frac{3}{16} = \frac{51}{16}$, $\int_3^{\infty} \frac{3}{x^4}\, dx \leq R_2 \leq \int_2^{\infty} \frac{3}{x^4}\, dx \Rightarrow \frac{1}{27} \leq R_2 \leq \frac{1}{8}$.

     (b) $R_n \leq \int_n^{\infty} \frac{3}{x^4}\, dx = \frac{1}{n^3} \leq 0.001$ if $n \geq 10$.

25. (a) $s = \displaystyle\sum_{n=1}^{\infty} \frac{1}{n\sqrt{n}} \approx s_3 = 1 + \frac{1}{2\sqrt{2}} + \frac{1}{3\sqrt{3}}$, $\int_4^{\infty} x^{-3/2}\, dx \leq R_3 \leq \int_3^{\infty} x^{-3/2}\, dx \Rightarrow$
     $\frac{2}{\sqrt{4}} \leq R_3 \leq \frac{2}{\sqrt{3}}$, i.e., $1 \leq R_3 \leq \frac{2}{\sqrt{3}}$.

     (b) $R_n \leq \int_n^{\infty} x^{-3/2}\, dx = \frac{2}{\sqrt{n}} \leq 0.0001$ if $n \geq 400,000,000$.

26. $\displaystyle\sum_{n=0}^{\infty} \frac{1}{n\sqrt{n}+3}$ converges by the comparison test because $\frac{1}{n\sqrt{n}+3} \leq \frac{1}{n^{3/2}}$ and $\displaystyle\sum_{n=1}^{\infty} \frac{1}{n^{3/2}}$
    converges since it is a p-series with $p = \frac{3}{2} > 1$.

27. $\displaystyle\sum_{n=2}^{\infty} \frac{1}{\sqrt{n}-1}$ diverges by the comparison test because $\frac{1}{\sqrt{n}-1} \geq \frac{1}{n^{1/2}}$ and $\displaystyle\sum_{n=1}^{\infty} \frac{1}{n^{1/2}}$
    diverges since it is a p-series with $p = \frac{1}{2} \leq 1$.

28. $\displaystyle\sum_{n=0}^{\infty} \frac{3^n}{4^n+1}$ converges by the comparison test because $\frac{3^n}{4^n+1} \leq \left(\frac{3}{4}\right)^n$ and $\displaystyle\sum_{n=0}^{\infty} \left(\frac{3}{4}\right)^n$
    converges since it is a geometric series with $r = \frac{3}{4}$ and $|r| < 1$.

29. $\displaystyle\sum_{n=0}^{\infty} \frac{3}{2n^2-3}$ converges by the comparison test because $\frac{3}{2n^2-3} \leq \frac{3}{2n^2-n^2} = \frac{3}{n^2}$ for
    $n \geq 2$ and $\displaystyle\sum_{n=1}^{\infty} \frac{1}{n^2}$ converges since it is a p-series with $p = 2 > 1$.

30. $\sum\limits_{n=0}^{\infty} \frac{2^n+1}{3^n}$ converges by the comparison test because $\frac{2^n+1}{3^n} \le \frac{2^n+2^n}{3^n} = \frac{2\cdot2^n}{3^n}$ for $n \ge 0$ and $\sum\limits_{n=0}^{\infty} \left(\frac{2}{3}\right)^n$ converges since it is a geometric series with $r = \frac{2}{3}$ and $|r| < 1$.

31. $\sum\limits_{n=0}^{\infty} \frac{2^n+n}{e^n}$ converges by the comparison test because $\frac{2^n+n}{e^n} \le \frac{2^n+2^n}{e^n} = \frac{2\cdot2^n}{e^n}$ for $n \ge 0$ and $\sum\limits_{n=0}^{\infty} \left(\frac{2}{e}\right)^n$ converges since it is a geometric series with $r = \frac{2}{e}$ and $|r| < 1$.

32. $\sum\limits_{n=1}^{\infty} \frac{1}{\sqrt{n}+n}$ diverges by the comparison test because $\frac{1}{\sqrt{n}+n} \ge \frac{1}{n+n} = \frac{1}{2n}$ for $n \ge 1$ and $\sum\limits_{n=1}^{\infty} \frac{1}{n}$ diverges since it is a p-series with $p = 1 \le 1$.

33. $\sum\limits_{n=1}^{\infty} \frac{\sqrt{n}-1}{n+1}$. $a_n = \frac{\sqrt{n}-1}{n+1} \sim \frac{\sqrt{n}}{n} = \frac{1}{\sqrt{n}} = b_n \Rightarrow \lim\limits_{n\to\infty} \frac{a_n}{b_n} = 1 > 0$ and $< \infty$ and $\sum\limits_{n=1}^{\infty} b_n$ diverges $\Rightarrow \sum\limits_{n=1}^{\infty} a_n$ diverges by the limit comparison test.

34. $\sum\limits_{n=0}^{\infty} \frac{n^3+2n-1}{n^4+n^3+2}$. $a_n = \frac{n^3+2n-1}{n^4+n^3+2} \sim \frac{n^3}{n^4} = \frac{1}{n} = b_n \Rightarrow \lim\limits_{n\to\infty} \frac{a_n}{b_n} = 1 > 0$ and $< \infty$ and $\sum\limits_{n=1}^{\infty} b_n$ diverges $\Rightarrow \sum\limits_{n=0}^{\infty} a_n$ diverges by the limit comparison test.

35. $\sum\limits_{n=1}^{\infty} \frac{\sqrt[3]{n^2+1}}{n^2+n-1}$. $a_n = \frac{\sqrt[3]{n^2+1}}{n^2+n-1} \sim \frac{n^{2/3}}{n^2} = \frac{1}{n^{4/3}} = b_n \Rightarrow \lim\limits_{n\to\infty} \frac{a_n}{b_n} = 1 > 0$ and $< \infty$ and $\sum\limits_{n=1}^{\infty} b_n$ converges $\Rightarrow \sum\limits_{n=1}^{\infty} a_n$ converges by the limit comparison test.

36. $\sum\limits_{n=2}^{\infty} \frac{1}{n^{2/3}\ln(n)}$. $a_n = \frac{1}{n^{2/3}\ln(n)}$. Let $b_n = \frac{1}{n}$. Then $\lim\limits_{n\to\infty} \frac{a_n}{b_n} = \lim\limits_{n\to\infty} \frac{n^{1/3}}{\ln(n)} = \infty$ and $\sum\limits_{n=1}^{\infty} b_n$ diverges $\Rightarrow \sum\limits_{n=2}^{\infty} a_n$ diverges by the limit comparison test.

37. $\sum\limits_{n=2}^{\infty} \frac{\ln(n)}{n^2}$. $a_n = \frac{\ln(n)}{n^2}$. Let $b_n = \frac{1}{n^{3/2}}$. Then $\lim\limits_{n\to\infty} \frac{a_n}{b_n} = \lim\limits_{n\to\infty} \frac{\ln(n)}{n^{1/2}} = 0$ and $\sum\limits_{n=1}^{\infty} b_n$ converges $\Rightarrow \sum\limits_{n=2}^{\infty} a_n$ converges by the limit comparison test.

38. $\sum\limits_{n=1}^{\infty} \frac{\ln(1+\frac{1}{n})}{\sqrt{n}}$. $a_n = \frac{\ln(1+\frac{1}{n})}{\sqrt{n}} = \frac{n\ln(1+\frac{1}{n})}{n\sqrt{n}} = \frac{\ln[(1+\frac{1}{n})^n]}{n\sqrt{n}} \sim \frac{1}{n^{3/2}} = b_n \Rightarrow$ $\lim\limits_{n\to\infty} \frac{a_n}{b_n} = \lim\limits_{n\to\infty} \ln[(1+\frac{1}{n})^n] = \ln(e) = 1 > 0$ and $< \infty$ and $\sum\limits_{n=1}^{\infty} b_n$ converges $\Rightarrow \sum\limits_{n=1}^{\infty} a_n$ converges by the limit comparison test.

39. $\sum_{n=2}^{\infty} \frac{[\ln(n)]^3}{n\sqrt{n}}$. $a_n = \frac{[\ln(n)]^3}{n^{3/2}}$. Let $b_n = \frac{1}{n^{4/3}}$. Then $\lim_{n\to\infty} \frac{a_n}{b_n} = \lim_{n\to\infty} \frac{[\ln(n)]^3}{n^{1/6}} = 0$ and

$\sum_{n=1}^{\infty} b_n$ converges $\Rightarrow \sum_{n=2}^{\infty} a_n$ converges by the limit comparison test.

40. $\sum_{n=1}^{\infty} \frac{(-1)^n}{n^{2/3}}$ converges by the alternating series test since $b_n = \frac{1}{n^{2/3}} > 0$, $\{b_n\}$ is decreasing for $n \geq 1$ and $\lim_{n\to\infty} b_n = 0$.

41. $\sum_{n=0}^{\infty} \frac{(-1)^n}{2+\sin(n)}$ diverges by the nth-term test since $\lim_{n\to\infty} \frac{(-1)^n}{2+\sin(n)} \neq 0$.

42. $\sum_{n=2}^{\infty} \frac{(-1)^n}{\sqrt{\ln(n)}}$ converges by the alternating series test since $b_n = \frac{1}{\sqrt{\ln(n)}} > 0$, $\{b_n\}$ is decreasing for $n \geq 2$ and $\lim_{n\to\infty} b_n = 0$.

43. $\sum_{n=2}^{\infty} \frac{(-1)^n n}{e^n \ln(n)}$ converges by the alternating series test since $b_n = \frac{n}{e^n \ln(n)} > 0$, $\{b_n\}$ is decreasing for $n \geq 2$ and $\lim_{n\to\infty} b_n = 0$.

44. $\sum_{n=1}^{\infty} \frac{(-1)^n - 1}{n}$ diverges since $\sum_{n=1}^{\infty} \frac{(-1)^n}{n}$ converges and $\sum_{n=1}^{\infty} \frac{1}{n}$ diverges.

45. $\sum_{n=1}^{\infty} \frac{1 + (-1)^n n}{n^2}$ converges since both $\sum_{n=1}^{\infty} \frac{1}{n^2}$ and $\sum_{n=1}^{\infty} \frac{(-1)^n}{n}$ converge (Theorem 6.8).

46. (a) $\sum_{n=1}^{\infty} \frac{(-1)^{n-1}}{n^2} \approx s_3 = 1 - \frac{1}{4} + \frac{1}{9} = \frac{31}{36}$, $|R_3| < b_4 = \frac{1}{16}$.

(b) $|R_n| < b_{n+1} = \frac{1}{(n+1)^2} \leq 0.0001$ if $n \geq 99$.

47. (a) $\sum_{n=0}^{\infty} \frac{(-1)^n}{n^3+1} \approx s_2 = 1 - \frac{1}{2} + \frac{1}{9} = \frac{11}{18}$, $|R_2| < b_3 = \frac{1}{28}$.

(b) $|R_n| < b_{n+1} = \frac{1}{(n+1)^3+1} \leq \frac{1}{1,001}$ if $n \geq 9$.

48. $\sum_{n=2}^{\infty} \frac{(-1)^n}{n-1}$ converges by the alternating series test but $\sum_{n=2}^{\infty} \left| \frac{(-1)^n}{n-1} \right| = \sum_{n=2}^{\infty} \frac{1}{n-1}$

diverges. Hence, $\sum_{n=2}^{\infty} \frac{(-1)^n}{n-1}$ converges conditionally.

49. $\sum_{n=1}^{\infty} \frac{(-1)^{n+1}}{n\sqrt{n}}$ converges absolutely since $\sum_{n=1}^{\infty} \left| \frac{(-1)^{n+1}}{n\sqrt{n}} \right| = \sum_{n=1}^{\infty} \frac{1}{n\sqrt{n}}$ converges.

50. $\sum_{n=0}^{\infty} \frac{(-1)^n \sqrt{n}}{n+1}$ converges by the alternating series test but $\sum_{n=0}^{\infty} \left| \frac{(-1)^n \sqrt{n}}{n+1} \right| = \sum_{n=2}^{\infty} \frac{\sqrt{n}}{n+1}$

diverges. Hence, $\sum_{n=0}^{\infty} \frac{(-1)^n \sqrt{n}}{n+1}$ converges conditionally.

51. $\displaystyle\sum_{n=1}^{\infty}\frac{(-2)^n}{n^2}$ diverges by the nth-term test since $\displaystyle\lim_{n\to\infty}\frac{(-2)^n}{n^2}\neq 0$.

52. $\displaystyle\sum_{n=2}^{\infty}\frac{(-1)^n[\ln(n)]^2}{n}$ converges by the alternating series test since $b_n=\frac{[\ln(n)]^2}{n}>0$, $\{b_n\}$ is decreasing for $n\geq 8$ and $\displaystyle\lim_{n\to\infty}b_n=0$. Since $\displaystyle\sum_{n=2}^{\infty}\left|\frac{(-1)^n[\ln(n)]^2}{n}\right|=\sum_{n=2}^{\infty}\frac{[\ln(n)]^2}{n}$ diverges, $\displaystyle\sum_{n=2}^{\infty}\frac{(-1)^n[\ln(n)]^2}{n}$ converges conditionally.

53. $\displaystyle\sum_{n=1}^{\infty}\frac{(-2)^n}{3^n-1}$ converges absolutely since $\displaystyle\sum_{n=1}^{\infty}\left|\frac{(-2)^n}{3^n-1}\right|=\sum_{n=1}^{\infty}\frac{2^n}{3^n-1}$ converges.

54. $\displaystyle\sum_{n=1}^{\infty}\frac{2^n(n+1)^3}{3^n\,n^2}$ converges by the ratio test since $\displaystyle\lim_{n\to\infty}\left|\frac{a_{n+1}}{a_n}\right|=\lim_{n\to\infty}\frac{2^{n+1}(n+2)^3}{3^{n+1}(n+1)^2}\frac{3^n\,n^2}{2^n(n+1)^3}$ $=\frac{2}{3}<1$.

55. $\displaystyle\sum_{n=0}^{\infty}\frac{3^{n-1}\,n^2}{2^{n+1}(n+1)^4}$ diverges by the ratio test since $\displaystyle\lim_{n\to\infty}\left|\frac{a_{n+1}}{a_n}\right|=$ $\displaystyle\lim_{n\to\infty}\frac{3^n(n+1)^2}{2^{n+2}(n+2)^4}\frac{2^{n+1}(n+1)^4}{3^{n-1}\,n^2}=\frac{3}{2}>1$.

56. $\displaystyle\sum_{n=0}^{\infty}\frac{n^3+2n^2-1}{n!}$ converges by the ratio test since $\displaystyle\lim_{n\to\infty}\left|\frac{a_{n+1}}{a_n}\right|=$ $\displaystyle\lim_{n\to\infty}\frac{(n+1)^3+2(n+1)^2-1}{(n+1)!}\frac{n!}{n^3+2n^2-1}=0<1$.

57. $\displaystyle\sum_{n=0}^{\infty}\frac{2n}{(n+1)!}$ converges by the ratio test since $\displaystyle\lim_{n\to\infty}\left|\frac{a_{n+1}}{a_n}\right|=$ $\displaystyle\lim_{n\to\infty}\frac{2(n+1)}{(n+2)!}\frac{(n+1)!}{2n}=0<1$.

58. $\displaystyle\sum_{n=1}^{\infty}\frac{(n!)^2}{n^2(2n)!}$ converges by the ratio test since $\displaystyle\lim_{n\to\infty}\left|\frac{a_{n+1}}{a_n}\right|=$ $\displaystyle\lim_{n\to\infty}\frac{[(n+1)!]^2}{(n+1)^2(2n+2)!}\frac{n^2(2n)!}{(n!)^2}=\lim_{n\to\infty}\frac{n^2}{(2n+2)(2n+1)}=\frac{1}{4}<1$.

59. $\displaystyle\sum_{n=1}^{\infty}\frac{n!}{3\cdot6\cdot9\cdots(3n)}$ converges by the ratio test since $\displaystyle\lim_{n\to\infty}\left|\frac{a_{n+1}}{a_n}\right|=$ $\displaystyle\lim_{n\to\infty}\frac{(n+1)!}{3\cdot6\cdot9\cdots(3n)(3n+3)}\frac{3\cdot6\cdot9\cdots(3n)}{n!}=\lim_{n\to\infty}\frac{n+1}{3n+3}=\frac{1}{3}<1$.

60. $\displaystyle\sum_{n=0}^{\infty}\frac{(2n+1)!}{n!(n+1)!}$ diverges by the ratio test since $\displaystyle\lim_{n\to\infty}\left|\frac{a_{n+1}}{a_n}\right|=$ $\displaystyle\lim_{n\to\infty}\frac{(2n+3)!}{(n+1)!(n+2)!}\frac{n!(n+1)!}{(2n+1)!}=\lim_{n\to\infty}\frac{(2n+3)(2n+2)}{(n+2)(n+1)}=4>1$.

61. $\displaystyle\sum_{n=0}^{\infty}\frac{n!(n+3)!}{(2n+3)!}$ converges by the ratio test since $\displaystyle\lim_{n\to\infty}\left|\frac{a_{n+1}}{a_n}\right|=$ $\displaystyle\lim_{n\to\infty}\frac{(n+1)!(n+4)!}{(2n+5)!}\frac{(2n+3)!}{n!(n+3)!}=\lim_{n\to\infty}\frac{(n+1)(n+4)}{(2n+5)(2n+4)}=\frac{1}{4}<1$.

62. $\sum\limits_{n=2}^{\infty} \frac{(-n)^n}{[\ln(n)]^{2n}}$ diverges by the root test since $\lim\limits_{n\to\infty} |a_n|^{1/n} = \lim\limits_{n\to\infty} \frac{n}{[\ln(n)]^2} = \infty > 1$.

63. $\sum\limits_{n=0}^{\infty} \frac{(-1)^n n^{2n}}{2^n(n^2+1)^n}$ converges by the root test since $\lim\limits_{n\to\infty} |a_n|^{1/n} = \lim\limits_{n\to\infty} \frac{n^2}{2(n^2+1)} = \frac{1}{2} < 1$.

Chapter 6 Exercises – page 243

1. At $n = 0$, $s_0 = 1$ and $\frac{1-r^{n+1}}{1-r} = 1$ and the formula is true. Assume $s_n = \frac{1-r^{n+1}}{1-r}$.
   Then $s_{n+1} = s_n + r^{n+1} = \frac{1-r^{n+1}}{1-r} + r^{n+1} = \frac{1-r^{n+1}+(1-r)r^{n+1}}{1-r} = \frac{1-r^{n+2}}{1-r}$.

2. Let $s_n = \sum\limits_{k=1}^{n} a_k$ and, for $n \geq m$, $t_n = \sum\limits_{k=m}^{n} a_k$. If $m = 1$, then $s_n = t_n$. If
   $m \geq 2$, then $s_n = s_{m-1} + t_n$ for every $n \geq m$. Hence, $\lim\limits_{n\to\infty} s_n$ exists if and only
   if $\lim\limits_{n\to\infty} (s_{m-1} + t_n)$ exists, if and only if $\lim\limits_{n\to\infty} t_n$ exists, since s_{m-1} is a constant.
   Thus, $\sum\limits_{n=1}^{\infty} a_n$ converges if and only if $\sum\limits_{n=m}^{\infty} a_n$ converges for every integer $m \geq 1$.

3. The function $f(x) = \frac{1}{x \ln(x)\{\ln[\ln(x)]\}}$ is positive, decreasing and continuous for
   $x \geq 16 > e^e$ and $\int_{16}^{\infty} f(x)\,dx = \ln\{\ln[\ln(x)]\}\big|_{16}^{\infty} = \infty$. Hence, the series diverges
   by the integral test.

4. $\sum\limits_{n=1}^{\infty} \frac{1}{1+2+3+\cdots+n} = \sum\limits_{n=1}^{\infty} \frac{2}{n(n+1)} = \sum\limits_{n=1}^{\infty} a_n$ converges by the limit comparison test with
   $b_n = \frac{1}{n^2}$.

5. $\sum\limits_{n=1}^{\infty} \frac{n}{1+4+9+\cdots+n^2} = \sum\limits_{n=1}^{\infty} \frac{6}{(n+1)(2n+1)} = \sum\limits_{n=1}^{\infty} a_n$ converges by the limit comparison test
   with $b_n = \frac{1}{n^2}$.

6. Let $\sum\limits_{n=1}^{\infty} a_n$ be a finite series, i.e., $a_n = 0$ for $n \geq m$, where $m \geq 1$ is an integer.
   Then $s_n = \sum\limits_{k=1}^{n} |a_k| = \sum\limits_{k=1}^{m} |a_k| = s_m$ for all $n \geq m \Rightarrow \lim\limits_{n\to\infty} s_n = \lim\limits_{n\to\infty} s_m = s_m \Rightarrow$
   $\sum\limits_{n=1}^{\infty} |a_n|$ converges and, hence, $\sum\limits_{n=1}^{\infty} a_n$ converges absolutely.

7. $a_n = r^n \Rightarrow r^n = r^{n-1} + r^{n-2} \Rightarrow r^2 - r - 1 = 0 \Rightarrow r_1, r_2 = \frac{1\pm\sqrt{5}}{2}$, $a_n = c_1 r_1^n + c_2 r_2^n$
   $\Rightarrow c_1 r_1 + c_2 r_2 = a_1 = 1$ and $c_1 r_1^2 + c_2 r_2^2 = a_2 = 1 \Rightarrow c_1 = \frac{1}{\sqrt{5}}$ and $c_2 = \frac{-1}{\sqrt{5}} \Rightarrow$
   $a_n = \frac{1}{\sqrt{5}}\left(\frac{1+\sqrt{5}}{2}\right)^n - \frac{1}{\sqrt{5}}\left(\frac{1-\sqrt{5}}{2}\right)^n = \frac{1}{2^n\sqrt{5}}[(1+\sqrt{5})^n - (1-\sqrt{5})^n]$, $n \geq 1$.

C.7 Chapter 7 Solutions

Exercises 7.1 – page 251

1. $\sum\limits_{n=0}^{\infty} \frac{x^n}{4^n} = 1 + \frac{x}{4} + \frac{x^2}{16} + \frac{x^3}{64} + \frac{x^4}{256}$.

2. $\sum\limits_{n=0}^{\infty} \frac{(x-2)^n}{\sqrt{n+1}} = 1 + \frac{x-2}{\sqrt{2}} + \frac{(x-2)^2}{\sqrt{3}} + \frac{(x-2)^3}{2} + \frac{(x-2)^4}{\sqrt{5}}$.

3. $\sum\limits_{n=0}^{\infty} \frac{(x+1)^n}{(-3)^n} = 1 - \frac{x+1}{3} + \frac{(x+1)^2}{9} - \frac{(x+1)^3}{27} + \frac{(x+1)^4}{81}$.

4. $\sum\limits_{n=1}^{\infty} \frac{(x+2)^n}{n^2} = (x+2) + \frac{(x+2)^2}{4} + \frac{(x+2)^3}{9} + \frac{(x+2)^4}{16} + \frac{(x+2)^5}{25}$.

5. $\sum\limits_{n=0}^{\infty} \frac{x^{2n}}{\sqrt{n+1}} = 1 + \frac{x^2}{\sqrt{2}} + \frac{x^4}{\sqrt{3}} + \frac{x^6}{2} + \frac{x^8}{\sqrt{5}}$.

6. $\sum\limits_{n=1}^{\infty} \frac{(x-3)^{3n}}{n\sqrt{n}} = (x-3)^3 + \frac{(x-3)^6}{2\sqrt{2}} + \frac{(x-3)^9}{3\sqrt{3}} + \frac{(x-3)^{12}}{8} + \frac{(x-3)^{15}}{5\sqrt{5}}$.

7. $\sum\limits_{n=0}^{\infty} 2^n(x-1)^n + \sum\limits_{n=0}^{\infty} \frac{1}{n+1}(x-1)^n = \sum\limits_{n=0}^{\infty} \left[2^n + \frac{1}{n+1}\right](x-1)^n$.

8. $\alpha \sum\limits_{n=0}^{\infty} a_n(x-a)^n + \beta \sum\limits_{n=0}^{\infty} b_n(x-a)^n = \sum\limits_{n=0}^{\infty} (\alpha a_n + \beta b_n)(x-a)^n$.

9. $3 + 2x - 5x^2 + \sum\limits_{n=0}^{\infty} b_n x^n = \sum\limits_{n=0}^{\infty} c_n x^n \Rightarrow c_0 = 3 + b_0,\ c_1 = 2 + b_1,\ c_2 = -5 + b_2,$
$c_n = b_n,\ n \geq 3$.

10. $2 + (x-3) - (x-3)^4 + \sum\limits_{n=0}^{\infty} b_n(x-3)^n = \sum\limits_{n=0}^{\infty} c_n(x-3)^n \Rightarrow c_0 = 2 + b_0,\ c_1 = 1 + b_1,$
$c_2 = b_2,\ c_3 = b_3,\ c_4 = -1 + b_4,\ c_n = b_n,\ n \geq 5$.

11. $\sum\limits_{n=0}^{\infty} c_n x^n = c_0 + c_1 x + c_2 x^2 + c_3 x^3 + c_4 x^4 + c_5 x^5 + \cdots = (c_0 + c_2 x^2 + c_4 x^4 + \cdots) +$
$(c_1 x + c_3 x^3 + c_5 x^5 + \cdots) = \sum\limits_{k=0}^{\infty} c_{2k} x^{2k} + \sum\limits_{k=0}^{\infty} c_{2k+1} x^{2k+1}$.

12. $\sum\limits_{n=0}^{\infty} \frac{2^n x^n}{n+1}$, $R = \lim\limits_{n\to\infty} \left|\frac{c_n}{c_{n+1}}\right| = \lim\limits_{n\to\infty} \frac{2^n}{n+1} \frac{n+2}{2^{n+1}} = \frac{1}{2}$. $|x| < \frac{1}{2} \Rightarrow -\frac{1}{2} < x < \frac{1}{2}$. At $x = -\frac{1}{2}$, $\sum\limits_{n=0}^{\infty} \frac{(-1)^n}{n+1}$ converges, and at $x = \frac{1}{2}$, $\sum\limits_{n=0}^{\infty} \frac{1}{n+1}$ diverges $\Rightarrow I = \left[-\frac{1}{2}, \frac{1}{2}\right)$.

13. $\sum\limits_{n=0}^{\infty} \frac{x^n}{n^2+1}$, $R = \lim\limits_{n\to\infty} \left| \frac{c_n}{c_{n+1}} \right| = \lim\limits_{n\to\infty} \frac{(n+1)^2+1}{n^2+1} = 1$. $|x| < 1 \Rightarrow -1 < x < 1$. At

$x = \pm 1$, $\sum\limits_{n=0}^{\infty} \frac{(\pm 1)^n}{n^2+1}$ converges $\Rightarrow I = [-1, 1]$.

14. $\sum\limits_{n=0}^{\infty} \frac{\sqrt{n}(x-6)^n}{n^3+1}$, $R = \lim\limits_{n\to\infty} \left| \frac{c_n}{c_{n+1}} \right| = \lim\limits_{n\to\infty} \frac{\sqrt{n}}{n^3+1} \frac{(n+1)^3+1}{\sqrt{n+1}} = 1$. $|x - 6| < 1 \Rightarrow$

$-1 < x - 6 < 1 \Rightarrow 5 < x < 7$. At $x = 5$, $\sum\limits_{n=0}^{\infty} \frac{\sqrt{n}(-1)^n}{n^3+1}$ converges, and at $x = 7$,

$\sum\limits_{n=0}^{\infty} \frac{\sqrt{n}}{n^3+1}$ converges $\Rightarrow I = [5, 7]$.

15. $\sum\limits_{n=0}^{\infty} \frac{(-1)^n(x-1)^n}{2n+1}$, $R = \lim\limits_{n\to\infty} \left| \frac{c_n}{c_{n+1}} \right| = \lim\limits_{n\to\infty} \frac{2n+3}{2n+1} = 1$. $|x - 1| < 1 \Rightarrow -1 < x - 1 < 1$

$\Rightarrow 0 < x < 2$. At $x = 0$, $\sum\limits_{n=0}^{\infty} \frac{1}{2n+1}$ diverges, and at $x = 2$, $\sum\limits_{n=0}^{\infty} \frac{(-1)^n}{2n+1}$ converges $\Rightarrow$

$I = (0, 2]$.

16. $\sum\limits_{n=0}^{\infty} \frac{(x+1)^n}{2^n}$, $R = \lim\limits_{n\to\infty} \left| \frac{c_n}{c_{n+1}} \right| = \lim\limits_{n\to\infty} \frac{2^{n+1}}{2^n} = 2$. $|x + 1| < 2 \Rightarrow -2 < x + 1 < 2 \Rightarrow$

$-3 < x < 1$. At $x = -3$, $\sum\limits_{n=0}^{\infty} (-1)^n$ diverges, and at $x = 1$, $\sum\limits_{n=0}^{\infty} 1$ diverges $\Rightarrow$

$I = (-3, 1)$.

17. $\sum\limits_{n=0}^{\infty} \frac{2^n(2x-4)^n}{\sqrt{n+1}} = \sum\limits_{n=0}^{\infty} \frac{4^n(x-2)^n}{\sqrt{n+1}}$, $R = \lim\limits_{n\to\infty} \left| \frac{c_n}{c_{n+1}} \right| = \lim\limits_{n\to\infty} \frac{4^n}{\sqrt{n+1}} \frac{\sqrt{n+2}}{4^{n+1}} = \frac{1}{4}$. $|x - 2| < \frac{1}{4}$

$\Rightarrow -\frac{1}{4} < x - 2 < \frac{1}{4} \Rightarrow \frac{7}{4} < x < \frac{9}{4}$. At $x = \frac{7}{4}$, $\sum\limits_{n=0}^{\infty} \frac{(-1)^n}{\sqrt{n+1}}$ converges, and at $x = \frac{9}{4}$,

$\sum\limits_{n=0}^{\infty} \frac{1}{\sqrt{n+1}}$ diverges $\Rightarrow I = \left[\frac{7}{4}, \frac{9}{4} \right)$.

18. $\sum\limits_{n=0}^{\infty} \frac{2^n(6-3x)^n}{n+1} = \sum\limits_{n=0}^{\infty} \frac{(-6)^n(x-2)^n}{n+1}$, $R = \lim\limits_{n\to\infty} \left| \frac{c_n}{c_{n+1}} \right| = \lim\limits_{n\to\infty} \frac{6^n}{n+1} \frac{n+2}{6^{n+1}} = \frac{1}{6}$. $|x - 2| < \frac{1}{6}$

$\Rightarrow -\frac{1}{6} < x - 2 < \frac{1}{6} \Rightarrow \frac{11}{6} < x < \frac{13}{6}$. At $x = \frac{11}{6}$, $\sum\limits_{n=0}^{\infty} \frac{1}{n+1}$ diverges, and at $x = \frac{13}{6}$,

$\sum\limits_{n=0}^{\infty} \frac{(-1)^n}{n+1}$ converges $\Rightarrow I = \left(\frac{11}{6}, \frac{13}{6} \right]$.

19. $\sum\limits_{n=0}^{\infty} \frac{(x-3)^{2n}}{2^n}$, $\lim\limits_{n\to\infty} \left| \frac{a_{n+1}}{a_n} \right| = \lim\limits_{n\to\infty} \left| \frac{(x-3)^{2n+2}}{2^{n+1}} \frac{2^n}{(x-3)^{2n}} \right| = \frac{|x-3|^2}{2} < 1$ if and only if

$|x - 3| < \sqrt{2} \Rightarrow R = \sqrt{2}$. $|x - 3| < \sqrt{2} \Rightarrow -\sqrt{2} < x - 3 < \sqrt{2} \Rightarrow$

$3 - \sqrt{2} < x < 3 + \sqrt{2}$. At $x = 3 \pm \sqrt{2}$, $\sum\limits_{n=0}^{\infty} 1$ diverges $\Rightarrow I = (3 - \sqrt{2}, 3 + \sqrt{2})$.

20. $\sum\limits_{n=0}^{\infty} \frac{x^{3n}}{\sqrt{n^2+1}}$, $\lim\limits_{n\to\infty} \left| \frac{a_{n+1}}{a_n} \right| = \lim\limits_{n\to\infty} \left| \frac{x^{3n+3}}{\sqrt{(n+1)^2+1}} \frac{\sqrt{n^2+1}}{x^{3n}} \right| = |x|^3 < 1$ if and only if $|x| < 1$

$\Rightarrow R = 1.$ $|x| < 1 \Rightarrow -1 < x < 1.$ At $x = -1$, $\sum\limits_{n=0}^{\infty} \frac{(-1)^n}{\sqrt{n^2+1}}$ converges, and at $x = 1$, $\sum\limits_{n=0}^{\infty} \frac{1}{\sqrt{n^2+1}}$ diverges $\Rightarrow I = [-1, 1).$

21. $\sum\limits_{n=0}^{\infty} (3x - 2)^{2n}$, $\lim\limits_{n\to\infty} \left|\frac{a_{n+1}}{a_n}\right| = \lim\limits_{n\to\infty} \left|\frac{(3x-2)^{2n+2}}{(3x-2)^{2n}}\right| = |3x - 2|^2 < 1$ if and only if $|3x - 2| < 1$, i.e., $\left|x - \frac{2}{3}\right| < \frac{1}{3} \Rightarrow R = \frac{1}{3}.$ $\left|x - \frac{2}{3}\right| < \frac{1}{3} \Rightarrow -\frac{1}{3} < x - \frac{2}{3} < \frac{1}{3} \Rightarrow \frac{1}{3} < x < 1.$ At $x = \frac{1}{3}$ and at $x = 1$, $\sum\limits_{n=0}^{\infty} 1$ diverges $\Rightarrow I = \left(\frac{1}{3}, 1\right).$

22. $\sum\limits_{n=1}^{\infty} \frac{3^{n+1}(n^2+1)}{2^n \sqrt{n}} (x + 2)^n$, $R = \lim\limits_{n\to\infty} \left|\frac{c_n}{c_{n+1}}\right| = \lim\limits_{n\to\infty} \frac{3^{n+1}(n^2+1)}{2^n \sqrt{n}} \frac{2^{n+1}\sqrt{n+1}}{3^{n+2}[(n+1)^2+1]} = \frac{2}{3}.$

$|x + 2| < \frac{2}{3} \Rightarrow -\frac{2}{3} < x + 2 < \frac{2}{3} \Rightarrow -\frac{8}{3} < x < -\frac{4}{3}.$ At $x = -\frac{8}{3}$, $\sum\limits_{n=1}^{\infty} \frac{3(-1)^n(n^2+1)}{\sqrt{n}}$ diverges, and at $x = -\frac{4}{3}$, $\sum\limits_{n=1}^{\infty} \frac{3(n^2+1)}{\sqrt{n}}$ diverges $\Rightarrow I = \left(-\frac{8}{3}, -\frac{4}{3}\right).$

23. $\sum\limits_{n=0}^{\infty} \frac{2^{2n}(x-3)^n}{n!}$, $R = \lim\limits_{n\to\infty} \left|\frac{c_n}{c_{n+1}}\right| = \lim\limits_{n\to\infty} \frac{2^{2n}}{n!} \frac{(n+1)!}{2^{2n+2}} = \lim\limits_{n\to\infty} \frac{n+1}{4} = \infty \Rightarrow I = (-\infty, \infty).$

24. $\sum\limits_{n=0}^{\infty} \frac{(2n)!}{(n!)^2} x^n$, $R = \lim\limits_{n\to\infty} \left|\frac{c_n}{c_{n+1}}\right| = \lim\limits_{n\to\infty} \frac{(2n)!}{(n!)^2} \frac{[(n+1)!]^2}{(2n+2)!} = \lim\limits_{n\to\infty} \frac{(n+1)^2}{(2n+2)(2n+1)} = \frac{1}{4}.$

25. $\sum\limits_{n=1}^{\infty} \frac{[(n-1)!]^2}{(2n)!} (x - 1)^{2n}$, $\lim\limits_{n\to\infty} \left|\frac{a_{n+1}}{a_n}\right| = \lim\limits_{n\to\infty} \left|\frac{(n!)^2(x-1)^{2n+2}}{(2n+2)!} \frac{(2n)!}{[(n-1)!]^2(x-1)^{2n}}\right| = \lim\limits_{n\to\infty} \frac{n^2|x-1|^2}{(2n+2)(2n+1)} = \frac{|x-1|^2}{4} < 1$ if and only if $|x - 1| < 2 \Rightarrow R = 2.$

26. (a) $\left(\sum\limits_{n=0}^{\infty} a_n x^n\right) \left(\sum\limits_{n=0}^{\infty} b_n x^n\right) = \sum\limits_{n=0}^{\infty} c_n x^n$, $c_n = \sum\limits_{k=0}^{n} a_k b_{n-k} = \sum\limits_{k=0}^{n} a_{n-k} b_k.$

(b) $\left[\sum\limits_{n=0}^{\infty} a_n (x - a)^n\right] \left[\sum\limits_{n=0}^{\infty} b_n (x - a)^n\right] = \sum\limits_{n=0}^{\infty} c_n (x - a)^n$,

$c_n = \sum\limits_{k=0}^{n} a_k b_{n-k} = \sum\limits_{k=0}^{n} a_{n-k} b_k.$

Exercises 7.2 – page 279

1. $f(x) = \frac{1}{1+2x} = \sum\limits_{n=0}^{\infty} (-2x)^n = \sum\limits_{n=0}^{\infty} (-2)^n x^n$, $|-2x| < 1 \Rightarrow |x| < \frac{1}{2} = R.$

2. $f(x) = \frac{6}{2-x} = \frac{3}{1-\frac{x}{2}} = 3\sum\limits_{n=0}^{\infty} \left(\frac{x}{2}\right)^n = \sum\limits_{n=0}^{\infty} \frac{3}{2^n} x^n$, $\left|\frac{x}{2}\right| < 1 \Rightarrow |x| < 2 = R.$

3. $f(x) = \frac{1}{3+x} = \frac{1}{3} \frac{1}{1+\frac{x}{3}} = \frac{1}{3} \sum\limits_{n=0}^{\infty} \left(-\frac{x}{3}\right)^n = \sum\limits_{n=0}^{\infty} \frac{(-1)^n}{3^{n+1}} x^n$, $\left|-\frac{x}{3}\right| < 1 \Rightarrow |x| < 3 = R.$

4. $f(x) = \frac{2x}{4-x} = \frac{x}{2}\frac{1}{1-\frac{x}{4}} = \frac{x}{2}\sum_{n=0}^{\infty}\left(\frac{x}{4}\right)^n = \sum_{n=0}^{\infty}\frac{1}{2^{2n+1}}x^{n+1}$, $\left|\frac{x}{4}\right| < 1 \Rightarrow |x| < 4 = R$.

5. $f(x) = \frac{1}{6+2x} = \frac{1}{6}\frac{1}{1+\frac{x}{3}} = \frac{1}{6}\sum_{n=0}^{\infty}\left(-\frac{x}{3}\right)^n = \sum_{n=0}^{\infty}\frac{(-1)^n}{2\cdot 3^{n+1}}x^n$, $\left|-\frac{x}{3}\right| < 1 \Rightarrow |x| < 3 = R$.

6. $f(x) = \frac{1}{1-x^2} = \sum_{n=0}^{\infty}(x^2)^n = \sum_{n=0}^{\infty}x^{2n}$, $|x^2| < 1 \Rightarrow |x| < 1 = R$.

7. $f(x) = \frac{1}{2+x^3} = \frac{1}{2}\frac{1}{1+\frac{x^3}{2}} = \frac{1}{2}\sum_{n=0}^{\infty}\left(-\frac{x^3}{2}\right)^n = \sum_{n=0}^{\infty}\frac{(-1)^n}{2^{n+1}}x^{3n}$, $\left|-\frac{x^3}{2}\right| < 1 \Rightarrow R = 2^{1/3}$.

8. $f(x) = \frac{1}{1-x} - \frac{1}{1-3x} = \sum_{n=0}^{\infty}x^n - \sum_{n=0}^{\infty}(3x)^n = \sum_{n=0}^{\infty}(1-3^n)x^n$, $|x| < 1$ and $|3x| < 1 \Rightarrow$ $|x| < \frac{1}{3} = R$.

9. $f(x) = \frac{1}{2+x} + \frac{1}{3-2x} = \frac{1}{2}\frac{1}{1+\frac{x}{2}} + \frac{1}{3}\frac{1}{1-\frac{2x}{3}} = \frac{1}{2}\sum_{n=0}^{\infty}\left(-\frac{x}{2}\right)^n + \frac{1}{3}\sum_{n=0}^{\infty}\left(\frac{2x}{3}\right)^n =$
$\sum_{n=0}^{\infty}\left[\frac{(-1)^n}{2^{n+1}} + \frac{2^n}{3^{n+1}}\right]x^n$, $\left|-\frac{x}{2}\right| < 1$ and $\left|\frac{2x}{3}\right| < 1 \Rightarrow |x| < 2$ and $|x| < \frac{3}{2} \Rightarrow R = \frac{3}{2}$.

10. $f(x) = \frac{x^2+1}{x^2-1} = -(x^2+1)\sum_{n=0}^{\infty}x^{2n} = -\sum_{n=0}^{\infty}x^{2n} - \sum_{n=0}^{\infty}x^{2n+2} = -\sum_{n=0}^{\infty}x^{2n} - \sum_{n=1}^{\infty}x^{2n} =$
$-1 - \sum_{n=1}^{\infty}x^{2n} - \sum_{n=1}^{\infty}x^{2n} = -1 - \sum_{n=1}^{\infty}2x^{2n}$, $|x^2| < 1 \Rightarrow R = 1$.

11. $f(x) = e^{-x} = \sum_{n=0}^{\infty}\frac{1}{n!}(-x)^n = \sum_{n=0}^{\infty}\frac{(-1)^n}{n!}x^n$, $R = \infty$.

12. $f(x) = e^{-3x} = \sum_{n=0}^{\infty}\frac{1}{n!}(-3x)^n = \sum_{n=0}^{\infty}\frac{(-3)^n}{n!}x^n$, $R = \infty$.

13. $f(x) = e^x = e^2 e^{x-2} = e^2\sum_{n=0}^{\infty}\frac{1}{n!}(x-2)^n = \sum_{n=0}^{\infty}\frac{e^2}{n!}(x-2)^n$, $R = \infty$.

14. $f(x) = e^x = e^{-2}e^{x+2} = e^{-2}\sum_{n=0}^{\infty}\frac{1}{n!}(x+2)^n = \sum_{n=0}^{\infty}\frac{e^{-2}}{n!}(x+2)^n$, $R = \infty$.

15. $f(x) = e^{-3x^2} = \sum_{n=0}^{\infty}\frac{1}{n!}(-3x^2)^n = \sum_{n=0}^{\infty}\frac{(-3)^n}{n!}x^{2n}$, $R = \infty$.

16. $f(x) = e^{-3x} = e^{-3}e^{-3(x-1)} = e^{-3}\sum_{n=0}^{\infty}\frac{1}{n!}[-3(x-1)]^n = \sum_{n=0}^{\infty}\frac{e^{-3}(-3)^n}{n!}(x-1)^n$, $R = \infty$.

17. $f(x) = \sin(2x) = \sum_{k=0}^{\infty}\frac{(-1)^k}{(2k+1)!}(2x)^{2k+1} = \sum_{k=0}^{\infty}\frac{(-1)^k 2^{2k+1}}{(2k+1)!}x^{2k+1}$, $R = \infty$.

18. $f(x) = \cos(3x) = \sum\limits_{k=0}^{\infty} \frac{(-1)^k}{(2k)!}(3x)^{2k} = \sum\limits_{k=0}^{\infty} \frac{(-1)^k 3^{2k}}{(2k)!}x^{2k}$, $R = \infty$.

19. $f(x) = \sin(x) = \sin[\pi + (x - \pi)] = \sin(\pi)\cos(x - \pi) + \cos(\pi)\sin(x - \pi) =$
    $-\sin(x - \pi) = \sum\limits_{k=0}^{\infty} \frac{(-1)^{k+1}}{(2k+1)!}(x - \pi)^{2k+1}$, $R = \infty$.

20. $f(x) = \cos(x) = \cos[\pi + (x - \pi)] = \cos(\pi)\cos(x - \pi) - \sin(\pi)\sin(x - \pi) =$
    $-\cos(x - \pi) = \sum\limits_{k=0}^{\infty} \frac{(-1)^{k+1}}{(2k)!}(x - \pi)^{2k}$, $R = \infty$.

21. $\tan^{-1}(x) = \sum\limits_{n=0}^{\infty} \frac{(-1)^n}{2n+1}x^{2n+1}$, $|x| < 1$, $\Rightarrow \tan^{-1}(2x) = \sum\limits_{n=0}^{\infty} \frac{(-1)^n}{2n+1}(2x)^{2n+1} =$
    $\sum\limits_{n=0}^{\infty} \frac{(-1)^n 2^{2n+1}}{2n+1}x^{2n+1}$, $|2x| < 1 \Rightarrow |x| < \frac{1}{2} = R$.

22. $\frac{1}{x-1} = \frac{1}{1+(x-2)} = \sum\limits_{n=0}^{\infty} (-1)^n(x - 2)^n$, $|x - 2| < 1$, $\Rightarrow$
    $\ln(x - 1) = \int \frac{1}{x-1}\,dx = \sum\limits_{n=0}^{\infty} \frac{(-1)^n}{n+1}(x - 2)^{n+1} + C$, $x = 2 \Rightarrow C = 0 \Rightarrow$
    $\ln(x - 1) = \sum\limits_{n=1}^{\infty} \frac{(-1)^{n-1}}{n}(x - 2)^n$, $R = 1$.

23. $\frac{1}{x} = \frac{1}{2+(x-2)} = \frac{1}{2}\frac{1}{1+\frac{x-2}{2}} = \frac{1}{2}\sum\limits_{n=0}^{\infty} \left(-\frac{x-2}{2}\right)^n = \sum\limits_{n=0}^{\infty} \frac{(-1)^n}{2^{n+1}}(x - 2)^n$, $\left|-\frac{x-2}{2}\right| < 1$, $\Rightarrow$
    $\ln(x) = \int \frac{1}{x}\,dx = \sum\limits_{n=0}^{\infty} \frac{(-1)^n}{2^{n+1}(n+1)}(x - 2)^{n+1} + C$, $x = 2 \Rightarrow C = \ln(2) \Rightarrow$
    $\ln(x) = \sum\limits_{n=0}^{\infty} \frac{(-1)^n}{2^{n+1}(n+1)}(x - 2)^{n+1} + \ln(2)$, $|x - 2| < 2 = R$.

24. $\frac{1}{1+(x-2)^2} = \sum\limits_{n=0}^{\infty} [-(x - 2)^2]^n = \sum\limits_{n=0}^{\infty} (-1)^n(x - 2)^{2n}$, $|x - 2| < 1$, $\Rightarrow$
    $\tan^{-1}(x - 2) = \int \frac{1}{1+(x-2)^2}\,dx = \sum\limits_{n=0}^{\infty} \frac{(-1)^n}{2n+1}(x - 2)^{2n+1} + C$, $x = 2 \Rightarrow C = 0 \Rightarrow$
    $\tan^{-1}(x - 2) = \sum\limits_{n=0}^{\infty} \frac{(-1)^n}{2n+1}(x - 2)^{2n+1}$, $R = 1$.

25. $f(x) = \frac{4}{\sqrt{4+x}} = 2\left(1 + \frac{x}{4}\right)^{-1/2}$, $\alpha = -\frac{1}{2}$, $\binom{\alpha}{k} = \frac{(-1)^k(2k)!}{2^{2k}(k!)^2}$, $k \geq 0$, $\Rightarrow$
    $\frac{4}{\sqrt{4+x}} = 2\sum\limits_{k=0}^{\infty} \frac{(-1)^k(2k)!}{2^{2k}(k!)^2}\left(\frac{x}{4}\right)^k = \sum\limits_{k=0}^{\infty} \frac{(-1)^k(2k)!}{2^{4k+1}(k!)^2}x^k$, $\left|\frac{x}{4}\right| < 1 \Rightarrow |x| < 4 = R$.

26. $f(x) = \frac{x^2}{\sqrt[3]{1+x}} = x^2(1+x)^{-1/3}$, $\alpha = -\frac{1}{3}$, $\binom{\alpha}{k} = \frac{(-1)^k \cdot 1 \cdot 4 \cdot 7 \cdots (3k-2)}{3^k k!}$, $k \geq 1$, $\Rightarrow \frac{x^2}{\sqrt[3]{1+x}} =$
    $x^2\left[1 + \sum\limits_{k=1}^{\infty} \frac{(-1)^k \cdot 1 \cdot 4 \cdot 7 \cdots (3k-2)}{3^k k!}x^k\right] = x^2 + \sum\limits_{k=1}^{\infty} \frac{(-1)^k \cdot 1 \cdot 4 \cdot 7 \cdots (3k-2)}{3^k k!}x^{k+2}$, $|x| < 1 = R$.

27. $f(x) = x\sqrt{1+x^2} = x(1+x^2)^{1/2}$, $\alpha = \frac{1}{2}$, $\binom{\alpha}{k} = \frac{(-1)^{k-1}(2k-2)!}{2^{2k-1}k!(k-1)!}$, $k \geq 1$, $\Rightarrow$

$x\sqrt{1+x^2} = x\left[1 + \sum_{k=1}^{\infty}\frac{(-1)^{k-1}(2k-2)!}{2^{2k-1}k!(k-1)!}x^{2k}\right] = x + \sum_{k=1}^{\infty}\frac{(-1)^{k-1}(2k-2)!}{2^{2k-1}k!(k-1)!}x^{2k+1}$, $R = 1$.

28. $f(x) = \frac{x}{(1-x^3)^{3/2}} = x(1-x^3)^{-3/2}$, $\alpha = -\frac{3}{2}$, $\binom{\alpha}{k} = \frac{\left(-\frac{3}{2}\right)\left(-\frac{5}{2}\right)\cdots\left(-\frac{2k+1}{2}\right)}{k!} =$

$\frac{(-1)^k \cdot 3 \cdot 5 \cdots (2k+1)}{2^k k!} = \frac{(-1)^k(2k+1)!}{2^{2k}(k!)^2}$, $k \geq 0$, $\Rightarrow \frac{x}{(1-x^3)^{3/2}} = x\sum_{k=0}^{\infty}\frac{(-1)^k(2k+1)!}{2^{2k}(k!)^2}(-x^3)^k =$

$\sum_{k=0}^{\infty}\frac{(2k+1)!}{2^{2k}(k!)^2}x^{3k+1}$, $|x| < 1 = R$.

29. $e^x = 1 + x + \frac{1}{2}x^2 + \frac{1}{6}x^3 + \cdots$ and $\sin(x) = x - \frac{1}{6}x^3 + \cdots \Rightarrow e^x\sin(x) =$
$\left(1 + x + \frac{1}{2}x^2 + \frac{1}{6}x^3 + \cdots\right)\left(x - \frac{1}{6}x^3 + \cdots\right) \Rightarrow T_4(x) = T_3(x) = x + x^2 + \frac{1}{3}x^3$.

30. $f(x) = \frac{\cos(x)}{1+\sin(x)} = \frac{1 - \frac{1}{2}x^2 + \frac{1}{24}x^4 + \cdots}{1 + x - \frac{1}{6}x^3 + \cdots} \Rightarrow T_4(x) = 1 - x + \frac{1}{2}x^2 - \frac{1}{3}x^3 + \frac{5}{24}x^4$.

31. $f(x) = (x^2+1)\cos(x) = (1+x^2)\left(1 - \frac{1}{2}x^2 + \frac{1}{24}x^4 + \cdots\right) \Rightarrow T_4(x) = 1 + \frac{1}{2}x^2 - \frac{11}{24}x^4$.

32. $\frac{1}{x} = \frac{1}{1+(x-1)} = \sum_{n=0}^{\infty}(-1)^n(x-1)^n \Rightarrow \ln(x) = \int\frac{1}{x}\,dx = \sum_{n=0}^{\infty}\frac{(-1)^n}{n+1}(x-1)^{n+1} + C$,

$x = 1 \Rightarrow C = 0 \Rightarrow \ln(x) = \sum_{n=1}^{\infty}\frac{(-1)^{n-1}}{n}(x-1)^n$, $x = 1 + (x-1) \Rightarrow x\ln(x) =$

$[1 + (x-1)][(x-1) - \frac{1}{2}(x-1)^2 + \frac{1}{3}(x-1)^3 - \frac{1}{4}(x-1)^4 + \cdots] =$
$(x-1) + \frac{1}{2}(x-1)^2 - \frac{1}{6}(x-1)^3 + \frac{1}{12}(x-1)^4 + \cdots$,

$\frac{1}{2-x} = \frac{1}{1-(x-1)} = \sum_{n=0}^{\infty}(x-1)^n = 1 + (x-1) + (x-1)^2 + (x-1)^3 + \cdots \Rightarrow \frac{x\ln(x)}{2-x} =$

$[(x-1) + \frac{1}{2}(x-1)^2 - \frac{1}{6}(x-1)^3 + \frac{1}{12}(x-1)^4 + \cdots][1 + (x-1) + (x-1)^2 + (x-1)^3 + \cdots]$
$\Rightarrow T_4(x) = (x-1) + \frac{3}{2}(x-1)^2 + \frac{4}{3}(x-1)^3 + \frac{17}{12}(x-1)^4$.

33. $\sin(x) = \sum_{k=0}^{\infty}\frac{(-1)^k}{(2k+1)!}x^{2k+1} \Rightarrow \sin\left(\frac{1}{2}\right) = \sum_{k=0}^{\infty}\frac{(-1)^k}{2^{2k+1}(2k+1)!} = \sum_{k=0}^{\infty}(-1)^k b_k$ is alternating,

$|R_k| < b_{k+1} = \frac{1}{2^{2k+3}(2k+3)!}$, $k = 1 \Rightarrow |R_1| < \frac{1}{2^5 5!} \approx 0.00026 < 0.001 \Rightarrow$
$\sin\left(\frac{1}{2}\right) \approx s_1 = \frac{1}{2} - \frac{1}{48} = \frac{23}{48} \approx 0.47916$. The value by calculator is 0.47942, with an absolute difference of $0.00026 < 0.001$.

34. $\cos(x) = \sum_{k=0}^{\infty}\frac{(-1)^k}{(2k)!}x^{2k} \Rightarrow \cos(\sqrt{x}) = \sum_{k=0}^{\infty}\frac{(-1)^k}{(2k)!}x^k \Rightarrow \int_0^1\cos(\sqrt{x})\,dx =$

$\sum_{k=0}^{\infty}\frac{(-1)^k}{(k+1)(2k)!}x^{k+1}\Big|_0^1 = \sum_{k=0}^{\infty}\frac{(-1)^k}{(k+1)(2k)!} = \sum_{k=0}^{\infty}(-1)^k b_k$ is alternating, $|R_k| < b_{k+1} =$

$\frac{1}{(k+2)(2k+2)!}$, $k = 2 \Rightarrow |R_2| < \frac{1}{2880} \approx 0.0003 < 0.001 \Rightarrow$
$\int_0^1\cos(\sqrt{x})\,dx \approx s_2 = 1 - \frac{1}{4} + \frac{1}{72} = \frac{55}{72} \approx 0.7638$, correct to 3 decimal places.

35. $\frac{1}{\sqrt{1+t}} = \sum_{k=0}^{\infty}\frac{(-1)^k(2k)!}{2^{2k}(k!)^2}t^k \Rightarrow \int_0^{\frac{1}{2}}\frac{1}{\sqrt{1+x^8}}\,dx = \sum_{k=0}^{\infty}\frac{(-1)^k(2k)!}{(8k+1)2^{2k}(k!)^2}x^{8k+1}\Big|_0^{\frac{1}{2}} =$

$\sum_{k=0}^{\infty} \frac{(-1)^k(2k)!}{(8k+1)2^{10k+1}(k!)^2} = \sum_{k=0}^{\infty}(-1)^k b_k$ is alternating, $|R_k| < b_{k+1} = \frac{(2k+2)!}{(8k+9)2^{10k+11}[(k+1)!]^2}$,

$k = 0 \Rightarrow |R_0| < b_1 = \frac{1}{9\cdot2^{10}} = \frac{1}{9216} \approx 0.000108 < 0.001 \Rightarrow$

$\int_0^{\frac{1}{2}} \frac{1}{\sqrt{1+x^8}}\,dx \approx s_0 = \frac{1}{2} = 0.5$, correct to 3 decimal places.

36. $\lim\limits_{x\to 0} \frac{x(e^{3x}-1)^2\cos^2(x)}{\sin^3(x)} = \lim\limits_{x\to 0} \frac{x\left(3x+\frac{9}{2}x^2+\cdots\right)^2\left(1-\frac{1}{2}x^2+\cdots\right)^2}{\left(x-\frac{1}{6}x^3+\cdots\right)^3} = \lim\limits_{x\to 0} \frac{x^3\left(3+\frac{9}{2}x+\cdots\right)^2\left(1-\frac{1}{2}x^2+\cdots\right)^2}{x^3\left(1-\frac{1}{6}x^2+\cdots\right)^3} =$

$\lim\limits_{x\to 0} \frac{\left(3+\frac{9}{2}x+\cdots\right)^2\left(1-\frac{1}{2}x^2+\cdots\right)^2}{\left(1-\frac{1}{6}x^2+\cdots\right)^3} = 9.$

37. $\lim\limits_{x\to 0} \frac{(x^2-1)(e^{-x}+x-1)\cos(x)}{x\sin(3x)} = \lim\limits_{x\to 0} \frac{(x^2-1)\left(\frac{1}{2}x^2-\frac{1}{6}x^3+\cdots\right)\left(1-\frac{1}{2}x^2+\cdots\right)}{x\left(3x-\frac{27}{6}x^3+\cdots\right)} = -\frac{1}{6}.$

38. $\lim\limits_{x\to 0} \frac{(x+2)^3\ln(1-x)}{\sin(2x)\cos(3x)} = \lim\limits_{x\to 0} \frac{(x+2)^3\left(-x-\frac{1}{2}x^2-\cdots\right)}{\left(2x-\frac{8}{6}x^3+\cdots\right)\left(1-\frac{9}{2}x^2+\cdots\right)} = -4.$

39. $\lim\limits_{x\to 0-} \frac{x\sqrt{4x^4-x^5}}{\tan^3(2x)\cos^2(3x^2)} = \lim\limits_{x\to 0-} \frac{x^3\sqrt{4-x}}{\left(2x+\frac{8}{3}x^3+\cdots\right)^3\left(1-\frac{9}{2}x^4+\cdots\right)^2} = \frac{1}{4}.$

40. $|R_n(x)| \le \frac{e^z}{(n+1)!}|x|^{n+1}$, $x = \frac{1}{3} \Rightarrow 0 \le z \le \frac{1}{3} \Rightarrow 0 \le e^z \le e^{1/3} < e \Rightarrow$
$\left|R_n\left(\frac{1}{3}\right)\right| < \frac{e}{3^{n+1}(n+1)!} \le 0.0001$ if $3^{n+1}(n+1)! \ge 10000e \approx 27,182.8$, and $n = 4$
$\Rightarrow 3^{n+1}(n+1)! = 3^5 5! = 29,160 > 27,182.8 \Rightarrow \sqrt[3]{e} \approx 1 + \frac{1}{3} + \frac{1}{2\cdot9} + \frac{1}{6\cdot27} + \frac{1}{24\cdot81} \approx$
1.395575. The value by calculator is 1.395612, with an absolute difference of
$0.000037 < 0.0001$.

41. $f(x) = \ln(1-x) = \sum_{n=1}^{\infty} \frac{-1}{n}x^n$ and $x = \frac{1}{10} \Rightarrow \ln(0.9) = \sum_{n=1}^{\infty} \frac{-1}{n\cdot10^n}$. $f^{(n+1)}(z) =$
$\frac{-n!}{(1-z)^{n+1}} \Rightarrow R_n(x) = \frac{f^{(n+1)}(z)x^{n+1}}{(n+1)!} = \frac{-x^{n+1}}{(1-z)^{n+1}(n+1)} \Rightarrow R_n\left(\frac{1}{10}\right) = \frac{-1}{(1-z)^{n+1}(n+1)10^{n+1}}$.
$0 \le z \le \frac{1}{10} \Rightarrow 0 \le \frac{1}{1-z} \le \frac{10}{9} \Rightarrow \left|R_n\left(\frac{1}{10}\right)\right| \le \frac{1}{9^{n+1}(n+1)} < 0.001$ if $9^{n+1}(n+1) >$
$1,000$. $n = 2 \Rightarrow 9^{n+1}(n+1) = 9^3\cdot3 = 2,187 > 1,000$, and $\ln(0.9) \approx -\frac{1}{10} - \frac{1}{200} =$
$-\frac{21}{200} = -0.105$. The value by calculator is -0.10536, with an absolute difference
of $0.00036 < 0.001$.

42. $f(x) = \sin(x) = \sin[a+(x-a)] = \sin(a)\cos(x-a) + \cos(a)\sin(x-a) =$
$\sin(a)\sum_{k=0}^{\infty} \frac{(-1)^k}{(2k)!}(x-a)^{2k} + \cos(a)\sum_{k=0}^{\infty} \frac{(-1)^k}{(2k+1)!}(x-a)^{2k+1} = \sum_{n=0}^{\infty} c_n(x-a)^n$, with
$c_{2k} = \frac{(-1)^k\sin(a)}{(2k)!}$ and $c_{2k+1} = \frac{(-1)^k\cos(a)}{(2k+1)!}$, $k \ge 0$, and $R = \infty$.

43. $f(x) = \cos(x) = \cos[a+(x-a)] = \cos(a)\cos(x-a) - \sin(a)\sin(x-a) =$
$\cos(a)\sum_{k=0}^{\infty} \frac{(-1)^k}{(2k)!}(x-a)^{2k} - \sin(a)\sum_{k=0}^{\infty} \frac{(-1)^k}{(2k+1)!}(x-a)^{2k+1} = \sum_{n=0}^{\infty} c_n(x-a)^n$, with
$c_{2k} = \frac{(-1)^k\cos(a)}{(2k)!}$ and $c_{2k+1} = \frac{(-1)^{k+1}\sin(a)}{(2k+1)!}$, $k \ge 0$, and $R = \infty$.

44. $e^{ix} = \sum\limits_{n=0}^{\infty} \frac{1}{n!}(ix)^n = \sum\limits_{k=0}^{\infty} \frac{1}{(2k)!}(ix)^{2k} + \sum\limits_{k=0}^{\infty} \frac{1}{(2k+1)!}(ix)^{2k+1} =$

$\sum\limits_{k=0}^{\infty} \frac{(-1)^k}{(2k)!}x^{2k} + \sum\limits_{k=0}^{\infty} \frac{i(-1)^k}{(2k+1)!}x^{2k+1} = \cos(x) + i\sin(x).$

45. (a) If $ab \geq 0$, then $ab = |ab| = |a||b|$. If $ab < 0$, then $ab = -|ab| < |ab| = |a||b|$. Hence, $ab \leq |a||b|$.

  (b) $(a+b)^2 = a^2 + 2ab + b^2 \leq a^2 + 2|a||b| + b^2 = |a|^2 + 2|a||b| + |b|^2 = (|a| + |b|)^2$
  $\Rightarrow \sqrt{(a+b)^2} \leq \sqrt{(|a| + |b|)^2} \Rightarrow |a+b| \leq |a| + |b|.$

  (c) Since $\sum\limits_{n=0}^{\infty} |a_n x^n|$ converges for $|x| < R_1$ and $\sum\limits_{n=0}^{\infty} |b_n x^n|$ converges for $|x| < R_2$, $\sum\limits_{n=0}^{\infty} (|a_n x^n| + |b_n x^n|)$ converges for $|x| < \min\{R_1, R_2\}$. Since $|(a_n + b_n)x^n| = |a_n x^n + b_n x^n| \leq |a_n x^n| + |b_n x^n|$ by part (b), $\sum\limits_{n=0}^{\infty} |(a_n + b_n)x^n|$ converges for $|x| < \min\{R_1, R_2\}$, by the comparison test. Hence, $R \geq \min\{R_1, R_2\}.$

C.8   Chapter 8 Solutions

Exercises 8.1 – page 297

1. If f is periodic with period T, then $f(x+T) = f(x)$ and $f(x) = f((x-T)+T) = f(x-T)$, $f(x \pm 2T) = f((x \pm T) \pm T) = f(x \pm T) = f(x)$, etc. Hence, $f(x+nT) = f(x)$ for every integer n.

2. $f(x) = x^2 + 1$ for $-1 \leq x < 2$ and $f(x+3) = f(x)$ for all x. Since f has period 3, $f(5) = f(-1) = 2$, $f(7) = f(1) = 2$, $f(-4) = f(-1) = 2$, $f(783) = f(0) = 1$ and $f(-291) = f(0) = 1$.

3. Multiply $f(x) = \frac{a_0}{2} + \sum\limits_{n=1}^{\infty} \left[a_n \cos\left(\frac{n\pi x}{L}\right) + b_n \sin\left(\frac{n\pi x}{L}\right)\right]$ by $\sin\left(\frac{m\pi x}{L}\right)$, where $m \geq 1$ is any integer, integrate from $-L$ to L and reverse the order of summation and integration to obtain $\int_{-L}^{L} f(x)\sin\left(\frac{m\pi x}{L}\right) dx = \frac{a_0}{2}\int_{-L}^{L}\sin\left(\frac{m\pi x}{L}\right) dx$

$+ \sum\limits_{n=1}^{\infty} \left[a_n \int_{-L}^{L}\cos\left(\frac{n\pi x}{L}\right)\sin\left(\frac{m\pi x}{L}\right) dx + b_n \int_{-L}^{L}\sin\left(\frac{n\pi x}{L}\right)\sin\left(\frac{m\pi x}{L}\right) dx\right].$

The first integral on the right is $\int_{-L}^{L}\sin\left(\frac{m\pi x}{L}\right) dx = -\frac{L}{m\pi}\cos\left(\frac{m\pi x}{L}\right)\Big|_{-L}^{L} = 0$. Employing the trigonometric identity $\cos(a)\sin(b) = \frac{1}{2}[\sin(a+b) - \sin(a-b)]$ with $a = \frac{n\pi x}{L}$ and $b = \frac{m\pi x}{L}$, we obtain

$\int_{-L}^{L}\cos\left(\frac{n\pi x}{L}\right)\sin\left(\frac{m\pi x}{L}\right) dx = \frac{1}{2}\int_{-L}^{L}\left\{\sin\left[\frac{(n+m)\pi x}{L}\right] - \sin\left[\frac{(n-m)\pi x}{L}\right]\right\} dx = 0.$ If $n \neq m$, then the trigonometric identity $\sin(a)\sin(b) = \frac{1}{2}[\cos(a-b) - \cos(a+b)]$ with $a = \frac{n\pi x}{L}$ and $b = \frac{m\pi x}{L}$ gives

$\int_{-L}^{L} \sin\left(\frac{n\pi x}{L}\right) \sin\left(\frac{m\pi x}{L}\right) dx = \frac{1}{2} \int_{-L}^{L} \left\{ \cos\left[\frac{(n-m)\pi x}{L}\right] - \cos\left[\frac{(n+m)\pi x}{L}\right] \right\} dx = 0.$

If $n = m \geq 1$, then, employing the trigonometric identity $\sin^2(a) = \frac{1}{2}[1 - \cos(2a)]$ with $a = \frac{m\pi x}{L}$, we obtain $\int_{-L}^{L} \sin^2\left(\frac{m\pi x}{L}\right) dx = \frac{1}{2} \int_{-L}^{L} \left[1 - \cos\left(\frac{2m\pi x}{L}\right)\right] dx = \frac{1}{2} \left[x - \frac{L}{2m\pi} \sin\left(\frac{2m\pi x}{L}\right)\right]\Big|_{-L}^{L} = L.$ Thus, $b_m = \frac{1}{L} \int_{-L}^{L} f(x) \sin\left(\frac{m\pi x}{L}\right) dx$, $m \geq 1$.

4. $f(x) = \left\{ \begin{array}{ll} 0, & -2 \leq x < 0 \\ 1, & 0 \leq x < 2 \end{array} \right\}$ and $f(x + 4) = f(x)$ for all x. $T = 4$, $L = 2$,

$a_n = \frac{1}{2} \int_{-2}^{2} f(x) \cos\left(\frac{n\pi x}{2}\right) dx = \frac{1}{2} \int_{0}^{2} \cos\left(\frac{n\pi x}{2}\right) dx = \frac{1}{n\pi} \sin\left(\frac{n\pi x}{2}\right)\Big|_{0}^{2} = 0$, $n \geq 1$,

$a_0 = \frac{1}{2} \int_{0}^{2} 1\, dx = 1$, $b_n = \frac{1}{2} \int_{0}^{2} \sin\left(\frac{n\pi x}{2}\right) dx = -\frac{1}{n\pi} \cos\left(\frac{n\pi x}{2}\right)\Big|_{0}^{2} = \frac{[1-(-1)^n]}{n\pi}$. The Fourier series of f is $\frac{1}{2} + \sum_{n=1}^{\infty} \frac{[1-(-1)^n]}{n\pi} \sin\left(\frac{n\pi x}{2}\right)$.

5. $f(x) = \left\{ \begin{array}{ll} 0, & 0 \leq x < 1 \\ x, & 1 \leq x < 2 \end{array} \right\}$ and $f(x + 2) = f(x)$ for all x. $T = 2$, $L = 1$,

$a_n = \int_{0}^{2} f(x) \cos(n\pi x) dx = \int_{1}^{2} x \cos(n\pi x) dx = \frac{x}{n\pi} \sin(n\pi x)\Big|_{1}^{2} - \frac{1}{n\pi} \int_{1}^{2} \sin(n\pi x) dx = \frac{1}{n^2\pi^2} \cos(n\pi x)\Big|_{1}^{2} = \frac{1-(-1)^n}{n^2\pi^2}$, $n \geq 1$, $a_0 = \int_{1}^{2} x\, dx = \frac{x^2}{2}\Big|_{1}^{2} = \frac{3}{2}$,

$b_n = \int_{1}^{2} x \sin(n\pi x) dx = -\frac{x}{n\pi} \cos(n\pi x)\Big|_{1}^{2} + \frac{1}{n\pi} \int_{1}^{2} \cos(n\pi x) dx = -\frac{2}{n\pi} + \frac{1}{n\pi} \cos(n\pi)$

$= \frac{(-1)^n - 2}{n\pi}$, $n \geq 1$. The Fourier series of f is

$\frac{3}{4} + \sum_{n=1}^{\infty} \left[\frac{1-(-1)^n}{n^2\pi^2} \cos(n\pi x) + \frac{(-1)^n - 2}{n\pi} \sin(n\pi x) \right].$

6. $f(x) = 2x - 3$ for $2 \leq x < 5$ and $f(x + 3) = f(x)$ for all x. $T = 3$, $L = \frac{3}{2}$,

$a_n = \frac{2}{3} \int_{2}^{5} (2x-3) \cos\left(\frac{2n\pi x}{3}\right) dx = \frac{1}{n\pi} (2x-3) \sin\left(\frac{2n\pi x}{3}\right)\Big|_{2}^{5} - \frac{2}{n\pi} \int_{2}^{5} \sin\left(\frac{2n\pi x}{3}\right) dx = \frac{1}{n\pi} \left[7 \sin\left(\frac{10n\pi}{3}\right) - \sin\left(\frac{4n\pi}{3}\right)\right] + \frac{3}{n^2\pi^2} \cos\left(\frac{2n\pi x}{3}\right)\Big|_{2}^{5} = \frac{6}{n\pi} \sin\left(\frac{4n\pi}{3}\right) + \frac{3}{n^2\pi^2} \left[\cos\left(\frac{10n\pi}{3}\right) - \cos\left(\frac{4n\pi}{3}\right)\right] = \frac{6}{n\pi} \sin\left(\frac{4n\pi}{3}\right)$, $n \geq 1$, $a_0 = \frac{2}{3} \int_{2}^{5} (2x - 3) dx = \frac{2}{3}[x^2 - 3x]\Big|_{2}^{5} = 8$, $b_n = \frac{2}{3} \int_{2}^{5} (2x - 3) \sin\left(\frac{2n\pi x}{3}\right) dx = -\frac{1}{n\pi} (2x-3) \cos\left(\frac{2n\pi x}{3}\right)\Big|_{2}^{5} + \frac{2}{n\pi} \int_{2}^{5} \cos\left(\frac{2n\pi x}{3}\right) dx = -\frac{1}{n\pi} \left[7 \cos\left(\frac{10n\pi}{3}\right) - \cos\left(\frac{4n\pi}{3}\right)\right] + \frac{3}{n^2\pi^2} \sin\left(\frac{2n\pi x}{3}\right)\Big|_{2}^{5} = -\frac{6}{n\pi} \cos\left(\frac{4n\pi}{3}\right)$. The Fourier series of f is

$4 + \sum_{n=1}^{\infty} \left[\frac{6}{n\pi} \sin\left(\frac{4n\pi}{3}\right) \cos\left(\frac{2n\pi x}{3}\right) - \frac{6}{n\pi} \cos\left(\frac{4n\pi}{3}\right) \sin\left(\frac{2n\pi x}{3}\right) \right].$

7. $f(x) = \frac{1}{x}$ for $0 < x \leq 1$ and $f(x + 1) = f(x)$ for all x. f is not piecewise continuous because $\lim_{x \to 0+} f(x) = \infty$. The discontinuity at 0 is not a finite jump.

8. $f(x) = \left\{ \begin{array}{ll} 0, & -1 \leq x < 0 \\ -x, & 0 \leq x < 1 \end{array} \right\}$ and $f(x + 2) = f(x)$ for all x.

(a) $T = 2$, $L = 1$, $a_n = \int_{0}^{1} -x \cos(n\pi x) dx = -\frac{x}{n\pi} \sin(n\pi x)\Big|_{0}^{1} + \frac{1}{n\pi} \int_{0}^{1} \sin(n\pi x) dx = -\frac{1}{n^2\pi^2} \cos(n\pi x)\Big|_{0}^{1} = \frac{[1-(-1)^n]}{n^2\pi^2}$, $n \geq 1$, $a_0 = \int_{0}^{1} -x\, dx = -\frac{x^2}{2}\Big|_{0}^{1} = -\frac{1}{2}$,

$b_n = \int_0^1 -x \sin(n\pi x)\, dx = \frac{x}{n\pi} \cos(n\pi x)\big|_0^1 - \frac{1}{n\pi} \int_0^1 \cos(n\pi x)\, dx = \frac{(-1)^n}{n\pi}$. The Fourier series of f is $-\frac{1}{4} + \sum\limits_{n=1}^{\infty} \left[\frac{1-(-1)^n}{n^2\pi^2} \cos(n\pi x) + \frac{(-1)^n}{n\pi} \sin(n\pi x) \right]$.

(b) The graph of f is displayed in Figure C.1.

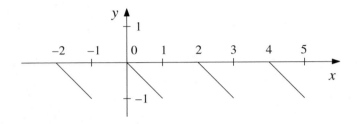

Figure C.1: The graph of f.

(c) At $x = 0$, the series converges to $f(0) = 0$.
At $x = \frac{1}{2}$, the series converges to $f\left(\frac{1}{2}\right) = -\frac{1}{2}$.
At $x = 1$, the series converges to $\frac{1}{2}[f(1+) + f(1-)] = -\frac{1}{2}$.
At $x = 18$, the series converges to $f(18) = f(0) = 0$.
At $x = 18.5$, the series converges to $f(18.5) = f\left(\frac{1}{2}\right) = -\frac{1}{2}$.
At $x = 19$, the series converges to $\frac{1}{2}[f(19+) + f(19-)] = \frac{1}{2}[f(1+) + f(1-)] = -\frac{1}{2}$.

9. $f(x) = x^2$ for $0 \le x < 2$ and $f(x+2) = f(x)$ for all x.

(a) $T = 2$, $L = 1$, $a_n = \int_0^2 x^2 \cos(n\pi x)\, dx = \frac{1}{n\pi} x^2 \sin(n\pi x)\big|_0^2 - \frac{2}{n\pi} \int_0^2 x \sin(n\pi x)\, dx = \frac{2}{n^2\pi^2} x \cos(n\pi x)\big|_0^2 - \frac{2}{n^2\pi^2} \int_0^2 \cos(n\pi x)\, dx = \frac{4}{n^2\pi^2}$, $n \ge 1$, $a_0 = \int_0^2 x^2 dx = \frac{x^3}{3}\big|_0^2 = \frac{8}{3}$, $b_n = \int_0^2 x^2 \sin(n\pi x)\, dx = -\frac{1}{n\pi} x^2 \cos(n\pi x)\big|_0^2 + \frac{2}{n\pi} \int_0^2 x \cos(n\pi x)\, dx = -\frac{4}{n\pi} + \frac{2}{n^2\pi^2} x \sin(n\pi x)\big|_0^2 - \frac{2}{n^2\pi^2} \int_0^2 \sin(n\pi x)\, dx = -\frac{4}{n\pi} + \frac{2}{n^3\pi^3} \cos(n\pi x)\big|_0^2 = -\frac{4}{n\pi}$, $n \ge 1$. The Fourier series of f is $\frac{4}{3} + \sum\limits_{n=1}^{\infty} \left[\frac{4}{n^2\pi^2} \cos(n\pi x) - \frac{4}{n\pi} \sin(n\pi x) \right]$.

(b) The graph of f is displayed in Figure C.2.

(c) At $x = 3$, the series converges to $f(3) = f(1) = 1$.
At $x = 8$, the series converges to $\frac{1}{2}\left[f(8-) + f(8+) \right] = 2$.
At $x = -10$, the series converges to 2.

10. $f(x) = x^3$ for $-1 \le x < 1$ and $f(x+2) = f(x)$ for all x. $T = 2$, $L = 1$, and f is odd. Hence, its Fourier series is a sine series, with $b_n = 2\int_0^1 x^3 \sin(n\pi x)\, dx = -\frac{2}{n\pi} x^3 \cos(n\pi x)\big|_0^1 + \frac{6}{n\pi} \int_0^1 x^2 \cos(n\pi x)\, dx = -\frac{2(-1)^n}{n\pi} + \frac{6}{n^2\pi^2} x^2 \sin(n\pi x)\big|_0^1 -$

$\frac{12}{n^2\pi^2}\int_0^1 x\sin(n\pi x)\,dx = -\frac{2(-1)^n}{n\pi}+\frac{12}{n^3\pi^3}x\cos(n\pi x)\big|_0^1-\frac{12}{n^3\pi^3}\int_0^1\cos(n\pi x)\,dx = -\frac{2(-1)^n}{n\pi}$
$+\frac{12(-1)^n}{n^3\pi^3}$. The Fourier series of f is the sine series $\sum_{n=1}^{\infty}\left[\frac{12(-1)^n}{n^3\pi^3}-\frac{2(-1)^n}{n\pi}\right]\sin(n\pi x)$.

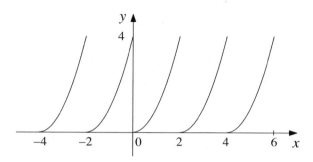

Figure C.2: The graph of f in Solution 9.

11. $f(x) = \left\{ \begin{array}{cc} -1, & -2 \le x < 0 \\ 1, & 0 \le x < 2 \end{array} \right\}$ and $f(x+4) = f(x)$ for all x.

(a) The graph of f is displayed in Figure C.3.

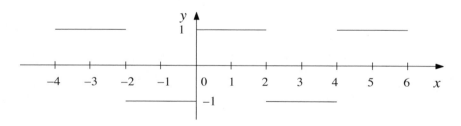

Figure C.3: The graph of f.

(b) $T = 4$, $L = 2$ and f is odd. Hence, its Fourier series is a sine series, with
$b_n = \int_0^2 \sin\left(\frac{n\pi x}{2}\right)dx = -\frac{2}{n\pi}\cos\left(\frac{n\pi x}{2}\right)\big|_0^2 = \frac{2}{n\pi}[1-(-1)^n]$, $n \ge 1$.

The Fourier series of f is the sine series $\sum_{n=1}^{\infty}\frac{2[1-(-1)^n]}{n\pi}\sin\left(\frac{n\pi x}{2}\right)$.

12. $f(x) = x^2$ for $-1 \le x < 1$ and $f(x+2) = f(x)$ for all x. $T = 2$, $L = 1$ and f is even. Hence, its Fourier series is a cosine series, with $a_n = 2\int_0^1 x^2\cos(n\pi x)\,dx = \frac{2}{n\pi}x^2\sin(n\pi x)\big|_0^1-\frac{4}{n\pi}\int_0^1 x\sin(n\pi x)\,dx = \frac{4}{n^2\pi^2}x\cos(n\pi x)\big|_0^1-\frac{4}{n^2\pi^2}\int_0^1\cos(n\pi x)\,dx = \frac{4(-1)^n}{n^2\pi^2}$, $n \ge 1$, $a_0 = 2\int_0^1 x^2\,dx = \frac{2}{3}$. The Fourier series of f is the cosine series $\frac{1}{3} + \sum_{n=1}^{\infty}\frac{4(-1)^n}{n^2\pi^2}\cos(n\pi x)$.

13. $f(x) = \left\{ \begin{array}{ll} 1 - x^2, & 0 \le x \le 1 \\ 1 - (x-2)^2, & 1 < x < 2 \end{array} \right\}$ and $f(x+2) = f(x)$ for all x.

(a) The graph of f is displayed in Figure C.4.

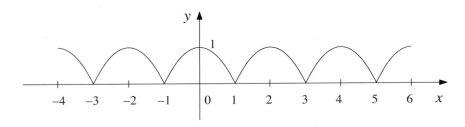

Figure C.4: The graph of f.

(b) $T = 2$, $L = 1$ and f is even. Hence, its Fourier series is a cosine series, with $a_n = 2 \int_0^1 (1 - x^2) \cos(n\pi x)\, dx = \frac{2}{n\pi}(1 - x^2) \sin(n\pi x)\big|_0^1 +$ $\frac{4}{n\pi} \int_0^1 x \sin(n\pi x)\, dx = -\frac{4}{n^2\pi^2} x \cos(n\pi x)\big|_0^1 + \frac{4}{n^2\pi^2} \int_0^1 \cos(n\pi x)\, dx = -\frac{4(-1)^n}{n^2\pi^2}$, $n \ge 1$, $a_0 = 2 \int_0^1 1 - x^2\, dx = 2x - \frac{2}{3}x^3\big|_0^1 = \frac{4}{3}$. The Fourier series of f is the cosine series $\frac{2}{3} + \sum_{n=1}^{\infty} \frac{4(-1)^{n-1}}{n^2\pi^2} \cos(n\pi x)$. The series converges to $f(x)$ for all x since f is continuous everywhere and f' is piecewise continuous.

(c) $x = 0 \Rightarrow 1 = f(0) = \frac{2}{3} + \sum_{n=1}^{\infty} \frac{4(-1)^{n-1}}{n^2\pi^2} \Rightarrow \sum_{n=1}^{\infty} \frac{(-1)^{n-1}}{n^2} = \frac{\pi^2}{12}$.

14. (a) The area under $y = f(x)$ for $-1 \le x \le 2$ is the same as the area under $y = f(x)$ for $5 \le x \le 8$.

(b) The area under $y = f(x)$ for $-1 \le x \le 0$ is the same as the area under $y = f(x)$ for $2 \le x \le 3$, and the interval $0 \le x \le 2$ is common to both integrals: $\int_{-1}^{2} f(x)\, dx = \int_{-1}^{0} f(x)\, dx + \int_{0}^{2} f(x)\, dx = \int_{2}^{3} f(x)\, dx + \int_{0}^{2} f(x)\, dx = \int_{0}^{3} f(x)\, dx$.

15. For any real number α, employ the T-periodicity of f and make the change of variable $y = x + T$ to obtain $\int_{\alpha}^{\alpha+T} f(x)\, dx = \int_{\alpha}^{0} f(x)\, dx + \int_{0}^{\alpha+T} f(x)\, dx = \int_{\alpha+T}^{T} f(y-T)\, dy + \int_{0}^{\alpha+T} f(x)\, dx = \int_{\alpha+T}^{T} f(y)\, dy + \int_{0}^{\alpha+T} f(x)\, dx = \int_{\alpha+T}^{T} f(x)\, dx + \int_{0}^{\alpha+T} f(x)\, dx = \int_{0}^{T} f(x)\, dx$. It follows that $\int_{\alpha}^{\alpha+T} f(x)\, dx = \int_{0}^{T} f(x)\, dx = \int_{\beta}^{\beta+T} f(x)\, dx$ for any real α and β.

16. $f(x) = \left\{ \begin{array}{ll} -\cos(x), & -\pi \le x < 0 \\ \cos(x), & 0 \le x < \pi \end{array} \right\}$ and $f(x + 2\pi) = f(x)$ for all x. $T = 2\pi$, $L = \pi$ and f is odd since $f(-x) = -f(x)$. Hence, the Fourier series of f is a sine

series, with $b_n = \frac{2}{\pi} \int_0^\pi \cos(x)\sin(nx)\,dx = \frac{1}{\pi}\int_0^\pi \sin[(1+n)x] - \sin[(1-n)x]\,dx$

$= \frac{1}{\pi}\left\{ \frac{\cos[(1-n)x]}{1-n} - \frac{\cos[(1+n)x]}{1+n} \right\}\Big|_0^\pi = \frac{(-1)^{n-1}-1}{\pi}\left(\frac{1}{1-n} - \frac{1}{1+n} \right) = \frac{2n[(-1)^{n-1}-1]}{\pi(1-n^2)}.$

The Fourier series of f is the sine series $\displaystyle\sum_{n=1}^\infty \frac{2n[(-1)^{n-1}-1]}{\pi(1-n^2)}\sin(nx)$.

Exercises 8.2 – page 311

1. The Fourier series of f on $[0,6]$ has the form $\frac{a_0}{2} + \displaystyle\sum_{n=1}^\infty \left[a_n\cos\left(\frac{n\pi x}{3} \right) + b_n\sin\left(\frac{n\pi x}{3} \right) \right]$.

2. The Fourier series of f on $[-3,5]$ has the form
   $\frac{a_0}{2} + \displaystyle\sum_{n=1}^\infty \left[a_n\cos\left(\frac{n\pi x}{4} \right) + b_n\sin\left(\frac{n\pi x}{4} \right) \right]$.

3. The Fourier series of $f(x) = \left\{ \begin{array}{ll} 1, & 0 \le x < 1 \\ 2, & 1 \le x \le 2 \end{array} \right\}$ is

   $\frac{a_0}{2} + \displaystyle\sum_{n=1}^\infty [a_n\cos(n\pi x) + b_n\sin(n\pi x)]$, $a_0 = \int_0^1 1\,dx + \int_1^2 2\,dx = 3$,

   $a_n = \int_0^1 \cos(n\pi x)\,dx + \int_1^2 2\cos(n\pi x)\,dx = 0$, $n \ge 1$,

   $b_n = \int_0^1 \sin(n\pi x)\,dx + \int_1^2 2\sin(n\pi x)\,dx = -\frac{1}{n\pi}\cos(n\pi x)\big|_0^1 - \frac{2}{n\pi}\cos(n\pi x)\big|_1^2 =$
   $\frac{1}{n\pi}[1 - (-1)^n] - \frac{2}{n\pi}[1 - (-1)^n] = \frac{1}{n\pi}[(-1)^n - 1]$, $n \ge 1$.

   The Fourier series is $\frac{3}{2} + \displaystyle\sum_{n=1}^\infty \frac{[(-1)^n - 1]}{n\pi}\sin(n\pi x)$.

4. The Fourier series of $f(x) = \left\{ \begin{array}{ll} 2, & 0 \le x \le \pi \\ 0, & \pi < x \le 2\pi \end{array} \right\}$ is

   $\frac{a_0}{2} + \displaystyle\sum_{n=1}^\infty [a_n\cos(nx) + b_n\sin(nx)]$, $a_0 = \frac{1}{\pi}\int_0^{2\pi} f(x)\,dx = \frac{1}{\pi}\int_0^\pi 2\,dx = 2$,

   $a_n = \frac{1}{\pi}\int_0^{2\pi} f(x)\cos(nx)\,dx = \frac{1}{\pi}\int_0^\pi 2\cos(nx)\,dx = \frac{2}{n\pi}\sin(nx)\big|_0^\pi = 0$, $n \ge 1$,

   $b_n = \frac{1}{\pi}\int_0^{2\pi} f(x)\sin(nx)\,dx = \frac{1}{\pi}\int_0^\pi 2\sin(nx)\,dx = -\frac{2}{n\pi}\cos(nx)\big|_0^\pi =$
   $\frac{2}{n\pi}[1 - (-1)^n]$, $n \ge 1$. The Fourier series is $1 + \displaystyle\sum_{n=1}^\infty \frac{2[1-(-1)^n]}{n\pi}\sin(nx)$.

5. The Fourier series of $f(x) = x$ on $[2,4]$ is $\frac{a_0}{2} + \displaystyle\sum_{n=1}^\infty [a_n\cos(n\pi x) + b_n\sin(n\pi x)]$,

   $a_0 = \int_2^4 x\,dx = \frac{x^2}{2}\big|_2^4 = 6$, $a_n = \int_2^4 x\cos(n\pi x)\,dx =$
   $\frac{1}{n\pi}x\sin(n\pi x)\big|_2^4 - \frac{1}{n\pi}\int_2^4 \sin(n\pi x)\,dx = \frac{1}{n^2\pi^2}\cos(n\pi x)\big|_2^4 = 0$, $n \ge 1$,

   $b_n = \int_2^4 x\sin(n\pi x)\,dx = -\frac{1}{n\pi}x\cos(n\pi x)\big|_2^4 + \frac{1}{n\pi}\int_2^4 \cos(n\pi x)\,dx =$
   $-\frac{2}{n\pi} + \frac{1}{n^2\pi^2}\sin(n\pi x)\big|_2^4 = -\frac{2}{n\pi}$, $n \ge 1$. The Fourier series is $3 - \displaystyle\sum_{n=1}^\infty \frac{2}{n\pi}\sin(n\pi x)$.

6. The Fourier series of $f(x) = x^3$ on $[1, 3]$ is

$\frac{a_0}{2} + \sum\limits_{n=1}^{\infty} [a_n \cos(n\pi x) + b_n \sin(n\pi x)]$, $a_0 = \int_1^3 x^3 \, dx = \frac{x^4}{4}\Big|_1^3 = 20$,

$a_n = \int_1^3 x^3 \cos(n\pi x) \, dx = \frac{1}{n\pi}x^3 \sin(n\pi x)\Big|_1^3 - \frac{3}{n\pi}\int_1^3 x^2 \sin(n\pi x) \, dx =$

$\frac{3}{n^2\pi^2}x^2 \cos(n\pi x)\Big|_1^3 - \frac{6}{n^2\pi^2}\int_1^3 x \cos(n\pi x) \, dx = \frac{24(-1)^n}{n^2\pi^2} - \frac{6}{n^3\pi^3}x \sin(n\pi x)\Big|_1^3 +$

$\frac{6}{n^3\pi^3}\int_1^3 \sin(n\pi x) \, dx = \frac{24(-1)^n}{n^2\pi^2} - \frac{6}{n^4\pi^4}\cos(n\pi x)\Big|_1^3 = \frac{24(-1)^n}{n^2\pi^2}$, $n \geq 1$,

$b_n = \int_1^3 x^3 \sin(n\pi x) \, dx = -\frac{1}{n\pi}x^3 \cos(n\pi x)\Big|_1^3 + \frac{3}{n\pi}\int_1^3 x^2 \cos(n\pi x) \, dx = \frac{26(-1)^{n-1}}{n\pi} +$

$\frac{3}{n^2\pi^2}x^2 \sin(n\pi x)\Big|_1^3 - \frac{6}{n^2\pi^2}\int_1^3 x \sin(n\pi x) \, dx = \frac{26(-1)^{n-1}}{n\pi} + \frac{6}{n^3\pi^3}x \cos(n\pi x)\Big|_1^3 -$

$\frac{6}{n^3\pi^3}\int_1^3 \cos(n\pi x) \, dx = \frac{26(-1)^{n-1}}{n\pi} + \frac{12(-1)^n}{n^3\pi^3}$, $n \geq 1$. The Fourier series is

$10 + \sum\limits_{n=1}^{\infty}\left\{\frac{24(-1)^n}{n^2\pi^2}\cos(n\pi x) + \left[\frac{26(-1)^{n-1}}{n\pi} + \frac{12(-1)^n}{n^3\pi^3}\right]\sin(n\pi x)\right\}$.

7. The sine series of f on $[0, 6]$ has the form $\sum\limits_{n=1}^{\infty} b_n \sin\left(\frac{n\pi x}{6}\right)$.

8. The sine series of $f(x) = \left\{\begin{array}{ll} x, & 0 \leq x < 1 \\ 0, & 1 \leq x \leq 2 \end{array}\right\}$ is $\sum\limits_{n=1}^{\infty} b_n \sin\left(\frac{n\pi x}{2}\right)$,

$b_n = \int_0^1 x \sin\left(\frac{n\pi x}{2}\right) dx = -\frac{2}{n\pi}x \cos\left(\frac{n\pi x}{2}\right)\Big|_0^1 + \frac{2}{n\pi}\int_0^1 \cos\left(\frac{n\pi x}{2}\right) dx$

$= -\frac{2}{n\pi}\cos\left(\frac{n\pi}{2}\right) + \frac{4}{n^2\pi^2}\sin\left(\frac{n\pi x}{2}\right)\Big|_0^1 = -\frac{2}{n\pi}\cos\left(\frac{n\pi}{2}\right) + \frac{4}{n^2\pi^2}\sin\left(\frac{n\pi}{2}\right)$, $n \geq 1$.

The sine series is $\sum\limits_{n=1}^{\infty}\left[\frac{4}{n^2\pi^2}\sin\left(\frac{n\pi}{2}\right) - \frac{2}{n\pi}\cos\left(\frac{n\pi}{2}\right)\right]\sin\left(\frac{n\pi x}{2}\right)$.

9. The sine series of $f(x) = \left\{\begin{array}{ll} x, & 0 \leq x < 1 \\ 2 - x, & 1 \leq x \leq 2 \end{array}\right\}$ is $\sum\limits_{n=1}^{\infty} b_n \sin\left(\frac{n\pi x}{2}\right)$,

$b_n = \int_0^2 f(x) \sin\left(\frac{n\pi x}{2}\right) dx = \int_0^1 x \sin\left(\frac{n\pi x}{2}\right) dx + \int_1^2 (2 - x) \sin\left(\frac{n\pi x}{2}\right) dx =$

$-\frac{2}{n\pi}x \cos\left(\frac{n\pi x}{2}\right)\Big|_0^1 + \frac{2}{n\pi}\int_0^1 \cos\left(\frac{n\pi x}{2}\right) dx - \frac{2}{n\pi}(2 - x) \cos\left(\frac{n\pi x}{2}\right)\Big|_1^2 -$

$\frac{2}{n\pi}\int_1^2 \cos\left(\frac{n\pi x}{2}\right) dx = -\frac{2}{n\pi}\cos\left(\frac{n\pi}{2}\right) + \frac{4}{n^2\pi^2}\sin\left(\frac{n\pi x}{2}\right)\Big|_0^1 + \frac{2}{n\pi}\cos\left(\frac{n\pi}{2}\right) -$

$\frac{4}{n^2\pi^2}\sin\left(\frac{n\pi x}{2}\right)\Big|_1^2 = \frac{4}{n^2\pi^2}\sin\left(\frac{n\pi}{2}\right) + \frac{4}{n^2\pi^2}\sin\left(\frac{n\pi}{2}\right) = \frac{8}{n^2\pi^2}\sin\left(\frac{n\pi}{2}\right)$, $n \geq 1$.

The sine series is $\sum\limits_{n=1}^{\infty} \frac{8}{n^2\pi^2}\sin\left(\frac{n\pi}{2}\right) \sin\left(\frac{n\pi x}{2}\right)$.

10. $f(x) = x^2$ for $0 \leq x \leq 2$.

(a) $\sum\limits_{n=1}^{\infty} b_n \sin\left(\frac{n\pi x}{2}\right)$, $b_n = \int_0^2 x^2 \sin\left(\frac{n\pi x}{2}\right) dx = -\frac{2}{n\pi}x^2 \cos\left(\frac{n\pi x}{2}\right)\Big|_0^2 +$

$\frac{4}{n\pi}\int_0^2 x \cos\left(\frac{n\pi x}{2}\right) dx = -\frac{8}{n\pi}\cos(n\pi) + \frac{8}{n^2\pi^2}x \sin\left(\frac{n\pi x}{2}\right)\Big|_0^2 -$

$\frac{8}{n^2\pi^2}\int_0^2 \sin\left(\frac{n\pi x}{2}\right) dx = -\frac{8}{n\pi}(-1)^n + \frac{16}{n^3\pi^3}\cos\left(\frac{n\pi x}{2}\right)\Big|_0^2 =$

$-\frac{8}{n\pi}(-1)^n + \frac{16}{n^3\pi^3}\cos(n\pi) - \frac{16}{n^3\pi^3} = \frac{8}{n\pi}(-1)^{n-1} + \frac{16}{n^3\pi^3}[(-1)^n - 1], \; n \geq 1.$

The sine series is $\sum\limits_{n=1}^{\infty} \left\{\frac{8}{n\pi}(-1)^{n-1} + \frac{16}{n^3\pi^3}[(-1)^n - 1]\right\} \sin\left(\frac{n\pi x}{2}\right).$

(b) The graph of the odd, 4-periodic extension $\tilde{f}$ of f to $\mathbb{R}$ is displayed in Figure C.5.

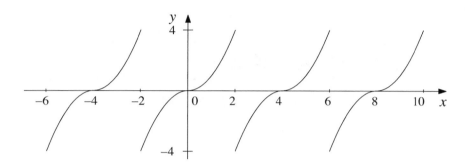

Figure C.5: The odd, 4-periodic extension $\tilde{f}$ of f to $\mathbb{R}$.

(c) The series converges to $f(x)$ on $[0, 2)$. At $x = 2$, the series converges to $0 \neq f(2)$.

(d) At $x = 3$, the series converges to $\tilde{f}(3) = \tilde{f}(-1) = -\tilde{f}(1) = -f(1) = -1$ since $\tilde{f}$ is 4-periodic and odd.

At $x = 8$, the series converges to $\tilde{f}(8) = \tilde{f}(0) = f(0) = 0$ since $\tilde{f}$ is 4-periodic.

At $x = -10$, by 4-periodicity, the series converges to

$\frac{1}{2}\left[\tilde{f}(-10+) + \tilde{f}(-10-)\right] = \frac{1}{2}\left[\tilde{f}(2+) + \tilde{f}(2-)\right] = \frac{1}{2}(-4 + 4) = 0.$

11. The cosine series of f on $[0, 6]$ has the form $\frac{a_0}{2} + \sum\limits_{n=1}^{\infty} a_n \cos\left(\frac{n\pi x}{6}\right).$

12. The cosine series of $f(x) = \left\{\begin{array}{ll} 1, & 0 \leq x < \frac{1}{2} \\ 2, & \frac{1}{2} \leq x \leq 1 \end{array}\right\}$ is $\frac{a_0}{2} + \sum\limits_{n=1}^{\infty} a_n \cos(n\pi x),$

$a_0 = 2\int_0^{\frac{1}{2}} 1\, dx + 2\int_{\frac{1}{2}}^{1} 2\, dx = 3, \; a_n = 2\int_0^{\frac{1}{2}} \cos(n\pi x)\, dx + 2\int_{\frac{1}{2}}^{1} 2\cos(n\pi x)\, dx =$

$\frac{2}{n\pi}\sin(n\pi x)\Big|_0^{\frac{1}{2}} + \frac{4}{n\pi}\sin(n\pi x)\Big|_{\frac{1}{2}}^{1} = -\frac{2}{n\pi}\sin\left(\frac{n\pi}{2}\right), \; n \geq 1.$

The cosine series is $\frac{3}{2} - \sum\limits_{n=1}^{\infty} \frac{2}{n\pi}\sin\left(\frac{n\pi}{2}\right)\cos(n\pi x).$

13. The cosine series of $f(x) = x^3$ on $[0, 1]$ is $\frac{a_0}{2} + \sum\limits_{n=1}^{\infty} a_n \cos(n\pi x),$

$a_0 = 2\int_0^1 x^3\, dx = \frac{1}{2}, \; a_n = 2\int_0^1 x^3 \cos(n\pi x)\, dx =$

$\frac{2}{n\pi}x^3 \sin(n\pi x)\big|_0^1 - \frac{6}{n\pi}\int_0^1 x^2 \sin(n\pi x)\,dx = \frac{6}{n^2\pi^2}x^2 \cos(n\pi x)\big|_0^1 -$
$\frac{12}{n^2\pi^2}\int_0^1 x\cos(n\pi x)\,dx = \frac{6(-1)^n}{n^2\pi^2} - \frac{12}{n^3\pi^3}x\sin(n\pi x)\big|_0^1 + \frac{12}{n^3\pi^3}\int_0^1 \sin(n\pi x)\,dx =$
$\frac{6(-1)^n}{n^2\pi^2} - \frac{12}{n^4\pi^4}\cos(n\pi x)\big|_0^1 = \frac{6(-1)^n}{n^2\pi^2} + \frac{12}{n^4\pi^4}[1 - (-1)^n],\ n \geq 1.$
The cosine series is $\frac{1}{4} + \sum\limits_{n=1}^{\infty} \left\{ \frac{6(-1)^n}{n^2\pi^2} + \frac{12[1-(-1)^n]}{n^4\pi^4} \right\} \cos(n\pi x).$

14. The cosine series of $f(x) = \sin(x)$ on $[0,3]$ is $\frac{a_0}{2} + \sum\limits_{n=1}^{\infty} a_n \cos\left(\frac{n\pi x}{3}\right)$,

$a_0 = \frac{2}{3}\int_0^3 \sin(x)\,dx = -\frac{2}{3}\cos(x)\big|_0^3 = \frac{2}{3}[1 - \cos(3)]$,
$a_n = \frac{2}{3}\int_0^3 \sin(x)\cos\left(\frac{n\pi x}{3}\right)dx = \frac{1}{3}\int_0^3 \left\{\sin\left[\left(1 + \frac{n\pi}{3}\right)x\right] + \sin\left[\left(1 - \frac{n\pi}{3}\right)x\right]\right\}dx =$
$-\frac{1}{3}\left\{\frac{\cos\left[\left(1+\frac{n\pi}{3}\right)x\right]}{1 + \frac{n\pi}{3}}\Big|_0^3 + \frac{\cos\left[\left(1-\frac{n\pi}{3}\right)x\right]}{1 - \frac{n\pi}{3}}\Big|_0^3\right\} = -\left\{\frac{\cos(3+n\pi)-1}{3+n\pi} + \frac{\cos(3-n\pi)-1}{3-n\pi}\right\} =$
$-\left\{\frac{(-1)^n\cos(3)-1}{3+n\pi} + \frac{(-1)^n\cos(3)-1}{3-n\pi}\right\} = [1 - (-1)^n\cos(3)]\left(\frac{1}{3+n\pi} + \frac{1}{3-n\pi}\right) =$
$\frac{6[1-(-1)^n\cos(3)]}{9 - n^2\pi^2},\ n \geq 1.$ The cosine series is

$\frac{1}{3}[1 - \cos(3)] + \sum\limits_{n=1}^{\infty} \frac{6[1-(-1)^n\cos(3)]}{9-n^2\pi^2}\cos\left(\frac{n\pi x}{3}\right).$

15. $f(x) = x^2$ on $[-2, 2]$.

   (a) The graph of the 4-periodic extension $\tilde{f}$ of f to $\mathbb{R}$ is displayed in Figure C.6.

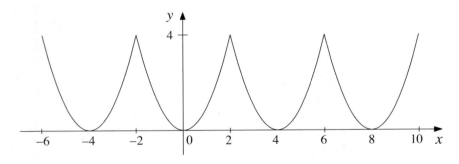

Figure C.6: The 4-periodic extension $\tilde{f}$ of f to $\mathbb{R}$.

   (b) The Fourier series of f converges to $\tilde{f}(x)$ for all x because $\tilde{f}$ is continuous everywhere and $\tilde{f}'$ is piecewise continuous.

   (c) Since $\tilde{f}$ is even, the Fourier series of f is the cosine series $\frac{a_0}{2} + \sum\limits_{n=1}^{\infty} a_n \cos\left(\frac{n\pi x}{2}\right)$,

   $a_0 = \int_0^2 x^2 dx = \frac{x^3}{3}\big|_0^2 = \frac{8}{3},\ a_n = \int_0^2 x^2 \cos\left(\frac{n\pi x}{2}\right)dx = \frac{2}{n\pi}x^2 \sin\left(\frac{n\pi x}{2}\right)\big|_0^2 -$
   $\frac{4}{n\pi}\int_0^2 x\sin\left(\frac{n\pi x}{2}\right)dx = \frac{8}{n^2\pi^2}x\cos\left(\frac{n\pi x}{2}\right)\big|_0^2 - \frac{8}{n^2\pi^2}\int_0^2 \cos\left(\frac{n\pi x}{2}\right)dx = \frac{16(-1)^n}{n^2\pi^2}$,

   $n \geq 1.$ The cosine series is $\frac{4}{3} + \frac{16}{\pi^2}\sum\limits_{n=1}^{\infty} \frac{(-1)^n}{n^2}\cos\left(\frac{n\pi x}{2}\right).$

16. $f(x) = \left\{ \begin{array}{ll} x, & 0 \le x < 1 \\ 1, & 1 \le x \le 2 \end{array} \right\}$.

(a) The graph of the odd, 4-periodic extension $\tilde{f}$ of f to $\mathbb{R}$ is displayed in Figure C.7.

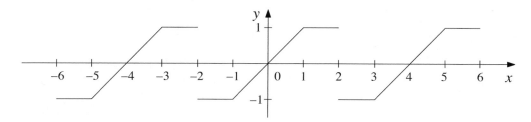

Figure C.7: The graph of the odd, 4-periodic extension $\tilde{f}$ of f to $\mathbb{R}$.

(b) The sine series of f is $\sum_{n=1}^{\infty} b_n \sin\left(\frac{n\pi x}{2}\right)$, $b_n = \int_0^2 f(x) \sin\left(\frac{n\pi x}{2}\right) dx =$

$\int_0^1 x \sin\left(\frac{n\pi x}{2}\right) dx + \int_1^2 \sin\left(\frac{n\pi x}{2}\right) dx = \left. -\frac{2x}{n\pi} \cos\left(\frac{n\pi x}{2}\right)\right|_0^1 + \frac{2}{n\pi} \int_0^1 \cos\left(\frac{n\pi x}{2}\right) dx -$

$\left. \frac{2}{n\pi} \cos\left(\frac{n\pi x}{2}\right)\right|_1^2 = -\frac{2}{n\pi} \cos\left(\frac{n\pi}{2}\right) + \left. \frac{4}{n^2\pi^2} \sin\left(\frac{n\pi x}{2}\right)\right|_0^1 - \frac{2}{n\pi} \cos(n\pi) + \frac{2}{n\pi} \cos\left(\frac{n\pi}{2}\right)$

$= \frac{4}{n^2\pi^2} \sin\left(\frac{n\pi}{2}\right) - \frac{2}{n\pi}(-1)^n$, $n \ge 1$. The sine series is

$\sum_{n=1}^{\infty} \left[\frac{4}{n^2\pi^2} \sin\left(\frac{n\pi}{2}\right) - \frac{2(-1)^n}{n\pi} \right] \sin\left(\frac{n\pi x}{2}\right)$. The series converges to $f(x)$ on $[0, 2)$.

(c) At $x = 0$, the series converges to $\tilde{f}(0) = f(0) = 0$.
At $x = 1$, the series converges to $\tilde{f}(1) = f(1) = 1$.
At $x = 2$, the series converges to $\frac{1}{2}\left[\tilde{f}(2+) + \tilde{f}(2-)\right] = \frac{1}{2}(-1 + 1) = 0$.

At $x = 78$, employing the 4-periodicity of $\tilde{f}$, the series converges to
$\frac{1}{2}\left[\tilde{f}(78+) + \tilde{f}(78-)\right] = \frac{1}{2}\left[\tilde{f}(2+) + \tilde{f}(2-)\right] = 0$.
At $x = 79$, since $\tilde{f}$ is 4-periodic and odd, the series converges to
$\tilde{f}(79) = \tilde{f}(-1) = -\tilde{f}(1) = -f(1) = -1$.

(d) The graph of the even, 4-periodic extension $\tilde{f}$ of f to $\mathbb{R}$ is displayed in Figure C.8.

(e) The cosine series of f is $\frac{a_0}{2} + \sum_{n=1}^{\infty} a_n \cos\left(\frac{n\pi x}{2}\right)$, $a_0 = \int_0^2 f(x) dx =$

$\int_0^1 x \, dx + \int_1^2 1 \, dx = \frac{1}{2} + 1 = \frac{3}{2}$, $a_n = \int_0^2 f(x) \cos\left(\frac{n\pi x}{2}\right) dx = \int_0^1 x \cos\left(\frac{n\pi x}{2}\right) dx$

$+ \int_1^2 \cos\left(\frac{n\pi x}{2}\right) dx = \left. \frac{2x}{n\pi} \sin\left(\frac{n\pi x}{2}\right)\right|_0^1 - \frac{2}{n\pi} \int_0^1 \sin\left(\frac{n\pi x}{2}\right) dx + \left. \frac{2}{n\pi} \sin\left(\frac{n\pi x}{2}\right)\right|_1^2 =$

$\frac{2}{n\pi} \sin\left(\frac{n\pi}{2}\right) + \frac{4}{n^2\pi^2} \cos\left(\frac{n\pi x}{2}\right) \Big|_0^1 - \frac{2}{n\pi} \sin\left(\frac{n\pi}{2}\right) = \frac{4}{n^2\pi^2} \left[\cos\left(\frac{n\pi}{2}\right) - 1\right]$, $n \geq 1$.

The cosine series is $\frac{3}{4} + \sum_{n=1}^{\infty} \frac{4}{n^2\pi^2} \left[\cos\left(\frac{n\pi}{2}\right) - 1\right] \cos\left(\frac{n\pi x}{2}\right)$, and converges to $f(x)$ for all x in $[0, 2]$.

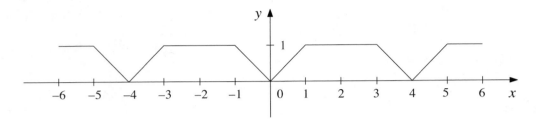

Figure C.8: The graph of the even, 4-periodic extension $\tilde{f}$ of f to $\mathbb{R}$.

(f) At $x = 0$, the series converges to $\tilde{f}(0) = f(0) = 0$.
At $x = 1$, the series converges to $\tilde{f}(1) = f(1) = 1$.
At $x = 2$, the series converges to $\tilde{f}(2) = f(2) = 1$.
At $x = 78$, since $\tilde{f}$ is 4-periodic, the series converges to
$\tilde{f}(78) = \tilde{f}(2) = f(2) = 1$.
At $x = 79$, since $\tilde{f}$ is 4-periodic and even, the series converges to
$\tilde{f}(79) = \tilde{f}(-1) = \tilde{f}(1) = f(1) = 1$.

17. $f(x) = \left\{ \begin{array}{ll} 1, & 0 \leq x < \frac{\pi}{2} \\ 0, & \frac{\pi}{2} \leq x \leq \pi \end{array} \right\}$.

(a) The sine series of f is $\sum_{n=1}^{\infty} b_n \sin(nx)$, $b_n = \frac{2}{\pi} \int_0^{\pi} f(x) \sin(nx)\, dx =$

$\frac{2}{\pi} \int_0^{\frac{\pi}{2}} \sin(nx)\, dx = -\frac{2}{n\pi} \cos(nx) \Big|_0^{\frac{\pi}{2}} = \frac{2}{n\pi} \left[1 - \cos\left(\frac{n\pi}{2}\right)\right]$, $n \geq 1$.

The sine series is $\sum_{n=1}^{\infty} \frac{2}{n\pi} \left[1 - \cos\left(\frac{n\pi}{2}\right)\right] \sin(nx)$, and converges to $f(x)$ on $(0, \pi]$ except at $\frac{\pi}{2}$.

(b) The cosine series of f is $\frac{a_0}{2} + \sum_{n=1}^{\infty} a_n \cos(nx)$, $a_0 = \frac{2}{\pi} \int_0^{\pi} f(x)\, dx =$

$\frac{2}{\pi} \int_0^{\frac{\pi}{2}} 1\, dx = 1$, $a_n = \frac{2}{\pi} \int_0^{\pi} f(x) \cos(nx)\, dx = \frac{2}{\pi} \int_0^{\frac{\pi}{2}} \cos(nx)\, dx = \frac{2}{n\pi} \sin(nx) \Big|_0^{\frac{\pi}{2}}$

$= \frac{2}{n\pi} \sin\left(\frac{n\pi}{2}\right)$, $n \geq 1$. The cosine series is $\frac{1}{2} + \sum_{n=1}^{\infty} \frac{2}{n\pi} \sin\left(\frac{n\pi}{2}\right) \cos(nx)$, and converges to $f(x)$ on $[0, \pi]$ except at $\frac{\pi}{2}$.

(c) The Fourier series of f is $\frac{a_0}{2} + \sum\limits_{n=1}^{\infty} [a_n \cos(2nx) + b_n \sin(2nx)]$,

$a_0 = \frac{1}{\frac{\pi}{2}} \int_0^\pi f(x)\,dx = \frac{2}{\pi} \int_0^{\frac{\pi}{2}} 1\,dx = 1$, $a_n = \frac{1}{\frac{\pi}{2}} \int_0^\pi f(x) \cos(2nx)\,dx =$

$\frac{2}{\pi} \int_0^{\frac{\pi}{2}} \cos(2nx)\,dx = \frac{1}{n\pi} \sin(2nx) \Big|_0^{\frac{\pi}{2}} = 0$, $n \geq 1$, $b_n = \frac{1}{\frac{\pi}{2}} \int_0^\pi f(x) \sin(2nx)\,dx$

$= \frac{2}{\pi} \int_0^{\frac{\pi}{2}} \sin(2nx)\,dx = -\frac{1}{n\pi} \cos(2nx) \Big|_0^{\frac{\pi}{2}} = \frac{1}{n\pi} [1 - \cos(n\pi)] = \frac{1}{n\pi} [1 - (-1)^n]$,

$n \geq 1$. The Fourier series is $\frac{1}{2} + \sum\limits_{n=1}^{\infty} \frac{1-(-1)^n}{n\pi} \sin(2nx)$, and converges to $f(x)$

on $(0, \pi)$ except at $\frac{\pi}{2}$.

(d) The series may be simplified to $\frac{1}{2} + \sum\limits_{k=0}^{\infty} \frac{2}{(2k+1)\pi} \sin[2(2k+1)x]$. Then

$x = \frac{\pi}{4} \Rightarrow 1 = f\left(\frac{\pi}{4}\right) = \frac{1}{2} + \sum\limits_{k=0}^{\infty} \frac{2(-1)^k}{(2k+1)\pi} \Rightarrow \sum\limits_{k=0}^{\infty} \frac{(-1)^k}{2k+1} = \frac{\pi}{4}$.

Chapter 8 Exercises – page 313

1. $f(x) = \left\{ \begin{array}{ll} x - 3, & 3 \leq x < 4 \\ 1, & 4 \leq x < 5 \\ 6 - x, & 5 \leq x \leq 6 \end{array} \right\}$.

(a) The graph of the 3-periodic extension $\tilde{f}$ of f to $\mathbb{R}$ is displayed in Figure C.9.

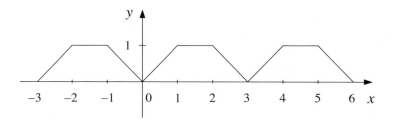

Figure C.9: The graph of the 3-periodic extension $\tilde{f}$ of f to $\mathbb{R}$.

(b) Since f is even, the Fourier series of f is the cosine series $\frac{a_0}{2} + \sum\limits_{n=1}^{\infty} a_n \cos\left(\frac{n\pi x}{3}\right)$

on $[0, 3]$, $a_0 = \frac{2}{3} \int_0^3 f(x)\,dx = \frac{2}{3} \int_0^1 x\,dx + \frac{2}{3} \int_1^2 dx + \frac{2}{3} \int_2^3 (3 - x)\,dx =$

$\frac{1}{3} x^2 \Big|_0^1 + \frac{2}{3} x \Big|_1^2 + \left(2x - \frac{1}{3} x^2\right) \Big|_2^3 = \frac{4}{3}$, $a_n = \frac{2}{3} \int_0^3 f(x) \cos\left(\frac{n\pi x}{3}\right) dx =$

$\frac{2}{3} \int_0^1 x \cos\left(\frac{n\pi x}{3}\right) dx + \frac{2}{3} \int_1^2 \cos\left(\frac{n\pi x}{3}\right) dx + \frac{2}{3} \int_2^3 (3 - x) \cos\left(\frac{n\pi x}{3}\right) dx =$

$\frac{2}{n\pi} x \sin\left(\frac{n\pi x}{3}\right) \Big|_0^1 - \frac{2}{n\pi} \int_0^1 \sin\left(\frac{n\pi x}{3}\right) dx + \frac{2}{n\pi} \sin\left(\frac{n\pi x}{3}\right) \Big|_1^2 + \frac{2}{n\pi} (3-x) \sin\left(\frac{n\pi x}{3}\right) \Big|_2^3 +$

$\frac{2}{n\pi} \int_2^3 \sin\left(\frac{n\pi x}{3}\right) dx = \frac{2}{n\pi} \sin\left(\frac{n\pi}{3}\right) + \frac{6}{n^2\pi^2} \cos\left(\frac{n\pi x}{3}\right) \Big|_0^1 + \frac{2}{n\pi} \sin\left(\frac{2n\pi}{3}\right) -$

$\frac{2}{n\pi}\sin\left(\frac{n\pi}{3}\right) - \frac{2}{n\pi}\sin\left(\frac{2n\pi}{3}\right) - \frac{6}{n^2\pi^2}\cos\left(\frac{n\pi x}{3}\right)\Big|_2^3 = \frac{6}{n^2\pi^2}\cos\left(\frac{n\pi}{3}\right) - \frac{6}{n^2\pi^2} -$

$\frac{6}{n^2\pi^2}\cos(n\pi) + \frac{6}{n^2\pi^2}\cos\left(\frac{2n\pi}{3}\right) = \frac{6}{n^2\pi^2}\left[\cos\left(\frac{n\pi}{3}\right) - 1 - \cos(n\pi) + \cos\left(\frac{2n\pi}{3}\right)\right]$

$= \frac{6}{n^2\pi^2}\left\{[1 + (-1)^n]\left[\cos\left(\frac{n\pi}{3}\right) - 1\right]\right\}, n \geq 1,$ employing

$\cos\left(\frac{n\pi}{3}\right) + \cos\left(\frac{2n\pi}{3}\right) = \cos\left(\frac{n\pi}{3}\right) + \cos\left(-\frac{2n\pi}{3}\right) = \cos\left(\frac{n\pi}{3}\right) + \cos\left(\frac{n\pi}{3} - n\pi\right) =$

$\cos\left(\frac{n\pi}{3}\right) + \cos\left(\frac{n\pi}{3}\right)\cos(n\pi).$ The cosine series is

$\frac{2}{3} + \frac{3}{\pi^2}\sum_{k=1}^{\infty}\frac{1}{k^2}\left[\cos\left(\frac{2k\pi}{3}\right) - 1\right]\cos\left(\frac{2k\pi x}{3}\right).$

(c) The series converges to $\tilde{f}(x)$ for all x since $\tilde{f}$ is continuous everywhere and $\tilde{f}'$ is piecewise continuous.

2. (a) $F(x) = f(x)$ at $x = 0$ and at $x = L$ if $f(0) = f(L)$.

   (b) $S(x) = f(x)$ at $x = 0$ if $f(0) = 0$; $S(x) = f(x)$ at $x = L$ if $f(L) = 0$.

   (c) $C(x) = f(x)$ at $x = 0$ and at $x = L$ regardless of the values $f(0)$ and $f(L)$.

3. (a) $\int_0^L \sin\left(\frac{n\pi x}{L}\right)\sin\left(\frac{m\pi x}{L}\right)dx = \frac{1}{2}\int_0^L\left\{\cos\left[\frac{(n-m)\pi x}{L}\right] - \cos\left[\frac{(n+m)\pi x}{L}\right]\right\}dx = 0$ if $n \neq m$, for any $m, n \geq 1$.

   (b) $\int_0^L \cos\left(\frac{n\pi x}{L}\right)\cos\left(\frac{m\pi x}{L}\right)dx = \frac{1}{2}\int_0^L\left\{\cos\left[\frac{(n-m)\pi x}{L}\right] + \cos\left[\frac{(n+m)\pi x}{L}\right]\right\}dx = 0$ if $n \neq m$, for any $m, n \geq 0$.

   (c) If $f(x) = \sum_{n=1}^{\infty} b_n\sin\left(\frac{n\pi x}{L}\right)$, then, for any integer $m \geq 1$,

   $\int_0^L f(x)\sin\left(\frac{m\pi x}{L}\right)dx = \sum_{n=1}^{\infty} b_n\int_0^L\sin\left(\frac{n\pi x}{L}\right)\sin\left(\frac{m\pi x}{L}\right)dx =$

   $b_m\int_0^L\sin^2\left(\frac{m\pi x}{L}\right)dx = \frac{L}{2}b_m \Rightarrow b_m = \frac{2}{L}\int_0^L f(x)\sin\left(\frac{m\pi x}{L}\right)dx.$

   (d) If $f(x) = \frac{a_0}{2} + \sum_{n=1}^{\infty} a_n\cos\left(\frac{n\pi x}{L}\right)$, then, for any integer $m \geq 0$,

   $\int_0^L f(x)\cos\left(\frac{m\pi x}{L}\right)dx = \frac{a_0}{2}\int_0^L\cos\left(\frac{m\pi x}{L}\right)dx +$

   $\sum_{n=1}^{\infty} a_n\int_0^L\cos\left(\frac{n\pi x}{L}\right)\cos\left(\frac{m\pi x}{L}\right)dx = \frac{L}{2}a_m \Rightarrow$

   $a_m = \frac{2}{L}\int_0^L f(x)\cos\left(\frac{m\pi x}{L}\right)dx.$

4. Since f and g are continuous and f' and g' are piecewise continuous, the Fourier series of f and g converge to $f(x)$ and $g(x)$, respectively, for all x, by Theorem 8.1. Since the two series are equal, $f(x) = g(x)$ for all x. It follows, that

   $a_n = \frac{1}{L}\int_{-L}^L f(x)\cos\left(\frac{n\pi x}{L}\right)dx = \frac{1}{L}\int_{-L}^L g(x)\cos\left(\frac{n\pi x}{L}\right)dx = c_n, n \geq 0,$ and

   $b_n = \frac{1}{L}\int_{-L}^L f(x)\sin\left(\frac{n\pi x}{L}\right)dx = \frac{1}{L}\int_{-L}^L g(x)\sin\left(\frac{n\pi x}{L}\right)dx = d_n, n \geq 1.$

5. (a) The fundamental period of f is 6. The sine series of f is $\sum_{n=1}^{\infty} b_n\sin\left(\frac{n\pi x}{3}\right),$

   with $b_n = \frac{2}{3}\int_0^3\left[2\sin\left(\frac{\pi x}{3}\right) - 3\sin\left(\frac{4\pi x}{3}\right) + 4\sin\left(\frac{5\pi x}{3}\right)\right]\sin\left(\frac{n\pi x}{3}\right)dx, n \geq 1.$ By Exercise 3(a), $b_n = 0$ if $n \neq 1, 4, 5, b_1 = \frac{2}{3}\int_0^3 2\sin^2\left(\frac{\pi x}{3}\right)dx = 2,$

$b_4 = \frac{2}{3}\int_0^3 -3\sin^2\left(\frac{4\pi x}{3}\right) dx = -3$, and $b_5 = \frac{2}{3}\int_0^3 4\sin^2\left(\frac{5\pi x}{3}\right) dx = 4$. Thus, the sine series of f is $f(x)$ itself. This is due to the fact that $f(x)$ has the form of a finite sine series, namely, $\sum_{n=1}^{\infty} c_n \sin\left(\frac{n\pi x}{3}\right)$, with $c_1 = 2$, $c_4 = -3$, $c_5 = 4$ and $c_n = 0$ otherwise. By Exercise 4, $f(x) = \sum_{n=1}^{\infty} c_n \sin\left(\frac{n\pi x}{3}\right) = \sum_{n=1}^{\infty} b_n \sin\left(\frac{n\pi x}{3}\right) \Rightarrow b_n = c_n$ for all $n \geq 1$, and, hence, $f(x)$ is its own sine series.

(b) The fundamental period of f is 8. As in part (a), the cosine series of f is $f(x)$.

(c) The fundamental period of f is 4. As in part (a), the Fourier series of f is $f(x)$.

C.9   Chapter 9 Solutions

Exercises 9.1 – page 326

1. (a) $f(x) = \frac{3}{x+2}$ is analytic at all points except $x = -2$.

   (b) $f(x) = \frac{x^2+1}{x^2-4}$ is analytic at all points except $x = \pm 2$.

   (c) $f(x) = \tan(x)$ is analytic at all points except $x = (2n+1)\frac{\pi}{2}$.

   (d) $f(x) = \frac{x+1}{e^x-1}$ is analytic at all points except $x = 0$.

   (e) $f(x) = \sqrt{x+2}$, $x \geq -2$, is analytic at all points $x > -2$.

2. Division of $1 + x$ into $1 - x + x^2$ gives $f(x) = \frac{1-x+x^2}{1+x} =$
$1 - 2x + 3x^2 - 3x^3 + 3x^4 - \cdots = 1 - 2x + \sum_{n=2}^{\infty} 3(-1)^n x^n$.

3. (a) $\sum_{n=2}^{\infty} a_n x^n = a_2 x^2 + a_3 x^3 + a_4 x^4 + a_5 x^5 + \cdots$.

   (b) $\sum_{n=2}^{\infty} a_n x^n = \sum_{m+2=2}^{\infty} a_{m+2} x^{m+2} = \sum_{m=0}^{\infty} a_{m+2} x^{m+2} =$
$a_2 x^2 + a_3 x^3 + a_4 x^4 + a_5 x^5 + \cdots$.

   (c) $\sum_{m=0}^{\infty} a_{m+2} x^{m+2} = \sum_{n=0}^{\infty} a_{n+2} x^{n+2} = a_2 x^2 + a_3 x^3 + a_4 x^4 + a_5 x^5 + \cdots$.

   (d) $\sum_{n=2}^{\infty} a_n x^n = \sum_{n+2=2}^{\infty} a_{n+2} x^{n+2} = \sum_{n=0}^{\infty} a_{n+2} x^{n+2} = a_2 x^2 + a_3 x^3 + a_4 x^4 + a_5 x^5 + \cdots$.

4. $\sum_{n=0}^{\infty} n a_n x^n + \sum_{n=0}^{\infty} a_n x^{n+2} = 0 \Rightarrow 0 + a_1 x + \sum_{n=2}^{\infty} n a_n x^n + \sum_{n=0}^{\infty} a_n x^{n+2} = 0 \Rightarrow$
$a_1 x + \sum_{n=0}^{\infty} [(n+2)a_{n+2} + a_n] x^{n+2} = 0 \Rightarrow a_1 = 0$ and $(n+2)a_{n+2} + a_n = 0$, $n \geq 0$,

$\Rightarrow a_1 = 0$ and $a_{n+2} = \frac{-a_n}{n+2}$, $n \geq 0$. Then $a_1 = 0 \Rightarrow a_3 = 0 \Rightarrow a_5 = 0$, etc., i.e., $a_{2k+1} = 0$ for all $k \geq 0$. Also, $n = 0 \Rightarrow a_2 = \frac{-a_0}{2}$, $n = 2 \Rightarrow a_4 = \frac{-a_2}{4} = \frac{a_0}{2 \cdot 4}$, $n = 4 \Rightarrow a_6 = \frac{-a_4}{6} = \frac{-a_0}{2 \cdot 4 \cdot 6} = \frac{(-1)^3 a_0}{2^3 \cdot 1 \cdot 2 \cdot 3}$, and, in general, $a_{2k} = \frac{(-1)^k}{2^k k!} a_0$, $k \geq 0$, and a_0 is arbitrary.

5. $y'' + xy' + 2y = 0$.

(a) $y = \sum\limits_{n=0}^{\infty} a_n x^n$, $y' = \sum\limits_{n=0}^{\infty} n a_n x^{n-1}$, $y'' = \sum\limits_{n=0}^{\infty} n(n-1) a_n x^{n-2}$, $y'' + xy' + 2y = 0$

$\Rightarrow \sum\limits_{n=0}^{\infty} n(n-1) a_n x^{n-2} + \sum\limits_{n=0}^{\infty} n a_n x^n + \sum\limits_{n=0}^{\infty} 2 a_n x^n = 0 \Rightarrow$

$\sum\limits_{n=0}^{\infty} \left[(n+2)(n+1) a_{n+2} + n a_n + 2 a_n \right] x^n = 0 \Rightarrow$

$(n+2)(n+1) a_{n+2} + (n+2) a_n = 0 \Rightarrow a_{n+2} = \frac{-a_n}{n+1}$, $n \geq 0$.

(b) $n = 0 \Rightarrow a_2 = \frac{-a_0}{1}$, $n = 2 \Rightarrow a_4 = \frac{-a_2}{3} = \frac{a_0}{1 \cdot 3}$, $n = 4 \Rightarrow a_6 = \frac{-a_4}{5} = \frac{-a_0}{1 \cdot 3 \cdot 5}$, $n = 6 \Rightarrow a_8 = \frac{-a_6}{7} = \frac{a_0}{1 \cdot 3 \cdot 5 \cdot 7}$, etc., and, in general, $a_{2k} = \frac{(-1)^k a_0}{1 \cdot 3 \cdot 5 \cdots (2k-1)} = \frac{(-1)^k \cdot 2 \cdot 4 \cdot 6 \cdots (2k) a_0}{(2k)!} = \frac{(-1)^k 2^k k! a_0}{(2k)!}$, $k \geq 0$.

$n = 1 \Rightarrow a_3 = \frac{-a_1}{2}$, $n = 3 \Rightarrow a_5 = \frac{-a_3}{4} = \frac{a_1}{2 \cdot 4}$, $n = 5 \Rightarrow a_7 = \frac{-a_5}{6} = \frac{-a_1}{2 \cdot 4 \cdot 6}$, and, in general, $a_{2k+1} = \frac{(-1)^k a_1}{2 \cdot 4 \cdot 6 \cdots (2k)} = \frac{(-1)^k a_1}{2^k k!}$, $k \geq 0$. $y = \sum\limits_{n=0}^{\infty} a_n x^n =$

$\sum\limits_{k=0}^{\infty} a_{2k} x^{2k} + \sum\limits_{k=0}^{\infty} a_{2k+1} x^{2k+1} = a_0 \sum\limits_{k=0}^{\infty} \frac{(-1)^k 2^k k!}{(2k)!} x^{2k} + a_1 \sum\limits_{k=0}^{\infty} \frac{(-1)^k}{2^k k!} x^{2k+1} =$

$a_0 y_1 + a_1 y_2$ is the general solution, and y_1 and y_2 are two independent solutions.

(c) $y_1(x) = 1 - x^2 + \frac{1}{3} x^4 - \frac{1}{15} x^6 + \cdots$, $y_2(x) = x - \frac{1}{2} x^3 + \frac{1}{8} x^5 - \frac{1}{48} x^7 + \cdots$.

(d) $y_2 = \sum\limits_{k=0}^{\infty} \frac{(-1)^k}{2^k k!} x^{2k+1} = x \sum\limits_{k=0}^{\infty} \frac{1}{k!} \left(-\frac{x^2}{2} \right)^k = x e^{-\frac{x^2}{2}}$.

(e) Since the equation has no singular points, $R = \infty$ for both series.

(f) $y(0) = 0 \Rightarrow a_0 = 0$ and $y'(0) = 2 \Rightarrow a_1 = 2$. Thus, $y = 2 y_2 = 2x e^{-\frac{x^2}{2}}$.

6. $(1 + x^2) y'' - 4xy' + 6y = 0$.

(a) $y = \sum\limits_{n=0}^{\infty} a_n x^n$, $y' = \sum\limits_{n=0}^{\infty} n a_n x^{n-1}$, $y'' = \sum\limits_{n=0}^{\infty} n(n-1) a_n x^{n-2}$,

$(1 + x^2) y'' - 4xy' + 6y = 0 \Rightarrow$

$(1 + x^2) \sum\limits_{n=0}^{\infty} n(n-1) a_n x^{n-2} - 4x \sum\limits_{n=0}^{\infty} n a_n x^{n-1} + 6 \sum\limits_{n=0}^{\infty} a_n x^n = 0 \Rightarrow$

$\sum\limits_{n=0}^{\infty} n(n-1) a_n x^{n-2} + \sum\limits_{n=0}^{\infty} n(n-1) a_n x^n - \sum\limits_{n=0}^{\infty} 4n a_n x^n + \sum\limits_{n=0}^{\infty} 6 a_n x^n = 0 \Rightarrow$

$\sum\limits_{n=0}^{\infty} \left[(n+2)(n+1) a_{n+2} + n(n-1) a_n - 4n a_n + 6 a_n \right] x^n = 0 \Rightarrow$

$$\sum_{n=0}^{\infty}[(n+2)(n+1)a_{n+2}+(n^2-5n+6)a_n]x^n = 0 \Rightarrow$$
$$(n+2)(n+1)a_{n+2}+(n-2)(n-3)a_n = 0 \Rightarrow a_{n+2} = \frac{-(n-2)(n-3)a_n}{(n+2)(n+1)}, \ n \ge 0.$$

(b) $n=0 \Rightarrow a_2 = -3a_0$, $n=2 \Rightarrow a_4 = 0$, $n=4 \Rightarrow a_6 = 0$, etc. Hence, $a_{2k} = 0$ for $k \ge 2$. $n=1 \Rightarrow a_3 = -\frac{1}{3}a_1$, $n=3 \Rightarrow a_5 = 0$, $n=5 \Rightarrow a_7 = 0$, etc. Hence, $a_{2k+1} = 0$ for $k \ge 2$. Thus, $y = a_0 + a_1x + a_2x^2 + a_3x^3 = a_0 + a_1x - 3a_0x^2 - \frac{1}{3}a_1x^3 = a_0(1-3x^2)+a_1\left(x-\frac{1}{3}x^3\right)$ is the general solution, with a_0 and a_1 arbitrary, and $y_1 = 1-3x^2$ and $y_2 = x-\frac{1}{3}x^3$ are two linearly independent solutions.

(c) $y(0) = -3 \Rightarrow a_0 = -3$ and $y'(0) = 1 \Rightarrow a_1 = 1$. Hence, $y = -3(1-3x^2)+(x-\frac{1}{3}x^3) = -3+x+9x^2-\frac{1}{3}x^3.$

7. $y'' + xy' - 2y = 0.$ $y = \sum_{n=0}^{\infty} a_nx^n$, $y' = \sum_{n=0}^{\infty} na_nx^{n-1}$, $y'' = \sum_{n=0}^{\infty} n(n-1)a_nx^{n-2}$,
$$y'' + xy' - 2y = 0 \Rightarrow \sum_{n=0}^{\infty} n(n-1)a_nx^{n-2} + \sum_{n=0}^{\infty} na_nx^n - \sum_{n=0}^{\infty} 2a_nx^n = 0 \Rightarrow$$
$$\sum_{n=2}^{\infty} n(n-1)a_nx^{n-2} + \sum_{n=0}^{\infty} (n-2)a_nx^n = 0 \Rightarrow (n+2)(n+1)a_{n+2}+(n-2)a_n = 0$$
$\Rightarrow a_{n+2} = -\frac{(n-2)a_n}{(n+1)(n+2)}$, $n \ge 0$. $n=0 \Rightarrow a_2 = \frac{2a_0}{1\cdot2} = a_0$, $n=2 \Rightarrow a_4 = 0$, $n=4 \Rightarrow a_6 = 0$, etc. Hence, $a_{2k} = 0$ for $k \ge 2$. $n=1 \Rightarrow a_3 = \frac{a_1}{2\cdot3} = \frac{a_1}{3!}$, $n=3 \Rightarrow a_5 = \frac{-a_3}{4\cdot5} = \frac{-a_1}{5!}$, $n=5 \Rightarrow a_7 = \frac{-3a_5}{6\cdot7} = \frac{3a_1}{7!}$, $n=7 \Rightarrow a_9 = \frac{-5a_7}{8\cdot9} = \frac{-3\cdot5a_1}{9!}$, $n=9 \Rightarrow a_{11} = \frac{-7a_9}{10\cdot11} = \frac{3\cdot5\cdot7a_1}{(11)!}$, etc., and, in general, $a_{2k+1} =$
$$\frac{(-1)^{k+1}\cdot1\cdot3\cdot5\cdot7\cdots(2k-3)\,a_1}{(2k+1)!} = \frac{(-1)^{k+1}\cdot1\cdot3\cdot5\cdot7\cdots(2k-3)\,a_1}{(2k+1)!}\frac{2\cdot4\cdot6\cdots(2k-2)}{2\cdot4\cdot6\cdots(2k-2)} = \frac{(-1)^{k+1}(2k-2)!a_1}{(2k+1)!2^{k-1}(k-1)!},$$
$k \ge 1$. The general solution is $y = a_0y_1 + a_1y_2$, where $y_1 = 1 + x^2$ and $y_2 = x + \sum_{k=1}^{\infty} \frac{(-1)^{k+1}(2k-2)!}{(2k+1)!2^{k-1}(k-1)!}x^{2k+1}$ are two linearly independent solutions.

8. $(2+x^2)y'' + 2xy' - 2y = 0.$ $y = \sum_{n=0}^{\infty} a_nx^n$, $y' = \sum_{n=0}^{\infty} na_nx^{n-1}$,
$$y'' = \sum_{n=0}^{\infty} n(n-1)a_nx^{n-2}, \ (2+x^2)y'' + 2xy' - 2y = 0 \Rightarrow$$
$$\sum_{n=0}^{\infty} 2n(n-1)a_nx^{n-2} + \sum_{n=0}^{\infty} n(n-1)a_nx^n + \sum_{n=0}^{\infty} 2na_nx^n - \sum_{n=0}^{\infty} 2a_nx^n = 0 \Rightarrow$$
$$\sum_{n=0}^{\infty} 2n(n-1)a_nx^{n-2} + \sum_{n=0}^{\infty} (n^2+n-2)a_nx^n = 0 \Rightarrow$$
$2(n+2)(n+1)a_{n+2}+(n+2)(n-1)a_n = 0 \Rightarrow a_{n+2} = \frac{-(n-1)a_n}{2(n+1)}$, $n \ge 0$.
$n=1 \Rightarrow a_3 = 0 \Rightarrow a_5 = 0$, etc., and $a_{2k+1} = 0$ for $k \ge 1$.
$n=0 \Rightarrow a_2 = \frac{a_0}{2}$, $n=2 \Rightarrow a_4 = \frac{-a_2}{2\cdot3} = \frac{-a_0}{2^2\cdot3}$, $n=4 \Rightarrow a_6 = \frac{-3a_4}{2\cdot5} = \frac{a_0}{2^3\cdot5}$,
etc., and, in general, $a_{2k} = \frac{(-1)^{k-1}a_0}{2^k(2k-1)}$. Hence, $y = a_1x + a_0 + \sum_{k=1}^{\infty} \frac{(-1)^{k-1}a_0}{2^k(2k-1)}x^{2k} =$
$$a_1x + a_0\left(1 + \sum_{k=1}^{\infty} \frac{(-1)^{k-1}}{2^k(2k-1)}x^{2k}\right) = a_1y_1 + a_0y_2.$$

9. $y'' + e^x y = 0$.

(a) $y = a_0 + a_1 x + a_2 x^2 + a_3 x^3 + a_4 x^4 + a_5 x^5 + \cdots$, $y' = a_1 + 2a_2 x + 3a_3 x^2 + 4a_4 x^3 + 5a_5 x^4 + \cdots$, $y'' = 2a_2 + 6a_3 x + 12a_4 x^2 + 20a_5 x^3 + \cdots$,
$e^x = 1 + x + \frac{1}{2}x^2 + \frac{1}{6}x^3 + \frac{1}{24}x^4 + \frac{1}{120}x^5 + \cdots$,
$e^x y = a_0 + (a_0 + a_1)x + \left(\frac{1}{2}a_0 + a_1 + a_2\right)x^2 + \left(\frac{1}{6}a_0 + \frac{1}{2}a_1 + a_2 + a_3\right)x^3 + \cdots$,
$y'' + e^x y = 0 \Rightarrow (2a_2 + a_0) + (6a_3 + a_0 + a_1)x + \left(12a_4 + \frac{1}{2}a_0 + a_1 + a_2\right)x^2 + \left(20a_5 + \frac{1}{6}a_0 + \frac{1}{2}a_1 + a_2 + a_3\right)x^3 + \cdots = 0 \Rightarrow a_2 = \frac{-a_0}{2}$, $a_3 = \frac{-a_0 - a_1}{6}$,
$a_4 = \frac{-a_1}{12}$, $a_5 = \frac{a_0}{40} - \frac{a_1}{60} \Rightarrow y = a_0 + a_1 x - \frac{a_0}{2}x^2 - \frac{1}{6}(a_0 + a_1)x^3 - \frac{a_1}{12}x^4 + \left(\frac{a_0}{40} - \frac{a_1}{60}\right)x^5 + \cdots$.

(b) $a_0 = 1$ and $a_1 = 0 \Rightarrow y_1 = 1 - \frac{1}{2}x^2 - \frac{1}{6}x^3 + \frac{1}{40}x^5 + \cdots$, $a_0 = 0$ and $a_1 = 1$
$\Rightarrow y_2 = x - \frac{1}{6}x^3 - \frac{1}{12}x^4 - \frac{1}{60}x^5 + \cdots$.

10. Legendre's equation of order ν, $(1 - x^2)y'' - 2xy' + \nu(\nu + 1)y = 0$.

(a) $y = \sum\limits_{n=0}^{\infty} a_n x^n$, $y' = \sum\limits_{n=0}^{\infty} na_n x^{n-1}$, $y'' = \sum\limits_{n=0}^{\infty} n(n-1)a_n x^{n-2} \Rightarrow$

$\sum\limits_{n=0}^{\infty} n(n-1)a_n x^{n-2} - \sum\limits_{n=0}^{\infty} n(n-1)a_n x^n - \sum\limits_{n=0}^{\infty} 2na_n x^n + \sum\limits_{n=0}^{\infty} \nu(\nu+1)a_n x^n = 0$

$\Rightarrow \sum\limits_{n=0}^{\infty} n(n-1)a_n x^{n-2} + \sum\limits_{n=0}^{\infty} [\nu(\nu+1) - n(n+1)]a_n x^n = 0$

$\Rightarrow \sum\limits_{n=0}^{\infty} \{(n+2)(n+1)a_{n+2} + [\nu(\nu+1) - n(n+1)]a_n\}x^n = 0$

$\Rightarrow a_{n+2} = \frac{n(n+1) - \nu(\nu+1)}{(n+1)(n+2)}a_n$, $n \geq 0$.

(b) If $\nu = m \geq 0$ is an integer, then the recursion relation becomes
$a_{n+2} = \frac{n(n+1) - \nu(\nu+1)}{(n+1)(n+2)}a_n = \frac{n(n+1) - m(m+1)}{(n+1)(n+2)}a_n$, $n \geq 0$,
and $n = m \Rightarrow a_{m+2} = 0$, $n = m+2 \Rightarrow a_{m+4} = 0$, $n = m+4 \Rightarrow a_{m+6} = 0$, etc., which shows that one of the series solutions truncates at $a_m x^m$. If m is even, then $y_1 = a_0 + a_2 x^2 + \cdots + a_m x^m$ is a polynomial, and if m is odd, then $y_2 = a_1 x + a_3 x^3 + \cdots + a_m x^m$ is a polynomial.

(c) If $m = 0$, then $P_0(x) = a_0$, and $P_0(1) = 1 \Rightarrow a_0 = 1$. Hence, $P_0(x) = 1$.
If $m = 1$, then $P_1(x) = a_1 x$, and $P_1(1) = 1 \Rightarrow a_1 = 1$. Hence, $P_1(x) = x$.
If $m = 2$, then $P_2(x) = a_0 + a_2 x^2$, with a_2 given by the recursion relation with $n = 0$: $a_2 = \frac{-2 \cdot 3}{1 \cdot 2}a_0 = -3a_0 \Rightarrow P_2(x) = a_0 - 3a_0 x^2 = a_0(1 - 3x^2)$.
Then $P_2(1) = 1 \Rightarrow -2a_0 = 1 \Rightarrow a_0 = -\frac{1}{2} \Rightarrow$
$P_2(x) = -\frac{1}{2} + \frac{3}{2}x^2 = \frac{1}{2}(3x^2 - 1)$.
If $m = 3$, then $P_3(x) = a_1 x + a_3 x^3$, with a_3 given by the recursion relation with $n = 1$: $a_3 = \frac{1 \cdot 2 - 3 \cdot 4}{2 \cdot 3}a_1 = -\frac{5}{3}a_1 \Rightarrow P_3(x) = a_1\left(x - \frac{5}{3}x^3\right)$. Then $P_3(1) = 1 \Rightarrow a_1 = -\frac{3}{2} \Rightarrow P_3(x) = \frac{1}{2}(5x^3 - 3x)$.

Exercises 9.2 – page 332

1. $f(x) = x^2 - x + 2$ on $[0, 2]$ and $f(x + 2) = f(x)$ for all x. $f(x) =$
$\frac{a_0}{2} + \sum\limits_{n=1}^{\infty} [a_n \cos(n\pi x) + b_n \sin(n\pi x)]$, $a_0 = \int_0^2 (x^2 - x + 2)\, dx = \left(\frac{x^3}{3} - \frac{x^2}{2} + 2x\right)\Big|_0^2 =$
$\frac{14}{3}$, $a_n = \int_0^2 (x^2 - x + 2) \cos(n\pi x)\, dx = \frac{1}{n\pi}(x^2 - x + 2)\sin(n\pi x)\big|_0^2 -$
$\frac{1}{n\pi}\int_0^2 (2x-1)\sin(n\pi x)\, dx = \frac{1}{n^2\pi^2}(2x-1)\cos(n\pi x)\big|_0^2 - \frac{2}{n^2\pi^2}\int_0^2 \cos(n\pi x)\, dx = \frac{4}{n^2\pi^2}$,
$n \geq 1$, $b_n = \int_0^2 (x^2 - x + 2)\sin(n\pi x)\, dx = -\frac{1}{n\pi}(x^2 - x + 2)\cos(n\pi x)\big|_0^2 +$
$\frac{1}{n\pi}\int_0^2 (2x-1)\cos(n\pi x)\, dx = -\frac{2}{n\pi} + \frac{1}{n^2\pi^2}(2x-1)\sin(n\pi x)\big|_0^2 - \frac{2}{n^2\pi^2}\int_0^2 \sin(n\pi x)\, dx =$
$-\frac{2}{n\pi} + \frac{2}{n^3\pi^3}\cos(n\pi x)\big|_0^2 = -\frac{2}{n\pi}$, $n \geq 1$. $y'' + 3y = f(x) \Rightarrow$
$y = \frac{c_0}{2} + \sum\limits_{n=1}^{\infty} [c_n \cos(n\pi x) + d_n \sin(n\pi x)]$, $c_0 = \frac{a_0}{3} = \frac{14}{9}$, $c_n = \frac{a_n}{3 - n^2\pi^2} = \frac{4}{n^2\pi^2(3 - n^2\pi^2)}$,
$d_n = \frac{b_n}{3 - n^2\pi^2} = \frac{-2}{n\pi(3 - n^2\pi^2)}$.

2. $f(x) = x^2 - 2x$ on $[-1, 3]$ and $f(x + 4) = f(x)$ for all x. $f(x) =$
$\frac{a_0}{2} + \sum\limits_{n=1}^{\infty} \left[a_n \cos\left(\frac{n\pi x}{2}\right) + b_n \sin\left(\frac{n\pi x}{2}\right)\right]$, $a_0 = \frac{1}{2}\int_{-1}^3 (x^2 - 2x)\, dx = \left(\frac{x^3}{6} - \frac{x^2}{2}\right)\Big|_{-1}^3 =$
$\frac{2}{3}$, $a_n = \frac{1}{2}\int_{-1}^3 (x^2 - 2x)\cos\left(\frac{n\pi x}{2}\right)\, dx = \frac{1}{n\pi}(x^2 - 2x)\sin\left(\frac{n\pi x}{2}\right)\big|_{-1}^3 -$
$\frac{1}{n\pi}\int_{-1}^3 (2x - 2)\sin\left(\frac{n\pi x}{2}\right)\, dx = \frac{4}{n^2\pi^2}(x-1)\cos\left(\frac{n\pi x}{2}\right)\big|_{-1}^3 - \frac{4}{n^2\pi^2}\int_{-1}^3 \cos\left(\frac{n\pi x}{2}\right)\, dx =$
$\frac{16}{n^2\pi^2}\cos\left(\frac{n\pi}{2}\right)$, $n \geq 1$, $b_n = \frac{1}{2}\int_{-1}^3 (x^2 - 2x)\sin\left(\frac{n\pi x}{2}\right)\, dx =$
$-\frac{1}{n\pi}(x^2 - 2x)\cos\left(\frac{n\pi x}{2}\right)\big|_{-1}^3 + \frac{1}{n\pi}\int_{-1}^3 (2x-2)\cos\left(\frac{n\pi x}{2}\right)\, dx = \frac{4}{n^2\pi^2}(x-1)\sin\left(\frac{n\pi x}{2}\right)\big|_{-1}^3$
$- \frac{4}{n^2\pi^2}\int_{-1}^3 \sin\left(\frac{n\pi x}{2}\right)\, dx = \frac{-16}{n^2\pi^2}\sin\left(\frac{n\pi}{2}\right)$, $n \geq 1$. $y'' + 4y = f(x) \Rightarrow$
$y = \frac{c_0}{2} + \sum\limits_{n=1}^{\infty} \left[c_n \cos\left(\frac{n\pi x}{2}\right) + d_n \sin\left(\frac{n\pi x}{2}\right)\right]$, $c_0 = \frac{a_0}{4} = \frac{1}{6}$,
$c_n = \frac{a_n}{4 - \frac{n^2\pi^2}{4}} = \frac{64\cos\left(\frac{n\pi}{2}\right)}{n^2\pi^2(16 - n^2\pi^2)}$, $d_n = \frac{b_n}{4 - \frac{n^2\pi^2}{4}} = \frac{-64\sin\left(\frac{n\pi}{2}\right)}{n^2\pi^2(16 - n^2\pi^2)}$.

3. $f(x) = x - x^2$ on $[0, 1]$, odd, 2-periodic. $f(x) = \sum\limits_{n=1}^{\infty} b_n \sin(n\pi x)$,
$b_n = 2\int_0^1 (x - x^2)\sin(n\pi x)\, dx = -\frac{2}{n\pi}(x - x^2)\cos(n\pi x)\big|_0^1 +$
$\frac{2}{n\pi}\int_0^1 (1 - 2x)\cos(n\pi x)\, dx = \frac{2}{n^2\pi^2}(1 - 2x)\sin(n\pi x)\big|_0^1 + \frac{4}{n^2\pi^2}\int_0^1 \sin(n\pi x)\, dx =$
$-\frac{4}{n^3\pi^3}\cos(n\pi x)\big|_0^1 = \frac{4[1 - (-1)^n]}{n^3\pi^3}$, $n \geq 1$. $y'' - 3y = f(x) \Rightarrow y = \sum\limits_{n=1}^{\infty} d_n \sin(n\pi x)$,
$d_n = \frac{b_n}{-3 - n^2\pi^2} = \frac{-4[1 - (-1)^n]}{n^3\pi^3(3 + n^2\pi^2)}$.

4. $f(x) = \left\{ \begin{array}{ll} x, & 0 \leq x < 1 \\ 2 - x, & 1 \leq x \leq 2 \end{array} \right\}$, odd, 4-periodic. $f(x) = \sum\limits_{n=1}^{\infty} b_n \sin\left(\frac{n\pi x}{2}\right)$,
$b_n = \frac{8}{n^2\pi^2}\sin\left(\frac{n\pi}{2}\right)$ by Section 8.2, Exercise 9. $y'' + 3y = f(x) \Rightarrow$
$y = \sum\limits_{n=1}^{\infty} d_n \sin\left(\frac{n\pi x}{2}\right)$, $d_n = \frac{b_n}{3 - \frac{n^2\pi^2}{4}} = \frac{32\sin\left(\frac{n\pi}{2}\right)}{n^2\pi^2(12 - n^2\pi^2)}$.

5. $f(x) = 1 - x$ on $[0, 1]$, even, 2-periodic. $f(x) = \frac{a_0}{2} + \sum\limits_{n=1}^{\infty} a_n \cos(n\pi x)$, $a_0 = 1$ and $a_n = \frac{2[1-(-1)^n]}{n^2\pi^2}$, $n \geq 1$, by Example 8.20 in Section 8.2. $y'' + y = f(x) \Rightarrow$ $y = \frac{c_0}{2} + \sum\limits_{n=1}^{\infty} c_n \cos(n\pi x)$, $c_0 = a_0 = 1$, $c_n = \frac{a_n}{1-n^2\pi^2} = \frac{2[1-(-1)^n]}{n^2\pi^2(1-n^2\pi^2)}$.

6. $f(x) = \left\{ \begin{array}{ll} x, & 0 \leq x < 1 \\ 1, & 1 \leq x \leq 2 \end{array} \right\}$, even, 4-periodic. $f(x) = \frac{a_0}{2} + \sum\limits_{n=1}^{\infty} a_n \cos\left(\frac{n\pi x}{2}\right)$, $a_0 = \frac{3}{2}$, $a_n = \frac{4}{n^2\pi^2}\left[\cos\left(\frac{n\pi}{2}\right) - 1\right]$, $n \geq 1$, by Exercise 16(e) in Section 8.2. $y'' + 4y = f(x) \Rightarrow y = \frac{c_0}{2} + \sum\limits_{n=1}^{\infty} c_n \cos\left(\frac{n\pi x}{2}\right)$, $c_0 = \frac{a_0}{4} = \frac{3}{8}$, $c_n = \frac{a_n}{4-\frac{n^2\pi^2}{4}} = \frac{4}{n^2\pi^2\left(4-\frac{n^2\pi^2}{4}\right)}\left[\cos\left(\frac{n\pi}{2}\right) - 1\right] = \frac{16}{n^2\pi^2(16-n^2\pi^2)}\left[\cos\left(\frac{n\pi}{2}\right) - 1\right]$.

7. $f(x) = 2x - x^2$ on $[0, 2]$ and $f(x + 2) = f(x)$ for all x. Since f is even, $f(x) = \frac{a_0}{2} + \sum\limits_{n=1}^{\infty} a_n \cos(n\pi x)$, $a_0 = 2\int_0^2 (2x - x^2)\, dx = 2\left(x^2 - \frac{x^3}{3}\right)\Big|_0^2 = \frac{8}{3}$, $a_n = 2\int_0^2 (2x - x^2)\cos(n\pi x)\, dx = \frac{2}{n\pi}(2x - x^2)\sin(n\pi x)\Big|_0^2 -$ $\frac{2}{n\pi}\int_0^2 (2-2x)\sin(n\pi x)\, dx = \frac{4}{n^2\pi^2}(1-x)\cos(n\pi x)\Big|_0^2 + \frac{4}{n^2\pi^2}\int_0^2 \cos(n\pi x)\, dx = \frac{-8}{n^2\pi^2}$, $n \geq 1$. $y'' + 2y = f(x) \Rightarrow y = \frac{c_0}{2} + \sum\limits_{n=1}^{\infty} c_n \cos(n\pi x)$, $c_0 = \frac{a_0}{2} = \frac{4}{3}$, $c_n = \frac{a_n}{2-n^2\pi^2} = \frac{-8}{n^2\pi^2(2-n^2\pi^2)}$.

8. $f(x) = \sin(2\pi x)$ on $[0, 1]$, even, 2-periodic. $f(x) = \frac{a_0}{2} + \sum\limits_{n=1}^{\infty} a_n \cos(n\pi x)$, $a_0 = 2\int_0^1 \sin(2\pi x) = 0$. If $n \neq 2$, $a_n = 2\int_0^1 \sin(2\pi x)\cos(n\pi x)\, dx = \int_0^1 \{\sin[(2+n)\pi x] + \sin[(2-n)\pi x]\}dx = -\left\{\frac{\cos[(2+n)\pi x]}{(2+n)\pi} + \frac{\cos[(2-n)\pi x]}{(2-n)\pi}\right\}\Big|_0^1 = \frac{[1-(-1)^n]}{(2+n)\pi} + \frac{[1-(-1)^n]}{(2-n)\pi} = \frac{4[1-(-1)^n]}{\pi(4-n^2)}$. If $n = 2$, $a_2 = 2\int_0^1 \sin(2\pi x)\cos(2\pi x)\, dx = \int_0^1 \sin(4\pi x)\, dx = 0$. $y'' = f(x) \Rightarrow y = \frac{c_0}{2} + \sum\limits_{n=1}^{\infty} c_n \cos(n\pi x)$, $0 \cdot c_0 = a_0 = 0 \Rightarrow c_0$ is arbitrary, $c_2 = \frac{a_2}{-4\pi^2} = 0$, $c_n = \frac{a_n}{-n^2\pi^2} = \frac{-4[1-(-1)^n]}{n^2\pi^3(4-n^2)}$, $n \neq 2$.

Index